30
1005

MUNICIPAL AND RURAL SANITATION

Municipal and Rural SANITATION

VICTOR M. EHLERS, C.E.

Director, Division of Sanitary Engineering
Texas State Department of Health

ERNEST W. STEEL, C.E.

Professor of Sanitary Engineering
University of Texas

FIFTH EDITION

McGRAW-HILL BOOK COMPANY, INC.

New York Toronto London

1958

MUNICIPAL AND RURAL SANITATION

 Library of Congress Catalog Card Number 57-10904

II

THE MAPLE PRESS COMPANY, YORK, PA.

PREFACE

This book first appeared in 1927 as an attempt to place in one convenient volume the more important principles and practices of sanitation. A heavy demand for the book has necessitated later editions, revised to keep up with sanitation advances in a changing world. In preparing the fifth edition, we received much counsel as to the addition of new material and the expansion of other materials. To our friends who made these logical and well-founded suggestions, we can only reply that, had we followed them all, the book would have become several volumes instead of one.

The sanitation phase of public health work, reacting to the impact of technological development, has changed greatly within the last decade. The fifth edition has attempted to keep abreast of the changing field. Consequently, the user of previous editions will find that this edition is somewhat reorganized and contains considerable new material.

New chapters include Chaps. 16, Institutional Sanitation, and 18, Radiological Sanitation. Those completely rewritten are Chaps. 1, Communicable Diseases; 4, Excreta Disposal with Water Carriage; 5, Water; 8, Refuse Sanitation; 9, Insect Vector and Rodent Control. Extensive changes, however, have been made in the entire text.

The authors are grateful to many friends for suggestions and contributions, including the following: Fred C. Kluth, M.D., M. D. Hollis, Frank M. Stead, Malcolm C. Hope, Harry Hanson, Curtis M. Everts, Jerome Trichter, Edwin Ludewig, James A. Doull, Arthur E. Gorman, Harold L. Malone, John E. Kiker, Jr., Alfred H. Fletcher, Ralph K. Longaker, Emil T. Chanlett, Dr. E. F. Gloyna, Richard J. Hammerstrom, George R. Hayes, Jr., Dr. Samuel W. Simmons, Charles D. Spangler, Dr. Abel Wolman, Dr. H. B. Gotaas, Dr. Don Mason, Dr. Ken Herrold, Henry A. Holle, M.D., J. E. Peavy, M.D., Theodore J. Bauer, M.D., J. Lloyd Barron, Harold S. Adams, John F. Pierce, David B. Lee, Ernest M. Allen, W. T. Ballard, Don Knudson, Thad Patrick, Dean S. Mathews, Frank J. Von Zuben, Jr., Dr. Harry D. Pratt, Bayard F. Bjornson, Thomas B. Gaines, Ross W. Buck, Porter A. Stephens, R. E. Peel, George H. Walker, E. C. Nelson, H. L. Dabney, J. W. Hornburg, Dave Barker, H. E. Hargis, M. C. Wukasch, Warren J. Kaufman, and Mrs. Ella Belle Hammer; and to Ruby Turner for secretarial work, reading proofs, and preparing an index.

Thanks are especially due to some organizations whose staff members undoubtedly contributed time and effort in the interest of improving this volume. Among those are the Texas State Department of Health, the Robert A. Taft Sanitary Engineering Center, and the Communicable Disease Center of the Public Health Service.

A major part of the editorial work on this edition was handled by Clayton H. Billings, Associate Editor of *Public Works* magazine.

Victor M. Ehlers
Ernest W. Steel

CONTENTS

INTRODUCTION

Disease prevention has a comparatively short history. About the turn of the century the discovery that microscopic organisms could cause disease was followed by ever-increasing knowledge of methods of transmission. This knowledge naturally led to the development of methods of preventing communication. At the same time medical science was investigating such other fields as the noncommunicable diseases, nutrition, and hygiene from the standpoint of health conservation. Soon there had accumulated a vast store of knowledge that is sometimes called "preventive medicine," since its purpose is to prevent disease, as opposed to its older brother, curative medicine, which aims to save the person already attacked by disease.

While the individual may take advantage of preventive medicine by his own efforts, as by having his family physician vaccinate him against such diseases as smallpox and typhoid fever, in the main, prevention must be applied through community efforts.

Public Health Work. Obviously, preventive medicine would be limited in value if it were practiced only by the individual. An epidemic, for example, requires the efforts of all the skilled persons and facilities available for investigation of the source and prevention of further spread. Nor could one person conduct a campaign to eradicate mosquitoes, or improve the milk supply of a city, or reduce infant mortality by establishing maternity and child welfare clinics. Such efforts, which are carried out by an organization for the benefit of a community or certain classes of the community, are known as public health work. Mostly they are carried on at public expense, but note that the definition does not exclude work done by charitable organizations. Curative activities that are carried on at public expense, while generally considered charity or welfare work rather than preventive medicine, are not excluded entirely from public health work. Tuberculosis and the venereal diseases, for example, are prevented to a considerable degree by isolation and cure, in the case of the former, and quick cure at public expense, in the case of the latter.

Public health work includes the following activities: control of communicable diseases by means of immunization, isolation, etc.; maternity, infant, and preschool hygiene; school hygiene; control of the venereal diseases; control of tuberculosis; sanitation; recording of vital statistics. Sanitation is the principal subject of this book, but the other activities are briefly discussed in Chap. 21.

Sanitation. Sanitation is the prevention of diseases by eliminating or controlling the environmental factors which form links in the chain of transmission. An outline of this field of public health work follows:

1. Water supply
2. Wastes
   a. Excreta disposal, without water carriage
   b. Sewerage
   c. Garbage and rubbish disposal
3. Insect control
   a. Mosquitoes
   b. Flies
   c. Other
4. Rodent control
5. Food sanitation
   a. Milk
   b. Meat
   c. Other foods
   d. Food-processing and -handling establishments
6. Plumbing
7. Air conditioning and purification of the atmosphere
8. Lighting
9. Housing
10. Institutional sanitation
11. Industrial hygiene
12. Sanitation of swimming pools
13. Eradication of nuisances
14. Radiological protection

Some of the above activities also have value in producing comfort—for example, the eradication of non-disease-bearing mosquitoes, air conditioning of buildings, improvement of housing, and elimination of smoke, odors, and noise.

Sanitation is practiced by the sanitary inspector, the sanitarian, and the sanitary engineer or public health engineer. The sanitary inspector is a person who makes inspections as a means of enforcing sanitary regulations and who works under the supervision of a sanitarian or engineer. The sanitarian is a person who has had formal training in the fundamental sciences that apply to sanitation, such as biology, bacteriology, chemistry, and vital statistics. He should be able to translate the sanitary needs of a community into terms of sanitary regulations and procedures and train and supervise inspectors. The public health engineer or sanitary engineer[1] has received engineering training which he applies to the field of sanitation. He should be able to head a division of sanitation in industry and in a health department and to apply the principles of sanitary engineering to such diverse activities as air, water, and insect-control measures and the planning of community improvements, including housing.

[1] Attempts have been made to differentiate between a sanitary engineer and a public health engineer by considering the former as a specialist in the design and operation of municipal waterworks and sewerage works, including water treatment and sewage treatment. The public health engineer's field, by this classification, would be the whole field of sanitation.

CHAPTER 1

COMMUNICABLE DISEASES

1-1. Definitions. The term "contagious disease" is not in favor because of its vagueness. It may be considered as applying to those diseases communicated only by direct contact. Many of them, however, are also transmitted in other ways. Infectious diseases are those in which some known infection is communicated from person to person, not necessarily directly. This is also a vague and unsatisfactory term. Health officials prefer to apply the term "communicable disease" to all ailments which may be transmitted by any means from person to person or from animals to persons.

Reportable diseases are those which state laws, rules, or regulations, supplemented by municipal ordinances, require reporting to the health officer on the part of attending physicians. As to which diseases are to be reported, practice varies in different cities and states. In practically all of them the major communicable diseases, such as tuberculosis, plague, typhoid fever, yellow fever, diphtheria, scarlet fever, smallpox, measles, and the venereal diseases, are reportable. The other diseases may or may not be reportable. The classification systems established by the American Public Health Association[1] on reporting of diseases is an excellent guide.

An *epidemic* is the incidence of a communicable disease among a number of people to an extent that is recognized statistically as being well beyond the normal expectancy for the disease in a community in a definite period of time. Usually large groups are affected, but only a few persons might be. For example, five cases of smallpox, where the disease has been absent for years, might be termed an epidemic. A disease may be said to be *endemic* in an area if it is constantly present in some degree. An endemic disease may flare up at times and become epidemic.

A *sporadic* disease is one that occurs in occasional, scattered cases. A *pandemic* affects large numbers of people at the same time and transcends community boundaries. For instance, the influenza of 1918–1919 was pandemic.

Channels of infection are the means through which the body becomes infected by disease-producing agents. The channels may be the respiratory tract, the digestive tract, or the exterior surfaces of the body. Of these, the mouth is the portal of entry for the majority of infections.

Vehicles of infection are the means by which infectious agents are transported in causing disease. Water, food, insects, and inanimate objects may be vehicles of infection. Insect or rodent vehicles are sometimes called "vectors."

Carriers are persons who harbor pathogens[1] but show no symptoms of the disease. A state of infection exists in their respiratory, circulatory, or gastrointestinal system, or in other parts of their bodies, and the living infectious agent may be discharged in various secretions or excretions. Some of the diseases that carriers are known to harbor are typhoid, diphtheria, cholera, hookworm, scarlet fever, and cerebrospinal fever. The release of pathogens may be continuous or intermittent. Carriers can often be identified by laboratory examinations. The best public health practice requires the examination of the feces of all convalescents from typhoid fever to establish the fact that after recovery the patient will not continue to harbor the infectious agent. A small percentage of typhoid patients are likely to become carriers. The danger of their being employed in occupations connected with the preparation of food is apparent, and many epidemics have been traceable to this cause. Known carriers of typhoid fever are listed by many health departments and are not permitted to work in food-handling establishments.

The term "carrier" is sometimes applied to persons who harbor an infection but who may have attacks of the disease. Persons who are infected with malaria may be in this category. Many epidemiologists, however, restrict the word "carrier" to persons who have recovered from the disease with no remaining clinical symptoms.

Incubation period is the time elapsing between entrance of an infectious agent into the body and the appearance of signs or symptoms of the disease.

1-2. Methods of Communication. It was formerly supposed that the air was an important vehicle of infection and that diseases were due to miasmas floating about, particularly in damp or foggy night air. Investigations have shown, however, that the air is relatively free from bacteria and that its importance in the communication of disease has been greatly overestimated. Sunlight and dryness tend to kill some bacteria which have been discharged into the air. However, sunlight will not kill spores. Bacteria may be carried on dust particles. Air as it leaves the lungs, even in cases of diseases of the respiratory tract, is free from bacteria during quiet breathing. Sneezing, coughing, or forcible speaking, however, causes the exhaled air to carry with it droplets of moisture which

[1] This term refers to disease-producing organisms, virulent organisms, or infectious agents.

may be infectious. Droplets usually do not travel more than a few feet, although under unusual conditions they may be carried much farther. Droplet infection is a recognized method of communication of such diseases as common colds, tuberculosis, and influenza, although there are other methods of spread.

Water and food are involved in the communication of those diseases whose channel of infection is the mouth and intestinal tract. Water may contain infectious agents of typhoid and paratyphoid fever, dysentery and, in some parts of the world, cholera. Infectious agents usually enter water with the discharges of sick persons or carriers. Milk-borne epidemics of typhoid fever and scarlet fever were frequent in the past. Diphtheria is occasionally disseminated in this manner. Foods are often involved in the communication of typhoid and paratyphoid fever and dysentery. Milk and foods are usually contaminated by the hands of carriers or persons in the early stages of disease or by flies and other insects.

Fomites (inanimate objects that have come in contact with a sick person) also undoubtedly enter into the communication of disease to some extent. Not all fomites, however, are equally dangerous. Books, umbrellas, and similar objects are of little importance in spreading disease, but eating utensils, pencils which have been placed in the mouth, and fragments of food which have been nibbled upon are of great importance, particularly among children where close contact with such fomites is very likely. The common towel and drinking cup are also in this category. The transmission of disease through fomites may be considered an indirect-contact transmission. Another example of this type of transmission is putting the hand to the mouth after shaking hands with an infected person.

The communication of venereal diseases, whereby infectious agents are transmitted from a lesion to the mucous membrane of another, is an instance of infection by direct contact. Diseases may also be directly transmitted through kissing.

Animals are involved in the communication of certain diseases. Rabies is transmitted from dogs or other animals by bites. Tularemia is contracted by contact with infected rabbits. Brucellosis, or undulant fever, is carried from infected cows or goats by milk and also by direct contact with diseased cattle, goats, and hogs, slaughtered or alive.

Insects are the vectors of infection of several diseases. Malaria, yellow fever, dengue, and filariasis are carried by mosquitoes. Plague is carried from rats and other rodents by fleas. Epidemic typhus fever is carried by the body louse.

DISEASES COMMUNICATED BY INTESTINAL DISCHARGES

1-3. The intestinal diseases, because of their usual methods of communication, are exceedingly important to the sanitarian. They include typhoid fever, the paratyphoids, cholera, dysentery, poliomyelitis, hepatitis or infectious jaundice, hookworm disease, and a few other parasitic infections. Cholera has not been epidemic in this country for many years. It is endemic in India and Southwest Asia. Hepatitis or infectious jaundice, although possibly transmissible by nose and throat discharges, can also be communicated by fecal contamination of water or milk.

1-4. Typhoid Fever. The incidence of this disease has decreased very greatly in response to sanitation. For example, in 1946, a typical year, the American Medical Association reported that among 90 of the largest cities of the United States there were 60 that had no deaths from typhoid fever during that year. In 49 cities there had been no such deaths for

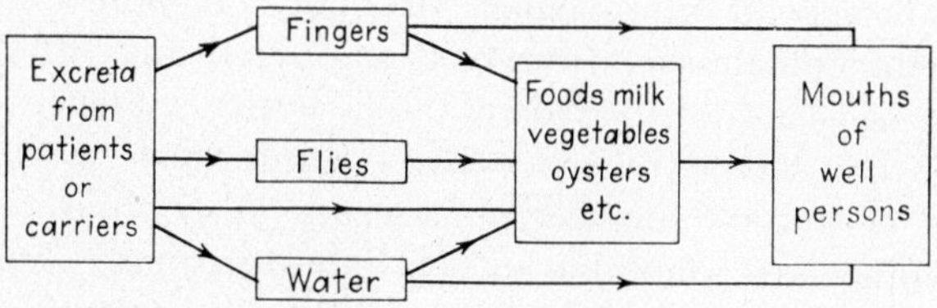

FIG. 1-1. How typhoid fever is spread. (*After Lumsden, U.S. Public Health Service.*)

two successive years. There were only a few localized outbreaks. The greatest death rate for typhoid in any city was 2.0 per 100,000. Before the application of sanitary measures the annual typhoid death rate in cities was likely to be from 50 to 80 per 100,000. The major part of this reduction was caused by water purification, later followed by improvement of milk supplies, detection of carriers, and immunization against the disease. The stronghold of typhoid fever at present is in small communities and institutions, where association of people is frequently not accompanied by adequate sanitary measures.

The disease, of course, is always caused by some serious sanitary defect, and it is still more prevalent than necessary, especially when it is considered that the methods of communication are fully understood and subject to easy control. Preventive measures include care as to the disposal of the feces and urine of the patients—the disinfection and disposal of the excreta to prevent its reaching drinking water or foods or being accessible to flies. Fomites and the hands of nurses should be disinfected. Carriers play a large part in the transmission of this disease. Female carriers are especially dangerous, since they are more likely to be engaged in the preparation of food. The typhoid epidemics that are not traceable to water are usually due to carriers infecting milk or other foods. Oysters may also be involved, but they are usually contaminated by the water in which they grow. Figure 1-1 shows graphically the means of transmission of typhoid. The control of typhoid fever will include the following expedients: disinfection of the discharges of patients, examination of convalescents to discover carriers, the purification of water, and the proper disposal of sewage. Obtaining the history of food handlers is of little merit, but there is possible value in questioning them.

Vaccination, which confers a degree of immunity from the disease, is another important preventive measure. Typhoid fever was formerly prevalent in armies, but vaccination has virtually eliminated it from modern wars. In civil life vaccination is usually applied to all persons who have come in contact with a patient. The vaccination of everyone would have the effect of not only raising the resistance to typhoid fever but also lessening the chances of susceptible persons' coming into contact with cases, thus working two ways. The requirement of vaccination for all food handlers is an improvement that may be applied in the future.

1-5. Typhoid Epidemics. Investigation of epidemics of typhoid fever is frequently necessary on the part of public health workers. If possible, the investigation should be made by a team which would include a physician and a sanitary engineer, a nurse, and other professional workers whose techniques are adaptable to field investigations. The procedure includes obtaining full histories of the cases and tracing the movements of each patient previous to his sickness, so that the sources of his food, milk, and water may be identified. Thus it may be learned that the parties involved used the same milk, attended the same banquet, or consumed food or ice cream prepared at the same place. A spot map is of great value and can easily be prepared by marking on a map of the city the location of the houses in which the infected persons live. If no points of contact are found, a spot map showing a wide distribution of the cases would possibly indicate water carriage of the disease. Cases occurring in the neighborhood of an industrial plant may mean pollution of the water supply by a cross connection (see Art. 5-34).

Typhoid epidemics have been found to be due to water contaminated by the discharges of patients or carriers. Milk-borne epidemics are usually due to milkers or other dairy attendants being carriers of the disease. One typhoid epidemic coming under the observation of the authors was apparently due to contamination of the teats and udders of cattle by sewage. Food contamination by carriers during preparation, food contamination by flies, the eating of vegetables fertilized with human excreta, and consumption of contaminated oysters have all been responsible for typhoid epidemics. Sporadic cases of typhoid fever are exceedingly difficult to trace. Usually they may be considered as due to a carrier or food contamination by flies. The drinking of unsafe water at roadsides by motorists has led to considerable typhoid that is also difficult to trace.

1-6. Paratyphoid Fever. There are three varieties of paratyphoid, known as the A, B, and C types according to the causative organism, all resembling typhoid fever in their symptoms although much milder in effects. Epidemics occur because of infected water, milk, and other foods. Carriers are also involved. Preventive methods are similar to those of typhoid.

1-7. Dysentery. There are several kinds of dysentery. The bacillary type is, as its name indicates, due to bacilli. The amoebic dysentery is due to an amoeba, which is a small animal, or protozoon, and not vegetative in nature, as are bacteria. Dysentery should not be confused with the diarrheas, which may be caused by various toxins irritating to the intestines.

Bacillary dysentery, which occurs very widely in armies, is also the primary cause of infant summer diarrhea. The bacilli can appear in the excreta for several weeks after apparent recovery, but there appear to be no permanent carriers. The methods of transmission and control are similar to those of typhoid fever.

An outbreak of amoebic dysentery originating in Chicago in 1933 and involving 1,049 known cases with 98 deaths served to focus attention upon this dangerous disease. Apparently dysentery of this type is far more prevalent in temperate regions than was supposed. It was formerly considered that the infection was usually spread through food contaminated by food handlers who were carriers. Facts uncovered by a study of the Chicago epidemic indicate that water carriage is more important than food contamination. The outbreak was caused by sewage entering the ice-water systems of two hotels. The organism (*Endamoeba histolytica*) forms cysts which are excreted in discharges from the bowels. In the cyst form, the amoeba exists outside the body until it dies or is swallowed by a susceptible animal or person. The cysts will live long periods in water but will be killed by dryness on the hands within ten minutes, at the longest, and generally within five minutes, a circumstance which leads to the conclusion by some investigators that food handlers are of small importance in transmitting the disease. It would seem, however, that the ten-minute life of the cysts on the hands of a food handler of unclean habits would suffice to allow contamination of foods, and this method of transmission should not be overlooked. The cysts are removed from water by the standard treatment, coagulation and filtration.

1-8. Poliomyelitis. The virus of poliomyelitis has been found in the nasal and respiratory passages and the intestinal tract of human beings and has been isolated from the secretions and excretions of these areas.

It is quite apparent that control measures should be directed toward preventing the spread of the virus from these sources. Such control measures as isolation and vaccination are indicated. Originally it was classed as a disease communicated by the nose and throat discharges. It appears that the virus of the disease is present in the nose and throat passages for only a few days in the early stages of the disease. Undoubtedly some transmission occurs during this period. It is now supposed, however, that feces are the principal means of transfer, although much remains to be learned. Houseflies and blowflies have been found to be infected, and food on which they have fed has been proved a source of infection. Fly-control campaigns, however, have had no effect in checking epidemics. The virus has been found in city sewage but only during short epidemic seasons. Some investigators believe that laundries and swimming pools may be involved. Any gathering where children come into close contact with one another, as in pools, should be avoided during the period when the disease is most prevalent, or at least during epidemics.

DISEASES COMMUNICATED BY NOSE AND THROAT DISCHARGES

1-9. The diseases that are communicated by discharges from the mouth and respiratory system are numerous and important. As their communication is dependent upon personal contact and personal habits rather than upon environmental factors, they are the most difficult to control. The diseases of this category are listed below:

Tuberculosis	Whooping cough	Pneumonia
Diphtheria	Cerebrospinal fever	Influenza
Measles	Smallpox	Common colds
Scarlet fever	Chickenpox	Septic sore throat

Of these diseases, smallpox and chickenpox may also be transmitted through material from pustules or lesions of the skin. The infection may be transmitted by direct contact, by droplets, fomites, or from hand to mouth. Scarlet fever, diphtheria, and septic sore throat may also be carried by milk. Poliomyelitis was formerly placed in this class and, while it apparently may be transmitted by nose and throat discharges, it is now supposed that fecal material is the more probable medium for transfer of the infection.

Except in the incidence of tuberculosis, which will be discussed below in greater detail, the control of these diseases is frequently directed toward isolation of the patient, disinfection of discharges, and perhaps quarantine and observation of persons who have come in contact with the patient. In smallpox and diphtheria epidemics, artificial immunity is given to contacts and is required for, or recommended to, all persons as a preventive measure. Influenza has proved difficult to control, partly because the virus which causes it can withstand drying for days and even weeks on clothing, bedding, and dust.

1-10. Tuberculosis. With the advent of mass X-ray surveys, the increasing availability of hospital beds, and the growing use of major chest surgery and antimicrobial drugs, the tuberculosis death rate has been declining, although this disease is still one of the leading causes of death. In the great majority of instances, however, recovery is possible. Since poor housing, overwork, worry, and insufficient and poor food diminish the power of resistance, tuberculosis is particularly prevalent among the poor. There are three distinct types of tuberculosis bacilli: human, avian, and bovine. The human type is pathogenic to man and also to cows and guinea pigs. The avian type affects birds and rabbits, but not man.

In man, bovine tuberculosis does not affect the lungs, but usually only the lymph glands or bones. It is responsible for about 0.5 per cent of all tuberculosis deaths and is most frequently found in children as a result of drinking contaminated cow's milk. The milk becomes contaminated either directly from a diseased udder or, more frequently, from the manure, which, in the case of infected animals, often contains tuberculosis bacilli.

Human tuberculosis is mainly transmitted through the sputum, although any or all of the body discharges may be infective. There are several theories as to the means by which the infectious material reaches a second person. The sputum may dry and pulverize, liberating the bacilli in dust which may be stirred up by sweeping or walking over floors. Crawling infants and playing children are likely to get such infectious material on their hands, which will later be placed in their mouths. The abrasive dust produced in many of the industries, when breathed for any length of time, appears to be conducive to tuberculosis. This is accounted for by the fact that such dust causes irritation of the lungs, creating a favorable place for the development of the chance infections mentioned previously.

Droplets from sneezing, coughing, etc., contain fresh and virile bacilli which may be inhaled or may fall upon food, hands, or other objects that are later carried to the mouth. Drinking cups and other utensils may also be involved. It appears that ingestion of bacilli, whether in food, droplets, or dust, will allow infection through the intestines in addition to direct infection of the lungs. In fact, some investigators claim that tuberculosis is acquired mainly, if not altogether, through the alimentary canal. It is possible for flies to carry the disease and also for it to be water-borne, although the latter is considered improbable.

The prevention of tuberculosis is a vast undertaking, involving such diverse matters as education of the infected persons themselves and their families; the elimination of tuberculous workers from food-handling occupations; safe disposal of the infectious material; the proper treatment of patients, and their segregation, where possible; the improvement of housing and industrial conditions; the tuberculin testing of cattle and the removal of tuberculous animals from dairy herds; and the pasteurization of milk.

OTHER COMMUNICABLE DISEASES

1-11. Arthropod-borne Diseases. The arthropods, which are animals having jointed limbs, include the insects and arachnids, some of which are important in disease transmission. They may be vectors, agents of infection, by inoculation into or through the skin or mucous membrane or by deposit of infective materials on fomites, food, or on the skin. Insects such as houseflies and cockroaches may be merely mechanical carriers of pathogenic organisms by reason of breeding or feeding in excrement and also by gaining access to food or milk. Examples of diseases transmitted in this manner are typhoid fever, paratyphoid fever, cholera, dysentery, and others already discussed.

The arthropod vector may be infected with microorganisms which undergo a cyclical change and multiplication within the body of the arthropod. Also, the pathogenic organism may undergo cyclical change within the vector but not multiply, or it may undergo no cyclical change but still multiply. In other cases the arthropod may be said to be hereditarily infective, having acquired the pathogenic organism from infected parents.

While houseflies and cockroaches may also harbor certain pathogens of gastroenteric infections, many diseases important in America are primarily transmitted by arthropods capable of inoculating human beings and other vertebrate animals, by virtue of having skin-piercing mouth parts. Included in this category are malaria, yellow fever, dengue, filariasis, relapsing fever, typhus fever, plague, encephalitis, Rocky Mountain spotted fever, and tularemia.

There are two types of *typhus fever*. Epidemic, or classical, typhus is carried by the body louse, which in feeding upon the infected person takes into its body with the blood some of the organisms of the disease. Upon the second host, however, it does not inject the disease directly into the blood, but infection results from the crushed body or feces of the louse being rubbed into a skin abrasion. Control of epidemic typhus includes bodily cleanliness and delousing of clothing and bedding. In Italy and elsewhere during the Second World War epidemics were prevented by using dust guns to blow 10 per cent DDT powder into sleeves and other openings of clothing while they were being worn. Another method used during the war was to moisten the clothing in a 1.5 to 2 per cent water emulsion of DDT. The DDT will usually retain its efficiency even after six launderings of the clothing. The eggs of the lice are not killed, and the adults may live for as long as twenty-four hours.

Endemic, or murine, typhus occurs in temperate, semitropical, and tropical areas. It is harbored by rats and transmitted to man and from rat to rat by the bites of rat fleas and rat mites. Rodent control will reduce this disease; this is discussed in Chap. 9.

Plague, primarily a disease of rats and other rodents, is transmitted to man by the bite of the rat's fleas, which, upon the death of the original host, will feed upon man until able to find another rat. Plague is of several types. As transmitted by fleas it is of the bubonic variety, which causes swelling of various glands. Should the lungs become infected, however, the pneumonic type results; this type may be transmitted directly to the lungs of others in a manner similar to the manner of transmission of pneumonia or pulmonary tuberculosis.

Relapsing fever, the tick-borne variety, is found in the Western United States and other parts of the American continents. Wild rodents are reservoirs, and ticks are responsible for transmission. In other parts of the world, the louse-borne variety may result when an infected louse is crushed into a bite wound or an abrasion of the skin.

Malaria, *yellow fever*, *dengue*, and *filariasis* are carried by mosquitoes and are discussed in Chap. 9. *Tularemia* (see Art. 1-12) is sometimes transmitted by ticks and blood-sucking flies. *Rocky Mountain spotted fever* occurs throughout most of the United States but is most prevalent in the Rocky Mountains and the Middle Atlantic seaboard. It is also found in Canada, Mexico, Colombia, and Brazil. Infected ticks are responsible for transmission, the variety depending upon the endemic location.

Birds or bird mites are suspected of being the principal reservoirs of infection from *arthropod-borne viral encephalitis*. It is transmitted by mosquitoes in the United States and ticks in Russia. There have been occasional epidemics of this disease in man in the United States (see Art. 1-12).

1-12. Diseases of Animals Transmissible to Man. The diseases mentioned in Art. 1-11 include some in which vertebrate animals are reservoirs and share the transmission cycle with arthropods, particularly murine typhus, plague, Rocky Mountain spotted fever, tularemia, and encephalitis. With the exception of tularemia and encephalitis, the diseases in the following discussion are those which have vertebrate animals as reservoirs and in which transmission is wholly or principally by means other than arthropods.

More than 80 diseases are known to involve vertebrate animals as reservoirs and are transmissible to humans. Bacterial and rickettsial diseases include brucellosis, bovine tuberculosis, Q fever, anthrax, leptospirosis, salmonellosis, tularemia, glanders, actinomycosis, and tetanus. Among the more important infections caused by viruses are rabies, psittacosis (ornithosis), encephalitis, and foot-and-mouth disease. Mycotic infections include ringworm of cats and dogs (*Microsporum* species) and ringworm of cattle (*Trichophyton* species). Also of importance are such parasitic infestations of animals as trichinosis, pork tapeworm (*Taenia solium*), beef tapeworm (*T. saginata*), hydatidosis, and broad fish tapeworm of man (*Diphyllobothrium latum*).

Brucellosis, or undulant fever—formerly known as Malta fever in man and as infectious abortion or Bang's disease in cattle, goats, and swine—may be transmitted to man by the ingestion of raw milk from infected animals or by direct or indirect contact with aborted fetuses, afterbirths, and other discharges that are released during or following abortion in animals. Abattoir workers occasionally contract the disease while slaughtering infected animals. Control measures consist of (1) compulsory pasteurization of all milk and milk products destined for human consumption, (2) periodic testing and elimination of infected animals, (3) the establishment of resistant herds by calfhood vaccination, and (4) the practice of sound sanitary husbandry. Cooking will eliminate the danger of contracting the disease through the consumption of meat.

Bovine tuberculosis has been virtually eliminated in this country; nevertheless, it still exists and serves as a potential threat. In other parts of the world it remains a serious economic and public health problem. It was discussed further in Art. 1-10.

Q fever is a disease of more recent times, having been first recognized during the mid-thirties in Australia. Of the domestic animals, cattle, sheep, and goats are the principal reservoirs of this disease. The infection in domestic animals is entirely asymptomatic. The organism is discharged in the milk and also with the birth fluids and membranes during parturition. Human infection occurs primarily from the inhalation of rickettsia-laden particles that contaminate the environment of cattle lots, meat-packing and -rendering plants, and wool-processing factories. Raw milk likewise may serve as a mode of transmission. Although several species of ticks have been found naturally infected, they are not considered important in the transmission of this disease. A control measure is pasteurization of milk products. Vaccines for preventing the disease in animals are in the exploratory phases.

Anthrax, the so-called "wool sorter's disease," occurs among textile and wool factory workers. Close to 90 per cent of the reported cases of human anthrax occur in this occupational group. It is primarily a disease of cattle and horses. Man may be infected through skin abrasions, the lungs, or the intestinal tract. Control measures consist of isolation and treatment of infected animals. Carcasses of infected animals should be incinerated or buried deeply with quicklime. The control of waste effluents from industries concerned with processing animals or animal products and the education of the employees of these establishments are also indicated. The disinfection, by steaming, of animal hair used for brushes—particularly shaving brushes—is required by the U.S. Public Health Service. The individual may disinfect his own brush by soaking it, with frequent agitation, for a period of four hours in a 10 per cent solution of formalin at 110°F.

Leptospirosis, also known as Weil's disease or hemorrhagic jaundice, occurs among rats, other rodents, dogs, swine, cattle, and occasionally other animals. Probably most human cases are caused by the ingestion of food or water which has been contaminated with rat urine or by swimming in water holes to which animals have access.

Salmonellosis is caused by a group of bacteria known as the *Salmonella* organisms. Poultry and meat products frequently become contaminated with *Salmonella* organisms from the contents of the intestinal tracts of these birds and animals when the processing or slaughtering operations are done in a careless or an insanitary manner. Such *Salmonella*-contaminated products can cause a serious form of food poisoning or diarrhea if they are not adequately cooked. Control would be attained by improving the methods of processing and slaughtering so that contamination of the carcass by fecal material will be at a minimum and by educating the public on the hygienic values of cooking poultry and meat products thoroughly.

Tularemia is usually contracted by man from rabbits, opossums, rodents, quail, and other game animals. The infection occurs during skinning or dressing and enters through a skin abrasion. The disease, though of long duration, is rarely fatal. Sick or sluggish animals, since they may be infected, should be avoided by hunters. This disease is also transmitted by certain biting insects and ticks.

Glanders has been eradicated from this country principally because of the reduction in horse population, the disappearance of the community horse-watering tanks, and the application of the Mallein test as a diagnostic technique. Glanders is still present in certain parts of the world, however.

Actinomycosis, also known as "lumpy jaw," frequently infects cattle and occasionally man. Infections in man usually occur among those rural dwellers who habitually place straw or grass blades in their mouths. Cattle with draining actinomycotic lesions may serve to contaminate the environment, thus increasing the opportunity for human infections to occur.

Rabies is a viral disease to which all warm-blooded animals are susceptible. It is most frequently observed in dogs; however, infections in cats, cattle, horses, other domestic animals, and many species of wild animals, such as skunks and foxes, are also very common. Rabid dogs are the source of most human infection. Transmission occurs by the entrance of virus-laden saliva into lesions or open wounds, which are generally caused by the bite of the rabid animal. The prevention of rabies is discussed in Chap. 19.

Psittacosis (ornithosis), also called "parrot fever," is a virus disease of parrots, parakeets, canaries, pigeons, and numerous other species of birds, including some of our domestic fowl—chickens, ducks, and turkeys. The disease is transmitted to man by direct contact with infected birds. In Texas, several outbreaks of psittacosis (ornithosis) have occurred among poultry plant workers who had processed infected turkeys. The inhalation of dispersed infectious particles appears to be the principal method of transmission. Man-to-man transmission has been reported; however, such occurrences are not common. The new broad-spectrum antibiotics are highly effective in the treatment of psittacosis, but prior to the use of these antibiotics the mortality rate of psittacosis was fairly high. Satisfactory control measures for this disease have not been completely worked out and for the most part have been directed at restricting the importation of psittacine birds into the country. Contact with visibly sick birds should be avoided. Apparently healthy birds have occasionally spread the disease. Banding of psittacine birds should be encouraged, so that birds suspected as a source of human psittacosis may be traced to their origin. Recent experiments offer some hope that antibiotics may be successfully used to eliminate aviary infection and thus to establish psittacosis-free aviaries.

Infectious encephalitis is recognized in three distinct types of mosquito-borne diseases in the United States. These are Western and Eastern equine encephalomyelitis and St. Louis encephalitis. Various species of wild and domestic birds have been identified as the basic reservoirs of these viruses. Certain species of mosquitoes are responsible for transmitting the disease from birds to horses and to man. Horses are not considered to be natural reservoirs of the Western and Eastern viruses but are merely terminal, end-chain victims to these agents, as is man. Control is achieved by continuous effective mosquito-abatement programs. Vaccines are being used with success in preventing the disease in horses.

Foot-and-mouth disease is caused by a virus to which all cloven-hoofed animals are susceptible, although cattle are primarily infected. It is transmitted to man through milk or milk products and possibly by the hands. It is rarely fatal to man. It is controlled through quarantine, isolation, and the slaughtering and burning of infected animals.

Ringworm is a general term used to describe mycotic or fungal infection of keratinized parts of the body (skin, hair, and nails). Children of prepuberty age are highly susceptible to the ringworm (*Microsporum canis*) of cats and dogs. Sizable outbreaks of *Microsporum* infection in school children have been traced to an infected cat or dog the children had been playing with. Adults are highly resistant to *Microsporum* species, but all ages are susceptible to *Trichophyton mentagrophytes* and *T. verrueosum*, which commonly infect cattle and horses. *Trichophyton* infections are commonly seen among rural dwellers. The forehead is frequently the site of infection because of the common habit of resting the forehead against the flank of the cow during the milking operation. Control primarily involves public education, pointing out the danger of permitting ringworm infection in pets and domestic animals to continue untreated. When animals are suspected as the source of human infection, they should be located and subjected to treatment. Ringworm infections are a serious problem in that they are exceedingly difficult to treat.

Trichinosis is caused by the larva of a parasitic nematode infecting man and animal hosts. The principal source of infection among humans is the meat of infected animals, particularly pork and occasionally wild game. Swine and many wild animals, including rats, are reservoirs of infection. Trichinosis occurs throughout the world, except among the native populations of the tropics, where swine are fed on root vegetables and ordinarily do not gain access to the flesh of animals. Control involves meat inspection, education of farmers and hog raisers in methods of hog production to minimize trichinosis infection, elimination of the practice of feeding uncooked garbage and offal to swine, and, of course, thorough cooking of fresh pork and all pork products.

Taeniasis, or tapeworm infection, involves various animal hosts. Common varieties that occur in man through the ingestion of flesh are those of beef, pork, and fish. The feces of an infected person constitute a reservoir of the disease. Transmission also occurs through direct hand-to-mouth transfer of the eggs and feces. The disease is prevalent wherever beef or pork is eaten raw or only slightly cooked. Prevention and control consist of proper sewage disposal, thorough cooking of beef and pork, and immediate treatment of human beings. Meat inspection is of little value in preventing beef tapeworm because of its comparatively light infection in cattle. The infection is more intense in swine, and pork inspection may lead to prevention in some cases.

Diphyllobothriasis, or the fish tapeworm infection, has as its source the flesh of infected fresh-water fish. As in the case of beef and pork tapeworm the feces of infected persons contain eggs and constitute a reservoir. However, the eggs must reach bodies of fresh water in order to mature, hatch, and infect the first intermediate host, copepods. The latter are eaten by susceptible fish, and the fish, in turn, become the second intermediate hosts. This disease is endemic in many parts of Europe and Asia; the Great Lakes Region, Eastern Canada, and Florida in North America; and Chile in South America. Prevention and control are accomplished by abating stream and lake pollution, establishing adequate sewage treatment, and thoroughly cooking fish or freezing it for twenty-four hours at minus 10°C.

Echinococcosis, or the dog-tapeworm infection, is relatively common in South America, Alaska, Eastern Australia, New Zealand, and the Middle East. Infection exists to some extent in England and Central Europe. A source of infection is feces containing eggs of the adult worm from dogs and some wild animals. The disease is transmitted through ingestion of contaminated food and water as well as hand-to-mouth transfer of eggs. Prevention lies in the control of slaughtering processes so that dogs do not have access to meat, licensing and periodic examination of dogs, incineration of dead animals, and education of the public in the dangers of close association with dogs.

1-13. Miscellaneous Diseases. *Venereal diseases* are transmitted by direct contact and rarely by towels, common drinking cups, closet seats, etc. Blindness in newborn infants may be due to gonorrheal infection. Many states require preventive treatment against this variety of blindness by the attending physician. Proper treatment is always successful.

Trachoma is a communicable disease of the eyes which may be transmitted by towels, handkerchiefs, or fingers.

Leprosy, called Hansen's disease, is caused by an acid-fast bacillus, *Mycobacterium leprae*. It affects chiefly the skin, mucous membrane, and peripheral nerves. According to Dr. Fred C. Kluth[5], comparatively little is known about transmission of the disease because the disease agent has not been cultured in an artificial medium and then transferred to animals or to human volunteers. Direct personal contact is likely to be the usual route. The disease occurs predominantly in the warm climates of China, India, Central Africa, Indonesia, Japan, and some Latin American republics. Though a far less important problem in the United States, the disease has been reported in Southern California, Florida, Louisiana, and southern Texas. Almost all patients can be classified in either the lepromatous or tuberculoid types. The lepromatous type[5] is the principal, if not the only, source of transmission of the disease. Untreated, it may shorten life or cause blindness or crippling. The tuberculoid type is not considered transmissible, but it may cause severe crippling. Treatment with sulfone drugs arrests the disease much more rapidly and in a larger proportion of patients than do older forms of treatment, but it is still a process which requires many years. The patient is considered infectious until the arrested stage is achieved. Adequate housing and cleanliness can greatly hamper the spread of this particular disease. In the United States the disease is controlled by treating volunteer patients at the Carville Sanitorium, where about 400 of the approximately 1,000 lepers in this country live under supervision in a state of isolation from the outside world.

GENERAL METHODS OF COMMUNICABLE DISEASE CONTROL

1-14. Immunization. Immunity is the power of living beings to resist infection. It varies in degree not only among persons but also in the same person from time to time, depending upon his physical condition. It may be natural or acquired. Certain diseases give immunity against a second attack, and immunity can also be artificially obtained by the introduction of a serum, toxin, vaccine, or virus. An outstanding example of the conferring of artificial immunity is the vaccination for smallpox. In this connection it should be noted that smallpox, as the result of virtually complete vaccination a generation ago, is showing a very low incidence rate for the disease. The absence of smallpox epidemics, however, has had the unfortunate effect of breeding contempt for the disease, with the result that vaccination has been neglected. In consequence there has been a rather alarming increase of cases during recent years. Other diseases for which artificial immunization may be given are typhoid, paratyphoid, diphtheria, rabies, and tetanus.

Prompt immunization of contacts is required by active city and county health departments in all cases of communicable diseases where immunization treatment is available. Application of this measure is exceedingly valuable in the prevention of epidemics.

1-15. Quarantine and Isolation. Quarantine has been applied since medieval times at Venice and elsewhere. It gets its name from the Italian word *quaranta*, meaning "forty," the number of days that suspected vessels were held in quarantine before being allowed to land goods or passengers. Maritime quarantine at ports of the United States is always administered by the U.S. PublicHealth Service. It applies to cholera, plague, louse-borne relapsing fever, smallpox, louse-borne typhus fever, yellow fever, and psittacosis. Upon arrival at United States ports, lepers who are United States citizens are sent to the leprosarium at Carville, La. Persons with diseases other than those named are allowed to enter, and the regulations of the local authorities are applied to them. Quarantine at areas other than ports is no longer considered effective, and in the United States it is applied only to smallpox by state, city, and county authorities. Contacts may be released from quarantine after their immunity has been established.

Isolation, as the term implies, involves the segregation of the patient. The degree of isolation depends upon the nature of the disease. For the most readily communicable diseases, such as smallpox and measles, strict isolation should be applied. This requires separate rooms for patients. In some cases of scarlet fever and diphtheria strict isolation is indicated. For yellow fever and dengue, covering the bed of the patient with a mosquito bar is sufficient isolation. In general, isolation is most easily obtained in hospitals. For safety in homes, careful and, preferably, trained attendants are required.

1-16. Control of Epidemics. This is one of the most important functions of health departments. Investigations and application of control measures are carried out by the division of communicable diseases, in some cases with the cooperation of the division of sanitation. In any event, for effective work a responsible head must be provided with undivided authority and legal backing.

The essentials in the prevention and control of epidemics may be summarized as follows:

1. Prompt notification to the health department of all communicable disease by the attending physician.

2. Analysis and investigation of reports by the health officials. This may include the preparation of graphs and spot maps showing where cases occurred and the time of occurrence, and the compilation of concise epidemiological histories.

3. Prompt hospitalization and isolation where necessary. Public health nurses should be available to give instructions as to isolation and disinfection in the home.

4. Immunization of contacts where practical.

5. Laboratory work directed toward verification of diagnosis, establishment of cure for release from isolation, detection of carriers, and tests of suspected water or milk, especially in gastroenteric diseases.

6. Special investigations by the division of sanitation in regard to food and water supplies and the application of emergency measures.

BIBLIOGRAPHY

1. "The Control of Communicable Diseases," 8th ed., American Public Health Association, New York, 1955.
2. Herms, William B.: "Medical Entomology," The Macmillan Company, New York, 1939.
3. McLaughlin, A. J.: "The Communicable Diseases," Harper & Brothers, New York, 1923.
4. Rosenau, M. J.: "Preventive Medicine and Hygiene," 7th ed., by Kenneth F. Maxcy, Appleton-Century-Crofts, Inc., New York, 1951.
5. Kluth, Fred C., research epidemiologist, Leonard Wood Foundation, unpublished correspondence.

CHAPTER 2

PRINCIPLES OF EXCRETA DISPOSAL

2-1. Excreta disposal, soil pollution, and the properties of the soil are closely related subjects. A study, therefore, of the soil and the chemical and biological processes which take place within it is essential to an understanding of sewage and excreta disposal and of that somewhat indefinite danger soil pollution. The various types of filter in which sewage is sometimes treated in order that it will be in a stable and non-putrefactive state are nothing more than attempts to duplicate soil conditions in such a manner that the processes of reduction can be controlled.

2-2. Soil Bacteria. The upper layers of the soil swarm with bacteria. The number varies with the richness of the soil and with the depth below the ground surface. In uncultivated sandy soil Houston found an average of 100,000 bacteria per gram, 1,500,000 per gram in garden soil, and 115,000,000 per gram in soil that had been polluted with sewage. These numbers include only the bacteria that can be conveniently grown in laboratory media. Actually the number must be far greater. The number of bacteria decreases greatly with the depth of the soil, until at a depth of 4 to 6 feet there is little or no bacterial activity, and the soil is completely sterile at 10 to 12 feet if there are no crevices and holes made by animals and no other disturbances. For this reason material which is to be reduced by soil bacteria should be applied close to the surface, preferably no deeper than 2 feet.

Nearly all the soil bacteria are saprophytic, *i.e.*, living upon dead organic matter. Soil conditions are unfavorable to the multiplication of pathogenic organisms and even to their existence in the soil for any great length of time. This is due to unfavorable temperature and moisture conditions and also to the enormous numbers of saprophytes preying upon, crowding out, or otherwise affecting the pathogens. The spores or seeds of certain bacteria which may cause wound infections, however, are often found in the soils of certain localities. These are anthrax, tetanus, and the so-called gas bacillus.

2-3. Nitrogen Cycle. The changes that take place in organic matter which is applied to the soil are well illustrated by the nitrogen cycle. The proteins which are among the constituents of the bodies of plants or animals may be taken as the starting point. Upon the death of the animal or plant, the dead tissues and cells are attacked by the putrefactive or saprophytic bacteria. The waste products, or excreta, of animals are subject to the same bacterial action. In order that this action may take place there must be favorable conditions as to moisture and temperature. This first decomposition is very complicated in nature, and odorous gases are among its products, but the nitrogen finally appears as ammonia. The various nitrifying bacteria of the soil, acting in the presence of air, then play their part by oxidizing the ammonia, first into nitrites, and then into nitrates. These represent stability and mineralization; no

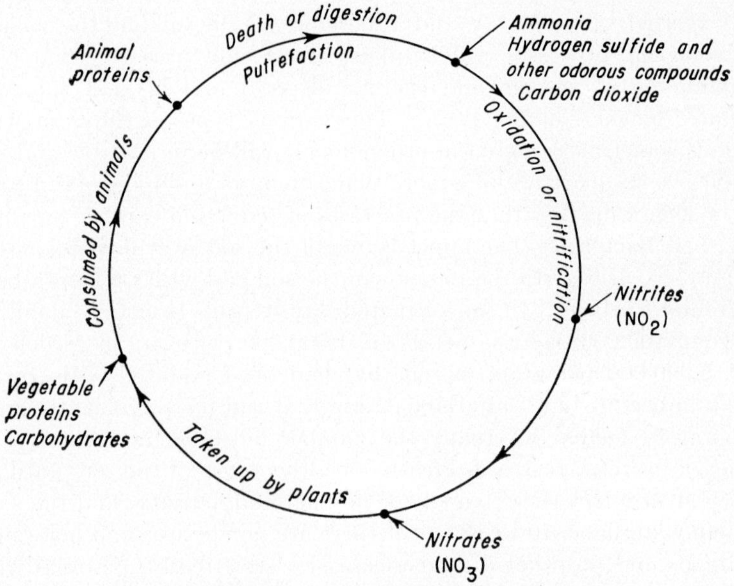

FIG. 2-1. Diagram illustrating the cycles of decay.

further reduction takes place in the continued presence of oxygen, and there is no more danger of odors. In all probability the pathogens will have been destroyed during these processes, although this cannot be depended upon. The nitrates which have been formed are now available as plant food to be taken up by the roots and converted into plant protein, which, in turn, will again undergo decay directly or will first be consumed by animals before continuing the cycle (see Fig. 2-1).

2-4. Other Cycles. Though less important to the sanitarian in his study of excreta disposal, other cycles which parallel the nitrogen cycle may be mentioned. In the case of sulfur, the first stage, or putrefaction, results in the formation of hydrogen sulfide and offensive odors. If oxygen is present, the so-called sulfur bacteria then cause oxidation of the hydrogen sulfide into inoffensive sulfates which are taken up by plants, and the cycle continues.

Carbon undergoes a somewhat similar change. It is present in the organic matter under discussion, such as cellulose, starch, and sugars. Fermentation takes place through the agency of microorganisms with carbon dioxide as the most important product. The carbon dioxide is taken up by the plants, unites with the water in them, and through the action of sunlight again forms starch and sugars.

It will be noted that the first stage of decay, or putrefaction, is accompanied by offensive odors. It is not until after the secondary action, or oxidation, which must take place in the presence of oxygen, that the organic matter has become inoffensive and available for use as food by the higher plants. An understanding of the essentials of this process is necessary in order to dispose of sewage properly.

2-5. Excreta Disposal without Water Carriage. Many houses, particularly those in rural areas, do not have running water available and therefore are without water-flushed toilets. This gives rise to that peculiarly rural problem, disposal of human excreta in some manner that will not be dangerous or cause nuisances. The dangers include possible pollution of ground or surface water; pollution of the ground surface, which may result in spread of hookworm disease; and access of flies to the excreta. The nuisances, of course, are offensive sights and odors. The various types of privies described in the following chapters differ in the treatment given to the excreta, but the commonest varieties—the pit, the bored-hole latrine, and the vault—provide a long period of storage for the putrefactive stage. If the excreta are kept rather dry by exclusion of surface or ground water or by drainage of liquid into the dry soil, production of odorous gases is very slow. Oxidation and stabilization occur by anaerobic bacteria splitting the more complex substances of the organic matter, and finally there is practical stabilization into a humus-like material with a strong musty smell. If the material is wet, as in a pit filled with ground water, the putrefactive stage proceeds much faster with the formation of much hydrogen sulfide and other offensive gases in the process known as septic action, which is employed in the septic tank. In either case several questions arise. How long will disease bacteria live in the excreta? Will they be able to travel through dry soil? How far may they be carried with ground water during its slow movement through the soil? These matters are discussed in Arts. 2-10 to 2-13.

2-6. Sewage Disposal in General. The term "sewage" is applied to a combination of the liquid wastes from residences, business buildings, and industrial establishments, together with such ground and surface water as may have entered the sewers. Domestic sewage is the liquid waste from residences, business buildings, and institutions, and contains only the wastes from water closets and the wash water from baths and kitchens. Industrial wastes are the liquids discharged into sewers from such industrial establishments as packing houses, breweries, and milk plants. Since this work is to cover residential sewage disposal only, the discussion will be confined to domestic sewage.

Domestic sewage is about 99.9 per cent water. Aside from the minerals originally present in the water, sewage contains paper, solids from the feces, urine, and soap and other substances introduced as a result of washing dishes, taking baths, and the like. About 40 per cent of the solids are in suspension and the balance in solution, the total solids amounting to 500 to 1,200 parts per million by weight. The actual amount of solids will, of course, be practically constant on a grams per capita basis, even though the parts per million may vary widely because of the different amounts of water used by families. Practically, however, these differences are of little importance in the case of residential sewage disposal but should be considered when designs are being made for large hotels or institutions and cities. Table 2-1 shows a typical

TABLE 2-1. CERTAIN CHARACTERISTICS OF A TYPICAL DOMESTIC SEWAGE

Characteristics	Raw sewage, ppm	Settled sewage, ppm	Final effluent,* ppm
Suspended solids	315	173	13.8
Total dissolved solids	423	411	415
Five-day biochemical oxygen demand	272	179	16.5
Ammonia nitrogen	17.7	14.4	3.4
Nitrites	0	0	0.52
Nitrates	0	0	3.7

* Following treatment by aeration in an activated sludge-process plant.

analysis of an average domestic sewage, raw and in various stages of treatment, expressed in parts per million.[1] Note the changes in the nitrogen content as treatment proceeds.

[1] Parts per million is a common sanitary engineering term used to express the weight of the contents of a sewage or water per million pounds of water. For example, in the sewage given in Table 2-1 the amount of dry suspended solids per million gallons would be calculated as follows:

$$\frac{1,000,000 \times 8.34 \times 315}{1,000,000} = 2,627 \text{ pounds}$$

Note: 1 gallon of water weighs 8.34 pounds. There is an increasing tendency among laboratory technicians to use the expression "milligrams per liter" instead of "parts per million." Because of the metric-system relationship, values are identical with either means of expression. The use of the newer term is recommended by "Standard Methods."

Sewage disposal methods are usually classified as primary or secondary treatment, although one or the other of the steps may be eliminated for various reasons. Primary treatment involves the removal of a portion of the suspended matter from the sewage by screening, or sedimentation, or both. In connection with sedimentation, the solids are stored in a tank under anaerobic conditions for putrefactive action. In the case of septic tanks this process takes place in the sedimentation chamber, while in Imhoff and other sedimentation tanks a separate chamber is provided for the anaerobic liquefaction.

Secondary treatment provides for the contact of the septic or other tank effluent with air, generally under conditions somewhat approximating those found in the soil. Filter beds, therefore, are porous beds of sand or crushed stone through which the sewage percolates, coming in contact with nitrifying and other aerobic bacteria coating the stones and oxidizing the organic matter. This process can, by elaborate installations, be carried to complete stability. Usually this is not an economical proceeding, and treatment is carried only as far as local conditions require, the state board of health being the arbiter in the matter if stream pollution is involved. Both local and state health authorities have jurisdiction if other health menaces or nuisances are likely to result.

Sewage can be treated on filters without primary treatment, although preliminary settling or screening, at the least, is advisable to take a large part of the load from the filters. Under some circumstances only primary treatment may be required by the state board of health. In general, artificial filters are used to furnish the aerobic reduction of sewage for municipalities and for large institutions, but such treatment requires skilled attention that is not always available for residences. Therefore other means are used, as described below.

2-7. Sewage Disposal for Residences. Safe and sanitary sewage disposal for residences must include oxidation or aerobic reduction in some form. The sewage is first run through a tank in which sedimentation of a part of the solids and septic action take place. The septic effluent, however, is still putrescible and may contain pathogens. It therefore must not be allowed to run into an open ditch or into a small stream without further treatment. While artificial filters can be provided for small residential plants, it is usually cheaper and more desirable to make use of the filtering properties of the soil. This is done by running the tank effluent through open-jointed tile pipe placed not more than 18 inches beneath the ground surface. This allows the sewage to percolate out into the soil where it is exposed to the oxidizing action of soil bacteria.

2-8. Coliform Organisms. These bacteria, which include *Escherichia coli*, live in the intestines of man and animals, large numbers being excreted with the feces. In water and sewage testing *E. coli* are usually classified with other organisms as "coliforms." This group of bacteria, which includes some organisms of nonfecal origin, react to the routine laboratory test in the same way as *E. coli*. They are discussed in more detail in Arts. 5-6 and 5-7. Coliforms will be present naturally, therefore, in sewage and in water or soil that has been polluted with sewage or excreta. They are numerous in the dust of city streets and houses. While these bacteria are not responsible for disease, they are exceedingly important to the sanitarian because their presence, which can be easily demonstrated in the laboratory, is an indication of pollution. In the earth they may be very abundant, particularly in cultivated soils where manure has been added and in pastures and fields where the soil has been polluted by the presence of animal excreta. Although less likely to be prevalent away from cultivation or traveled places, they appear never to be entirely absent. They are found only in the upper layers of the soil and rarely occur below a depth of 1 foot.

2-9. Soil Pollution and Health. The old idea that miasmas arose from the earth to cause fevers and other illness has been found to be mistaken. The diseases communicated through the agency of soil pollution include typhoid fever, paratyphoid, the dysenteries, and hookworm disease. The infection must be carried to the soil with human excreta and remain there for varying lengths of time. Hookworm disease is contracted by contact of the skin with the soil, usually through bare feet (see Arts. 19-1 to 19-5). Typhoid, paratyphoid, and the dysenteries may result from the eating of vegetables which have been fertilized by sewage or human excreta. There is also the possibility that a surface water or a ground water may be endangered. Since many rural homes must take water from wells and also care for excreta disposal, the possible effect of the latter upon ground-water pollution should be given careful consideration.

2-10. Length of Travel of Intestinal-disease Bacteria in the Soil. Obviously it is important to know just how far the intestinal-disease organisms will travel through the soil. If they are confined to the point at which they are deposited, there will be no danger of contamination of wells. On the other hand, if they move for long distances, the danger to ground-water supplies is very apparent. Dr. Kligler[1] found that typhoid and dysentery bacilli did not move horizontally into a soil to any extent. A pit privy, even when located above the ground-water table, may receive roof drippings or surface water during a rain. Accordingly, water was applied to determine whether the bacteria of typhoid could be washed downward. In porous soils they were carried vertically downward for 2 feet, while in denser soils the downward travel was only 1 foot. Observations indicated that coliforms can be washed downward 3 to 5 feet from a pit and the same distance from open-jointed tile pipes disposing of septic-privy and -tank effluent. The horizontal travel, as shown by coliforms, from pits and tile lines was only about 1 foot.

2-11. Length of Life of Intestinal-disease Bacteria in Septic Fluids. The bacilli of typhoid and dysentery were found to survive for only one to five days in the liquid of septic tanks and septic privies. Since the retention period for excreta in septic privies is considerably longer than five days, it is reasonable to suppose that the effluent from them will be reasonably safe and that such a privy and its disposal pipe may be located with little danger of serious results. The retention period in a septic tank is usually only wenty-four hours. Therefore, it is apparent that septic-tank effluent is potentially dangerous and should be treated accordingly.

2-12. Penetration of Disease Bacteria in Dry Soils. Infectious material does not move of itself; there must be some mechanical method of transportation. Normally this would be provided by water. In dry soil, therefore, no movement is to be anticipated.

2-13. Ground-water Pollution. Ground water results from rain water falling upon the surface of the ground and seeping downward into the porous soil. Should it encounter impervious material, such as rock, it will fill the interstices in the porous material and then move toward some outlet. This is illustrated in Fig. 5-1. The upper surface of the saturated portion of the soil is known as the "water table." Generally it is into such relatively shallow ground water that dug wells and bored or driven wells penetrate, and the bottom of the well must, of course, be below the water table. The water table may fluctuate vertically if there are variations in the rainfall. Above the water table the water is held by capillary action in the pores of the waterbearing formation. This capillary fringe will fluctuate as the water table changes, but there is no lateral motion in this water.

Figure 5-2 shows a deeper ground water. Here the rainfall has penetrated into an extensive porous formation which dips underground and is overlain and underlain by impervious formations. Here there is no water table, but the water will rise in the well above the porous formation because of the pressure of the mass of water above and toward the area where the rainfall has entered.

Ground water below the water table or in enclosed porous formations is in motion although its velocity is very slow, generally only a few feet per day. The actual rate will vary according to the permeability of the material through which the water is moving, and this in turn depends upon the size of the grains of which the material is composed; the velocity will be much slower through a fine sand than in a coarse sand and slower still in a mixture of clay and fine sand. In dense clays there may be practically no movement at all, even though they are saturated.

Human excreta, with its accompanying bacteria, may reach the ground water in two ways: (1) It may be washed downward through intervening soil to the ground water by rain occurring at the ground surface, or it may seep from a pit privy, a cesspool, or open-jointed sewage disposal pipes. Of course this may also occur when city sewers leak. (2) The cesspool or pit of the privy may penetrate the ground water and pollute it directly. A variation of this method would be polluted waters from a river or other body of surface water entering the ground water of a valley during flood periods. Normally, the flow of ground water would be toward the river.

Under the conditions mentioned in (1) above, bacteria which reach the ground water tend to be localized near its surface, and although there will be some diffusion, many of the organisms will be entrapped in the capillary water and remain there until they die. In Art. 2-10 it was stated that the downward movement of coliforms through otherwise dry soil, when aided by a constant drip of water, was 5 feet at most and of disease bacteria only 1 to 2 feet. For this reason wells (Figs. 5-14 and 5-15) are protected with watertight linings for at least 10 feet below the ground surface in order to ensure at least 10 feet of filtration of surface washings.

Cesspools contain solid excreta which undergo digestion, or decomposition, into finely divided material. A similar process occurs in pits which penetrate the ground water. The moving water carries with it both bacteria and the fine solids, which clog the soil. The chemical products of decomposition, the nitrites, nitrates, and ammonias which are in solution, will also pass into the ground water.

Several investigations that have been made are of interest. Those of Caldwell[2] and coworkers are of particular interest. A bored-hole latrine 15 inches in diameter and 16 feet deep was located in soil of varying characteristics, ranging from fine sand and sandy clay near the surface to coarse sand with little clay at the bottom. The water table varied from 5 to 11.5 feet below the ground surface, and the ground-water velocity varied from 3 to 8 feet per day. Wells were driven at various distances around the boring. Human feces, without water, were placed in the boring daily. The results were as follows. (1) Coliforms were recovered from the wells at a distance of 15 feet downstream from the latrine in three days. In the upper strata where the ground-water velocity was only 3 feet per day coliforms appeared at a distance of 10 feet after five weeks. After two months the greatest distance of coliform travel was noted: considerable numbers at 25 feet and occasional organisms at 35 feet. There were none in the upper strata, however, at 15 feet. Thereafter clogging of the sand caused a recession of the coliforms, and by the end of seven months they had retreated practically to the latrine. This effect of clogging upon the movement of pollution is known as "defense." (2) Chemical pollution traveled faster and farther than the coliforms, the maximum distance being 80 feet. Defense tended to reduce it also. (3) Pollution of both types moved in a well-defined stream bounded by unpolluted water. The stream tended to rise and fall vertically with the rise and fall of the water table. The coliform stream attained a maximum width of 3 feet at a distance of 15 feet from the latrine and thereafter narrowed, while the figures for chemical pollution were 5 and 25 feet, respectively.

The same investigations also included observations of a pit privy 8 feet 8 inches deep which extended into ground water moving through fine sand.

FIG. 2-2. A sanitary privy, properly mounded and curbed.

Here coliforms reached only slightly beyond 10 feet in three to four months. In nine months they could be found no farther than 5 feet from the pit. The maximum width of the stream was 4 feet at a distance of 5 feet from the pit. Chemical pollution, however, traveled a maximum distance of 310 feet, and at 80 feet, gross chemical pollution was noted. Odors could be noted in the water up to a distance of 195 feet. The maximum width of the stream was 25 feet at 80 feet from the privy, and its depth was a maximum of 7 feet after six months. It tended to drop toward the impermeable stratum which underlay the waterbearing material.

Dyer[3] and others in India also experimented with a bored-hole latrine 16 inches in diameter and 20 feet deep in an alluvial soil which was sandy loam near the surface with decreasing amounts of clay to all fine sand below 14 feet. The water-table level varied from 3 to 13 feet below the ground surface. Wells 12, 15, and 18 feet deep were driven around the latrine and were pumped daily. Human feces without water were placed in the latrine daily. Pollution appeared only down the ground-water stream from the latrine. Observations were made from November, 1941, to April, 1943. Coliforms were recovered 10 feet away from the latrine after two months, with large numbers at 5 feet. Thereafter the numbers diminished and organisms were virtually absent at 5 feet at the end of the period of observation. Chemical pollution was noted to a distance of only 15 feet and was more pronounced in the shallow wells. Investigations of the discharging of sewage into underground waters on a large scale have led the California State Water Pollution Control Board to report that "reclamation of sewage waters by direct recharge into underground aquifers is practical, and that operational considerations rather than public health considerations are the controlling factors."

From the investigations reported a few conclusions can be drawn:

1. Privy pits, bored-hole latrines, and cesspools should not penetrate the ground water. Preferably pits and latrines should terminate at least 5 feet above the water table, and cesspools, 10 feet. If this requirement can be complied with, the chance of ground-water pollution is practically nonexistent.

2. Occasional rises of ground water, caused by heavy rainfall, into pits or cesspools should be of no significance. Much of such pollution will probably be held in the capillary water as the water level falls again. In any case a continual feeding of bacteria into the water apparently is necessary for pollution to be noted at any great distance.

3. Wells should always be placed upstream in the ground-water flow from privy or cesspool. The upstream distance need not be far, but it should be remembered that heavy pumping of a well and a surcharge of liquid in a pit or cesspool above the water table may result in a temporary flow upstream.

4. Where a well must be placed downstream from a privy or cesspool which penetrates the ground water, the distance should be as great as convenient. There should be no danger of pollution with coliform organisms if the distance is at least 50 feet. If, however, the stream of chemical pollution enters the well, its effects may be noted, although chemical pollution is not a cause of disease.

5. Ground water moving in limestone or other fissured rock must be looked upon with suspicion. Tests will indicate its safety, but a newly constructed cesspool or other new source of pollution may make the water unsafe.

BIBLIOGRAPHY

1. Kligler, I. J.: "Investigation on Soil Pollution and Relation of Various Types of Privies to Spread of Intestinal Infections," Rockefeller Institute for Medical Research Monographs, no. 15, Oct. 10, 1921.
2. Caldwell, E. L., and L. W. Parr: *J. Infectious Diseases*, vol. 61, pp. 148, 180, 1937; vol. 62, pp. 225, 272, 1938.
3. Dyer, B. R., T. R. Bhaskaran, and C. C. Sekar: Investigations of Groundwater Pollution, *Indian J. Med. Research*, vol. 33, pp. 17, 23, 1945.
4. Gotaas, Harold B.: Report on the Investigation of Travel of Pollution, *State Water Pollution Control Board Pub.* 11, p. 8, 1954.
5. Rosenau, M. J.: "Preventive Medicine and Hygiene," 7th ed., by Kenneth F. Maxcy, Appleton-Century-Crofts, Inc., New York, 1951.
6. Smillie, Wilson G.: "Preventive Medicine and Public Health," 2d ed., The Macmillan Company, New York, 1952.

CHAPTER 3

EXCRETA DISPOSAL WITHOUT WATER CARRIAGE

3-1. At the present time and in all probability for many years to come, excreta will be disposed of without water carriage at the vast majority of farmhouses, at residences in the smaller towns and villages, and in the unsewered sections of the larger cities. While disposal with water is desirable, it is not practical under many conditions. It is possible, however, to dispose of the body wastes in a manner that will minimize or eliminate the transmission of disease involving soil and water pollution, animals, and flies.

The 1950 housing census[1] states that 738,000 rural dwelling units do not have any toilet facilities. Modern plumbing systems with water carriage of human wastes were found in only one-eighth of the farm houses in this country. Probably, in part because of increased prosperity in rural areas, these conditions have improved to some degree, but it is apparent that much progress is yet to be made. It should be recognized that many of the existing outdoor toilets are grossly insanitary—for example, the open-back surface type, which is little better than no toilet at all. At many of the rural schools the same condition applies and also in the small villages and unsewered portions of the larger towns. In the small town which boasts of its sewer system it is quite common to find that one-third of its area has no sewers and that the excreta disposal methods used there are as primitive as in a backward rural area. This is one reason why the small town has an unenviable record for incidence of typhoid fever, dysentery, and "summer complaint" of infants.

3-2. Requirements for Satisfactory Excreta Disposal. An excreta disposal method should satisfy the following requirements:

1. There should be no contamination of ground water that may enter springs or wells.
2. There should be no contamination of surface water.
3. The surface soil should not be contaminated. This requirement is to prevent hookworm disease (see Chap. 19).
4. Excreta should not be accessible to flies or animals.
5. There should be freedom from odors and unsightly conditions.

6. The method used should be simple and inexpensive as to construction and operation. This applies particularly to rural areas where the farmer may construct his own facilities.

In this chapter the pit, vault, septic, chemical, and box-and-can privies will be described in detail. They will be discussed briefly here in comparison with each other and in relation to the above requirements.

The *pit privy* is inexpensive and requires no operation. The fly hazard is nonexistent if the seat cover is down when the toilet is not in use, and it is not very great even if this precaution is neglected, for flies are not attracted in large numbers to dark places. Odors are negligible. There is no contamination of the ground surface or surface water. Usually there is no danger to wells or springs. This type is not adapted to areas where the ground water is high and keeps the pit filled with water. The pit fills up with excreta, etc., in the course of time, but it is always possible to dig a new pit and skid the slab and house over it.

The *vault privy* has the advantage of not contaminating ground water, surface water, or the soil. It is more expensive than the pit type and has important sanitary disadvantages. As constructed, flies can often enter and odors are likely to be present. Cleaning is necessary and unpleasant, and during this process surface soil contamination may occur, flies will be attracted, and the fecal matter must be buried at a proper location to prevent further hazards.

The *septic privy* is more expensive than the two privies already named, and requires the daily addition of water. There is no fly hazard, but mosquitoes may breed in the tank. There is no contamination of the ground surface or surface water, and there should be no danger of groundwater contamination if the overflow pipe is properly placed. There may be a septic odor noticeable at times from the tank contents. Sludge must be removed at long intervals. It is less offensive than the contents of vault privies but will contain some undigested fecal matter.

The *chemical toilet* is the most expensive in first cost and operation. The liquefied contents present no great difficulties in disposal. There is no fly hazard or danger of contamination of soil and water. While the toilet can be placed in the house with the tank located under the floor, it can produce offensive odors, and may be objectionable from that standpoint.

The *box-and-can privy* is not high in first cost, but continual attention must be given to the emptying and cleaning of cans. As operated, this toilet usually attracts flies and emits odors. There is no danger of soil or water contamination at the toilet, but improper disposal of the can contents may present all the sanitary hazards mentioned. This type of privy is little used at present.

THE PIT PRIVY

3-3. This is a hole in the ground with the toilet seat located directly over it. It has the great advantage of low cost and, if properly constructed and located, it solves the excreta disposal problem for the family which can afford nothing better. An old type of pit privy uses a timber slab or floor and riser. It has the advantage of ease of construction, but its life will be short, cracks will open in the floor and riser, flies will enter, and odors will escape. It should be discouraged in favor of the improved type which uses concrete for the slab and the riser. This concrete-slab privy is described in the following article.

A variation of the pit privy is the bored-hole latrine. It consists of a hole, usually bored with an earth auger, 10 to 25 inches in diameter and 15 to 25 feet deep. In loose soils it may be kept from caving by the use of woven tree branches, etc. A concrete slab is usually placed over it, and a seat may or may not be provided. The type without a seat is more acceptable to people in the primitive portions of Africa and Asia. This type of privy is cheap and easily replaced when filled, but its depth frequently presents the danger of ground-water pollution.

3-4. The Concrete-slab Pit Privy. This toilet has been adopted by many state health departments as the type favored for homes and schools where water is not available for sewerage.

The first problem is to decide upon the location of the privy, particularly with respect to the well. Usually, although not always, the ground water flows in the direction of the general slope of the land. Therefore the privy should be located downslope from the well. This cannot always be done, but there should be no danger if the pit does not penetrate into the ground water. In fact, pit privies do not function well if water stands in them. They are odorous; the pit contents do not compact; and probably they fill up sooner. If ground water does not enter the pit and the soil is uniformly compact, there should be no danger to a well at very short distances, although prudence dictates a distance of at least 50 feet. Some state health departments suggest at least 100 feet, and this should certainly be the rule if the ground-water table rises into the pit during a rainy period. If the ground water is permanently within a few feet of the ground surface, conditions are not favorable for pit privies and some other of the types discussed in this chapter should be chosen. Appendix A contains construction details.

Pit privies need very little attention or maintenance. The ventilation should keep the pit contents dry and small in bulk. Consequently a pit should serve for ten years or more, particularly if toilet paper is used and no garbage or other refuse is thrown in. Insofar as possible, water should be prevented from entering, but if it does, a cupful of kerosene dropped in at weekly intervals will discourage mosquito breeding; if, however, the seat cover is kept down and the ventilator is screened, there should be no breeding. Odors which occur can, in some cases, be controlled by the use of lime. No disinfectants should be used in the pit.

3-5. School Privies. In rural areas where running water is not available, pit privies can be constructed for use at schools by increasing the length of the pit and increasing the number of required seat units. Drainage from urinals should be discharged into a trench filled with large gravel or crushed stone.

TANK TOILETS

3-6. The Vault Toilet. This type of toilet was devised to prevent the possibility of polluting soil and ground water. It is of historical interest since it is the type, constructed of stone or brick, that was used in large ancient, medieval, and modern cities down to the time that water-carried

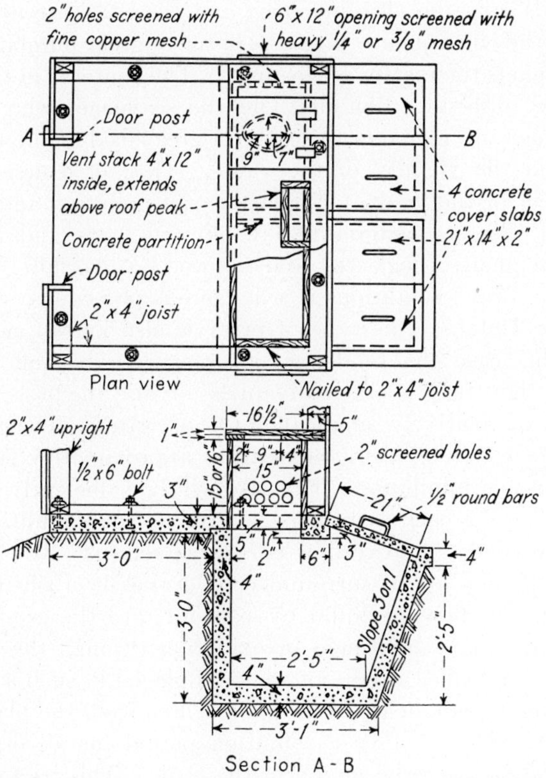

Fig. 3-1. Concrete-vault privy as recommended by the West Virginia State Board of Health.

sewerage was established. It consists of a watertight concrete vault over which the seat and house are placed. For the average family it is made with a capacity of 10 to 15 cubic feet and should function without emptying for a period of three to six months. The theory on which the vault toilet was originated is that the excreta would become dry and inoffensive so that they could be easily removed from the vault. This result, however, it fails to attain, as the contents tend to become liquid rather than dry. Some vaults have been made in two compartments and with two separate seats. In this case one seat with its compartment is used until full. This side is then closed and the other side is used until its capacity has been reached. By this time the excreta in the first compartment will have undergone complete decomposition, and the compartment may be emptied. This type of toilet, in order to be as sanitary as possible, should have self-closing seats and a watertight vault, and the back cover through which the emptying is done should be flytight. Ventilation is also advisable.

Experience has shown that the vault toilet does not come up to expectations. As a rule the cleaning door and the seats are not well maintained, with the consequence that flies enter in great numbers. Another serious problem is the matter of cleaning. The contents in the semiliquid state are very difficult to handle, and the scavenger who usually does such work generally manages to scatter a great deal of the material over the ground in the vicinity of the vault. This, of course, defeats the primary object of the vault, for it means soil pollution and the possible scattering of disease bacteria and hookworm eggs and larvae. The vaults are frequently neglected and allowed to overflow, and cleaning them under crowded conditions is a dangerous procedure.

3-7. Septic Toilet. This type of privy is also known as a liquefying tank. In this case the tendency of excreta to become liquid when enclosed in a tight tank is taken advantage of, and the process is aided by the addition of relatively small amounts of water. The tank, usually constructed of concrete, has a capacity of approximately 200 gallons, or 26 cubic feet, as a minimum. This size will be sufficiently large for five or six persons. For each extra person, 3 cubic feet of additional capacity should be provided. An overflow is constructed, usually of 4- or 6-inch drain tile with open joints, surrounded by gravel or crushed stone which will allow the overflowing liquid to seep out into the ground. Here it will receive secondary treatment or oxidation through the action of the soil bacteria. A baffle, usually of wood, is placed in such a manner that water and excreta cannot travel in a direct line from the place of deposit to the outlet. This ensures a retention period for all organic matter sufficient to allow bacterial action in the tank. This bacterial action is of an anaerobic nature and causes a liquefaction of parts of the products

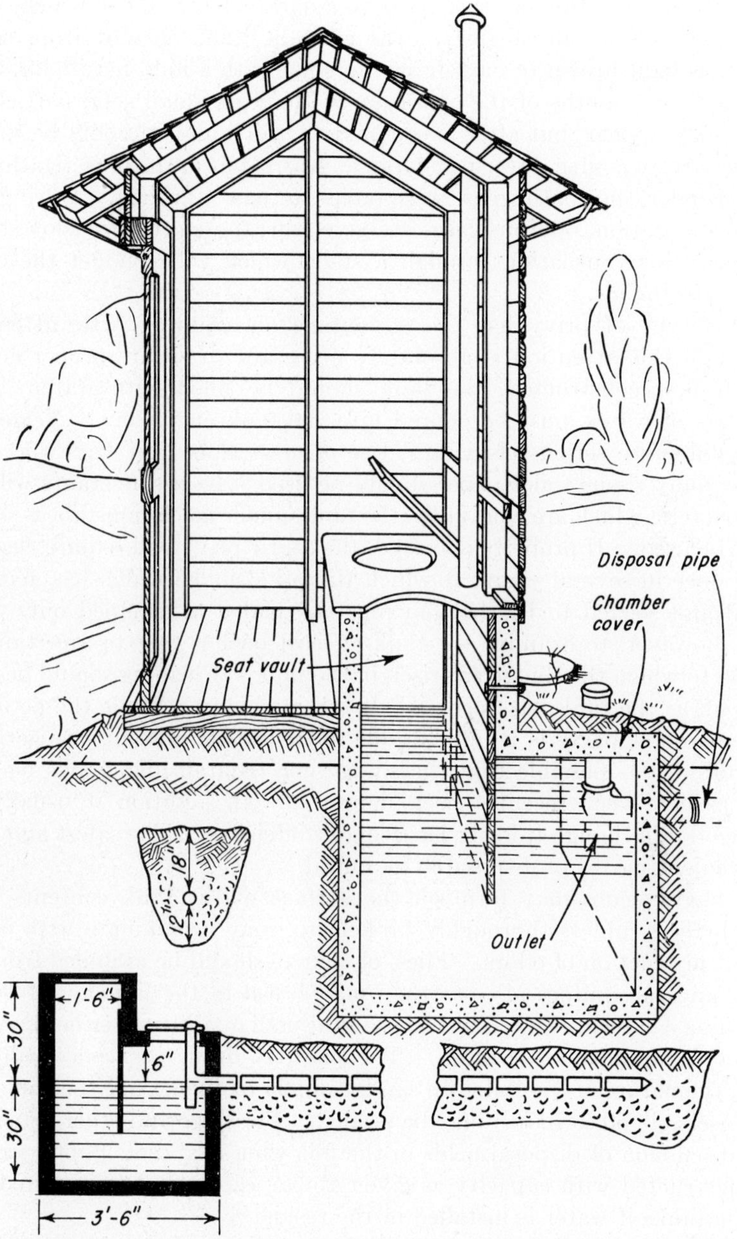

FIG. 3-2. The septic privy. (*Courtesy of Missouri State Board of Health.*)

and a transformation of other parts to a dark-colored sludge which, when well digested, is unrecognizable as excreta. The effluent from septic toilets is light brown to dark brown in color with a mild fecal odor. For the first few months of the operation of the tank small solid particles of feces may appear, but after longer periods the liquid will only be turbid. *E. coli* are, of course, present in large numbers, but in the investigations of Dr. Kligler, no pathogens were able to pass through. During the anaerobic action, odorous gases are given off; therefore, provision should be made for ventilation through a stack which will conduct the odors high into the air.

This type of privy has the advantage of requiring little attention, although this attention is absolutely necessary to ensure proper action. When first constructed, the tank should be filled with water. Two buckets of water must be poured into the tank every day. Neglect of this will cause serious clogging. Use of newspaper may have the same effect; only tissue toilet paper should be used. As disinfectants will kill the bacteria which are working in the tank, under no circumstances should they be used. If properly operated, the septic privy will require cleaning only once in several years, at which time the sludge which has accumulated and settled to the bottom must be bailed or pumped out. It is well, however, to examine the tank at least once a year to ascertain the depth to which the sludge has risen in the tank. Cleaning should be done as soon as the tank has become half full of sludge. While the action of the anaerobic bacteria is unfavorable to the existence of disease germs in the tank, it is possible that the sludge may contain dangerous bacteria which have very recently been deposited. In addition it usually has some odor, although it is not particularly offensive. The safest and most convenient means of disposal is by burial.

A heavy scum may form on the surface of the tank contents upon which feces, unless thoroughly broken up, may accumulate with consequent production of odors. Flies, of course, should be excluded from the tank and mosquitoes also, as they may breed in the liquid. Mosquito breeding can be prevented by the use of a small quantity of either kerosene or fuel oil applied once a week. The length of drain tile needed will vary with the nature of the soil. In sandy soil, 25 to 40 feet may be sufficient; in closer soil, 50 to 70 feet may be needed. For slope and other details see the discussion of disposal fields in the following chapter. Septic privies, if constructed with capacity as given above, can later be converted into septic tanks if water is installed in the residence.

The septic privy is an excellent method of sewage disposal. If properly operated, it fills all sanitary requirements with minimum chance of nuisances arising. The amount of attention it requires is small but absolutely essential, and some failures in this type of toilet have been reported because of neglect. Septic privies may be constructed of tile and also of metal. The firms selling such tanks have in many cases asserted that complete liquefaction of the product would be accomplished with absolutely no attention. This, of course, has also resulted in unsatisfactory service.

A similar type of septic closet, known as the Lumsden-Roberts-Stiles, or L. R. S. type, designed by the U.S. Public Health Service has been used to some extent. In this case two barrels or two concrete tanks are used. The first barrel or tank receives the excreta, and in it liquefaction takes place. The effluent then runs into the second container which is emptied from time to time. The barrels, if used, are of small capacity and short life. The concrete tanks are an improvement, but in either case the effluent must be handled.

3-8. Chemical Toilets. Most chemical toilets are made by commercial firms and are sold under various trade names. They consist of a tank, usually cylindrical in shape, some 2½ feet in diameter, 4 feet long for one seat, with 3 feet additional length for each extra seat, giving a capacity of 100 to 125 gallons per seat. The tanks are generally constructed of 14-gauge copper-bearing steel, metal of this sort being required to withstand the action of the chemical used. The toilet seats are placed directly over the tank and consist of vitrified china bowls with wooden seats and covers. Ventilation is obtained by a flue rising from the seat bowl through the roof. The operation of this toilet depends upon the action of a caustic disinfectant and water. Caustic soda is the most favorable in its action and is almost exclusively used. Caustic soda not only kills all the bacteria but also liquefies the solids. For each toilet seat 25 pounds of caustic soda is dissolved in 10 to 15 gallons of water. This solution is poured into the tank and should last for six to nine months. At the end of this period the tank must be drained or emptied in some other fashion. Most tanks are equipped with a drain plug or valve in the bottom or at one end from which the liquid runs through a pipe into a leaching pool. The leaching pool is merely a hole in the ground which has been covered over and from which the liquid fecal matter seeps into the earth. The discharge from chemical toilets has also been used as fertilizer. If no gravity drain has been provided, the tank must be emptied by bailing or pumping. Some tanks are provided with overflows so that there is a continuous but slight discharge into the leaching pool. In this case, however, 3 or 4 pounds of chemical dissolved in 5 gallons of water should be added each month. The tanks which are completely drained must be recharged with the full amount of the chemical—25 pounds per seat.

Chemical toilets are also provided with some form of agitator which should be worked each time after the toilet is used in order to mix the chemical and the excreta. If this is not done, there is a possibility that there will be considerable floating matter which, being untouched by the chemical, will putrefy and result in unpleasant odors. When the toilets are used in schools, the janitors should be instructed in their proper use.

Poor operation will result in bad odors, and experience indicates that poor operation is not uncommon. The most important points are proper charging with chemical and agitation. It is also advisable to use toilet paper exclusively. No other wastes except human excreta should be

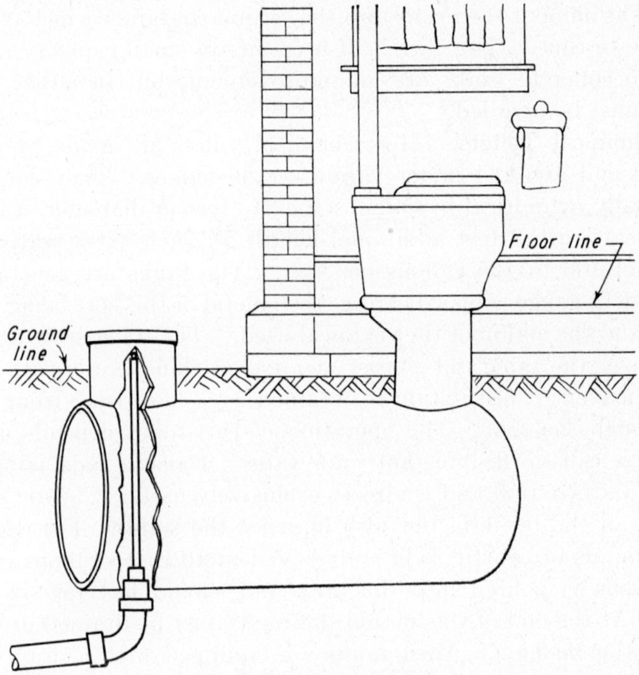

FIG. 3-3. Chemical toilet.

placed in the tank. Care should be taken after emptying a tank through the drain valve that the valve seats tightly when closed. Otherwise there is likely to be a leakage and a wasting of the chemical after recharging. If the leak is not noticed, this may result in an offensive condition in the tank.

Chemical tanks are also constructed in the form of a commode. This consists of a metal container which is equipped with an ordinary water-closet seat. The excreta fall directly into a pail having a capacity of about 10 gallons. The ventilating flue rises from the back. This type must, of course, be emptied at short intervals, approximately every week or ten days, and the charge of chemical will be 2 pounds or less.

Chemical toilets are useful only where it is not practical to install the water-carriage method. They are used by construction contractors in tropical areas and summer camps, and they have, in general, given fair service. If the toilets are properly charged, the material is completely sterilized so that there is no chance of disease dissemination. In areas where water pollution would not occur, certain chlorinated hydrocarbons, such as that known commercially as Chloroben, may be used to prevent the rapid decomposition of the contents of the tank. The action of the chlorinated hydrocarbons is not one of chemical change but, rather, serves to preserve the excreta present through inhibiting bacterial growth and action.

BOX-AND-CAN SYSTEM

3-9. Box-and-Can Privy. This consists of a metal can enclosed in a box, usually made of wood, the lid of which is the toilet seat. The can is removable through the top or side of the box which is hinged or otherwise made so that it can be opened. The box-and-can privy is sometimes used in the unsewered sections of cities and in small communities that do not have sewer systems. For satisfactory operation there should be a regular scavenger service, preferably under the supervision of the city authorities. This is necessary in order to ensure regular emptying and proper maintenance.

The box should be constructed of wood 1 inch thick, tongued and grooved and well stiffened with pieces of 1 by 2 or 2 by 2 at the corners. Ventilation is obtained by boring a row of holes in one side of the box an inch or two from the floor and running a galvanized pipe or wood flue from the box through the roof of the privy house. In order to exclude flies, screening of both the ventilating holes and the flue is necessary. A self-closing seat cover should also be used. Usually the top of the box through which the seat hole has been cut is hinged so that the scavenger can remove the can for emptying. In many cases the back of the box is the back wall of the privy house. A hinged door can be so placed that the scavenger can remove the can from the back of the toilet without entering it. Placing the toilets at the fence line along the alley makes for speed in scavenging. It is much more difficult, however, to keep the rear doors flytight than it is when the top or seat is hinged.

The cans are of galvanized iron, usually 14 to 16 inches in diameter and about the same in depth, with two handles. The scavenger removes the can and places it in his vehicle without emptying, putting a clean can in the place of the full one. A lid is placed upon the full can. After the conveyance has become loaded with cans, they are hauled to the point of disposal, emptied, and washed. Scavenging is done weekly, at ten-day intervals, or even biweekly. A truck or wagon is used to convey the cans to the points of disposal and washing. A double-deck truck can be constructed large enough to hold 40 to 50 cans, while 20 to 30 cans will be the limit of a wagon.

3-10. Administration of Box-and-Can System. The pail system was instituted in many small rural communities, but in many cases it was a dismal failure after a year or so of service, usually because it was not administered by the city or town government or because there was no governmental agency available to take it over. It has been found that installing such a system on the basis of voluntary payment by the toilet owners to a private scavenger is not successful. The best method is to require by ordinance a certain fee per can to be paid to the city. These ordinances generally require that payments be made quarterly in advance and that all toilets where sewerage cannot be obtained be of the box-and-can type and kept in good order. If the quarterly fees are not paid when due, there should be power under the privy ordinance to levy a fine upon the responsible persons. Practice varies as to whether the property owner or the tenant pays the fees, but in general the best results are obtained by collecting from the property owner. The fee should be made large enough to pay the cost of scavenging and the replacement of cans and other equipment. Charges should not be made too low, or there may be a tendency to avoid making sewer connections.

The box-and-can system is recommended only as a temporary measure in rapidly developing towns unable to finance sewage works and where soil conditions are unfavorable to pit privies.

3-11. Disposal of Collections. The material collected from the can sometimes presents a difficult disposal problem. It should never be deposited in running streams or open pits. Where a large sewer is available, the material can be dumped into it at some convenient point. Running water is usually supplied, and the cans are washed at the same time by means of a hose, the can washings also running into the sewer. As sticks, bricks, and other large objects are very frequently found in the cans, it is advisable to have a bar screen or grating over the opening to prevent the possibility of stoppage of the sewer. As the dumping process is likely to be accompanied by odors, it is advisable to place the dumping station at some point remote from habitations.

Can contents are sometimes emptied into the influent sewer at the entrance to the settling tank of the sewage treatment plant. Solids then settle with the sewage sludge and digest with it. In other cases a separate tank is provided for the can contents. They are dumped into the tank and water or sewage may be added, the liquid overflow in any case going to the settling tank of the sewage treatment plant. The solids either digest in the tank and are drawn off as digested sludge, or they may be pumped to a separate digestion tank. Such a procedure should be carried on only under the supervision of a qualified sanitary engineer, or trouble may arise.

Excreta or night soil has been disposed of by incineration. This, however, is almost impossible to accomplish without the production of very offensive odors. Burial is widely used. Trenches are dug, and the excreta deposited in them with immediate covering by replacement of the earth. Plenty of covering earth must be placed over the excreta or odors may escape. Fly larvae, which are frequently found in the contents of cans or vaults, may develop into flies which are able to penetrate several feet of loose earth. In any event the covering should not be less than 12 inches. Digestion of the excreta in the pit is slow—three or four years, possibly longer, being required to digest the contents completely.

BIBLIOGRAPHY

1. "United States Census of Housing, 1950: General Characteristics," U.S. Summary 1950 Housing Census Report H-A1.

CHAPTER 4

EXCRETA DISPOSAL WITH WATER CARRIAGE

4-1. Residences and institutions with running water will usually find it convenient to use a water-carried system of excreta disposal. Where there is no public sewer system, this involves a private sewer and sewage disposal plant. While the water-carried system allows toilets to be placed in the house, with an easy carriage of the wastes to the outside, the problem is complicated by the large increase in the bulk of the wastes caused by the addition of water. Again, the problem is particularly complicated where an individual must provide a private sewage treatment plant.

The problems of excreta disposal with water carriage are generally categorized as those of the individual sewage disposal systems or those of the municipal sewage disposal systems. Classed with individual sewage disposal systems are those serving residences, schools, camps, institutions, tourist courts, and others where municipal sewage disposal systems are not available. Municipal sewage disposal involves a collection system for an entire community and a central plant for the treatment and disposal of the wastes.

In the case of individual sewage disposal systems, too often the means of disposal to be used is a mere afterthought, to be solved by the digging of a cesspool or the building of a septic tank by a local workman who knows nothing of the principles of sewage treatment. Consequently, it is not strange that septic tanks are sometimes causes of trouble. Quite frequently in the neighborhood of the finest residences, there are ditches receiving tank effluent, or partially treated sewage, that vie with the more primitive toilets in terms of unpleasantness. In view of the difficulties encountered with such systems, individual sewage disposal systems cannot be recommended where a community sewerage system is available or could be organized.

INDIVIDUAL SEWAGE DISPOSAL SYSTEMS

4-2. Individual sewage disposal systems—those serving residences, tourist courts, camps, parks, churches, and the like—are likely to receive only a minimum amount of attention; therefore, the installations should be such that very little maintenance is required. The system should create no health hazards by contamination of drinking-water supplies or by exposure to rodents or insects which might serve as the means for transmission of disease. The system should be constructed so that a nuisance will not be created by odor or unsightly appearance. For individual sewage disposal systems, the septic tank system is one of the most acceptable methods. Cesspools are still used in some areas, although they are not generally recommended.

4-3. The Cesspool. The *cesspool* is the reverse of a well. The liquid wastes are run into a hole in the ground from which they seep off into the soil. The sides are usually lined with either brick or stone masonry, the joints laid without mortar so that the sewage will leach out. In the course of time the pores of the soil surrounding the cesspool may choke up, causing overflow. This results in a very offensive condition, one that is quite often encountered where cesspools are in use. The remedy is to dig a new pool. Cesspools sometimes receive the effluent from a septic tank, in which case they are less likely to become choked up. Others are constructed to receive wash water only, the closet wastes being conducted to a septic tank. When poorly covered, they allow odors to escape and are breeding places for mosquitoes. Cesspools are not, in general, recommended by health authorities because of the disadvantages cited. A pool might be used to advantage at an isolated home where underground formations are suitable, if there is no danger to the water supply. Cesspools are especially dangerous if they are located in limestone, for unfiltered sewage may then pass through crevices for long distances.

4-4. The Septic Tank, Principles. The septic tank is widely used in connection with sewage disposal from homes or other buildings where running water is available but where there are no sewers. It is simple to construct and requires little care or operation. It should be recognized, however, that it does not "purify" sewage. The tank effluent may contain disease bacteria and will still be putrescible.

Sewage is discharged into the tank, where it is retained, as quiescently as possible, for a period of twenty-four hours in residential tanks or for eight to twelve hours in tanks serving large numbers of people. During the retention period, from 60 to 70 per cent of the suspended solids of the sewage is removed, mostly by sedimentation, to form a semiliquid called sludge, which accumulates at the tank bottom; some of the solids, however, form floating scum. Both sludge and scum are acted upon by anaerobic bacteria to form gases and liquids. This is known as digestion, and during the process, pathogenic organisms are largely or completely destroyed; the solid matter is reduced in volume and changed in character. Well-digested sludge is very dark in color and homogeneous; it has a tarry odor and dries readily on sand beds. Dried sludge that is well digested forms a cake that is dark brown in color and granular in structure and that has only a slightly musty odor. Hookworm eggs may survive digestion and drying, but dried sludge is generally considered safe to use as fertilizer.

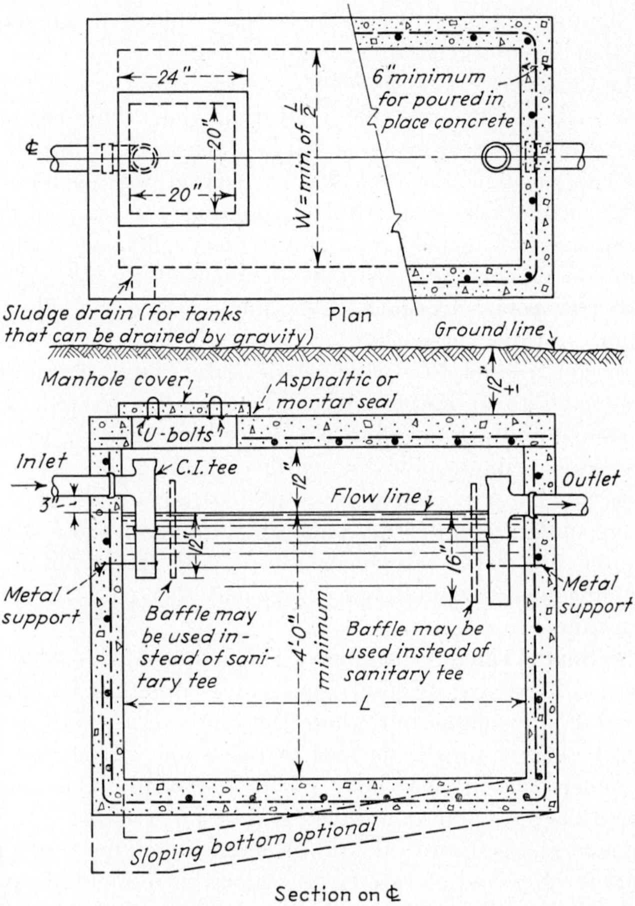

FIG. 4-1. Single-chamber septic tank. (*Individual Sewage Disposal Systems, Reprint* 2461, *U.S. Public Health Service.*)

Investigations made by the U.S. Public Health Service[1] have shown that the average accumulation of sludge in a septic tank is 0.92 cubic foot per person per year and that scum accumulation is 0.42 cubic foot per person per year. A properly designed septic tank must provide space for sewage retention to allow sedimentation and an additional volume for storage of scum and sludge between cleanings.

Direct currents between tank inlet and outlet must be prevented to ensure effective sedimentation. This is accomplished by using pipe tees with submerged ends as inlet and outlet or, as an alternative, a baffle wall at each end (see Fig. 4-1). The outlet pipe or baffle also retains the scum in the tank. About 75 per cent of the scum is submerged below the water line (flow line).

"Clear space" in a septic tank is the space between the upper level of the sludge and the lower level of the scum. It is established by the movement of sewage into and out of the tank. Its vertical dimension depends upon the depth of penetration of the outlet pipe or baffle and the plan area of the tank. The larger the plan area of the clear space, the lower the horizontal velocity and the more effective the sedimentation.

TABLE 4-1. CAPACITIES FOR SEPTIC TANKS SERVING INDIVIDUAL DWELLINGS

Number of bedrooms	Maximum number of persons served	Nominal liquid capacity of tank, gallons*	Recommended dimensions			
			Width	Length	Liquid depth	Total depth
2 or less	4	500	3′0″	6′0″	4′0″	5′0″
3	6	600	3′0″	7′0″	4′0″	5′0″
4	8	750	3′6″	7′6″	4′0″	5′0″
5	10	900	3′6″	8′6″	4′6″	5′6″
6	12	1,100	4′0″	8′6″	4′6″	5′6″
7	14	1,300	4′0″	10′0″	4′6″	5′6″
8	16	1,500	4′6″	10′0″	4′6″	5′6″

* Liquid capacity is based on the number of bedrooms in a dwelling. The total volume in cubic feet of a tank includes air space above liquid level.

As scum or sludge encroaches upon the clear space, horizontal velocity is increased, and solids are scoured out with the effluent. For tanks of usual dimensions the clear space is established at about 1 foot below the lower end of the outlet baffle or pipe, and the scum should not accumulate lower than 3 inches above the bottom of the outlet pipe or baffle. This means that with a 16-inch penetration of the outlet pipe or baffle the clear space will have a 15-inch vertical dimension. This, multiplied by the plan area of the tank, will give the minimum tank volume for sedimentation or sewage retention, and the rest of the tank volume is available for sludge and scum accumulation. Obviously, when the clear space has been reduced to 15 inches, the tank should be cleaned of sludge and scum.

Figure 4-1 shows a single-chamber septic tank. The greater depth at the influent end is favored by some health departments, since it may be expected that more settled solids will accumulate near the influent end; also, a greater depth at some point facilitates cleaning by pumping.

Two-chambered tanks were found to be somewhat more effective than single-chambered tanks in removing suspended solids. One-half of the required capacity is given to each chamber. The influent and effluent details of the cross wall are the same as provided for the tank influent and effluent. For a residential tank it is doubtful whether the extra expense of the cross wall is justified. Shallow tanks are somewhat more effective than deeper tanks, provided that the depth is not less than about 3 feet and that the required capacity is maintained. The dimensions shown in Table 4-1, however, are convenient and economical.

The remainder of the discussion is concerned with the more acceptable form of individual sewage disposal system, the septic tank, and the subsurface irrigation system.

4-5. Location of Septic Tanks. Septic tanks should be located so that they cannot contribute to the contamination of any spring or well or other potential source of domestic water supply. The tank should be at a minimum distance of 50 feet from such sources, and the surface drainage from the site should be away from all sources of water supply.

In locating the tank, consideration must also be given to the grade of the house sewer line and the contour of the ground where the subsurface tile for disposal of the liquid contents of the tank is to be laid. The recommended minimum grade for the house sewer is 1/8 inch per foot. The best performance is obtained from the subsurface drainage field if the tile is laid on a slope not exceeding 2 to 3 inches per 100 feet. Where the terrain will not permit the laying of straight laterals on a slope of 2 to 3 inches per 100 feet, the laterals might be allowed to follow the contours of the ground surface.

4-6. Septic-tank Details. There is some disagreement among state health departments as to the size of septic tanks for residential service. In general, it is believed that the minimum capacity should be 500 gallons below the flow line, with a space of not less than 1 foot above the flow line. Table 4-1 gives recommended dimensions and capacities related to contributors. The dimensions provide a clear space of 30 to 40 gallons per capita for each 15 inches of depth; with the usual water consumption for single families, this should provide a twenty-four-hour retention period for the sewage by the time that the tank should be cleaned. Sludge- and scum-storage space, calculated as 75 per cent of scum beneath the flow line, is provided for seven to nine years. It should be recognized that these figures are based upon average sludge and scum accumulations and that cleaning may be necessary at shorter intervals.

In Table 4-1 it will be noted that the number of bedrooms is related to tank capacity. This is preferable to consideration of actual inhabitants, as the number of bedrooms is a good indication of the probable maximum number of residents.

Table 4-2 gives dimensions and capacities for septic tanks to serve day schools and camps. These are based upon the fact that children are in school only a part of each weekday, not all week. Camp populations that may be served are also given. These figures are based upon the probability that water usage will be lower than in a residence and that the camp will not be used continuously. Tanks for schools and camps should preferably be specially designed, or, if the dimensions of Table 4-2 are used, the persons served, water-using habits, etc., should be checked against data given in Arts. 16-10 and 16-11. Tanks based on this table will probably require cleaning every two to three years.

TABLE 4-2. CAPACITIES FOR SEPTIC TANKS SERVING CAMPS AND DAY SCHOOLS

Maximum number of persons served		Nominal liquid capacity of tank, gallons*	Recommended dimensions			
Camps	Day schools		Width	Length	Liquid depth	Total depth
40	60	1,000	4′0″	8′6″	4′0″	5′0″
80	120	2,000	5′0″	11′0″	5′0″	6′3″
120	180	3,000	6′0″	13′6″	5′0″	6′3″
160	240	4,000	6′0″	18′0″	5′0″	6′3″
200	300	5,000	7′6″	18′0″	5′0″	6′6″
240	360	6,000	8′0″	20′0″	5′0″	6′6″
280	420	7,000	8′6″	20′0″	5′6″	7′0″
320	480	8,000	8′6″	23′0″	5′6″	7′0″

* Tanks with capacities in excess of 8,000 gallons should be designed for the specific requirements involved; however, in such cases the necessity for a more complete type of treatment should receive consideration.

Figure 4-2 shows a septic tank with a siphon chamber attached. The siphon chamber is filled from the septic tank and, when full, empties rapidly. The siphon chamber is of some advantage in the operation of a subsurface irrigation field as the quick rush of sewage doses the tile system more uniformly than can be expected by direct discharge from the tank. Time is also allowed for reaeration of the soil between doses. Siphons sometimes become inoperative, usually by clogging of the vent pipe, which can be seen in Fig. 4-2 on the left side of the bell section. They are little used except for large installations which will receive skilled operation.

Septic tanks are usually constructed of concrete. If made of brick, the interior should be carefully plastered with cement mortar to obtain a high degree of nonpermeability. Properly designed multicompartment tanks give as good or better performance than single-compartment tanks of the same total capacity[1]. If multicompartment tanks or tanks in series are used, each compartment or tank should have a capacity of at least 125 gallons, and the first unit should be as large or larger than the following unit or units. The inlet and outlet connections and baffles for each compartment should follow the principles set forth for inlet and outlet connections and baffles in single-compartment tanks, provided

Inside dimensions of septic tank		
No. of persons	Dimensions of tank	
	Inside width	Inside length
12	4′	8′
16	5′	9′
20	5′	10′
24	5′	11′

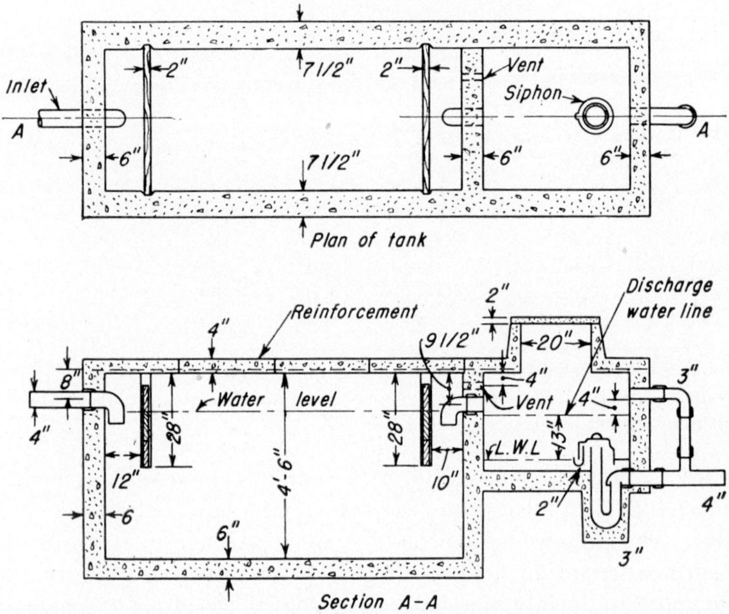

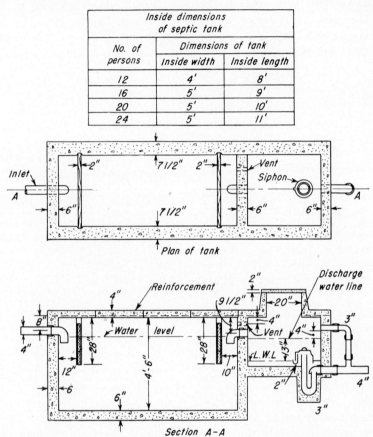

Fig. 4-2. Septic tank with siphon chamber as recommended by the New York State College of Agriculture, Cornell University. (*Extension Bull.* 48.)

such connections do not extend below the mid-depth of the liquid[2]. Lengths of concrete pipe 36 inches in diameter, with axes vertical, arranged to make a two-compartment tank, are satisfactory if requirements as to capacity and dimensions are satisfied. Steel tanks, cylindrical in shape, have also been used. If made of copper-bearing steel and coated with asphaltic paint, they should have a life of about seven years.

Tanks should be covered. The cover may be of narrow removable concrete slabs, or a manhole may be constructed in the cover. Tanks should be easily accessible for cleaning.

4-7. Condition of Septic-tank Effluent. A septic-tank effluent is not "purified." From 60 to 70 per cent of the suspended solids have been removed, but the dissolved solids still remain, together with soluble products of sludge decomposition. The effluent is dark in color and has a "septic" odor, which is caused by hydrogen sulfide and other odorous gases. Bacteria are present in great numbers. While many of them may differ in character from those of the original sewage, because the tank is a favorable breeding place for anaerobic bacteria, still there is no assurance that all pathogenic bacteria have been eliminated. At times the effluent may have large amounts of solids. This condition is usually caused by very great bacterial activity in the tank, which is responsible for much gas formation and turbulence.

The practice of discharging septic-tank effluent into ditches or on the ground surface causes nuisances and may be dangerous. The effluent requires further treatment to render it inoffensive.

4-8. Cleaning and Operation. As indicated above, residential tanks require removal of the indigestible residue of sludge and scum at intervals of seven to nine years, and larger tanks must be cleaned at shorter intervals. Tanks should be cleaned when an inspection indicates that scum and sludge are close to encroaching upon the required clear space. Inspection is difficult and involves determining scum thickness by means of a rod and a sampling of the sewage at various depths until sludge is encountered. The latter may be done by fastening a wide-mouthed bottle to a graduated stick and removing a stopper from the bottle by means of a wire. This is repeated at increasing depths until sludge is obtained in the bottle.

Tanks rarely, if ever, clog. If they are overfilled with sludge and scum, the sewage still passes through. However, raw solids remain in the tank, though an equal volume of digested or partially digested solids leaves. This is likely to make trouble in a tile disposal field or in any other method of secondary treatment that may be used.

Sludge and scum can be removed with a long-handled dipper or by means of a diaphragm pump. If the sludge is very compact, it may be necessary to agitate it with a jet of water or sewage so that the pump can take it. In areas where there are many septic tanks, there frequently are persons with pumps and tank trucks who clean them.

Large tanks are sometimes made with hopper bottoms with a sludge pipe leading from the lowest point and so arranged that by opening a valve the sludge can be drawn off. This arrangement is sometimes combined with a sludge-drying bed to which the sludge is run from the tank. The drying bed is made up of a 6- or 8-inch layer of cinders or fine gravel and underdrained by means of open-jointed pipelines 10 to 15 feet apart. The sludge is allowed to spread on the bed to a depth of about 8 inches, most of the liquid seeps away, and the solids dry to a cake. For small tanks the sludge may be dipped or bailed into a trench dug for the purpose, and earth is replaced over the sludge.

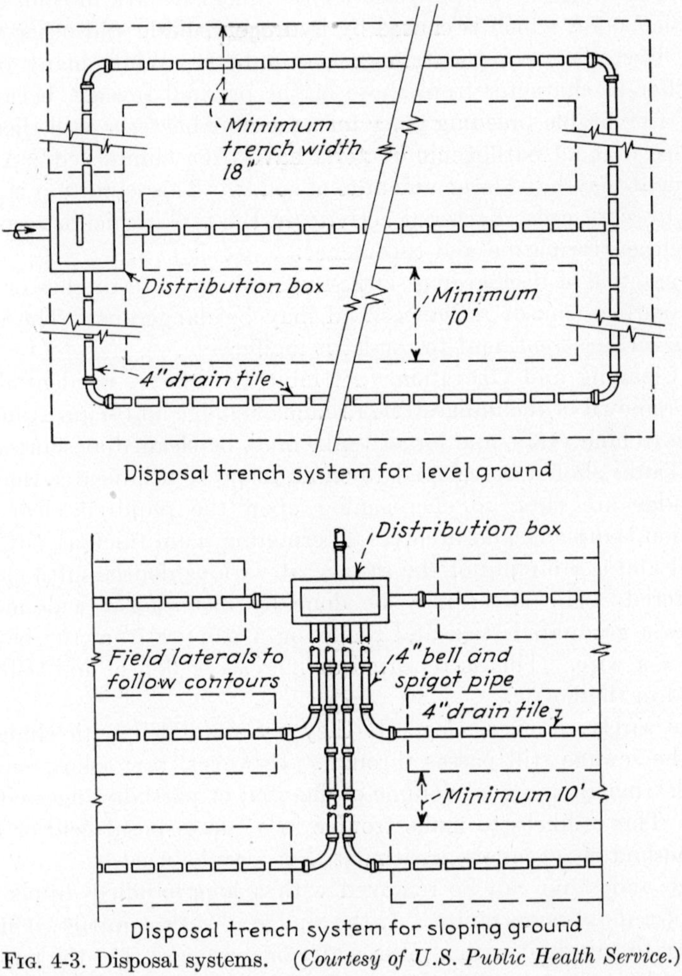

FIG. 4-3. Disposal systems. (*Courtesy of U.S. Public Health Service.*)

4-9. Distribution Box. A distribution box is a small tank which receives the effluent from the septic tank and from which the sewage enters the subsurface disposal field, sometimes called the absorption field. The distribution box regulates and equalizes the flow in all lines leaving the box and leading to the absorption field. The distribution box can also serve as an inspection manhole for observing the quality of the septic-tank effluent. The box should be connected to the septic tank with a tight line. The invert of the inlet pipe should be approximately 2 inches from the bottom. The outlet pipes may have the invert at the bottom of the box or approximately 1 inch above the bottom. The outlet pipes should all be at the same elevation. In addition to the advantages mentioned above, the distribution box makes it possible to shut off lines for repairs or to rest a part of the field when it becomes waterlogged.

4-10. The Soil-absorption Field. This method of septic-tank treatment and disposal is also called the tile disposal field or subsurface irrigation. It makes use of concrete or clay pipe laid with open joints so that the sewage can percolate into and through the soil. Filtration will remove suspended matters and aerobic soil bacteria, which obtain oxygen

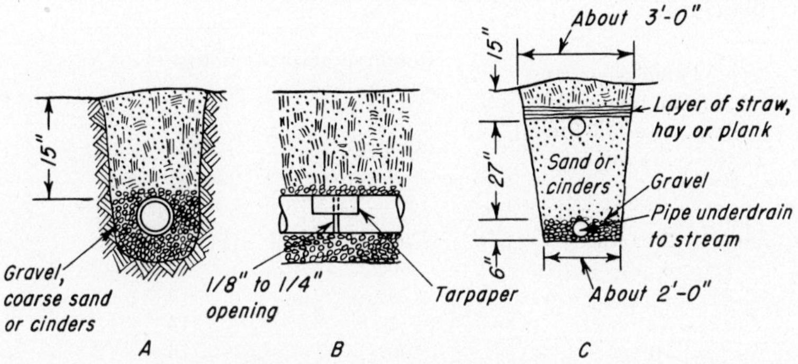

FIG. 4-4. (*A* and *B*) Arrangement of subsurface irrigation drains in ordinary soils. The opening between pipes varies from ⅛ inch or less near the upper end to ¼ inch at the lower end. (*C*) Arrangement in heavy clay soil. The layer of hay, straw, or plank prevents earth from clogging the sand or cinders. The underdrain empties into a stream.

from air in the soil pores and stabilize the organic matter, both suspended and dissolved, with which they come in contact. It is important that the receiving soil be naturally well drained, permeable, and of sufficient area. Heavy clay soils are not suitable, and limestone formations should be avoided, as fissures may allow unfiltered sewage to enter springs or wells.

In order to obtain a sufficient length of absorption trench, percolation tests may be made. A test is made as follows: A hole is dug or bored to the depth of the proposed pipe trench. It may be bored with an earth auger anywhere from 4 to 12 inches in diameter. The 4-inch hole is satisfactory and requires less work and water. After the hole is bored, the bottom and sides of the hole are scratched with a sharp instrument to provide a natural soil surface for the water to enter. All loose earth is then removed, and 2 inches of coarse sand or fine gravel is placed in the bottom to protect it from scouring or clogging by sediment.

The hole is then filled with clear water to a depth of 12 inches over the gravel. If necessary, it is refilled so that water will remain in it for at least four hours and preferably overnight. This is to allow the soil to become saturated and swelled as it will when the absorption field is operating. In very sandy soils swelling does not occur, and only saturation is needed.

If the water remains in the hole after the overnight period, the depth is adjusted to about 6 inches over the gravel, and after thirty minutes the drop in water level is measured. This drop is used to calculate the percolation rate, which is the time required for the water level to fall 1 inch, expressed in minutes. For example, if the water level drops 10 inches

TABLE 4-3. SOIL ABSORPTION FIELD DESIGN AREAS

Percolation rate (time required for water to fall 1 inch) in minutes	Required absorption area in bottom of trench, square feet	
	Residences, per bedroom	Schools, per person
2 or less	50	9
3	60	10
4	70	12
5	75	13
10	100	16
15	115	19
30	150	25
45	180	30
60	200	35
Over 60	Unsuitable for absorption system; investigate underground filter arrangement	

in thirty minutes, the percolation rate is three minutes per inch. If no water remains overnight in the hole, clear water is added to bring the water level to about 6 inches over the gravel. The drop in water level is then measured at thirty-minute intervals for 4 hours, more water being added as necessary. The drop that occurs in the last thirty minutes is used to calculate the percolation rate. Table 4-3 shows the absorption area, in square feet, required on the bottom of disposal trenches for different percolation rates. Table 4-4 gives trench dimensions, absorption areas per linear foot, and suggested spacing. In the absence of percolation tests, percolation areas provided per bedroom may vary from 50 square feet for most favorable soils to 100 square feet in average soils and 200 square feet or more in heavy soils. In any case a minimum of 150 square feet should be provided for each individual dwelling unit.

Seepage pits or filter wells are sometimes used where soil conditions are not favorable. They are holes located at the ends of the seepage pipes and at other points to catch sewage which the pipe cannot dispose of and from which seepage will take place into the deeper soil. They will be most effective if they penetrate into a soil more porous than that in which the pipe is placed. They should be covered and safeguarded against caving in. They are prohibited by some state health departments.

Plain-end drain tile 4 inches in diameter and 1 or 2 feet in length is generally used in the absorption fields. Ordinary sewer pipe, however, can also be used by placing the bell ends of the lengths downslope with the spigot centered in the bell by means of a small stone. In both straight-ended and ordinary sewer pipe, an opening of 1/4 inch should be left between lengths to allow the sewage to run out. The trench in

TABLE 4-4. SIZE AND MINIMUM SPACING REQUIREMENTS FOR DISPOSAL TRENCHES

Width of trench at bottom, inches	Depth of trench, inches	Effective absorption area, square feet per linear foot	Spacing of tile lines, feet*
18	18–30	1.5	6.0
24	18–30	2.0	6.0
30	18–36	2.5	7.5
36	24–36	3.0	9.0

* A greater spacing is desirable where the available area permits.

which the pipe is laid is filled with coarse sand, broken stone, gravel, cinders, or coke so that the pipe is surrounded for a distance of 6 inches on the bottom and sides and 2 inches on the top. This facilitates the taking up of sewage by the ground. To prevent earth or fine sand from entering and thereby clogging the open joints, the joints are protected with tar paper or with a layer of hay, straw, or plank, as indicated in Fig. 4-4. Since the bacterial activity of the soil is greatest near the ground surface, the pipe should not be placed too deep. On the other hand, if the disposal area is a field that will be plowed, sufficient covering must be given to protect the pipe from injury. For this reason, a depth of about 15 inches to the top of the pipe should be allowed. In northern climates where the ground freezes to a depth of 5 to 6 feet, it may be advisable to place the tile lines deeper than 15 inches, but never more than 3 feet. The trench may be dug below the frost line with the space between the pipe and the trench bottom filled with coarse gravel or crushed stone.

The grade given to the pipe should receive careful attention. If it is laid too steep there will be a rush of sewage to the lower ends with poor distribution closer to the tank. The best distribution is obtained by a slope or fall of 2 to 3 inches in 100 feet. The layout of the disposal pipe depends to some extent upon the shape and slope of the disposal field. The herringbone system has been used, but because Y-branches do not allow effective division of the sewage stream, other layouts are better.

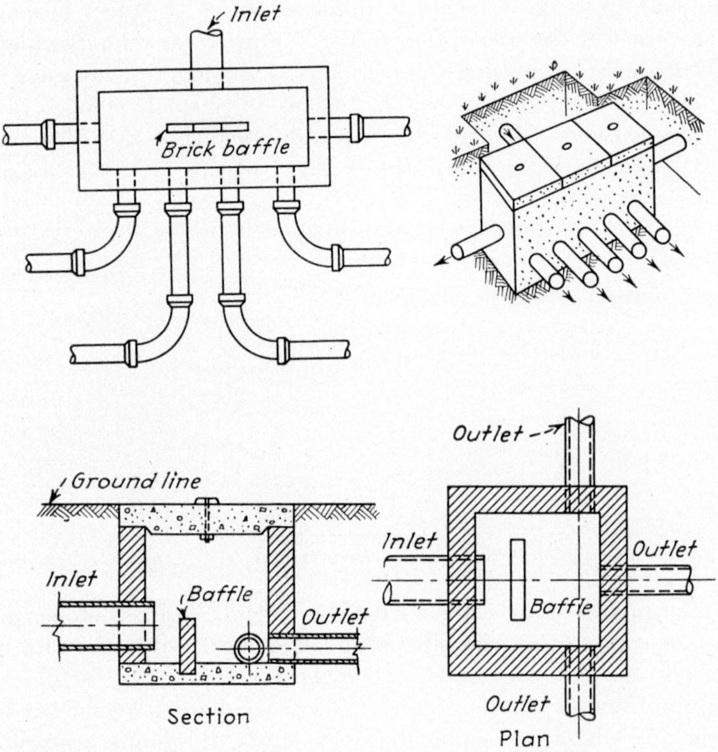

FIG. 4-5. Distribution boxes. (*Courtesy of U.S. Public Health Service.*)

If the ground slope allows, the pipe may be laid in straight lines or may follow contours, or it may be necessary to use a branch system. Since the horizontal distance of percolation through the soil will not ordinarily exceed 3 feet, the pipe branches are spaced as indicated in Table 4-4.

In soils with very low percolation rates an underground filter can be constructed, provided that the underdrain system has an outlet to some low point. The filter has an upper pipe to receive and discharge the septic-tank effluent and a lower underdrain, with 27 to 30 inches of cinders or coarse sand between, as shown in Fig. 4-4*C*. The trench area can

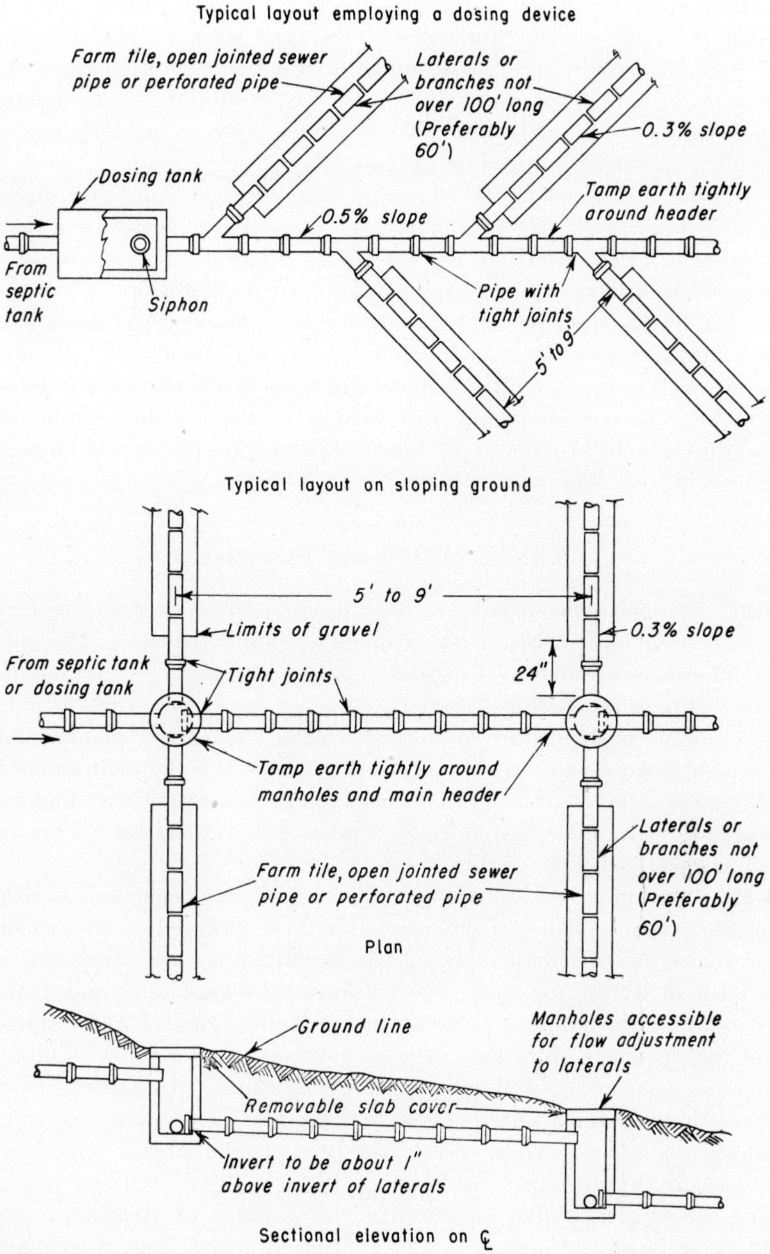

FIG. 4-6. Alternate layouts of absorption fields. (*After N.Y. State Dept. Health Bull.* 1 *and Univ. Florida Bull.* 23.)

be based upon the most favorable percolation rate of Table 4-3. The effluent from the underdrain will be clear and odorless, and should be free from pathogenic bacteria, although it should not be discharged where it may enter a body of water used for a water supply or for wading or swimming. It is desirable to obtain advice from a sanitary engineer prior to installation of an underground filter.

Since the earth and an underground filter recover from and digest a dose of sewage with the help of air, it is an advantage to have dosage intermittent rather than as a continuous trickle. This is one of the reasons that siphons are sometimes employed in septic tanks. But the same conditions may be obtained by having two separate units in the subsurface system with a switch box connecting them. Sewage is run into one section for a month or more and then diverted to the other section. This allows reaeration and drying of the resting section, does not imply a double amount of pipe. Half of the per capita allowance is placed in each section.

MUNICIPAL SEWAGE DISPOSAL

4-11. The principles that have been discussed in connection with residential sewage treatment are also applied by municipalities. The important differences are due to the greater size of the plants required and the larger volumes of sewage treated. Wastes from industrial establishments create problems in municipal sewage treatment plants. Also, more complicated methods are applicable because of the continuous and more expert attention that may be expected in connection with municipal treatment. The information given here is designed to aid operators of small sewage treatment plants.

4-12. Dilution. Sewage disposal by dilution has been used to a considerable extent by cities, particularly by those situated on the seacoast, large rivers, or the Great Lakes. As populations have increased and standards of living improved, the volumes of sewage requiring disposal have reached the point that treatment is being applied where dilution alone was formerly sufficient. Large volumes of water are required to dispose of raw sewage without offensive conditions. In general, twenty to forty times as much water as sewage is needed. Even with this volume of water available, however, other conditions in the stream, such as current and depth, must be considered.

The dilution available enters into the amount of treatment which must be given to the sewage. A city situated near a large river may be required by the state or Federal authorities to provide screening or sedimentation of the sewage, at least. If little dilution can be obtained, very complete treatment may be necessary.

4-13. Preliminary Treatment. Sewage frequently contains sand and other inorganic matter which should be removed before it is given further treatment. This is particularly true if the sewer system also receives storm water. The sewage, therefore, is passed through grit chambers, enlargements of channels in which the velocity is decreased sufficiently so that the heavy inorganic materials will settle, with the lighter organic matter remaining in suspension. Usually there are at least two grit chambers arranged so that the sewage flow can be diverted from one to the other. This permits removal of the grit when a chamber needs cleaning. In small sewage treatment plants, the grit is shoveled by hand from the chamber to wheelbarrows and is used to fill lowlands around the plant. A well-designed grit chamber should produce grit relatively free from organic matter. Cleaning is likely to be needed immediately after or even during a rainstorm; hence, the operator should be prepared to start cleaning operations promptly to prevent accumulation of grit throughout his plant. Apparatus for cleaning grit chambers mechanically, either intermittently or continuously, is used at some plants.

It is also necessary to remove sticks, rags, and other large floating materials which otherwise would form large amounts of scum on the sedimentation tank or clog the pumps. This is done by means of screens, usually constructed of iron bars with 1-inch or larger clear openings between them. Such screens need frequent cleaning, or they will clog and cause the sewage to overflow. The cleaning is done by means of rakes, and to facilitate this process the screen is placed at an angle of about 30 degrees to the bottom of the conduit and in such a manner that the openings allow an upward stroke of the rake. Large plants employ automatically cleaned screens. The screenings contain much water and are very offensive. They are sometimes allowed to drain for a time on a platform over the conduit. A liberal application of lime will prevent odors during this period. At small plants the screenings are usually buried.

4-14. Sedimentation of Sewage. Sedimentation consists of allowing sewage to run through a tank of such size that the velocity is low. This process has been universally used either as a preliminary treatment or as the only treatment if a large body of water is available for final disposal. The tanks operate continuously, and the retention period of the sewage may be from thirty minutes to three hours, depending upon the character of the sewage and the further treatment to be given. The sludge may be removed continuously with the aid of mechanical contrivances or drawn off at intervals from hoppers in the bottom. Septic and Imhoff tanks are special kinds of sedimentation tanks.

Plain sedimentation with separate sludge digestion is much used in present practice. The tanks may be rectangular or circular. They are usually constructed with slowly moving mechanisms having plows or blades which push the settled sludge to a hopper at the center or at one end of the tank. The sludge-moving mechanism may operate continuously or intermittently, as the operator deems necessary. Skimmers to remove the scum and discharge it to the sludge are usually included. The sludge may run by gravity or, more likely, may be pumped to a separate tank for digestion. The duties of the operator of a tank of this type are simple. He should see that the mechanism is operating properly

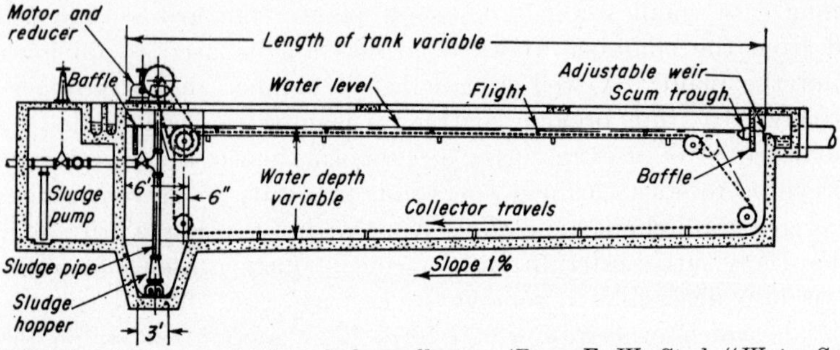

FIG. 4-7. Link-Belt straight-line sludge collector. (*From E. W. Steel, "Water Supply and Sewerage."*)

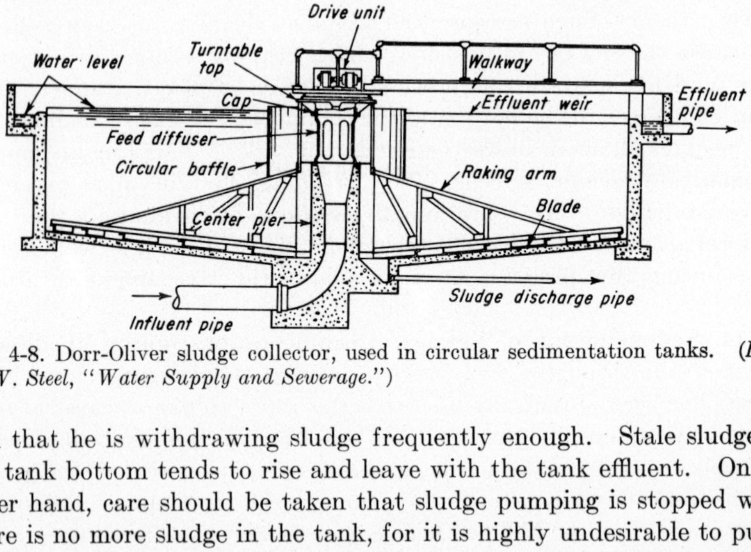

FIG. 4-8. Dorr-Oliver sludge collector, used in circular sedimentation tanks. (*From E. W. Steel, "Water Supply and Sewerage."*)

and that he is withdrawing sludge frequently enough. Stale sludge on the tank bottom tends to rise and leave with the tank effluent. On the other hand, care should be taken that sludge pumping is stopped when there is no more sludge in the tank, for it is highly undesirable to pump a large volume of sewage to the sludge-digestion tank. Figures 4-7 and 4-8 illustrate two types of sludge-collection mechanisms.

Chemical precipitation of sewage is also used. In this method certain chemicals are added to the sewage before it enters the sedimentation tank. The chemicals have the property of forming a heavy gelatinous floc which settles rapidly, carrying with it most of the suspended solids of the sewage. Lime, alum, ferrous sulfate, and particularly ferric chloride are used. Lime is used principally to add alkalinity to the sewage. Chemical precipitation has the advantage of greatly increasing the efficiency of sedimentation, but it is costly, requires careful chemical control, and produces a bulky sludge. This method is rarely used by small cities.

Septic tanks are much used for single residences and rarely by cities, even of small size. They are occasionally used for treating sewage from country clubs, rural schools, and public institutions. For such installations they are usually designed for a sewage-retention period of eight to twelve hours, and with sludge-retention capacities of 2 to 3 cubic feet per capita. Such tanks should be designed with hopper bottoms and pipes leading from them to allow easy withdrawal of sludge, or the sludge may be removed with a diaphragm pump. Partial withdrawal of the sludge, say at four- or six-month intervals, is more desirable than complete emptying. The raw sludge may be "seeded" by leaving some sludge, thus encouraging rapid digestion of the new raw solids.

The Imhoff tank, which gained its name from its inventor, Karl Imhoff of Germany, has been widely used. This tank is a variation of the septic tank. Two chambers are provided: the upper, or flow, chamber, through which the sewage passes at a very low velocity; and the lower, or sludge, chamber, in which anaerobic decomposition takes place. The solids of the sewage settle to the bottom of the upper chamber, which has sloping bottom walls. At the lowest point of the flow chamber is a slot through which the settled solids fall into the lower chamber. The slot is overlapped or trapped in such a way that gases generated in the sludge chamber cannot enter the flow chamber. A gas vent, also known as a scum chamber, is connected with the sludge chamber. The retention period in the upper chamber is short, usually about two hours. The capacity of the lower chamber is such that 2 to more than 3 cubic feet is provided for each person contributing sewage. Northern climates require the greater digestion space because of their lower mean annual temperatures.

Nuisance is sometimes caused at the gas vents by a black foam, which may reach such proportions as to spill over into the flow chamber. The foam is sometimes accompanied by very offensive odors. The odors can usually be reduced by placing lime in the gas vents, although this procedure may not stop the foaming. From 5 to 10 pounds of hydrated lime per 1,000 persons should be added daily until improvement is noted. This may require several weeks. Permanent improvement may be obtained by drawing off some of the sludge and using a hose to run water into the gas vents. Dumping well-rotted horse manure into the gas vents has resulted in improvement in some cases. This should also be done if the tank is completely emptied.

The sludge from the Imhoff tank is drawn off at intervals of one month to six weeks. Only the lower layers which have completely decomposed are drawn, however, some sludge being left to keep the tank seeded with anaerobic bacteria. The tank operator should remove all scum at least once a day from the sedimentation chamber. Disposal of the scum is most conveniently accomplished by placing it into the gas vents. The gas vents should be vigorously agitated daily by means of a wooden T-shaped contrivance to push down partially dried scum and release gas which is keeping it at the gas-vent surface. If this is not done, a

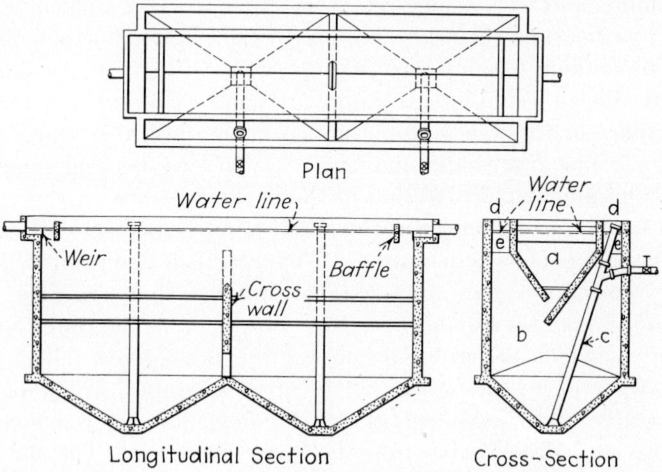

FIG. 4-9. Plan and sections of an Imhoff tank. (*a*) Sedimentation chamber; (*b*) sludge-digestion chamber; (*c*) sludge-withdrawal pipe; (*d*) gas chambers; (*e*) scum chambers.

heavy and deep plug of scum may form at the gas vents which will be difficult to remove. Careful attention to the operation details given here will increase efficiency of the plant and minimize odors.

4-15. Filtration. The treatment measures heretofore described reduce the oxygen required by the sewage to bring about stability, but the remaining demand must be satisfied to a large extent, or nuisance will result. The sewage filters described here are not true filters and provide little or no straining action. Primarily they serve two functions: to provide oxygen from the air and to provide surfaces where certain types of bacteria, the aerobes, can live and use that oxygen to oxidize the putrescible matter in the sewage to stable and inoffensive compounds, including nitrates and sulfates (see Fig. 2-1). Filters are frequently employed to accomplish this, and the two general types that are in use will be briefly described.

The *intermittent sand filter* consists of a layer of sand, not less than 30 inches deep, with underdrains, surrounded by gravel, to carry off the effluent. The settled sewage is applied by means of a dosing tank and siphon which discharge into troughs on the beds. The troughs have side openings which allow the sewage to flow on the sand, and blocks are placed under each sewage stream to prevent sand disturbance. After being applied to the filter for twenty-four hours, the sewage is switched to a second bed while the first bed rests. Usually three beds are worked in rotation. Intermittent sand filters must be dosed rather lightly, only 100,000 gallons per acre per day (considering the total acreage of the three beds; *i.e.*, beds totaling 3 acres could care for 300,000 gallons per day), but the effluent is better in quality than that resulting from any other type of treatment. The operator must be careful to see that dosing is properly done and that the beds are rotated. During the resting period, he should sweep or scrape off the dried sludge which accumulates on the sand surface. It may also be advisable to rake the sand surface occasionally. In the Northern states, where beds may freeze, the sand surface is raked into furrows leading from the dosing trough. Ice will form on the sewage surface between the furrows. This remains and forms a protective covering over the channel between the ridges. Intermittent sand filters produce excellent effluents.

Trickling filters are constructed of crushed stone or gravel of varying size placed in beds of varying depth. The sewage is applied to the bed surface, allowed to trickle over the stones, and collected in underdrains in the bed bottom. The oldest method of application is by means of sprays located at the surface of the bed. The sprays are operated intermittently by means of a dosing tank and siphon. A more favored method, now in general use, employs rotary distributors. The rotary distributor consists of two or more arms which are turned in a horizontal plane by the sewage as it escapes from orifices to fall on the bed. During the percolation through the bed, the sewage comes into contact with the bacterial film which has accumulated on the stones. The film is rather complicated biologically. Aerobic bacteria are the most important inhabitants, but there are also protozoa, algae, and, in the thicker portions, worms of various species. It is uncertain what part the organisms other than bacteria play, for it is the aerobic bacteria which reduce putrescibility by their oxidizing action. The film adsorbs solids which are worked upon by the organisms, after which they are released as a coagulated suspended material which is rather heavy and settles readily. A settling tank is provided to remove these solids before the effluent is discharged into a stream or otherwise disposed of.

Trickling filters are of two types: conventional, or standard, and high-rate, sometimes known as biofilters or aerofilters. In both types the sewage is first passed through a sedimentation tank, frequently called a primary tank. In the standard filter the bed is usually not less than 5 feet deep and the filter medium is crushed stone or gravel. A very commonly used size is 2½ to 3½ inches although 1½ to 2½ inches has been used. The dosing rate, or loading, is sometimes expressed as 2 to 4 million gallons per acre per day, with 2 to 2.5 million most common.

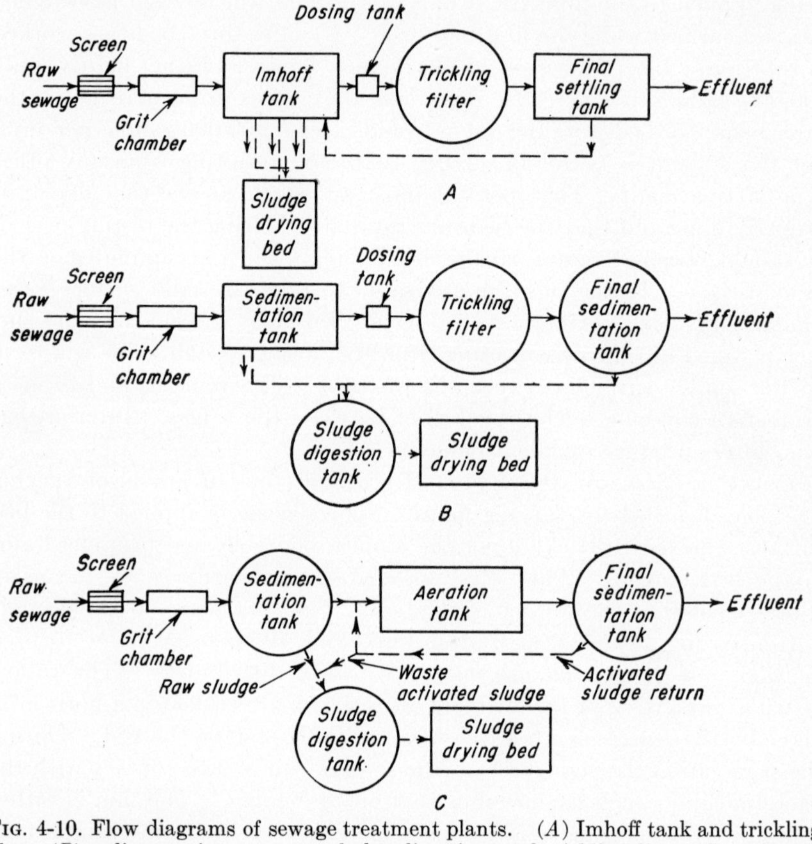

FIG. 4-10. Flow diagrams of sewage treatment plants. (*A*) Imhoff tank and trickling filter; (*B*) sedimentation, separate sludge digestion, and trickling filter; (*C*) activated sludge. Dashed lines show path of sludge.

A more logical method of expressing loading is in pounds of five-day biochemical oxygen demand per acre-foot of filter medium. State health departments specify limits for this and they vary from 250 to 600 pounds per acre-foot.[1]

The high-rate filters are loaded much more heavily—from 2,000 to 5,000 pounds of biochemical oxygen demand per acre-foot, with 3,000

[1] An acre-foot is a volume equal to an acre of area 1 foot thick, or 43,560 cubic feet, or 1,613 cubic yards.

most commonly used. The sewage loads are from 10 to 30 million gallons per acre per day, including any recirculated sewage. Filter media tend to be larger than for standard filters, at least 2½ to 3½ inches and in some cases 3 to 4 inches. Standard filter depths are usually less than those of the high-rate type. An important feature of the high-rate filter is the recirculation of sewage through the filter. Various recirculation schemes are used. A part of the filter effluent may be pumped back to the primary sedimentation tank to pass through it and the filter again, or effluent from the final tank may be pumped back to the entrance to the filter. Recirculation improves results by giving longer contact with the organic film on the stones, but the passage of a large volume of water through the filter washes off film before nitrification has had time to take place. Consequently, high-rate filter effluents may show good oxygen-demand reductions but little or no nitrification. Reduction of oxygen demand is by far the more important so far as quality of the effluent is concerned. Results of single-stage high-rate filtration, as described, are not as good as those of the standard filter.

Where results comparable to standard filters are desired, two high-rate filters are constructed and operated in series, sometimes with an intermediate sedimentation tank between them. Again, various recirculation schemes are used, the most common being to return part of the effluent from each filter to the influent of the same filter. The amount of sewage recirculated varies in different plants, the most widely used being a 1:1 recirculation, which means the recirculated sewage is equal in amount to the average flow to the plant. Loadings, where two filters are used, are based upon the total volume of filter medium.

Multiple high-rate filters, when properly designed and operated, can frequently accomplish results comparable to standard filters, at smaller first cost and with negligible addition to operating cost. In general, trickling filters can be designed to meet the sewage treatment needs for any situation. They are particularly well adapted to small installations because of their ability to take shock loads and their relative freedom from operating difficulty.

Sedimentation tanks generally have sludge-moving mechanisms and present no operating difficulties. Sludge and recirculation pumps will require attention. The devices used to apply the sewage to the filters, fixed sprays or rotating pipes, have nozzles or openings which clog and require cleaning. Should sewage stand on the bed or "pond," breaking the bed surface with a pick will remedy matters, although such a condition on a standard filter may indicate overloading. A small gray fly (*Psychoda*) sometimes breeds in filters in such numbers as to be a nuisance. A method of controlling them is to close the bed underdrain for twenty-four hours at intervals of a week or two. This floods the bed and drowns the fly larvae. Adults can be controlled by spraying resting places with DDT—a 5 per cent solution, emulsion, or suspension—at the rate of 1 quart per 250 square feet.

4-16. Activated Sludge. This method is used by both large and small cities but has been favored by the former. Sludge which has been aerated and thereby "activated" with aerobic bacteria is added to the settled sewage that is to be treated. The mixture of activated sludge and sewage is thoroughly agitated by compressed air, which is applied through porous diffusers at the bottom of the tank. At some plants mechanical methods, such as paddle wheels or impellers, are used to agitate the sewage-sludge mixture so that air will be absorbed from the atmosphere. The sludge, in its movement around in the sewage, together with the air, accomplishes

FIG. 4-11. Activated-sludge plant at Peoria, Ill. Diffused air is employed for aeration. (*Courtesy of Pacific Flush Tank Co. and Public Works Magazine.*)

the treatment. The solids in the sewage themselves coagulate into more sludge, leaving the liquid in a fairly well-nitrified condition. The sewage-sludge mixture is then allowed to settle, and the clear liquid is drawn off and discharged. Some of the sludge is retained for aeration and future addition to incoming sewage, while the balance must be disposed of by digestion or some other means. This system has the advantages of having a low first cost, being very flexible in its action, and giving a good effluent. The disadvantages are the skilled attention necessary, the high operating cost, and the large amounts of sludge which are produced and which must be disposed of.

The activated-sludge plant requires considerable attention on the part of the operator. He must ascertain the proportion of sludge which must be retained in the sewage-sludge mixture to obtain best results and so manipulate sludge wastage that this proportion is held. This is most easily done by taking a sample of the mixed liquid at the mid-point of the aeration tank in a liter graduate, allowing it to settle for thirty minutes, and noting the amount of sludge. About 20 per cent is commonly found to be desirable. An occasional trouble at activated-sludge plants is sludge bulking. This is characterized by a light fluffy sludge which will not settle normally in the secondary sedimentation tanks. The condition may be due to various reasons, such as underaeration, the presence of certain industrial wastes—especially those containing sugar or starch—or the presence of a filamentous fungus (*Sphaerotilus*) in the sludge. Chlorination of the sewage or use of lime to obtain a pH of 8 or more will help if fungi are causing the difficulty. Underaeration

FIG. 4-12. Activated-sludge plant at Carol City, Fla. Mechanical aeration is used. (*Courtesy of Yeomans Brothers Co. and Public Works Magazine.*)

can be remedied by using more air or, if this is not possible, by reducing the volume of sludge in the sewage-sludge mixture or bypassing the sewage around the aerating tank for a time until the sludge recovers. If injurious, industrial wastes may have to be eliminated from the sewage or perhaps treated at the industrial plant.

4-17. Oxidation Ponds. If sewage is retained in a pond or lagoon for a sufficient time, its biochemical oxygen demand will be satisfied in large part, and it will cease to be putrescible. This change is effected by aerobic bacteria, which use oxygen derived from the atmosphere and from the work of algae. The algae play an important part in this process. They are active in sunlight and break down the carbon dioxide, which is produced during the carbon cycle from the carbohydrates of the sewage, and use the carbon to produce more carbohydrates and release oxygen into the water[3]. Settled sewage is generally applied to ponds, and 1 acre of pond area is commonly provided for each 50 pounds of oxygen demand that must be satisfied each day. As an example: A sewage flow is 200,000 gallons per day and its biochemical oxygen demand after sedimentation is 110 parts per million. The pounds of oxygen demand to be satisfied daily will be $(200,000 \times 8.34 \times 110) \div 1,000,000$, or 183 pounds. (*Note:* 1 gallon of water weighs 8.34 pounds.) This weight of oxygen demand would require 3.66 acres. A rough method of approximation is 1,000 persons to 1 acre of pond area.

Oxidation ponds are constructed by building embankments of earth; more than one, operating in parallel or series, may be used. They must be properly designed. Shallow ponds permit penetration of sunlight to all parts of the sewage and thus encourage algae growth. On the other hand, rooted aquatic plants may then cause trouble and encourage mosquito breeding. A compromise is a depth of 3 feet. It is usual to discharge influent to the middle of a pond so that wind currents will cause some mixing; otherwise a concentration of influent sewage may result in odors. At some plants influent points may be changed to prevent such concentration.

Operation is simple and is little more than changing the sewage-entrance point, if this is possible and desirable; the removal of weeds which may grow on the embankments at the water edge; and mosquito control. Mosquitoes should give no trouble if marginal weeds are absent, but if they develop, the methods described in Chap. 9 can be applied. In warm, dry climates where the earth is porous, evaporation and percolation may dispose of the sewage. Effluents, where they occur, can be used for irrigation or discharged into streams.

4-18. Disinfection. Since the methods of sewage treatment described cannot be depended upon to eliminate all disease bacteria from sewage, the state health departments require that sewage be disinfected before it is discharged into a body of water which is used for bathing or other recreation or for a water supply. The action and use of the various forms of chlorine in purifying water are described in Art. 5-18, and a similar method is used in disinfecting sewage, except that larger doses are required because the larger amounts of organic matter in sewage tend to neutralize the chlorine. Chlorine residuals are not generally obtained, and dosages may be regulated by reductions in coliform organisms or total count. A 99.9 per cent reduction in coliforms, for example, may be considered as having eliminated the less resistant disease bacteria. Recommended dosages in parts per million by weight are as follows: sewage which has been settled only, including Imhoff-tank effluent, 10 or more; trickling filter effluent, 3 to 7; intermittent sand-filter effluent, 2; activated-sludge effluent, 5.

4-19. Sludge Disposal. In Art. 4-4, sludge decomposition or digestion in septic tanks was briefly described. In Imhoff tanks and separate sludge-digestion tanks, a similar process takes place. Speedy digestion is desirable, and this is obtained when the sludge temperature is fairly high (100°F), and when the acidity and alkalinity of the sludge are in proper balance—in other words, when the sludge is slightly on the alkaline side. Some digestion tanks are heated by means of pipe coils circulating hot water, while the slight alkalinity is retained by a proper relation between the amount of the incoming raw sludge and the well-digested sludge already in the tank. To ensure adequate capacity, tanks should be designed so that 2 to 6 cubic feet is allowed per person served. It is important that engineering studies be made in each case to determine the proper design figure. The operator must not, however, draw off too much well-digested sludge at one time, or the balance will be upset, with resultant odors and foaming. The separate digestion tank presents another problem. As sludge is pumped into it, an equal amount of liquid, known as supernatant liquid, is displaced and overflows. This is much clearer than the sludge, but it is very strong and will make trouble in a stream. It is usually returned to the plant with the raw sewage, but even there it places a heavy burden on the plant. Its volume should be kept as small as possible by careful control of sludge pumping.

The digested sludge is usually placed on beds of sand or cinders for drying. It dries into a dark-brown porous material, which is used for fertilizing or filling low places. The sludge which is produced by the activated-sludge treatment, unless it is digested, does not dry well on beds. If land is available, the sludge is sometimes discharged into lagoons or into low areas, where it forms a pond. Through vacuum filtration and chemical treatment, the sludge may be readily dewatered, and advantage may be taken of its fertilizing value, which is much higher than that of the sludge produced by other processes. When dried, it can be sold to commercial fertilizer manufacturers.

The gas produced by digesting sludge is normally composed of about 65 per cent methane, 30 per cent carbon dioxide, and the rest hydrogen and nitrogen. It resembles natural gas and can be used as fuel. Since about 0.6 cubic foot is produced per day per person contributing sewage, the amount is considerable, and at some municipal sewage treatment plants the gas is used for operating engines or, more often, for heating the sludge to promote quick digestion.

4-20. Irrigation. One of the earliest methods of disposal of sewage was to apply it to the land in intermittent doses, thereby taking advantage of the capacity of the soil for mineralizing nitrogenous material. This, however, requires a large area of porous, open soil to take care of large amounts of sewage. Crops such as hay or other cattle feed have been raised on land so treated. The growing of vegetables for human consumption in this manner is discouraged by health authorities.

While this means of sewage disposal is no longer a major method of treatment, it is being used to a considerable extent in the western part of the United States, where the rainfall is light and water is comparatively scarce. The sewage is applied in the same manner as irrigation water. The sewage has some nitrogenous elements which are useful as plant food, but they are present in such small amounts that they are of little consequence. The value of sewage in irrigation for cropping lies in its moisture content, and not in its organic constituents. Application to the land must be carefully supervised, or nuisances may result. It should be emphasized that irrigation with sewage is primarily a disposal method, and in some cities no soil cultivation or crop raising is practiced.

4-21. What Can Be Expected of Sewage Treatment. Sewage treatment has several purposes: (1) to render the sewage inoffensive so far as nuisances are concerned; (2) to prevent destruction of fish and other wildlife; (3) to reduce or eliminate the danger of contaminating water supplies, bathing areas, and shellfish. Insofar as these ends are accomplished, stream pollution is prevented. There are several factors which enter into a solution of the problem: (1) bodies of water which receive sewage, raw or treated, have a capacity for self-purification; (2) water which is to be used for public purposes will usually require treatment of some sort if it is derived from surface sources, and such treatment can take care of a considerable degree of pollution; and (3) cost of sewage treatment and water treatment must be kept at a reasonable figure, and degree of treatment directly affects cost.

A decision as to the amount of treatment a sewage will require calls for competent sanitary engineering judgment. State health department requirements must be satisfied, and these are based upon engineering knowledge. Such requirements, however, are subject to modification according to the situation. The preceding articles have indicated that there are many methods of sewage treatment, and various combinations of them will produce results that the engineer can predict with as much accuracy as is needful. He can also predict, after appropriate studies, the self-purifying capacities of a stream and its possible sanitary hazards. He can, therefore, prescribe sewage treatment that will meet the existing situation at a minimum cost. Accordingly, some sewage treatment plants provide screening only to remove large floating matter which might be unsightly in a ship channel or outer harbor. Others, which discharge into large rivers, may provide only sedimentation, with or without disinfection. Still others give full treatment, which includes sedimentation, then one of the oxidizing treatments, such as filtration or activated sludge, and disinfection.

Just as important as good engineering in plant planning and design is adequate operation of the plant. The skill and technical knowledge required will depend upon the size and complexity of the plant, but even the smallest plant deserves an operator who is conscientious and who has some knowledge of the principles of sewage treatment; otherwise the public investment in the plant will be largely wasted.

4-22. Industrial Wastes. Liquid wastes produced by meat-packing plants, creameries, breweries, textile plants, oil refineries, paper mills, and many other industries are known as industrial wastes. They are increasing in volume and constitute an increasing problem. In cities they are discharged into the sewers and add to the volume and strength of the sewage. This places a financial burden upon the city for treatment cost, which may be very great in the case of a small city which has a large waste-producing industry. The city which encourages the establishment of such an industry within its limits should also insist upon the industry's paying its share of treatment costs. Industries outside of city limits which pollute streams must be controlled by the state department of health or other governmental agency. Pollution of navigable streams or boundary streams is controlled by the Federal government or by interstate compacts.

Some industries, such as creameries, oil refineries, or manufacturers of chemicals, may produce wastes which are inimical to the bacteriological processes used in sludge digestion, sewage filtration, and activated-sludge treatment. These may have to be eliminated from the sewers and given special treatment at the industrial plants. It is encouraging to note that many industries in cities and elsewhere are assuming responsibility for reducing the strength and volume of their wastes and for treating them to prevent stream pollution.

The logical approach to the industrial-waste problem would be (1) to study the plant processes and reduce the volume of waste, if possible; (2) to control the discharge of the waste so that the wastes reach the plant during periods of low flow or to discharge the wastes at a constant rate over the twenty-four-hour period so that large amounts of waste are not discharged into the sewerage system in a short period of time; (3) to provide pretreatment so that the municipal sewage treatment plant is not overloaded or its operation interfered with; (4) to provide separate complete treatment for the industrial wastes.

In pretreatment or separate treatment of wastes, screening is an important initial step. Screening methods are available that in some instances provide sufficient solids removal. Removal of settleable solids by sedimentation, occasionally augmented by coagulation, will provide partial treatment that may be adequate for the larger receiving streams. Where chemicals are used for flocculation, increased efficiency of solids removal is gained at the expense of aggravating the problem of sludge disposal. Biological treatment is the most economical method for treatment of highly diluted organic wastes. Aeration facilities have been developed that are amenable to industrial-waste treatment, and activated sludge is believed to have a great potential in this field. Certain wastes ordinarily considered to be toxic, such as Kraft paper mill and phenolic wastes, have been successfully handled in activated-sludge systems. Biological filters, particularly of the high-rate type, have been used for economical treatment of numerous types of wastes. Anaerobic treatment processes have been successful in removing 95 per cent of the five-day biochemical oxygen demand and 90 per cent of the suspended solids at loadings up to 0.2 pound biochemical oxygen demand per cubic foot of digester volume per day. Toxic materials, such as cyanides and hexavalent chromium, may be rendered innocuous through chemical treatment. Land disposal methods have found their use in this field as well as in domestic sewage treatment; here spray irrigation, oxidation ponds, and deep injection wells have often been used. Incineration of combustible liquid waste is applied in some instances. An example is the centrifugation and incineration unit of Imperial Oil, Ltd., of Sarnia, Ontario.

4-23. Radioactive Wastes. The disposal of radioactive wastes is potentially a serious public health problem. Governmental projects and industries utilizing radioactive substances are concerned with the disposal of such wastes, and a great deal of research has been and is now being conducted to determine feasible methods of disposal. Only natural nuclear disintegration will render these radioactive products harmless, and nothing can be done to prevent or accelerate the rate of disintegration. The methods of disposal may be grouped into two classifications: storage and burial. Disposal by storage would involve storing the material until the radioactivity has been reduced to a nondangerous level. This method is practical only when the half-life of the substance is short. When burial is used as the means of disposal, the material may be buried in the earth or placed in concrete and buried at sea. Prior to burial, the radioactive material may be concentrated by coagulation and sedimentation, evaporation, or other methods. Precipitation and removal of some radioactive isotopes from water is possible by multiple passes through a sludge-blanket type of sedimentation basin. This would hardly be economically feasible except under very unusual conditions. Biological treatment systems have been investigated, and it has been found that biological processes can be utilized for certain radioactive wastes.

4-24. Training of Sewage Works Operators. It has long been recognized that a sewage treatment plant cannot perform efficiently unless it is under the supervision of an operator trained in sewage works operation. It is generally accepted now that certification or licensing of sewage plant operating personnel is advantageous, not only to the individual concerned, but also to the general public, to the local officials, and to state and local health departments. Training programs for treatment plant operators have a history of more than thirty years in the United States. Training programs in most states have been set up by the state or regional water- or sewage works association in cooperation with the state health department and a local college or university. Training is provided in the form of annual short schools at colleges or universities, correspondence courses, district or regional short schools, district water and sewage conferences, and state health department in-plant training programs.

Some states have laws requiring licensed or certified operators, but the training programs in most states are operated on a voluntary basis. The sewage works profession recognizes the need for a certification or licensing program and generally recommends that the program be compulsory, not voluntary. It is further recognized that the agency passing on the qualifications of the sewage plant operators should be the same agency that has supervision of plant operation. The personnel of the supervising agency may be assisted by a leading educator in the field of sanitary engineering in the state and also by a leader in the sewage works profession in the state, preferably a superintendent of sewage plant operation.

BIBLIOGRAPHY

1. "Studies on Household Disposal Systems," pt. III, U.S. Public Health Service, 1954.
2. "Statement of the Joint Committee on Rural Sanitation, on the Research Report," March, 1949.
3. Smallhorst, D. F., B. N. Walton, and Jack Myers: "The Use of Oxidation Ponds in Sewage Treatment," paper presented before the American Public Health Association, Engineering Section, Nov. 10, 1953.
4. Black, Hayse H.: The Future of Industrial Waste Treatment, *Sewage and Ind. Wastes*, vol. 26, no. 3, p. 300, March, 1954.
5. Black, Hayse H.: Industrial Waste Treatment Practice, *Civil Eng.*, October, 1955.
6. Hardenbergh, W. A.: "Sewerage and Sewage Treatment," 3d ed., International Textbook Company, Scranton, Pa., 1950.
7. Fair, G. M., and J. C. Geyer: "Water Supply and Wastewater Disposal," John Wiley & Sons, Inc., New York, 1954.
8. Metcalf, L., and H. P. Eddy: "Sewerage and Sewage Disposal," 2d ed., McGraw-Hill Book Company, Inc., New York, 1930.
9. Steel, E. W.: "Water Supply and Sewerage," 3d ed., McGraw-Hill Book Company, Inc., New York, 1953.
10. Theroux, F. R., E. F. Eldridge, and W. L. Mallmann: "Laboratory Manual for Chemical and Bacteriological Analysis of Water and Sewage," 3d ed., McGraw-Hill Book Company, Inc., New York, 1943.
11. "Standard Methods for the Examination of Water, Sewage, and Industrial Waste," 10th ed., American Public Health Association, New York, 1955.
12. "Manual for Sewage Plant Operators," 2d ed., Texas Water and Sewage Works Association, Austin, Tex., 1955.
13. Phelps, E. B.: "Stream Sanitation," John Wiley & Sons, Inc., New York.

CHAPTER 5

WATER—GENERAL CHARACTERISTICS, TREATMENT, AND PROTECTION

5-1. Practically all the water that appears in public or private supplies has been exposed to pollution, while falling as rain, while running over the ground surface or in streams, or while percolating through the soil. The growth of population in most areas of the United States and the increasing use of streams and other bodies of surface water for the disposal of wastes have been detrimental to water supplies, particularly to surface supplies and to a lesser extent to ground waters. The sanitary engineer has solved the problem of good water supplies for cities or other large consumers by treatment of water and also by treatment of liquid wastes. The small water supply for the rural home has not shared in the general improvement and will therefore receive special attention in this chapter, although the principles of water treatment will be briefly stated.

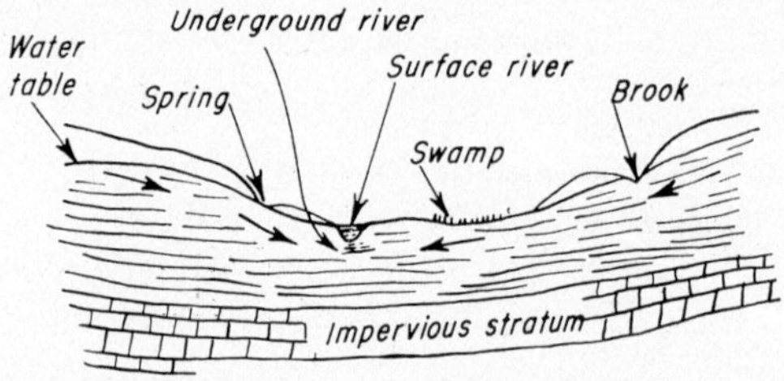

FIG. 5-1. How the ground-water surface or water table follows the contour of the land.

5-2. Underground Water. Of the rainfall, some runs off immediately to streams or other surface bodies of water, and some, the infiltration, goes into the soil. Of the infiltration, some is taken up by plants to be transpired from their leaves; some is held in the soil by capillary action; and some percolates through the soil. The percolating water passes vertically downward until it meets an impervious stratum of material, then moves in a nearly horizontal direction toward some outlet. As it saturates the upper soil it will develop a water table, which is at the elevation in the ground that the hydraulic conditions develop. Under these conditions, movement will usually be toward a valley bottom, the water table following roughly the ground surface and the outlet being the stream in the valley or the springs on the hillside. Wherever the water table outcrops at the ground surface, water will appear as a spring, pond, swamp, or stream. Flow from springs or from the banks or bottom of the river into the river itself is the dry-weather flow. If the river bed is of sand or gravel, there may be a well-defined water flow beneath the surface stream and in the same direction. In many cases the undersurface flow is present after a stream has dried. These conditions are shown in Fig. 5-1. When a well is drilled into such a formation, the water will rise into it to the elevation of the water table. Such a well is sometimes called a water-table or shallow well.

In some areas there are layers or strata of pervious materials which outcrop at the ground surface or just under the surface soil and then dip

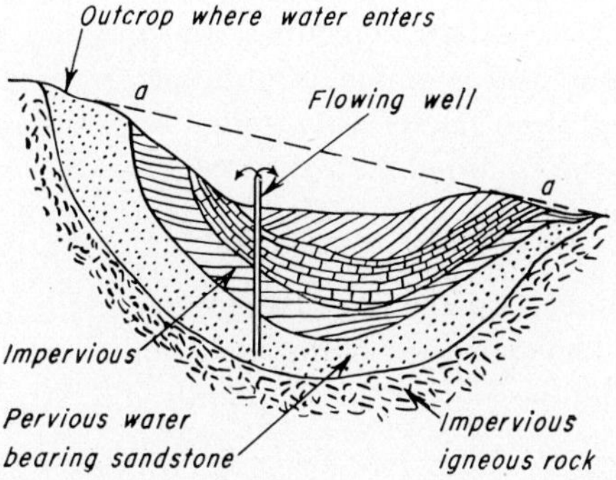

FIG 5-2. How artesian wells are formed. *aa* is the line to which the water would rise if the well casing were extended upward.

at some angle below the surface, becoming deeper with distance from the outcrop. Where such a geologic formation, or stratum, has other strata above and below it which are impervious, a water-carrying formation, or aquifer, results. It might be considered an underground reservoir through which water slowly moves toward some outlet, which might be at a great distance, possibly even under the sea. When a well is drilled into such a stratum, the water rises above the top of the aquifer and is known as an artesian well. If the water rises above the ground surface, it is a flowing artesian well (see Fig. 5-2).

Water-table wells are relatively shallow, and it is possible for water to enter them which has not percolated far through the soil. Artesian wells are deep, and the water they furnish has percolated long distances. Percolation through soil is rather slow. In gravels, velocities of 30 to 400 feet per day have been noted, depending upon size, while at the other extreme, velocities in waterbearing sandstone may be as low as 50 feet per year.

5-3. Impurities in Water. Pure water is not found in nature. As rain condenses in the atmosphere and falls toward the earth, it absorbs dust and such gases as carbon dioxide and oxygen. After reaching the surface of the ground, it immediately is exposed to pollution by organic matter. The polluting matter is dangerous if it includes the excreta of man. In any event, at the ground surface the water absorbs more carbon dioxide from the vegetation, as well as nitrogenous and other material from decomposed organic matter, and if it runs off into a stream it takes with it a considerable amount of suspended material, such as clay and sand.

The water which seeps into the ground is filtered naturally as it is drawn by gravity to the subsurface water, but it may or may not receive sufficient filtration to remove pollution. As it percolates through soil or rock, it dissolves and carries with it various mineral matters, the amount depending upon the distance of percolation and the minerals present. As the percolation continues, the original pollution tends to disappear, until the water which is obtained from deep wells may be expected to be free from bacteria and other organic matter.

To summarize, the common impurities of water can be listed as follows:

1. Entrained gases: carbon dioxide, hydrogen sulfide, methane, oxygen, nitrogen.

2. Dissolved minerals: calcium, magnesium, sodium, iron, manganese, their carbonates, bicarbonates, hydroxides, chlorides, sulfates, fluorides, nitrates, silica, and possibly other minerals discharged with industrial wastes.

3. Suspended and colloidal materials: bacteria, algae, fungi, protozoa, silt, and colloidal matter causing water to be acid or have color.

The type of treatment facilities needed to render the water palatable and satisfactory for its intended uses is determined by the types of impurities present and their concentrations.

5-4. Water and Disease. The most important of the water-borne diseases are those of the intestinal tract; they include typhoid fever, the paratyphoids, dysentery, and cholera. A few parasitic worms may also be disseminated by water. All are due to organisms from the intestinal discharges of patients or carriers which obtain entrance into drinking water. Other diseases which have been found, or suspected, to be transmissible by water include infectious hepatitis, gastroenteritis, tularemia, and tuberculosis. The disease gastroenteritis resembles food poisoning. It is not caused by specific organisms, but there is epidemiological evidence that it can be transmitted by water. The disposal of radioactive material also may bring about adverse physiological effects in human beings who consume water which contains these materials in concentrations above toxic limits.

Public health literature abounds in records of water-borne typhoid fever epidemics caused by the entrance of intestinal discharges from persons having typhoid fever, or from carriers of the disease, into surface sources of supply, shallow wells, or springs and wells penetrating limestone formations. Many factors have contributed to the tremendous decline in the incidence of water-borne diseases. Improved sanitation of public water systems—including improvement in water purification methods, operating practices, waste treatment facilities, and well construction—and vigilant laboratory control have played important roles.

Illness may also be caused by water which has been highly polluted with decaying organic matter, such as dead animals, even in the absence of specific disease germs. Digestive disturbances and diarrhea may

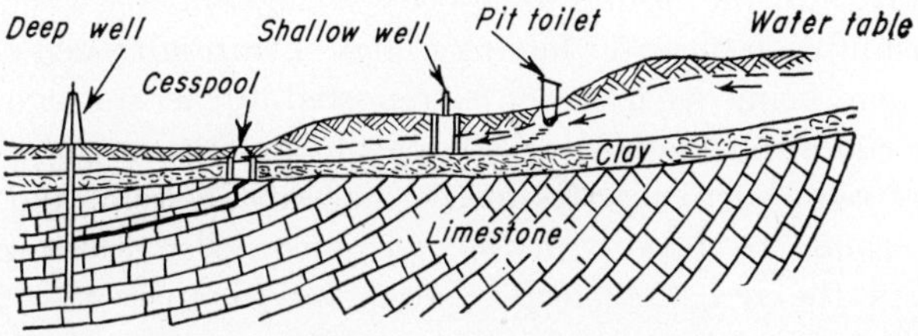

FIG. 5-3. How pollution may enter wells through soil pollution and by means of fissures in limestone.

result from such causes. Water containing very large numbers of bacteria has also been considered a cause of intestinal irritation, particularly in small children.

When a corrosive water is transported through pipes constructed of certain metals, the concentration of the metal in the water may reach toxic limits. The rate of reaction may vary in accordance with the amount of free or dissolved oxygen or carbon dioxide present, the concentrations of free mineral acids and acid salts such as alum and magnesium chloride, the temperature of the water, and the velocity of the water flowing through the pipes. Lead pipe has been used for transportation of hard waters without ill effects; however, it should not be used for the distribution of soft, acid water or water having a high concentration of oxygen or chlorides, for if any lead is dissolved in such water, it may have toxic effects. Lead is not found in natural waters.

In many areas ground water contains fluorides in excess of 1.5 parts per million, a proportion which causes fluorosis, or "mottled enamel," of the teeth. Such injury, however, occurs only during the formation period of permanent teeth, so that fluorosis only affects children up to around eight or nine years of age, after which the teeth do not become mottled or otherwise damaged by fluorides to any appreciable extent. During the early period of development, children living in regions where ground water has excessive fluorides should be given rain water or bottled water of low fluoride content for drinking, and this water should also be used in preparing their food. Since, however, appropriate amounts of fluorides in drinking water protect against dental caries, or tooth decay, it is most desirable to dilute water containing excessive fluorides with water which is "fluoride-free" or of low fluoride content in order to maintain a fluoride content of 1.0 to 1.5 parts per million. Individual household units for fluoride removal are available. These involve contact media, such as bone char, tricalcium phosphate, or activated alumina, which are replaced with new media when the unit is no longer effective in the removal of fluorides. A pilot plant using activated alumina has been established in one Texas city for removing fluoride from the public water supply, and the results have been successful.

The consumption of water having a high nitrate-nitrogen content or of milk formulas using such water is reported to be the cause of "blue babies," a condition known as "idiopathic" methemoglobinemia. The nitrates are reduced to nitrites in the digestive system, and these enter the blood stream to unite with the red blood cells, resulting in the discoloration of the red blood cells and in interference with the oxygen-carrying capacity of the blood. This condition may cause the death of infants only a few weeks old, but in many instances it is reported that rapid correction of the physiological deficiencies is made when infants suffering from this condition are provided with nitrate-free water. A nitrate-nitrogen concentration of 10 parts per million has been suggested as a safe upper limit.

There is no evidence that excessive concentrations of calcium, magnesium, carbonates, sulfates, chlorides, silicates, or other minerals commonly found in water are likely to form kidney or gallstones. Highly mineralized water, especially that which has a high sulfate content (in excess of 250 parts per million, theoretically combined with magnesium ions), may cause disorders of the alimentary tract in persons not accustomed to the water in a particular locality.

5-5. Chemical Examination of Water. A chemical analysis of a water indicates its history from its origin as rainfall to the point of collection. Water, originating as rain, upon reaching the earth's surface is soft, or relatively free from minerals, and has a tendency to become corrosive as it comes in contact with the earth's surface minerals or geological formations. It dissolves carbon dioxide, hydrogen sulfide, oxygen, methane, or other gaseous impurities, and such minerals as calcium, magnesium, iron, manganese, sodium, fluorides, chlorides, sulfates, silicates, carbonates, bicarbonates, and aluminum. It is also likely to pick up such organic impurities as ammonia nitrogen, nitrite nitrogen, nitrate nitrogen, and colloidal matter. The finely divided colloids may impart an undesirable color and will never settle without an artificial aid.

During the early stages of water-supply development, considerable attention was directed to the collection of chemical-analysis data, such as the chloride concentration and the presence of the nitrogen-cycle constituents cited in the preceding paragraph. Analysis for these characteristics was classified as a "sanitary chemical analysis" to obtain an indication of the sanitary quality of the water. Today this type of analysis is used primarily to appraise the efficiency of waste treatment facilities and is made in conjunction with routine sewage or industrial-waste analyses. It includes tests for suspended solids, biochemical oxygen demand, oxygen consumed, and hydrogen sulfide. In some instances, however, these data together with quantitative bacteriological examinations (most probable number) are used in appraising the sanitary aspects of surface-water sources subject to development for potable water supplies.

The routine chemical analysis made on developed water sources is usually to determine the acceptability of the water for drinking and household purposes, boiler use, manufacture of ice, preparation of beverages and foodstuffs, manufacture of paper, the dyeing of textiles, and other industrial usages. The results of these analyses also show what corrective treatment should be considered to reduce soap consumption, to improve boiler operation, to minimize corrosion, to prevent "red-water" troubles, to adjust treatment processes at the plant, and to solve special problems. All analysis results are expressed in terms of parts per million (pounds of indicated substance per million pounds of water) with the exception of pH, which is given as a number between 0 and 14 with a decimal fraction thereof. For example, water having a pH of 7.0 is neutral, neither acid nor basic, whereas a pH of less than 7.0 shows water to be acid, and a pH of more than 7.0 shows water to be basic or alkaline.

In collecting samples of water for chemical analysis, of either the routine or the sanitary type, a clean gallon glass container should be used. The cap or stopper should not be subject to corrosion. After thorough cleaning, the container should be rinsed with the water to be analyzed, and the water collected should be representative of the water normally available, unless special considerations are involved. All samples should be identified to show location of water-sample source (city, county, state), name of person collecting, purpose of chemical analysis, source of supply (well, spring, lake, stream, pond, etc.), point in system from which sample was collected (at well-pump discharge, prior to treatment, distribution-system tap, etc.), date of sample collection, and name and address of individual to whom the analytic report is to be sent. If the sample is collected from a well, the type and depth of the well should be given, and the water level, whether low, normal, or high, should be stated. A comment might also be made as to the physical appearance of the water during normal conditions.

5-6. Bacteriological Examination. Several types of determinations are available to the bacteriologist in evaluating the sanitary status of water quality. From a routine public health standpoint, it seems necessary to determine whether the water for drinking and household purposes is contaminated or whether it is safe. If only such information is desired, the routine examination is made to learn whether the laboratory test shows the presence or absence of coliform organisms, harmless bacteria which are used as indicative organisms. The coliform organisms are most commonly found in sewage, since they have their origin in the intestinal tract of warm-blooded animals. They are also found in soil and in water which has been subjected to pollution by dust, insects, birds, small animals, surface drainage, or flood waters or has been contaminated during construction of new, or rehabilitation of old, water facilities. Since the primary purpose of the "qualitative test" is to prove the effects of past contamination and the effects of pollutional hazards, the general opinion is that water samples for this examination should be secured only from individual water supplies which are protected adequately from contamination. Also, samples from new or repaired wells should not be submitted for bacteriological examination until the wells have been fully developed and disinfected with chlorine in an approved manner, since the water is exposed to contamination during the construction or rehabilitation program. Likewise, when new pumping equipment is installed or the existing equipment is withdrawn from the well for repairs, a similar procedure should be followed.

Quantitative tests estimating the density of coliform organisms may be made. These are useful in determining the extent of water treatment facilities necessary to render unprotected ground water and surface water safe for human consumption, in establishing the sanitary status of water for oyster production and recreational purposes, and in measuring the effects of the discharge of putrescible wastes into streams, lakes, or coastal waters. This type of bacteriological examination involves the collecting of water samples in sterilized containers, the immediate icing of the samples to inhibit multiplication or death of the coliform organisms, and the setting up of the laboratory examinations as promptly as possible. By using quantities of the sample varying in geometric series, *i.e.*, 0.01, 0.1, 1.0, and 10.0 milliliters, and by applying the usual test for coliform organisms, it is possible to determine a statistical estimate or the "most probable number" (MPN) of coliform organisms per 100 milliliters of water from tables or from calculations.

In addition to these tests, plate counts can be made which give information as to the total number of bacteria present per milliliter of water, even though the Public Health Service Drinking Water Standards[1] do not consider water quality from this standpoint. Also, in recent years the membrane filter has been in the process of development, and its use for determination of quantitative coliform density has been included in the tenth edition of "Standard Methods of Examination of Water, Sewage and Industrial Wastes"[5] as an optional procedure, approved by the Public Health Service, to be used in conjunction with the standard MPN procedures.

5-7. Method of Bacteriological Examination. An understanding of the method of bacteriological examination of water is of value to the sanitarian, although he may not be required to do more than interpret the reports of the tests. The total count of bacteria per milliliter is found by placing a milliliter of the sample on a sterilized glass plate which contains a sterile film of agar. The agar is a medium upon which the bacteria will multiply. The plate is then placed in an incubator and kept at a temperature of 35°C, or approximately body heat. After twenty-four hours the plate is examined. Under these favorable conditions of food and temperature each bacterium will have multiplied enormously and will have formed, with its increase, a colony on the agar. The colonies show up as spots which are visible to the naked eye and can be counted, thereby giving the number of bacteria in the original sample of water. In some cases the samples are also incubated at 20°C, which is approximately room temperature. At this temperature a different count will be obtained than at 35°C, but for public health work it is considered more indicative to find the count of the bacteria that multiply at body temperature.

Coliform organisms have the faculty of fermenting lactose, the fermentation being indicated by formation of gas trapped in small inverted tubes placed in larger test tubes, designated as fermentation tubes. A mixture of lactose broth and beef broth is placed into the larger tube, containing the inverted smaller tube, and is placed into an autoclave for sterilization. After sterilization and cooling of the tubes and liquid media, 10 milliliters of the water sample, by means of sterilized pipettes, is placed into each of the five tubes containing the media. In some instances, 100-milliliter samples of water are treated in lieu of 10-milliliter samples. The tubes containing the desired portions of the sample are placed in an incubator and are incubated for twenty-four hours at 35°C. At the end of the twenty-four-hour period of incubation, the number of the five tubes showing the presence of gas is recorded, and a loopful of the media in the tubes showing gas formation is transferred to sterilized tubes containing 2 per cent brilliant green bile lactose broth, to determine whether the gas production was due to coliform organisms or sporeformers, which also have the ability to ferment lactose.

The lactose tubes which did not show the production of gas at the end of twenty-four hours are left in the incubator for an additional twenty-four hours to allow more time for the slow lactose fermenters to grow and produce gas. If, at the end of forty-eight hours, gas is present in the tubes which did not show gas at the end of twenty-four hours, transfers are made from them to a brilliant green bile liquid confirmation medium, as was done at the end of the first twenty-four-hour period of incubation. After twenty-four and forty-eight hours' incubation, results of the tests with the brilliant green bile lactose broth are recorded. The formation of gas under these conditions constitutes a "confirmed test." Techniques are available for a "completed test" for absolute evidence of the presence of coliform organisms. They are not used, however, in routine bacterial analyses of drinking water.

The number of tubes showing positive results and the presence of coliform organisms are indicated on the analysis report. This information is used in computing compliance or noncompliance with the Public Health Service Drinking Water Standards, as outlined in Art. 5-9. A sample-analysis report card may show the absence of coliform organisms, or it may show that coliform organisms were found in one to five of the 10-milliliter portions tested for each sample. From a public health standpoint, however, any indication of contamination or the presence of coliform organisms should be sufficient to warrant immediate correction to remove existing contamination and to safeguard the water from subsequent contamination.

5-8. Collection of Samples for Bacteriological Analyses. Unless the sample is collected in a sterile bottle and every precaution is taken to prevent accidental contamination of the sample during its collection, the results of the bacteriological examination are meaningless. The following procedures should be meticulously observed:

1. Select a sampling tap which is in such a condition that leaking of water around the turnkey does not occur. The sampling tap should preferably be one of the nonwasher type, and the outlet should not have threads for connection of water hoses, etc. The location of the tap should also be relatively free from dust-borne contamination. Taps should also be selected at points where a representative water sample can be obtained.

2. Flush the faucet or sampling tap thoroughly to remove stagnant water from the supply line; then flame with a blowtorch, alcohol lamp, or other flaming device to remove contamination, which no doubt exists on the exterior and on portions of the interior of the sampling tap.

3. After flaming the sampling tap, open it and allow the water to run freely for at least five minutes to remove the water which may have been heated during the flaming operation and to cool the sampling tap.

(a)

(b)

(c)

FIG. 5-4. Collection of a water sample. (a) Flame faucet; (b) collect water sample; (c) package sample bottle. (*Photograph courtesy of Texas State Department of Health.*)

4. Remove the rubber band from the sterile bottle secured from a public health or commercial laboratory, leaving the paper, foil, or cloth hood in place. Grasp the bottle cap with the hood and turn cap to loosen. Holding the cap with the hood, remove the cap from the bottle and fill the container with the water to be tested to within ½ inch of the top. Replace the cap and rubber band with the hood still in place. Do not rinse the sample bottle with water to be tested or empty any material which might be present in the bottle before the sample is taken. While the bottle is being filled, hold the cap through the hood in your hand. Do not allow your fingers or any other object to come in contact with either the cap or the lip of the bottle.

5. Complete the sample-identification-analysis report card, giving all information requested by the laboratory performing the examination.

6. Examine samples as soon as possible after collection. If possible and practicable, keep the samples at 0 to 10°C until you are ready to examine them. Any deviation from the temperature requirement should be stated in the record of examination. If the water to be tested has a chlorine or chloramine residual present, sterilized bottles containing sodium thiosulfate should be used to neutralize it at the time of collection.

5-9. Department of Health, Education, and Welfare, Public Health Service Drinking Water Standards. On Jan. 22, 1913, the Secretary of the Treasury appointed a commission upon the recommendation of the Surgeon General, U.S. Public Health Service, to consider the establishment of a bacteriological quality standard for drinking water to be used in the administration of the Interstate Quarantine Regulations as they relate to the drinking water supplied to the public by common carriers operating in interstate commerce. On Oct. 21, 1914, the Treasury Department adopted the standards recommended by the commission. The original Standards were revised in 1925, 1942, and 1946. The 1946 Standards have been accepted by resolution by the American Water Works Association and also by the state departments of health as criteria of quality for all public water supplies with acceptable laboratory procedures to be followed as prescribed by the latest issue of "Standard Methods for the Examination of Water, Sewage and Industrial Wastes"[5].

Current standards of water quality from both the bacteriological- and chemical-analysis standpoint prescribe that the following be met:

3. AS TO BACTERIOLOGICAL QUALITY

3.21. Of all the standard 10-ml. portions examined per month in accordance with specified procedure, not more than ten (10) per cent shall show the presence of organisms of the coliform group.

3.22. Occasionally three or more of the five equal 10-ml. portions constituting a single standard sample may show the presence of organisms of the coliform group, provided that this shall not be allowable if it occurs in consecutive samples or in more than:

(*a*) Five per cent of the standard samples when 20 or more samples have been examined per month.
(*b*) One standard sample when less than 20 samples have been examined per month.

Provided further that when three or more of the five equal 10-ml. portions constituting a single standard sample show the presence of organisms of the coliform group, daily samples from the same sampling point shall be collected promptly and examined until the results obtained from at least two consecutive samples show the water to be of satisfactory quality.

3.23. Of all standard 100-ml. portions examined per month in accordance with the specified procedure, not more than 60 per cent shall show the presence of organisms of the coliform group.

3.24. Occasionally all of the five equal 100-ml. portions constituting a single standard sample may show the presence of organisms of the coliform group, provided that this shall not be allowable if it occurs in consecutive samples or in more than:

(*a*) 20 per cent of the standard samples when five or more samples have been examined per month.
(*b*) One standard sample when less than five samples have been examined per month.

Provided further that when all five of the standard 100-ml. portions constituting a single standard sample show the presence of organisms of the coliform group, daily samples from the same sampling point will be collected promptly and examined until the results obtained from at least two consecutive samples show the water to be of satisfactory quality.

4. AS TO PHYSICAL AND CHEMICAL CHARACTERISTICS

4.1. *Physical characteristics.*—The turbidity of the water shall not exceed 10 p. p. m. (silica scale), nor shall the color exceed 20 (standard cobalt scale). The water shall have no objectionable taste or odor.

4.2. *Chemical characteristics.*—The water shall not contain an excessive amount of soluble mineral substance, nor excessive amounts of any chemicals employed in treatment. Under ordinary circumstances, the analytical evidence that the water satisfies the physical and chemical standards given in sections 4.1 and 4.21 and simple evidence that it is acceptable for taste and odor will be sufficient for certification with respect to physical and chemical characteristics.

4.21. The presence of lead (Pb) in excess of 0.1 p. p. m., of fluoride in excess of 1.5 p. p. m., of arsenic in excess of 0.05 p. p. m., of selenium in excess of

0.05 p. p. m., of hexavalent chromium in excess of 0.05 p. p. m., shall constitute grounds for rejection of the supply.

These limits are given in parts per million by weight and a reference to the method of analysis recommended for each determination is given in section 4.31. Salts of barium, hexavalent chromium, heavy metal glucosides, or other substances with deleterious physiological effects shall not be added to the system for water treatment purposes.

Ordinarily analysis for these substances need be made only semiannually. If, however, there is some presumption of unfitness because of these elements, periodic determination for the element in question should be made more frequently.

Where experience, examination, and available evidence indicate that such substances are not present or likely to be present in the water supplies involved, semiannual examinations are not necessary, provided such omission is acceptable to the reporting agency and the certifying authority.

4.22. The following chemical substances which may be present in natural or treated waters should preferably not occur in excess of the following concentrations where other more suitable supplies are available in the judgment of the certifying authority. Recommended methods of analysis are given in section 4.3.

Copper (Cu) should not exceed 3.0 p. p. m.
Iron (Fe) and manganese (Mn) together should not exceed 0.3 p. p. m.
Magnesium (Mg) should not exceed 125 p. p. m.
Zinc (Zn) should not exceed 15 p. p. m.
Chloride (Cl) should not exceed 250 p. p. m.
Sulfate (SO_4) should not exceed 250 p. p. m.
Phenolic compounds should not exceed 0.001 p. p. m. in terms of phenol.

Total solids should not exceed 500 p. p. m. for a water of good chemical quality. However, if such water is not available, a total solids content of 1,000 p. p. m. may be permitted.

For chemically treated waters, i. e., lime softened, zeolite or other ion exchange treated waters, or any other chemical treatments, the following three requirements should be met:

(1) The phenolphthalein alkalinity (calculated as $CaCO_3$) should not be greater than 15 p. p. m. plus 0.4 times the total alkalinity. This requirement limits the permissible pH to about 10.6 at 25° C.

(2) The normal carbonate alkalinity should not exceed 120 p. p. m. Since the normal alkalinity is a function of the hydrogen ion concentration and the total alkalinity, this requirement may be met by keeping the total alkalinity within the limits suggested [in table on page 87] when the pH of the water is within the range given. These values apply to water at 25° C.

(3) If excess alkalinity is produced by chemical treatment, the total alkalinity should not exceed the hardness by more than 35 p. p. m. (calculated as $CaCO_3$).

pH range	*Limit for total alkalinity (p.p.m. as $CaCO_3$)*
8.0–9.6	400
9.7	340
9.8	300
9.9	260
10.0	230
10.1	210
10.2	190
10.3	180
10.4	170
10.5–10.6	160

5-10. Application of Drinking Water Standards. The Drinking Water Standards have been widely adopted by the states, cities, and other suppliers of water to the public, and time and use have demonstrated the practicability and value of the bacterial requirements.

The strict application of the criteria for chemical quality is somewhat difficult in certain areas, since water of the recommended total mineral content is not available for development, and the development of more remote sources of water supply is not practicable from an economical standpoint. In all instances, water made available for public use should not contain toxic materials, and it should be of such chemical quality as to be suitable for the intended beneficial usages.

5-11. Treatment of Water. The development of plant facilities for rendering contaminated surface water or ground water of questionable bacteriological quality safe and palatable for municipal and domestic purposes requires the application of the basic sanitary sciences, such as chemistry, bacteriology, biology, limnology, rheology, and sanitary engineering. Preliminary planning of water treatment plant works should include a comprehensive study of the catchment area: (1) size, topography, population density, surface geology; (2) sources of pollution; (3) sewage treatment facilities; (4) raw-water characteristics, including physical, chemical, bacteriological, and biological characteristics; (5) rainfall and runoff data; (6) evaporation data; (7) anticipated water-supply requirements, minimum, maximum, and average; (8) other items of importance in providing a safe water supply, adequate in amount for the community in question.

For the purpose of classifying and evaluating raw-water quality with respect to its treatment requirements, the U.S. Public Health Service has offered the following criteria:

Group I. Water Requiring No Treatment. This group is limited to underground waters not subject to any possibility of contamination, and meeting, in all respects, the requirements of the Public Health Service Drinking Water Standards, as shown by satisfactory, regular, and frequent sanitary inspections and laboratory tests.

Group II. Water Requiring Simple Chlorination, or Its Equivalent. This group includes both underground and surface waters subject to a low degree of contamination and meeting the requirements of the Public Health Service Drinking Water Standards in all respects except as to coliform bacterial content, which should average not more than 50 per 100 ml. in any month.

Group III. Waters Requiring Complete, Rapid-Sand Filtration Treatment or Its Equivalent, Together with Continuous Postchlorination. This group includes all waters requiring filtration treatment for turbidity and color removal, waters of high or variable chlorine demand; and waters polluted by sewage to such an extent as to be inadmissible to Groups I and II, but containing numbers of coliform bacteria averaging not more than 5,000 per 100 ml. in any one month and exceeding this number in not more than 20 per cent of the samples examined in any one month.

Group IV. Waters Requiring Auxiliary Treatment in Addition to Complete Filtration Treatment and Postchlorination. This group includes waters meeting the requirements of Group III with respect to the limiting monthly average coliform numbers, but showing numbers exceeding 5,000 per 100 ml. in more than 20 per cent of the samples examined during any one month and not exceeding 20,000 per 100 ml. in more than 5 per cent of the samples examined during any month.

Note. "Auxiliary treatment" as used here is presedimentation or prechlorination, or their equivalents, either separately or combined as may be necessary. Long-time storage, for periods of 30 days or more, represents a permanent and reliable safeguard which in many cases would provide something more than an effective substitute for one or both of the two other methods indicated.

Not only should the above bacterial requirements be met, but water acceptable for treatment should not contain any toxic or otherwise harmful substances or any organisms that are not readily and completely removable by the treatment facilities provided.

5-12. Storage and Plain Sedimentation. When surface water is confined in impounding reservoirs or natural lakes, the water undergoes purification by the action of sedimentation, sunlight, and oxidation. As a result of these natural means of purification, suspended matter, or turbidity, is considerably reduced, color is reduced by sunlight, putrescible matter is decomposed and oxidized by biological activity, and bacterial content is reduced. In view of the beneficial results obtained by long-time storage of water, it is advantageous to withdraw water directly from lakes instead of streams, which may receive contamination from the immediate watershed or from the local sources of pollution. Artificial reservoirs will make available raw water of more uniform quality and reduced turbidity, which will facilitate treatment. Presettling tanks or basins, if required or deemed advantageous, should be located or operated so that they will not receive flood waters. There should be at least two, in order to permit continuous operation under all circumstances, and they should be of sufficient capacity to afford a nominal retention period of at least one day and preferably two or three days. Provision should be made for rapid and convenient removal of sludge from the tanks. In the treatment of highly polluted water of variable quality, provision should be made for coagulation at the inlet or the outlet of the tanks whenever measures may be necessary.

5-13. Aeration. Aeration is a process whereby the water is brought into intimate contact with air to improve the quality of potable water. This process is used in an effort to accomplish the following:

1. To remove or reduce tastes and odors
2. To remove or reduce gases such as carbon dioxide, methane, or hydrogen sulfide
3. To increase the pH of water by the removal of carbon dioxide
4. To add gases
   a. Oxygen in the removal of iron and manganese
   b. Carbon dioxide after excess lime treatment used to soften water
5. To remove heat from deep well waters, which are at a higher temperature than desired upon their discharge at the earth's surface

It has been shown by various investigators that the rate of gas absorption by water is influenced most by the films of the gas at the water-gas interface, and it seems reasonable to assume that the greatest influence on the release of gases from water is also affected by these films, especially by the liquid film. The thickness of the films varies under different conditions. They are very thin when first formed and become considerably thicker shortly after formation. Other factors determining efficiency of aeration are the amount of agitation of the water and the agitation within the droplet, which affect film thickness; the maximum agitation being produced by the creation of falling droplets; temperature; solubility and concentration of the gas; vapor pressure of the gas; and barometric pressure.

Aerators may be classified as (1) injection aerators (perforated pipes, diffusers, air-lift pumps, mechanical patented devices), which permit the bubbling of air through water; (2) gravity aerators (inclined planes, cascades, perforated traps); and (3) pressure sprays or fountain aerators (orifices, nozzles).

5-14. Slow Sand Filter. Filtration of water through sand as a means of improving its quality has been used since 1829 when the first filter was built at London to treat Thames River water. This filter was the forerunner of the slow sand type which was developed in England and was used very largely in the United States until the early part of the twentieth century. A number of cities in the northeastern part of the United States still use slow sand filters. New installations are more likely to be of the rapid type, which is discussed later. The slow sand filter is well adapted for the treatment of slightly turbid water without preliminary coagulation and sedimentation. It does not completely clarify water with a turbidity higher than 50 parts per million except for a very short period of time. In the attempt to adapt it to the treatment of the waters of American rivers, which are frequently very turbid after rains, plain sedimentation was frequently given to reduce the turbidity to approximately 50 parts per million before treatment on the filters.

The filters consist of a layer of sand, 2 to 5 feet in depth, underlain by gravel. In the gravel are open-jointed pipes to carry off the filtered water to the clear-water reservoir. The water flows through the bed by gravity. The bulk of the suspended matter is caught on the surface and in the first few inches of the bed. The resulting layer of slimy silt or mud acts as an efficient strainer. Impurities are also removed by what might be considered as sedimentation in the minute openings between the grains of sand as the water moves very slowly through the sand bed, the matter taken out being held as a film on the surfaces of the grains. In addition to the physical process of sedimentation and straining, there appear to be other influences at work aiding in the purification process. This is evidenced by the fact that filters which have been in use for a considerable time give much better results than do new filters, possibly because of the accumulation of slimy film, which is organic and contains many living organisms, on the sand grains.

This type of filter is operated at the rate of about 3 to 6 million gallons per acre of filter area per day, the higher rate being more common where some preliminary treatment, such as sedimentation, is given to the water. Precautions are taken to see that the rate is kept uniform. A float-control valve is placed in the line supplying the filter, so that the depth of water over the filter is uniform at all times. The rate at which the water is allowed to pass through the sand is regulated by a rate controller, located in the effluent line which connects the underdrainage system of the filter with the clear-water reservoir.

After a certain period of operation, which depends upon the nature of the water treated, the upper layers of the sand become so clogged that cleaning is necessary. The filter bed is then thrown out of operation; the water is allowed to drain out; and the clogged layer of sand is scraped off. The dirty sand can be immediately washed and replaced, or it may be stored until the bed has become so thin from repeated scrapings that the sand must be replaced in order to ensure sufficient filtration. Special forms of apparatus are constructed for washing the sand. The lower limit as to thickness of bed before the sand must be replaced is 2 feet. The necessity for scraping the upper layers of the sand requires duplicate beds so that the demand may be taken care of at all times. Periods between scrapings may vary from three weeks to several months.

This type of filter is usually covered, owing to the fact that freezing weather and ice formation may result in serious trouble. This adds materially to the cost of construction as the beds are large, averaging from ½ to 1½ acres.

The bacterial efficiency of the slow sand filter is high. Operated at the higher rate mentioned above, 98 to 99 per cent removal of bacteria is obtained, while operation at 3 million gallons per acre per day, which was commonly the practice before the use of preliminary treatment and chlorination, will give efficiencies of 99.5 to 99.7 per cent. This type of filter will also remove some tastes and odors and is effective, to some extent, in color removal.

5-15. Coagulation and Sedimentation. The purpose of coagulation is to get the impurities of water into such a condition that they will settle out or be removed by rapid sand filters. In the coagulation process colloids, suspended material, and some dissolved solids are removed. Since color and a large portion of the suspended material in waters are colloidal in nature, the easiest way to remove these impurities is to coagulate them. By coagulation is meant the clumping together of colloidal particles to such an extent that they settle readily. The methods of coagulation may be outlined as follows:

1. Aging the colloidal matter (this method is too slow for modern water treatment plant operation)
2. Applying heat
3. Providing an antagonistic colloid
4. Altering pH
5. Adding an electrolyte or coagulant
6. Flocculating (slow stirring)

Of these, only the last three are used in water treatment.

Upon the addition of certain electrolytes, which are defined as coagulants, gelatinous flocs are formed which collect and/or adsorb colloidal particles. As the weight of the floc is gradually increased, settling takes place. In general waterworks practice, the coagulants used are aluminum sulfate (alum), ferric chloride, ferric sulfate, ferrous sulfate (copperas), chlorinated copperas, sodium aluminate.

Good coagulation requires a proper amount of the coagulant, an optimum pH value, efficient mixing of the coagulant with the water, and, after the rapid mix, a slow mix, sometimes called "flocculation," which encourages formation of floc masses and their adsorption and absorption of colloids and suspended particles. Mixing is done in baffled basins or by mechanical agitation, and flocculation is accomplished by slow-moving paddle wheels, operating in a tank having a detention period of twenty to forty minutes.

5-16. Sedimentation. Sedimentation basins may be rectangular with flat, sloping, or hopper bottoms; circular with flat or hopper bottoms; or rectangular with multiple bottoms or basins of the upflow-suspended-solids-contact type. The basins may or may not be equipped with facilities for continuous or intermittent sludge-removal facilities. In order to prevent the destruction of the floc formed from the time the coagulated water leaves the mixing or reaction chamber, the velocity of the water should be maintained at such a rate as to prevent settling or breaking up of the floc prior to entrance into the sedimentation basins. The sedimentation basins should be provided with inlet and outlet connections

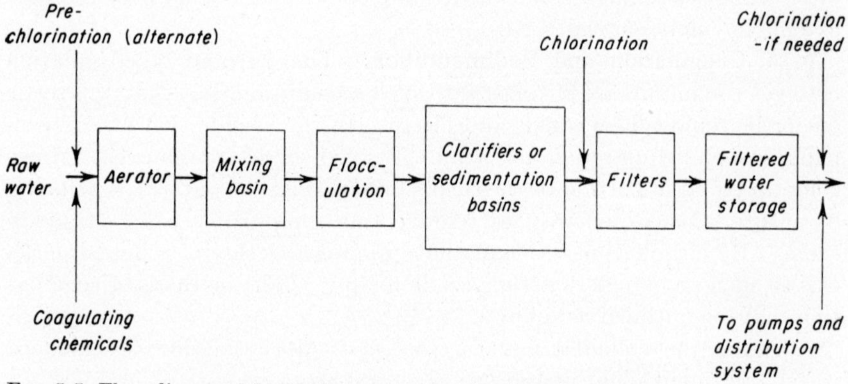

FIG. 5-5. Flow diagram of a modern water purification plant, employing coagulation, sedimentation, and rapid sand filtration.

arranged in a manner that will prevent short-circuiting of water flow, and the path of water flow should be long enough to permit settling of the floc and particles prior to reaching the outlet weir. In general practice when rectangular or circular basins without facilities for continuous sludge removal are provided, the theoretical retention period of the water in those basins is from six to eight hours, which also includes the retention period within flocculation units. The theoretical retention period for basins provided with facilities for mechanical, continuous sludge-removal facilities may be reduced to 4 or 4.5 hours, including flocculation time. The path of flow of the water in a basin may be horizontal, *i.e.*, introduced at one end of a rectangular basin and removed at the other, or introduced at the center of a circular basin and removed at the periphery. The path may also be vertical—introduced at the bottom and removed at the top. Concerning the use of the upflow-suspended-solids-contact clarification units, it may be pointed out that various state agencies charged with the responsibility of reviewing plans and specifications for water treatment plants have adopted varying policies regarding the recommended design practices to be met by the equipment manufacturers and suppliers.

5-17. Rapid Sand Filter. Rapid sand filters, which were developed in the United States about 1893, are also known as mechanical filters. With the development in water filtration, there began a new era in water treatment. It was concluded by leading water authorities of this period that the optimum filtration rate was 125 million gallons of water per acre of filter surface per day (2 gallons per square foot per minute), that water

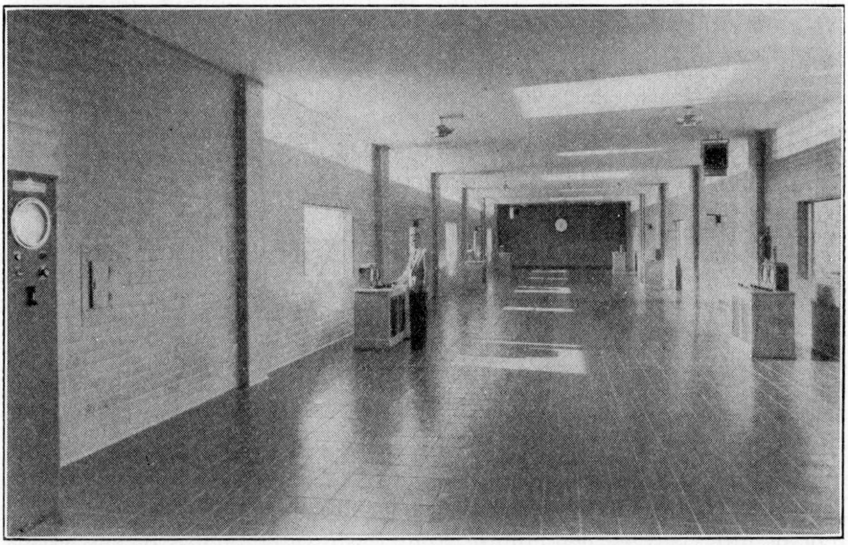

FIG. 5-6. Filter control chamber, water purification plant of the North Texas Water District, Wylie, Tex. (*Courtesy of Forrest and Cotton, Consulting Engineers.*)

to be filtered at these high rates, in comparison with slow-sand-filter rates, would need to be clarified prior to filtration, and also that water coagulants would need to be applied to the raw water to accelerate sedimentation. The present rapid sand filter is composed of the tank, or filter box; the inlet and distribution system; the effluent, or underdrain, system; the filtering medium, usually sand underlain by gravel, or anthracite coal graded in particle size; rate-of-flow controllers; loss-of-head gauges; and operating tables. In recent years, many filters of this type have also been provided with surface wash systems.

Usually, in conventional-type filters, the coagulated water, having a turbidity of about 10 parts per million upon leaving the sedimentation basins, flows through pipe or channels to the filter gullet, to which are attached the filter wash-water troughs. The coagulated water is distributed uniformly over the filter bed, which consists of 20 to 30 inches of filter sand, having an effective size ranging between 0.35 and 0.45 millimeter and a uniformity coefficient of between 1.4 and 1.8. The filter medium may also be Anthrafilt, as supplied by the Anthracite Equipment Corporation, Wilkes-Barre, Pa., which meets the specifications of the American Water Works Association. When filter sand is used, it is supported by 16 to 24 inches of gravel, ranging in size from ⅛ inch to 2½ inches in diameter, which is usually arranged in three to five layers with each layer containing material about twice the size of the material above it. After passing through the filtering medium, the water enters the underdrain system. Such systems are of various designs, but all are intended to collect the filtered water as well as distribute the wash water. Features in some are the elimination of metallic elements subject to corrosion and the avoidance of the necessity for a gravel layer. Some of these are the Wheeler, Wagner, Leopold Duplex, or Aloxite filter bottoms. Otherwise, the underdrain system consists of a central manifold with perforated pipe laterals, pipe laterals with brass strainers, or perforated plates.

As filtration proceeds, the flocculant material containing suspended matter, silt, clay, algae, bacteria, and other impurities causes clogging of the filter. When the loss-of-head approaches 7 to 8 feet, the backwashing of filters is indicated. To carry out this operation the influent valve is closed, and the water level in the filter unit is allowed to drop to the top of the wash-water troughs. The effluent valve is then closed and the waste valve opened. The wash-water valve is then opened gradually until fully open or to the point that the filter sand has been expanded 40 to 50 per cent by the supply of 15 to 20 gallons of treated water per square foot of filter surface per minute from wash-water pumps or the wash-water tank. After the filter has been washed a sufficient time to clean the sand, the wash-water valve is closed; the waste-water drain valve is closed after draining out the dirty water from the filter wash-water trough and gullet; and the influent and effluent valves are opened to place the filter unit back into service.

It is important that the rate of filtration should not exceed the rate for which the filter units were designed. The rate-of-flow controllers located in the filter effluent line are utilized to maintain a constant rate of filtration regardless of the time which has elapsed between washings. A rate-of-flow controller may also be placed in the line carrying water for backwashing of filters, if variable flows are likely to occur.

To obtain maximum operating efficiency of rapid sand filters, every effort should be made to check regularly the condition of the filter beds for "mud balls," crevicing, algae growths, unusual flow patterns, etc. At periodic intervals, standard bacterial plate counts may be made on water samples secured before and after filtration for each unit to determine the cleanliness of the medium.

5-18. Chlorination. Even though surface water is aerated, coagulated, settled, and filtered, the bacteria and microorganisms responsible for water-borne diseases are likely to be present in the treated water unless the water is disinfected continuously to destroy them. Also, in many instances water from protected wells is disinfected with chlorine gas or chlorine compounds primarily to maintain a chlorine residual in the water throughout the distribution system. This acts as a safeguard against contamination which might occur during main repairs or through faulty plumbing installations. Continuous disinfection of the water, however, should not be used as a substitute for strict plumbing inspection and control. All new and repaired sections of a water distribution system as well as water storage reservoirs and new pump-station facilities which come in contact with water should be sterilized to eliminate the contamination which may have entered the water system during the construction or rehabilitation program. All sterilization procedures should be checked by bacteriological examinations to be sure that the procedure followed has been effective. It may be pointed out that disinfection means the killing of the pathogens, the disease-producing organisms, while sterilization means the killing of all living organisms. Chlorine or its compounds are generally used for this purpose.

The rate of disinfection depends primarily upon the concentration of the agent and the period of contact; however, temperature and pH also play important roles. When chlorine compounds are used, the oxidizing power of the product expressed as chlorine gas (Cl_2) is termed "available chlorine."

In the disinfection of water, a variety of chlorine compounds are available for use, namely, bleaching powder ($CaOCl_2$), having an available chlorine content of 33.5 to 39 per cent; calcium hypochlorite [$Ca(OCl)_2$], sold under such trade names as HTH, Pittchlor, Hoodchlor, Perchloron, etc., having an available chlorine content of 70 per cent; sodium hypochlorite solutions ($NaOCl$), containing 3 to 5 per cent or 10 to 16 per cent by weight of available chlorine, sold under trade names such as Clorox, Purex, Hypro, White Magic, Nubora, Sani Chlor, White Rose, etc.; and liquid chlorine sold in cylinders of 10, 15, 25, 100, and 150 pounds, 2,000-pound drums, and railroad single-unit tank cars having capacities of 32,000, 60,000, or 110,000 pounds of liquid chlorine.

In the use of chlorinated lime (bleaching powders), high-strength calcium hypochlorite, or the other powdered chlorine compounds with various concentrations of available chlorine, a 1 per cent solution is made up and applied to the water at a constant rate by means of mechanical devices known as hypochlorinators. The required dosage varies with the degree of organic pollution and the minerals or gases present which are subject to oxidation. The dosage should be sufficient not only to meet the "chlorine demand" of the water but also to maintain a chlorine residual of at least 0.05 to 0.10 part per million in the water being supplied at distant points of the water distribution system. At times of threatened or prevalent outbreaks of water-borne disease, the residual free chlorine should be increased preferably to a minimum of 0.2 to 0.3 part per million in all parts of the distribution system, regardless of undesirable tastes and odors which may be present in the water being supplied during this period. In many water systems, residuals of 1.0

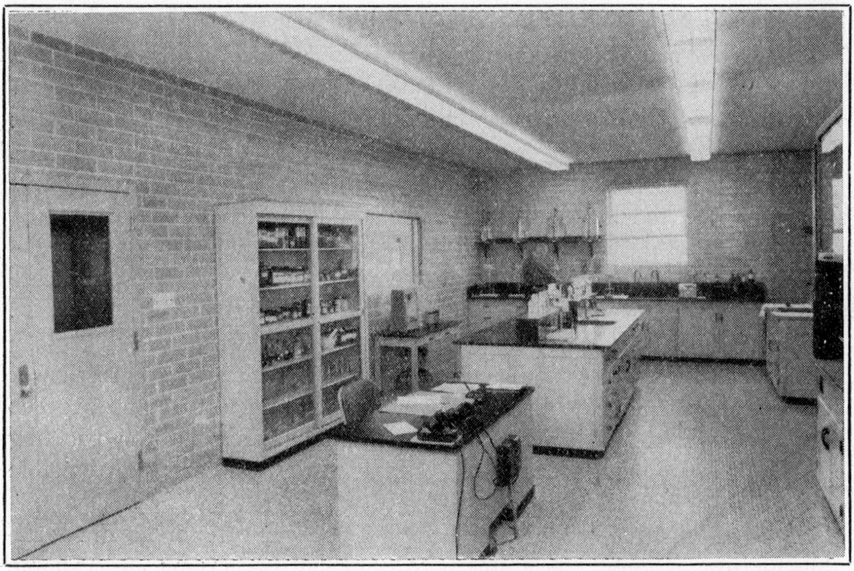

FIG. 5-7. A modern purification plant laboratory, at the plant of the North Texas Water District, Wylie, Tex. (*Courtesy of Forrest and Cotton, Consulting Engineers.*)

part per million or greater are routinely maintained. Frequent tests should be made on water samples collected at the plant discharge sampling tap and taps at representative points within the distribution system to determine the chlorine residual content of the water.

5-19. The Orthotolidine Test. This simple color test is made by the use of orthotolidine solution. Add 10 drops of orthotolidine solution to 1 ounce of water. If the water sample changes to a canary yellow, sufficient chlorine has been applied to overcome the "chlorine demand" of the water, and an excess or residual chlorine content of 0.2 to 0.3 part per million exists. Should a deep-orange color be developed, too much chlorine has been applied. A blue color denotes excessive alkalinity in the water, and the water sample should be acidified prior to adding the orthotolidine solution; or additional drops of orthotolidine solution, which is acid, may be added to neutralize the alkalinity. Chlorine comparators can be obtained from chemical supply houses; these have containers and droppers for making the orthotolidine test and they also provide colored glass disks so that residuals can be accurately determined.

5-20. Chlorine Dosage and Application. To prepare 50 gallons of a 1 per cent available chlorine solution, the following calculations are used:

1. 50 gallons of water × 8.34 pounds per gallon = 417 pounds.
2. 1 per cent of this weight = 4.17 pounds of chlorine gas.
3. If 70 per cent available chlorine compound is used, 4.17 ÷ 0.70 = 6.0 pounds of 70 per cent available chlorine compound required to produce 4.17 pounds of chlorine.
4. Therefore, if 6.0 pounds of the chlorine compound is added to 50 gallons to secure a chlorine content of 4.17 pounds, each gallon of the chlorine solution will contain 4.17 pounds ÷ 50, or 0.083 pound of equivalent chlorine gas.

Now assume that 250 gallons of water per minute is to be treated at a dosage rate of 2.0 parts per million so as to meet the chlorine demand and allow for a chlorine residual of 0.3 part per million and that it is desired to know the amount of 1 per cent solution which will be required per ten hours of water plant operation at this rate of continuous treatment.

1. 250 gallons per minute × ten hours × sixty minutes per hour = 150,000 gallons of water to be treated during period of operation.
2. 150,000 gallons × 8.34 pounds per gallon = 1,251,000 pounds of water.
3. $\frac{1{,}251{,}000 \text{ pounds}}{1{,}000{,}000 \text{ pounds}} \times 2.0 = 2.5$ pounds of equivalent chlorine gas.
4. 2.5 pounds equivalent chlorine gas ÷ 0.70 = 3.6 pounds of 70 per cent calcium hypochlorite.
5. Since 6.0 pounds of 70 per cent calcium hypochlorite is required to prepare 50 gallons of 1 per cent solution, then $\frac{3.6}{6.0} \times 50$, or 30 gallons of this solution would be required to disinfect the water as specified by the example given above.

In the preparation of hypochlorite solutions, a sludge of calcium carbonate and inert materials will be deposited in the container in which the hypochlorite is mixed with water. Therefore, it is advisable to carry out the mixing in an earthenware crock or rubber-lined barrel, and to decant the chlorine solution into another container of similar materials. Since calcium carbonate will deposit on orifices and the valves of hypochlorinators, it is recommended that soda ash (sodium carbonate) be added to the water used in making the chlorine solution so as to soften the water by precipitation of the calcium carbonate.

5-21. Chlorinators. At the larger water plant installations, disinfection of the water is accomplished by the use of liquid chlorine, which, under reduced pressure, becomes gaseous chlorine. The gaseous chlorine is either fed directly into the water through a porous diffuser or mixed with water by means of a chlorinator and fed as a solution to the water. Direct-feed chlorinators find application chiefly as emergency equipment

FIG. 5-8. Installation of chlorination equipment, San Jacinto Water Treatment Plant, Houston, Tex. (*Photograph courtesy of Jack F. Laws.*)

and on small installations where it is not possible to obtain a suitable water supply to operate solution-feed apparatus. Solution-feed chlorinators are much more widely used and are preferable in most cases because of greater capacity, flexibility of control and installation, and adaptability to widely varying requirements. Chlorinators, ranging in feed capacity from 0.1 pound per twenty-four hours to several thousand pounds per twenty-four hours, may be procured and operated by manual, program, or automatic controls. If direct-feed chlorinators are to be used, the pressure at the point of application must be below 20 pounds per square inch. If chlorinators of the solution type are to be used, such equipment must be operated by using these two water supplies: (1) an auxiliary water supply of city-water quality and relatively small in quantity at a pressure of between 25 and 75 pounds per square inch; and (2) an injector water supply with an approximate minimum quantity of 35 gallons per pound of chlorinator capacity at a pressure at least three times the pressure at the point of chlorine-solution application.

The simplest type of hypochlorinator consists of a device which feeds the solution of the hypochlorite at a constant rate to the water to be treated. This may be a small tank or head box in which a float-controlled valve maintains a constant head over an adjustable orifice. The constant-head tank is fed through the float valve from the solution tank. Hypochlorinators that include pumps which can be adjusted to feed chlorine solution at any desired rate are obtainable. They can inject the solution against pressure.

5-22. Chlorine Residual Maintained. Chlorine dosage is controlled by the residuals shown by the orthotolidine test. Two types of residuals are recognized. At most water treatment plants sufficient chlorine is added to the filtered water to obtain a residual of about 0.3 part per million as the water leaves the plant. This will usually require a dose of 0.5 part per million to 1.5 parts per million of chlorine. Such a residual will be a *combined available residual* because the chlorine is probably combined in large part with nitrogenous compounds to form chloramine. It is available for disinfective action but may cause a noticeably chlorinous odor.

If the chlorine dose is continuously increased, there is a consequent, but not exactly proportional, increase of the residual, while at some point there is a noticeable decrease of the residual. This is known as the *break point*. Beyond the break point the chlorine residual increases in direct proportion to the additional chlorine. It is not exactly known what occurs at the break point, but it is supposed that oxidation of nitrogenous and possibly of other matters has been completed and the residuals beyond that point are known as *free available residuals*. Usually no chlorinous odors are noticeable beyond the break point, and the free chlorine is more rapid in destroying bacteria than the combined chlorine. Free available residuals are desirable particularly for highly polluted and odorous waters but require large doses of chlorine. The break point of most waters occurs at about 6 parts per million.

Water is sometimes treated with ammonia and chlorine. This combination is known as chloramine. The combined available residual which results is long lasting but less rapid in action than a free residual. It sometimes prevents the formation of chlorinous odors.

5-23. Iron Removal. In the development of water resources for public or individual water systems, it may be necessary to treat the water to remove iron naturally present in the water. Iron, if in excess of 0.3 part per million, may form a colored precipitate which interferes with laundering and preparation of foods and drinks and causes staining of plumbing fixtures. It may also cause the water to have a chalybeate taste and may foster the growth of "iron bacteria," which impart undesirable tastes and odors to the water. To reduce the excessive iron content to such limits as to prevent these undesirable conditions, the following methods of treatment have been used: (1) oxidation by aeration, followed by sedimentation and filtration to remove the precipitated iron; (2) use of ordinary zeolites, or zeolites treated with pyrolusite, or beds composed entirely of pyrolusite; (3) use of lime or chlorine in a closed system ahead of pressure filters; (4) coagulation at pH values above 9.0; (5) use of limestone filters in conjunction with aeration units to remove carbon dioxide; (6) special iron-removal units using induced vacuum and anthracite coal beds; and (7) use of slow sand filters. The most effective form of treatment for a water is usually determined by trial.

5-24. Softening of Water. Hard water is the classification ordinarily given to a water that has a high soap-consuming power, or in which a lather cannot be produced without the use of an excessive quantity of soap. Hardness is caused by metallic ions which will form insoluble metal soaps. The principal hardness-producing ions are calcium and magnesium, but the presence of iron, manganese, copper, barium, zinc, and lead ions may cause slight increases in hardness. The adverse effects of hard water are many. However, the principal bad effects may be outlined as follows: (1) consumes soap; (2) clogs skin, discolors porcelain, stains and shortens life of fabrics, toughens and discolors vegetables; (3) gives difficulty in textile and paper manufacture, canning, and other industrial processes; (4) forms scale in boilers, resulting in great heat-transfer losses and danger of boiler failure.

Water softening is the process of removing totally, or in part, the hardness-producing ions. Two methods of softening are used: the lime-soda process, whereby calcium and magnesium ions are precipitated as calcium carbonate and magnesium hydroxide, respectively, to be removed by sedimentation and filtration; and the zeolite, or base-exchange process, whereby calcium and magnesium ions are replaced by the sodium ion from the zeolite.

5-25. Stabilization of Water. A lime-softened water remains supersaturated with respect to calcium carbonate for some time after the initial softening reaction has taken place. In the event that treatment with excess lime has resulted in supersaturation of the water, calcium carbonate will encrust the filter medium, and some of it will pass into the distribution system and form deposits in the mains, meters, and service connections. Manufacturers of patented upflow-suspended-solids-contact clarification units claim that the water passing through their units is well stabilized and that no further stabilization is required. However, in the event that stabilization is required at softening plants, consideration may be given to the installation of recarbonation units, which apply carbon dioxide to the water and cause the precipitation and sedimentation of calcium carbonate prior to filtration. Use of sodium hexametaphosphate in recent years has also found favor, since only the usual type of chemical-feeding equipment is required for a threshold treatment, and there is no danger of overdosing the water which might result in corrosion as in the case of recarbonation. In fact, hexametaphosphate is also claimed to be a corrosion inhibitor.

5-26. Fluoridation. Since 1946, it has been recognized that consumption of water containing from 1.0 to 1.5 parts per million of fluorine, as the fluoride, has reduced the amount of dental caries occurring. After noting that the decayed, missing, or filled rate (DMF) in children reared in areas where the water contains approximately 1.0 part per million of fluorine is much lower than the DMF rate in children routinely consuming water low in fluoride (0.3 to 0.4 part per million), some municipalities, upon approval of local dental and medical societies and officials of public health departments, have initiated the addition of fluoride-bearing chemicals to the water being supplied by public facilities. The application of sodium fluoride, sodium silicofluoride, hydrofluosilicic acid, hydrofluoric acid, or ammonium silicofluoride under laboratory control techniques has been initiated in many communities in the United States. These chemicals are applied by means of solution-type chemical feeders or dry feeders with solution pots, which cost from three hundred to a few thousand dollars depending upon feeder capacity and controls provided with feeder equipment. The dosage is determined by the natural fluoride content of the water available, which is supplemented to make available 1.0 part per million.

When fluorides are applied to water and fluorides are stored and handled at water treatment plants, special facilities should be provided to eliminate a dust hazard, the powdered fluoride compounds should be dyed a distinctive color, and all chemicals should be made inaccessible to unauthorized persons and visitors. Also, water-flow measuring devices, some control arrangement on the feeder to permit careful control of the accuracy of the feeding operation, and laboratory equipment for making frequent fluoride determinations of the water being supplied should be provided. Accurate records of fluoride application should be kept.

5-27. Corrosion and Control. Corrosion of water pipes or other metal coming into contact with water involves a surface phenomenon, electrochemical in nature. There are three forms of corrosion: (1) self-corrosion, exemplified by corrosion of iron in water, which is electrochemical in nature; (2) galvanic corrosion, exemplified by battery action between two dissimilar metals; and (3) electrolytic corrosion, brought about by stray electrical currents passing from water pipes into the ground, taking metal with them, and causing external pitting. Factors affecting rates of corrosion of the first type, which is most important, are (1) dissolved oxygen—without oxygen there is no corrosion; (2) carbon dioxide—causes deposition of carbonate coatings and also causes acid waters; (3) free mineral acids—decrease pH; alkalies increase it; (4) acid salts—such salts as aluminum chloride and magnesium chloride increase corrosion; (5) temperature—an increase in temperature increases rate of corrosion; and (6) velocity of water flow—an increase in velocity accelerates corrosion, since more oxygen or other impurities come in contact with metal. To control corrosion, it may be necessary to consider the following: (1) use of nonmetallic pipes; (2) use of metals most resistant to corrosion; (3) use of protective metal coatings on ferrous pipe; (4) treatment of water to secure high caustic alkalinity—saturation of calcium carbonate to cause it to deposit in the piping system under controlled conditions; use of sodium silicate; removal of dissolved gases by deactivation, deaeration, or degasifying; and cathodic protection.

5-28. Algae Control. Algae are a group of chlorophyll-bearing plants which occur as small microscopic individuals and may exist alone or in company with like individuals. Under favorable conditions, particularly as to sunlight and food, they may occur in such numbers as to make a water turbid or to give it an apparent color. They are undesirable because they impart odors and tastes to water. To control algal growths, attempts are made to reduce the available food supply, to poison the organisms by the addition of chemicals, or to control some physical factors that affect microscopic growths. In practice, the algae food supply in a body of water can be regulated by (1) proper conditioning of the watershed to prevent appreciable amounts of organic matter from reaching the reservoir; (2) application of such construction features as clearing, grubbing, and burning of vegetation; (3) preparation of shore lines to prevent water from coming in contact with vegetation; and (4) thorough cleaning of the reservoir bottom. When filtered or ground water is stored in clear wells or in ground or elevated storage tanks, these reservoirs should be covered so as to exclude sunlight, since darkness deprives the algae of energy for growth. Copper sulfate is widely used as a poison for eradication of algae and other microscopic organisms from impounded water. Even though it has been demonstrated that the consumption of water containing the small amounts of copper sulfate required for destruction of algal growths and microscopic organisms has not been proved dangerous to public health, the application of the copper sulfate should be carried out under intelligent and continual supervision. The upper limit of copper concentration that should be tolerated is 3.0 parts per million or less, as prescribed by the Public Health Service Drinking Water Standards. In considering the application of copper sulfate, it should be realized that fish may be adversely affected, although the tolerance varies from 0.14 part per million for trout to 2.10 parts per million for black bass. Copper sulfate dosages can be prescribed according to the species of alga, but ordinarily from 5 to 10 pounds per million gallons is used. Chlorine and chlorine dioxide can be used effectively to control algal growths, the dosages varying according to the form of organism causing difficulty.

Copper sulfate and chlorine are applied by placing the crystals or powdered chlorine compound in coarse bags, burlap bags, perforated buckets, or wire baskets and dragging these containers back and forth through the body of water to obtain uniform distribution of the chemicals in the impounded body of water. If local conditions permit, copper sulfate and chlorine may be applied by dry-feed or solution-feed machines so that all water can be treated as it passes through a narrow conduit or opening. Open treated-water reservoirs or swimming pools are treated for algae control by the preparation and application of a 5 per cent solution of copper sulfate or chlorine to walls and floors by means of mops, brushes, etc. When pipelines or other conduits contain troublesome growths, treatment with chlorine or chlorine dioxide can be provided as the water leaves the water plant and appropriate residuals can be maintained in the water throughout the distribution system. Algal growth can be destroyed by the addition of excess hydrate alkalinity, which brings about the removal of carbon dioxide, a necessity for the life processes of the plants.

5-29. Taste and Odor Control. Not only should every attempt be made to control algal growths in the impounded reservoir, flowing stream, or lake, but vigilant control should also be practiced at the water treatment plant. Should tastes and odors from algae be anticipated, the plant facilities might include aeration, facilities for pre- as well as post-chlorination, facilities for application of activated carbon and perhaps for chlorine dioxide treatment. Routine tests on the raw and treated water should be made to maintain records of the threshold odor present. Routine limnological examinations of raw water in various sections of the impounded water reservoir will be helpful in predicting the likely occurrence of the undesirable tastes and odors from algae growths present.

5-30. Demineralization of Saline Waters. In 1952, 2 million dollars was appropriated for the United States Department of the Interior to investigate the development of methods for the demineralization of saline waters, since present and future water-supply requirements show that a need exists to render the saline ground and surface waters suitable in chemical quality for beneficial uses. The results of the initial five years of study were so encouraging that research projects in this field continue. Formerly it was believed that the cost for demineralizing sea water was $400 to $500 per acre-foot of water; however, it is now thought that this cost can be reduced to approximately $120. Water demineralization equipment is available in units having capacities ranging from 1,000 to 100,000 gallons per day, and the cost of water conditioning by this equipment is lower than that of distillation, shipping by truck or boat, or distribution of water through long water-supply lines of small diameter. Research and development proposals under evaluation include critical-pressure devices, solar-distillation devices, absorption media, permeable selective membranes, molecular oil films, ultra-high-frequency currents, natural clay as ion-exchange material, electromagnetic effects, and a new type of absorption-refrigeration cycle.

Even though the results of the research studies undertaken in recent years have not brought forth an economical treatment method for demineralization of sea water to usable limits, it does appear that raw water having a salinity of 5,000 parts per million may be demineralized to a 40 per cent reduction in salt content for 15.4 to 21.3 cents per 1,000 gallons and power costs, depending upon whether the plant has a capacity of 0.3, 1.0, or 4.0 MGD.

5-31. Development of Ground-water Sources of Supply for Public Use. In the development of ground-water sources of supply, such as wells, springs, and infiltration galleries, adequate protection of the available water from sources of pollution should be emphasized. If the well is not protected from bacterial contamination, it must be considered as a "protected surface source of water supply" and given such treatment as necessary, depending upon the density of coliform organisms found to be present and the frequency with which they are found by regular bacteriological examinations.

In general practice, wells to be used in supplying water for public use are so located with reference to actual and potential sources of contamination as to minimize the possibility of contamination. Well construction is such as to give further protection in order to safeguard the bacteriological and chemical quality of the water.

The principal location requirements are that the number of people residing within a 300-foot radius of the well be at a minimum, that all residents within this zone be provided with sanitary sewerage service, that no tile or concrete sanitary sewers exist within 50 feet of the well, and that no outdoor privies, cesspools, septic-tank drain fields, or stock pens be located within 150 feet of the well. Drainage of the area should be such that runoff waters are diverted from the well and no flooding of sewage-polluted water will occur within 300 feet of the well. All abandoned water wells near the site chosen for a new well should also be plugged and sealed properly to prevent possible contamination of the ground-water formation.

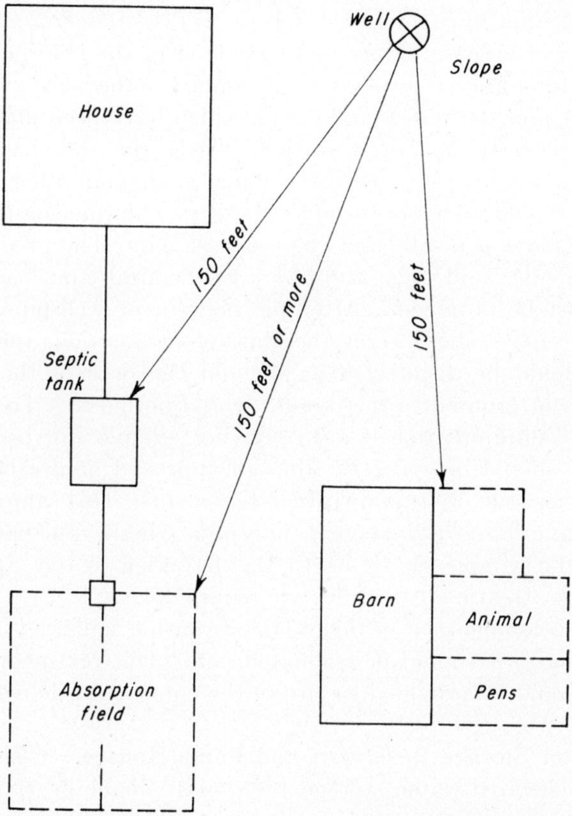

FIG. 5-9. A properly located well. (*Drawing courtesy of Texas State Department of Health.*)

In order to preserve the original quality of the ground water when tapped by a well, the well should be cased with high-grade steel or wrought-iron pipe with screw-type or welded joints. The casing should extend from a point 18 inches above the elevation of the finished floor of the pump house to the top of the shallowest water-producing formation to be developed. After the well casing has been suspended in the drill hole, the space between the casing and drill hole should be sealed by Portland cement grout. Sufficient grout should be used under pressure so that it can be forced up around the annular space between the casing and the drill hole and appear at the earth's surface. After the cementing operations have been completed and at least twenty-four hours' time has been allowed for the cement to set, the cement plug at bottom of the casing is removed by drilling. The bottom of the well is then completed, as required. If a gravel wall-type well is constructed, the gravel should be selected material, washed thoroughly and disinfected with high-strength calcium hypochlorite, sold as HTH, Perchloron, Pittchlor, Hoodchlor, and others, adding ½ to 1 pound of the chlorine compound per cubic yard of gravel as the gravel is applied to the well cavity between the drill hole and the screen and casing which have been placed into the well prior to the graveling operation. After the well has been fully developed to remove silt, debris, drilling mud, and other undesirable material, it should be again disinfected with a chlorine solution containing 40 to 50 parts per million of chlorine residual. The production tests should be made, and then samples for chemical and bacteriological analysis must be obtained. After the permanent well-pumping equipment has been installed, or at the time of installation, the completed well unit should be disinfected again, and the base of the well-pump motor sealed or grouted to the pump-foundation block. To ensure that intermittent contamination is not occurring, samples for bacteriological examination should be collected from an approved nonwasher sampling tap located on the well-pump discharge main. The sampling should proceed for five consecutive days to determine whether the bacteriological quality of the sample conforms to the Drinking Water Standards or whether water treatment facilities are required.

In the development of springs and infiltration galleries, the existing pollutional hazards should be evaluated, and such treatment as deemed necessary should be provided to ensure the continuous delivery of water of safe quality.

5-32. Water Storage Reservoirs and Pump Houses. Clear wells and ground- or elevated-water storage reservoirs should be constructed of durable materials and provided with covers that afford protection against contamination, dust, insects, and rain. Vents, manholes, and overflows should not permit contamination of the stored water. The inlet and outlet connections should be arranged to prevent short-circuiting of water flow and water stagnation. Clear wells or ground storage reservoirs must be thoroughly tight against external leakage and situated above the ground-water table. If drains are provided, they should not be directly connected to any waste or sewage collection system. Also, no sanitary sewer lines should be located within 50 feet of the reservoir or clear well, in case of underground installations, unless the sewer is of cast-iron pipe with leaded joints; if the sewer is of tile or concrete, it must be encased in concrete.

Pump pits or sub-ground-level pump rooms should be avoided. If direct-feed or solution-feed chlorinators are to be installed, they should be located in a separate, well-ventilated room of the pump station where the cylinders can be handled without extreme difficulty and the danger of damage to electrical controls by leakage of chlorine gas does not exist. All pump stations which require long periods of attendance by operators should have available sanitary facilities with approved means of sewage disposal. To facilitate the checking of water-system operation, meters and gauges for measuring the amount of water pumped and the water pressure at the plant site should be provided.

5-33. Distribution of Water. Even though water leaving the water plant may be of desirable chemical and bacteriological quality, the provision of substandard facilities for water distribution may greatly affect the quality of the water being supplied and result in many complaints concerning general water service. For these reasons, the following features of water distribution system planning should be given consideration:[1]

1. A water distribution system should be designed and constructed so as to provide at all times an adequate supply of water at ample pressure in all parts of the distribution system.

2. The safety and palatability of the water should not be impaired in any manner as it flows through the distribution system or any part thereof.

3. The system should be provided with sufficient valves and blowoffs so that necessary repairs can be made without undue interruption of service over any considerable area and the system can be flushed when required.

4. No unprotected open reservoir or physical cross connection with inferior water systems whereby unsafe water can enter the distribution system should be permitted.

5. The system should be tight against excessive leakage, and its various mains and branches should not be submerged by surface water or subjected to any other source of contamination.

6. The system should be designed so as to afford effective circulation of water, and only a minimum number of dead-end mains should exist.

7. The distribution system should be maintained in a sanitary manner, with due precautions against contamination of the water in any part of it as the result of necessary repairs, replacements, or extension of mains.

8. When new mains are installed, or old mains repaired, these mains should be filled with a strong chlorine solution (40 to 60 parts per million of chlorine) for at least twenty-four hours, and then flushed with water to be supplied normally by the mains. Following this main-sterilization

[1] These are based in part on the "Manual of Recommended Water-sanitation Practice"[2].

procedure, samples of water should be submitted for bacteriological examination and the disinfection repeated, if necessary, until favorable laboratory results are obtained.

9. Water mains should be laid, insofar as possible, 6 feet above the elevation of tile or concrete sanitary sewers at crossover points and at least 10 feet horizontally from such sanitary sewers when they are parallel. Where this recommended spacing is impossible because of local physical conditions, extra precautions should be taken to secure absolute and permanent tightness of water-pipe joints and to safeguard the water from contamination by sewage. In general practice this usually is attempted by encasing the sewer mains with concrete or replacing the tile or concrete sewer with cast-iron pipe having leaded joints within the suggested spacing distances.

5-34. Cross Connections. The distribution systems of many public water supplies are connected with other sources of water which are used only in emergencies. The emergency supplies may be of a public nature also, but used only when the regular supply fails or is inadequate to furnish all the water needed, say for a large fire. The emergency supply may be a river or lake from which the water is obtained without purification. Many industrial plants, in addition to the public supply, often have a private source of water for fire protection or other use, and in many cases the two supplies are connected. These connections between the public water supply and emergency or private supplies are known as cross connections. They should receive very close attention on the part of the sanitarian, as they are frequently responsible for water-borne epidemics, particularly those connected with private supplies. The trouble arises from the fact that the unsafe supply may be under higher pressure than the public supply with the result that unsafe water enters through leaky connections, or valves between the two supplies may be opened by unauthorized persons. A gate valve in a cross connection should be locked and sealed so that inspection will demonstrate whether the valve has been tampered with. However, gate valves may leak, with consequent danger. No connection of pipes or valves between public and private supplies should ever be allowed. Figure 5-10 illustrates the one method by which the dual supply may be obtained without danger.

Another type of cross connection that has recently proved itself to be very dangerous is that caused by faulty plumbing fixtures and poor plumbing installation in general. The danger results from possible back siphonage of dirty water from toilets, washbowls, etc., into the water-supply pipes or by direct cross connections between waste pipes and water pipes. The last is particularly likely in hotels and other large buildings having very complicated plumbing systems. The amoebic dysentery outbreak in Chicago in 1933 was caused by sewage from poor plumbing entering the refrigerated water system which served two hotels. A further discussion of poor plumbing and its relation to water supply is given in Art. 6-8.

Other types of cross connections which occur are found in swimming pools having fresh-water inlets placed beneath the water surface so that contaminated water may run back into the mains. At water treatment plants bypass pipes are sometimes found running from the raw-water pump discharge around the plant to a filtered-water tank, or in some other fashion so that untreated water may enter the water distribution

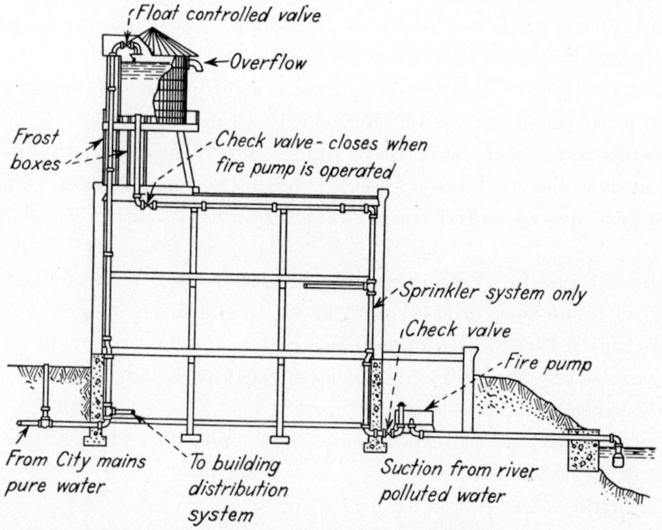

FIG. 5-10. Safe method of obtaining dual water supplies. (*Courtesy of Minnesota State Board of Health.*)

system. Filtered-water basins and raw-water basins may be placed side by side with a single wall between them, and this may leak.

At industrial plants and in commercial buildings cross connections other than to an auxiliary supply are all too common. Condenser water and cooling water may be returned to the building drinking water system, which in turn is connected with the public supply. Pumps which handle polluted water may be primed with water from the public supply in such a manner that possible contamination will result. Many industries have underwater inlets in tanks used for various purposes. The remedy, as for swimming pools, is a complete break or gap between the inlet pipe and the highest possible water level in the tank. In some cases actual connections have been made between the discharge lines of sewage-sump pumps and water lines so that sewage has been pumped into a supply pipe, although an extreme situation such as this is soon noted. Such mistakes can be prevented by a system of painting water-supply and drainage pipes in different colors throughout a plant.

In many cities elaborate and thorough cross-connection surveys have been made. The number of unsafe conditions found is usually surprising to the health and water authorities. The survey is followed, of course, by efforts to have matters remedied, which is a time-consuming task.

5-35. Laboratory Practice for Waterworks Operators. When surface waters must be given complete treatment, including aeration, coagulation and mixing, sedimentation, filtration and pre- and/or post-chlorination, then laboratory facilities for performing routine bacteriological and chemical control tests at the water treatment plant should be provided. The bacteriological examinations include:

1. Most probable numbers of coliform organisms in the raw water
2. Standard plate counts of bacteria at 20 or 35°C
3. Presumptive and confirmed tests for coliform organisms in the water sample collected from a tap located on the plant discharge main and on water samples collected from various points of the water distribution system

The specific chemical examinations considered at a particular location will vary with the type of treatment given to the raw water, but in general the following tests would be considered very useful:

1. "Jar tests" for determining coagulant dosages.
2. Alkalinity—raw, settled, filtered.
3. Total hardness—filtered, also raw if the water is softened.
4. Total solids—filtered.
5. Chlorides—filtered.
6. Fluorides—filtered, also raw and at points of distribution system if fluoridation is practiced.
7. Iron—raw and filtered.
8. Chlorine residual—at intermittent points of treatment, final, and at various points of the distribution system.
9. pH—raw, settled, filtered.
10. At periodic intervals, a complete chemical analysis should be made on the raw water, treated water, and water supplied at an active point of the distribution system. These complete analyses might include the following: total solids, silica residue, total alkalinity, total hardness, calcium, magnesium, iron, manganese, sodium (calculated), carbonate, bicarbonate, sulfate, chloride, fluoride, nitrate, and pH.

For effective sanitary control of ground-water systems, bacteriological examinations may be made on water samples secured from the various wells and also on samples collected from representative points of the distribution system in the numbers recommended by the Public Health

Service Drinking Water Standards, which approximate one sample per month per 1,000 population served by the facilities. If special treatment is given the well water, *i.e.*, softening, iron removal, fluoridation, and chlorination, then appropriate chemical control tests, as outlined above for surface-water systems, may be considered as desirable.

5-36. Sanitation and Development of Individual Water Facilities. Most of the water made available at farms, ranches, and residences in suburban or fringe areas of cities is derived from wells, springs, or cisterns; however, in some areas ground water is not available, or the available ground water is of undesirable chemical quality, and it has become necessary to develop surface sources of water supply. The water for the individual water-supply systems in many instances is not protected adequately from contamination, and proper sanitation and development of these small facilities should be emphasized to improve existing conditions. From a theoretical standpoint, these small water systems should be developed in a manner similar to that for water facilities for public use; however, due to the economic aspects, the provision of facilities to provide maximum protection of water quality may not be practical. Well drillers, water-system equipment suppliers and plumbers, as well as local, state, and Federal agencies interested in water-supply development, should make every effort to acquaint the layman with the features of water-supply development, operation, and maintenance required to ensure adequate protection or treatment of water to render the water thus made available potable for domestic use. The significance of bacteriological-analysis results should be understood, and the possible causes of contamination evaluated. Disinfection of water systems with chlorine after their construction, rehabilitation, and repair should be practiced. A comprehensive educational program covering individual water supplies will no doubt result in many needed improvements.

5-37. Springs. Contrary to popular belief, spring water is not always of good bacteriological quality. In many instances, springs are nothing more than very shallow wells with water derived from a water stratum composed of creviced limestone, sand, or gravel lying only a few feet below the earth's surface. Since it is not always practicable to determine accurately the depth of the stratum from which the water is produced or whether the water is protected from surface-water contamination by impervious formations, extreme precautions should be exercised in developing springs for drinking and household use.

If the spring water is to be used for drinking and household purposes, the spring should be protected from surface or runoff water, dust, insects, wildlife, and stock. The fissure from which water is flowing should be completely enclosed with a reservoir of concrete, tile, steel, or other impervious material. The walls of the reservoir should be of such depth as to penetrate the impervious formation beneath the water-producing stratum; the reservoir cover should be insect-, dust-, and rainproof; and a manhole of the raised curbing type having an overlapping cover, the edges of which terminate in a downward direction, should be provided with facilities for locking. To prevent the intermittent contamination of the spring through dipping by utensils, a water-discharge pipe should be provided which will permit the water to flow from the enclosure by gravity. If water is to be pumped from the spring to the point of use, it is preferable to allow the water to flow from the spring to a clear well reservoir where the pump is installed, in lieu of installing the pump at the spring enclosure.

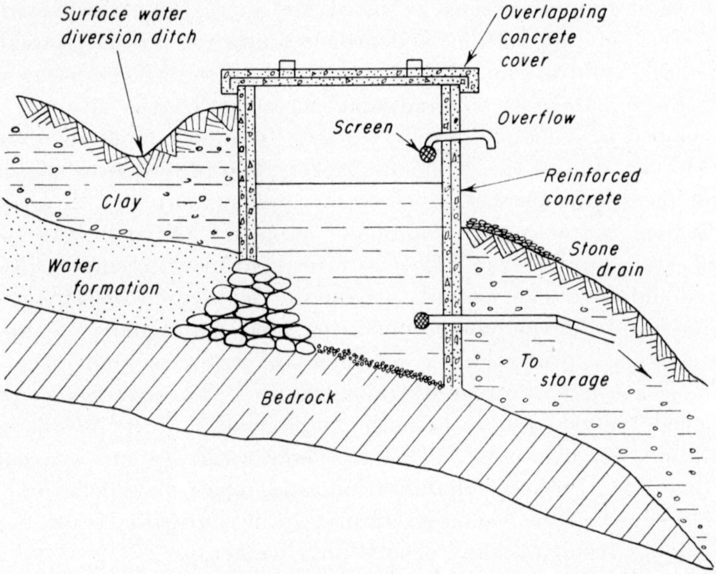

FIG. 5-11. A protected spring. (*Drawing courtesy of Texas State Department of Health.*)

Spring water should not be used with confidence for drinking or domestic purposes until bacteriological test results show that intermittent contamination is not occurring and that the water is of safe quality at all times. After a new or cleaned spring has been made ready for use, the entire spring enclosure should be disinfected with a chlorine solution and the installation flushed prior to submitting samples for laboratory examination. If satisfactory bacteriological examination results cannot be obtained, such treatment as filtration through sand and gravel and continuous disinfection may be considered. Also, should the spring water be considered too hard, too high in iron, or otherwise objectionable, special treatment to reduce or remove the troublesome mineral may be provided.

5-38. Cisterns. Ground-water supplies may not always be available; production from ground-water formation may be insufficient to meet domestic water demands; and the development of a surface-water system may be impossible in view of the large expenditure of funds required for such facilities. Under such local conditions, individuals find it necessary

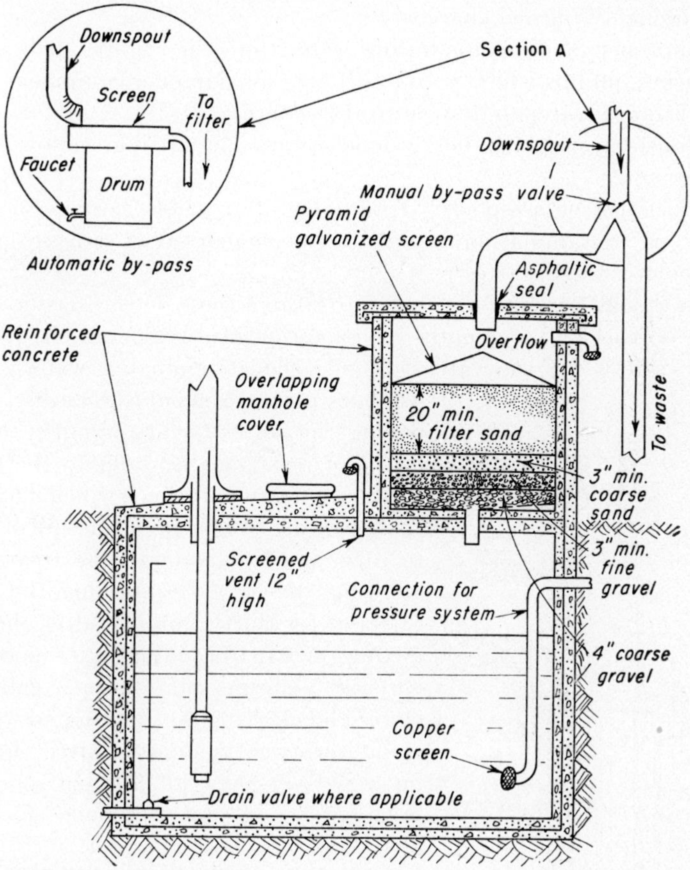

FIG. 5-12. Cistern with sand filter. (*Drawing courtesy of Texas State Department of Health.*)

to use rain water and to develop cistern supplies for household purposes. It should be realized, however, that cistern waters are subject to contamination, if the following defects are not corrected in the provision of such facilities:

1. Possibility of entrance of such contaminants as dust, soot, bird droppings, vermin from the roof or other catchment areas, and trash or soil which has accumulated in the gutters

2. Uncovered cisterns or tanks, existence of manhole covers which are not tight-fitting, or unscreened vents

3. No provision made for excluding from the cistern the first portion of each rainfall, until the roof or other collecting surface has become rinsed thoroughly

4. No provision made for a first-class filter of clean, well-selected sand and thoroughly burned charcoal

5. Improper facilities for raising water from the cistern, such as rope and bucket, pumps which require priming, or pumping equipment which allows leakage water to drain into the cistern

6. Cracks in walls of underground cisterns permitting shallow ground water to enter

7. Existence of cesspools, septic-tank drain fields, privies, or other sources of contamination located close enough to cisterns to permit entrance of sewage wastes

Even though precaution is taken to correct these defects, cistern water should be checked frequently by bacteriological examination to determine its safety. If the water is found to be contaminated, water used for drinking purposes should be treated (1) by boiling the water twenty minutes to sterilize it or bringing the water to the boiling point to kill any pathogens which may exist, (2) by adding two drops of tincture of iodine to each quart of water to be treated and allowing the water containing the iodine to stand for thirty minutes after thorough mixing, or (3) by adding 1 teaspoon of 1 per cent chlorine solution to 2 gallons of water and allowing the chlorinated water to stand for twenty minutes after thorough mixing. A 1 per cent chlorine solution is prepared by adding 1 teaspoon of chlorinated lime to 1 quart of water.

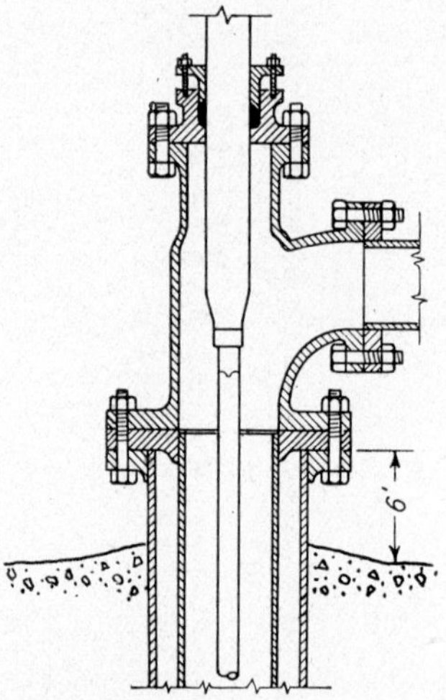

FIG. 5-13. Detail of well-casing-head protection. (*Courtesy of Minnesota State Board of Health.*)

5-39. Individual Well Supplies. Four general types of wells are constructed to procure water from water-producing strata: drilled, bored, driven, and dug. *Drilled wells* are deep enough to reach a plentiful and reliable source of water. Ordinarily, they should be constructed with a spudder, cable, or rotary-type drilling equipment in the same manner as wells provided to supply water for public use; however, costs for such installations are prohibitive for most individuals, and other means of providing protection of water quality are used. In view of the inferior well-construction practices usually followed, it is desirable to locate wells at distances greater than 150 feet from sources of contamination. To give some assurance that the water formation is protected from surface contamination and seepage water originating at shallow depths, the drilled well should be provided with steel or wrought-iron casing extending to at least the first impervious stratum below the earth's surface and preferably to the second impervious formation penetrated by the drill.

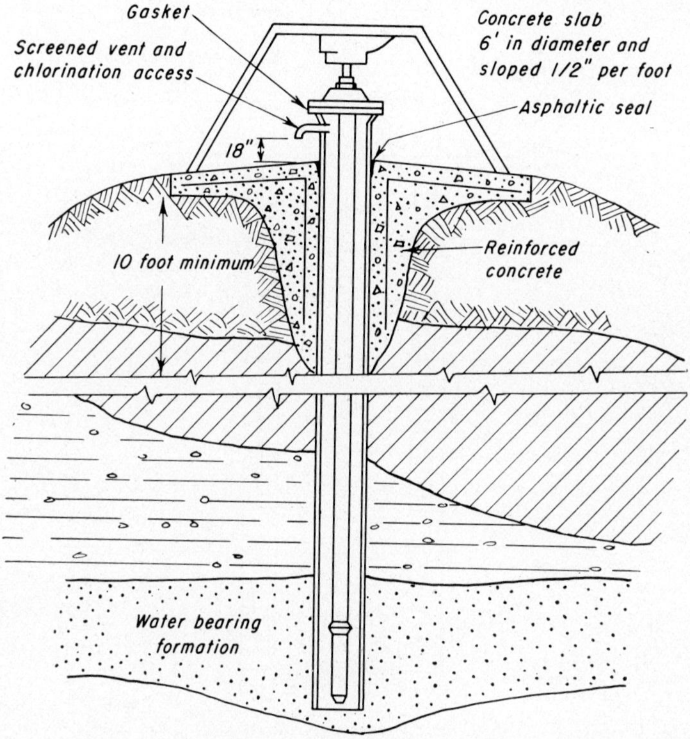

FIG. 5-14. A protected drilled well. *(Drawing courtesy of Texas State Department of Health.)*

A vulnerable part of the well from the standpoint of protection from surface contamination or from shallow ground water is the annular space which exists between the drill hole and the well casing. It is therefore desirable to cement the entire length of the casing placed into the well to prevent contamination of the well water by this route. To exclude possible entrance of surface water, pump-packing gland leakage, or rain water into the well, the well casing should extend at least 18 inches above the finished floor of the well house. The casing should be surrounded by a concrete pump-motor foundation block which allows 1 inch of the casing to extend above the top of it, and the well-pump motor base should be grouted or otherwise sealed to the foundation block. The well or well pump should be provided with a screened vent which terminates in a downward direction at such an elevation as to prevent possible submergence. If a well house is not to be provided, a concrete slab at least 6 feet by 6 feet by 6 inches should surround the well casing at the earth's surface.

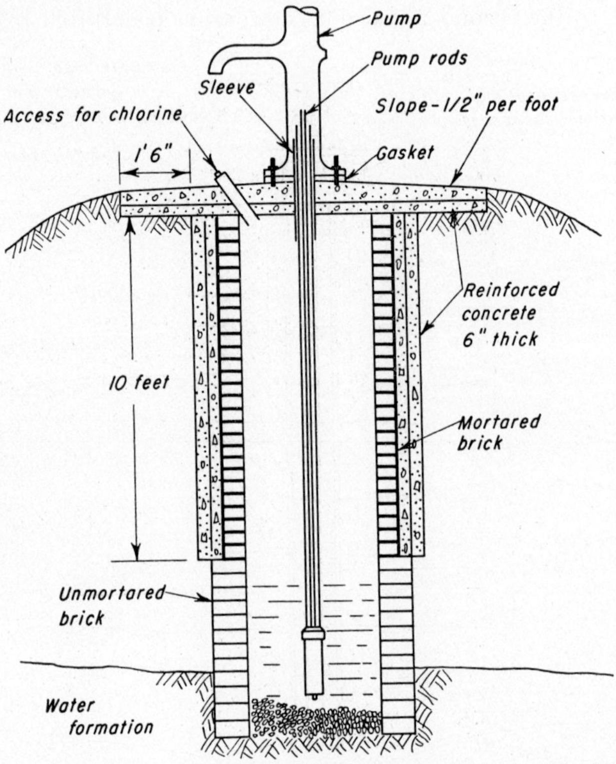

FIG. 5-15. A protected dug well. (*Drawing courtesy of Texas State Department of Health.*)

After the well has been constructed and developed and the permanent pumping equipment of a type which will not subject the water to contamination is installed, the well unit should be sterilized by applying at least 1 pound of chlorinated lime. This is placed into solution by adding it to 3 to 5 gallons of water. The solution is poured into the well, and mixing is accomplished by whatever means are available. All wells are subjected to contamination during construction and repairs, and this disinfection procedure should be followed by flushing the system thoroughly prior to submitting samples for bacteriological examination.

Bored wells may be constructed with the aid of hand or machine-driven augers. The same sanitary precautions and construction details are followed as for drilled wells to secure maximum protection of the water from possible contamination.

Driven wells are constructed by driving a pipe fitted with a well point with a pile driver or other driving device. Such installations are limited to localities where the waterbearing formations of sand or gravel lie at comparatively shallow depths and are not located below rock or shale formations which would prohibit the driving of the pipe.

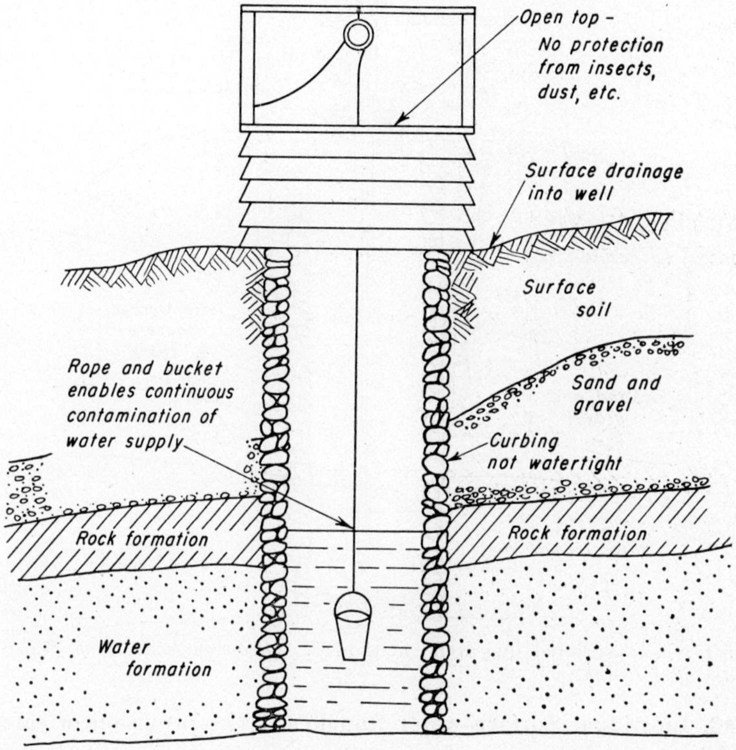

FIG. 5-16. Unsafe well. (*Drawing courtesy of Texas State Department of Health.*)

Dug wells are constructed with hand tools, and they are usually only deep enough to reach shallow water formations, the water production often being affected greatly during periods of drought. This type of well furnishes comparatively little water, and it is very difficult to maintain so as to be assured that a clear and safe water will be available at all times. In an attempt to safeguard the bacteriological quality of the water, the dug well, which is usually 2 or 3 feet in diameter, should be provided with a watertight curbing, constructed of stone, brick, tile, or metal, from the water-producing formation to 2 or 3 feet above ground elevation. No matter what the choice of curbing materials may be, it is advisable to place cement grout between the excavated well hole and the curbing for a depth of at least 10 feet and to provide a concrete slab at the earth's surface to prevent possible entrance of surface or shallow water. The cover over the well curbing should be of impervious material, should fit tight to exclude dust, insects, small animals, birds, rain water, and pump-packing gland leakage. The pump installed should not require priming, and it should be sealed to the well cover.

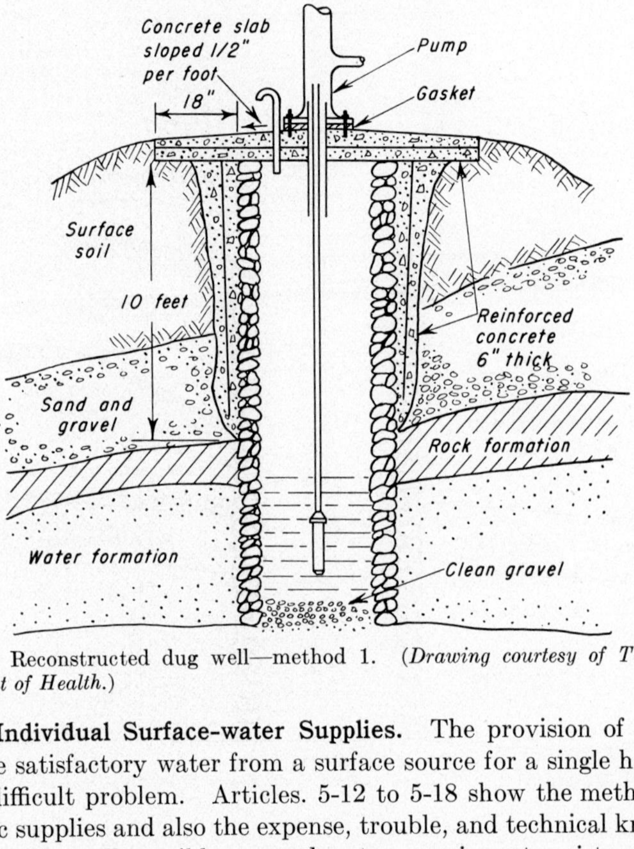

FIG. 5-17. Reconstructed dug well—method 1. (*Drawing courtesy of Texas State Department of Health.*)

5-40. Individual Surface-water Supplies. The provision of safe and otherwise satisfactory water from a surface source for a single home presents a difficult problem. Articles. 5-12 to 5-18 show the methods used for public supplies and also the expense, trouble, and technical knowledge required. If at all possible, ground-water or rain-water cisterns should be used.

If the surface water to be used is relatively clear, the water that is to be drunk or used for cooking may be run through one of the commercial stone filters and then boiled. Disinfection using chlorine (Arts. 5-18 and 5-20) or iodine may also be used. Two drops of tincture of iodine to a quart of water will disinfect it, but thorough mixing and a thirty-minute contact period should be provided.

If the water is noticeably turbid at all times, the water may be pumped to a covered concrete tank that provides an average storage period of about thirty days. This is expensive and requires provision for emptying and cleaning the tank. The water to be drunk can then be treated as suggested in the preceding paragraph. An alternative is to apply the settled water to a small slow sand filter constructed and operated as indicated in Art. 5-14. The effluent should be disinfected by one of the methods mentioned.

Another alternative which requires skilled operation is to apply the water from the source, if it is very clear, or from the concrete tank men-

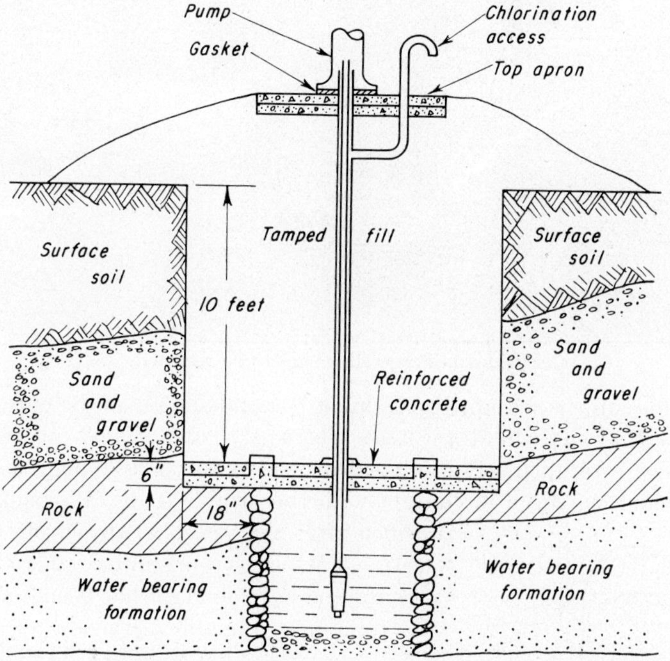

FIG. 5-18. A reconstructed dug well—method 2. (*Drawing courtesy of Texas State Department of Health.*)

tioned above, to one or more pressure filters, giving doses of a coagulant to the water as it enters the pressure filter. Pressure filters and their operation are described in Chap. 7. Such filters must be backwashed with filtered water. The filtered water to be drunk should be disinfected.

5-41. Drinking Fountains. The common drinking cup is implicated in the spread of tonsillitis, tuberculosis, diphtheria, syphilis, and other diseases. The recognition of the dangers of the common drinking cup has resulted in drinking fountains of various sorts replacing it in schools, factories, and public buildings. All drinking fountains, however, cannot be considered as satisfactory. Those in which the water rises vertically

FIG. 5-19. This well is sure to be polluted.

through a cup-shaped apparatus must be condemned, as the cup quickly becomes dirty and the drain holes frequently clog. Those in which the water rises intermittently in a vertical jet are especially dangerous as the water which has been in contact with the drinker's lips falls back to the orifice after the water is turned off. If the vertical jet runs constantly, there is still ground for suspicion as it has been found that bacteria may remain at the top of the jet. The safest drinking fountain provides a diagonal jet with guards so placed that the mouths of users cannot touch the orifice and so that the drippings from the mouth cannot possibly fall on it. The matter of prevention of all contact of the mouth with the orifice is important. A double diagonal jet with the two streams meeting beyond the guard is safe and also convenient to drink from as the velocity of the water is somewhat checked. The water outlet, or orifice, should be above the rim of the bowl so that a stoppage will not submerge it and thereby cause a cross connection or contaminate the orifice edges.

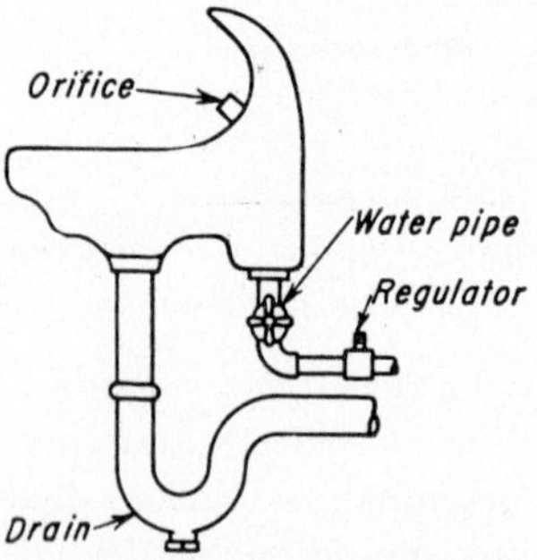

FIG. 5-20. Satisfactory type of drinking fountain.

5-42. Bottled Water. In establishing rules and regulations covering the production, processing, distribution, and sale of drinking water dispensed from bottles, cartons, cans, drums, tanks, or other containers and classified as natural, distilled, or demineralized, the following items might be considered[3]:

A. *Sources of Supply:* All natural and demineralized water must be procured from a source supplying water free from contamination unless approved supplemental treatment is given. Distilled water or sterile pyrogen-free water from vapor-compression water stills [should][1] originate from approved sources of supply. This requirement [must] be met even though it would be possible to render raw water from an unapproved source free from contamination by distillation methods. Water supply facilities are considered as approved upon compliance with the recommended standards of design [adopted by the agency responsible for the supervision of potable water systems. Mineral waters consumed for various therapeutic reasons do] conform with the drinking water standards from a chemical standpoint.

B. *General Requirements for Bottling Plants:*

1. Floors. The floors of all rooms where water is processed or the finished product stored [should] be constructed of concrete or other equally impervious and easily cleanable material and [should] be smooth, properly drained, provided with trapped drains and kept clean.

2. Walls and Ceilings. Walls and ceilings in rooms where water containers are filled and capped [should] be constructed and sealed in such a manner as to prevent the finished product from being contaminated and [should] be kept clean.

3. Doors and Windows. Unless other effective means are provided to prevent the [entrance] of insects, all openings into rooms where containers are sterilized, filled and capped [should] be effectively screened, and screen doors [should] open outward and be self-closing.

4. Lighting and Ventilation. All rooms [should] be well lighted and adequately ventilated.

5. Miscellaneous Protection from Contamination. The various plant operations [should] be so located and conducted as to prevent any contamination of the water or cleaned equipment. All means necessary for the elimination of insects [should] be used. Container filling and sterilization [should] be in a separate room from loading and unloading operations.

6. Toilet Facilities. Toilet rooms [should] not open directly into the container filling rooms and the doors of all toilet rooms [should] be self-closing. Toilet rooms [should] be kept in a clean condition, in good repair, and well ventilated and [should] not be used as dressing rooms.

7. Facilities for Washing and Disinfecting the Hands. Facilities for washing the hands [should] be provided on each floor, should be convenient to the toilet facilities, and should include hot and cold running water, soap, and approved sanitary towels. [Common towels are] prohibited. Conspicuous signs [should]

[1] The words in brackets in these quoted passages are editorial changes from the original document.

be posted in all toilet rooms which read as follows: "All Employees MUST Wash Hands Before Returning to Work." If manual or hand-filling methods are used, a solution containing an approved bactericidal agent [should] be placed near the location of the container filling operations. The operator [should] disinfect his hands in this solution each time he resumes container filling operations after periods of interruption. The management [should] require those employees who fill the containers or who otherwise handle these containers prior to filling them to follow this procedure.

8. Sanitary Piping. All piping used to conduct water to the filling operation [should] be of a type which can easily be cleaned, which is non-corrosive, and which will prevent toxic materials from entering the water being transported.

9. Containers and Equipment. All multi-use containers and equipment with which water comes in contact [should] be constructed in such a manner as to be easily cleaned and [should] be kept in good repair.

10. Plumbing and Disposal of Waste. All plumbing and equipment will be installed in accordance with the laws of the state . . . and local plumbing codes. All liquid wastes [should] also be disposed of in accordance with the laws of the state . . . and local ordinances.

11. Refuse and Garbage Disposal. All accumulation of broken bottles, rubbish and garbage [should] be kept in appropriate receptacles or containers with tight-fitting covers and [should] be removed from the bottling plant daily.

12. Cleaning and Bactericidal Treatment. All processed water containers and equipment (except single service containers) [should] be thoroughly cleaned after each usage. All multi-use containers and equipment [should] be subjected to an approved bactericidal process before usage. In the cleaning of bottles or multi-use containers to be filled, the temperature of the washing solution [should] not be less than 120°F and the alkalinity of such a solution [should] at all times be equivalent to the alkalinity of a 3 per cent [sodium hydroxide] solution. Bactericidal treatment [should] consist of the use of chlorine at 100 ppm for two minutes, hot water at 180°F for two minutes, or any other type [of] treatment which is approved by the . . . Department of Health. No plant [should] practice the refilling of bottles or multi-use containers unless: (a) it uses at all times a mechanical bottle washer which [should] be maintained in a state of full efficiency at all times, or (b) it provides facilities accomplishing equal treatment.

13. Storage of Containers and Equipment. After bactericidal treatment as prescribed above, all containers, unless immediately filled, [should] be stored so as to prevent contamination.

14. Handling of Containers, Caps, Covers and Equipment. All containers, caps, covers and equipment [should] be handled in such a manner as to prevent contamination.

15. Storage of Caps, Parchment Paper, Corks and Single-service Containers. Caps, parchment paper, corks and single-service containers [should] be purchased and stored only in sanitary tubes, cartons or boxes, and [should] be kept in a clean, dry place.

16. Capping. Capping [should] be done so as to prevent contamination. All caps and corks [should] be subjected to an approved bactericidal treatment prior to use.

17. Transportation of Water. All containers and tanks used in the transportation of water to be processed or to be sold in bulk [should] be sealed and protected against contamination. These containers and tanks [should] be subjected to a thorough cleaning and a bactericidal treatment prior to filling with water to be processed at a plant or sold in bulk. This treatment [should] be accomplished by flushing the containers or tanks every 7 days and steaming them at least at monthly intervals. Bactericidal treatment using 100 ppm residual chlorine for two minutes is also considered satisfactory. The containers and tanks [should] be labeled in accordance with the labeling requirements of [the state agency having jurisdiction].

18. Bacteriological Analysis. As a minimum requirement, every processor [should] submit . . . every two weeks for bacteriological analysis a sample of each type of water processed and distributed by the plant. All samples [should] be taken from the filled container. When a water sample indicates the presence of coliform organisms, the operator [should] immediately take corrective action and [should] submit daily samples until the results obtained from at least two consecutive samples show the water to be satisfactory in accordance with drinking water standards. All records of bacteriological analyses made shall be maintained on file at the plant where the water is processed. The Local Health Officer [should] have the power to prevent the continuation of bottled water processing if the quality of the finished product endangers public health.

19. Chemical Analysis. At least once each year a complete chemical analysis [should] be made on all types of water offered for sale. If a change in the water facilities is made which would alter the chemical quality, appropriate supplemental analyses [should] be made. All water must conform with physical and chemical quality limits prescribed in *USPHS Drinking Water Standards.* Mineral water, however, need not meet mineral concentrations prescribed in [the] standards.

All records of chemical analyses must be maintained on file at the plant where the water is bottled or canned, and [also] copies of analysis reports submitted to the [state department of health having jurisdiction].

20. Certificates of Competency. No [vendor should] offer for sale drinking water unless the production, processing and treatment is at all times under the supervision of [competent personnel]. . . . Individuals engaged in handling and dispensing drinking water from tank trucks [should be] likewise required to be certified.

21. Personnel Health. All employees working or engaged in the business of processing or transporting drinking water [should] be required to obtain a health card or certificate of health in conformance with the laws of the state . . . and the city where the bottling plant is located. This health card or certificate of health when issued [should] acknowledge the fact that the employee is free of communicable disease.

22. Personnel Cleanliness. All persons engaged in processing water [should] wear clean garments and [should] keep their hands clean at all times.

23. Labeling. Each container [should] bear a label approved by the State Department of Health [having jurisdiction], labels to be affixed to the container before it leaves the plant. Each label [should] show the following:

(a) The type of water, such as "Distilled Water," "Demineralized Water," "Spring Water," etc.

(b) The name and address of the processor.

(c) The source of the natural water sold.

(d) Claims of medicinal and health-giving properties [should] not be [allowed] on labels nor [should] references as to bacterial purity [be acceptable].

(e) No untrue or misleading statements [should] appear on the label.

5-43. Manufacture of Ice. The danger of water-borne disease transmission by the consumption of ice or of beverages or raw food cooled or refrigerated by contact with contaminated ice is apparent, even though it is somewhat difficult to trace epidemics of these diseases as being brought about by such a medium. To assure the proper protection of the bacteriological quality of ice, however, the following items should be considered[4]:

1. a. All water used in the manufacture of ice sold for human or domestic consumption [should] meet [Public Health Service] Drinking Water Standards from a bacteriological quality standpoint. Also, water used [should] not contain any materials which will be detrimental to health.

b. Frequent tests (at least four per month) [should] be made to determine the bacteriological quality of the water secured from a privately owned water supply, which is used in the manufacture of ice intended for human consumption.

c. Similar tests [should] also be made of the ice manufactured to determine defects during freezing and ice handling operations. All ice in cakes, cubes, or in the form of crushed, sized or flake ice [should] be inspected for foreign objects and not sold or offered for human consumption if foreign objects are found.

2. Water systems supplying water to ice plants or to facilities [for] producing ice at point of use [should] be protected in such a manner as to prevent possible contamination of the water, and adequate treatment facilities [should] be provided, as required, to render the water safe for human consumption. Such water systems [should] also be operated in such a manner as to be assured that water of safe quality is being used. No cross connections between a safe water and an unsafe supply [should] be permitted.

3. a. Equipment used at ice plants or as a part of the facilities producing ice at point of use [should] not be permitted to come in contact with the floor or other sources of contamination. Plant structures and equipment [should] be maintained in such a condition as to prevent the entrance of foreign solids or liquid wastes into the water during freezing.

b. In order to minimize the possibility of contamination of the ice during freezing, the operator employed on the tank floor [should] use footwear which is limited to use only on the tank room floor. This footwear cannot be worn when leaving the tank room floor for any purpose. Only authorized persons [should] be permitted on the tank room floor or within the ice storage rooms. Signs [should] be posted stating that only authorized persons are allowed on the tank room floor and in ice storage vaults. Spitting in the ice plant and cold storage rooms [should be] prohibited.

c. All freezing tank covers [should] be maintained in good repair and in a sanitary condition. Covers [should] be removed from [the] tank room, if thorough cleaning is required. Submerging or spraying ice cans for removal of ice cakes from them in or with unsafe water [should be] prohibited.

4. All portable can fillers, core sucking devices, and drop tubes [should] be handled in such a manner as to prevent their contamination. If at any time equipment is suspected as having been contaminated by improper handling, this equipment [should] be sterilized by means described in Section 9.

5. All air supplied for water agitation [should] be filtered to exclude dust and other foreign material. Air intakes [should] be arranged in such a manner as to minimize dust in air used.

6. Ice storage vaults [should] be kept in a sanitary condition. All storage vaults provided with drains [should] be maintained in such a condition as to prevent possible flooding of rooms with waste material. All vaults . . . which will be normally used at temperatures above freezing [should] be provided with suitable drains. To prevent possible contamination of ice, all accumulations of rust, fungus growths, molds or slimes [should] be controlled. Meats, vegetables, other foods, flowers, etc. [should] not be placed in direct contact with ice intended to be sold for human consumption. Bins, racks or other receptacles used for the storage of meats and foods [should] be kept in a sanitary condition. At points of public use or consumption no foods, beverages, or other materials [should] be refrigerated or stored in direct contact with ice in containers used for storing ice available for human consumption.

7. The ice loading platform and chutes [should] be maintained in a sanitary condition. All ice during delivery [should] be covered to minimize contamination by dust. Ice delivery trucks and other vehicles transporting ice [should] be operated and maintained so as to prevent possible contamination of the ice. Upon delivery of ice for human consumption at an establishment, the recipient [should be] responsible for the protection of the quality of the ice. . . .

8. a. Crushed or ground ice intended for human consumption [should] be crushed or ground in a sanitary manner. The crushing or grinding of ice for human consumption on wagons, trucks or other vehicles [should] be permitted only upon approval by the local or State health authorities, when appropriate steps have been taken to safeguard the crushed or ground ice and equipment from contamination.

b. The crushing, grinding, sizing, cubing or other operations associated with processing of such ice at fixed locations [should] be carried on in a manner as to prevent contamination of the finished product or the equipment used.

9. After long periods of interrupted plant operation, or if contamination occurs, all freezing cans, can fillers, core suction devices, and water agitators [should] be [disinfected] by steam, if available, or by submergence into a chlorine solution containing at least 100 ppm of chlorine residual for a period of two minutes, after the equipment has been cleaned thoroughly.

10. Adequate handwashing and toilet facilities [should] be provided and maintained in a sanitary condition at the ice plant. If drinking fountains are provided for patrons, they [should] be of the approved angle jet type and be located so that it will not be necessary for persons to walk across the ice loading platform. All liquid and solid wastes [should] be disposed [of] by approved methods.

BIBLIOGRAPHY

1. Public Health Service Drinking Water Standards, 1946, *Public Health Repts.*, vol. 61, no. 11, pp. 371–384, 1946.
2. Manual of Recommended Water Sanitation Practice, *Public Health Repts.*, vol. 58, no. 1, pp. 84–111, 1943.
3. "Minimum Standards for Production, Processing and Distribution, Bottled Drinking Water," Texas State Department of Health, 1952.
4. "Minimum Standards Covering Manufacture, Storage, and Distribution of Ice Sold for Human Consumption, Including Ice Produced at Point of Use," Texas State Department of Health, 1954.
5. "Standard Methods for the Examination of Water, Sewage, and Industrial Waste," 10th ed., American Public Health Association, New York, 1955.
6. Individual Water Supply Systems, *U.S. Public Health Service Bull.* 24, 1950.
7. "Safe Water for Farm and Suburban Homes," Texas State Department of Health.
8. Babbitt, H. E., and J. J. Doland: "Water Supply Engineering," 5th ed., McGraw-Hill Book Company, Inc., New York, 1955.
9. Steel, E. W.: "Water Supply and Sewerage," 3d ed., McGraw-Hill Book Company, Inc., New York, 1953.
10. Hardenbergh, W. A.: "Water Supply and Purification," 3d ed., International Textbook Company, Scranton, Pa., 1952.
11. Fair, G. M., and J. C. Geyer, "Water Supply and Waste-water Disposal," John Wiley & Sons, Inc., New York, 1954.

CHAPTER 6

PLUMBING

6-1. The importance of safe methods of sewage collection and disposal is realized by all sanitarians. One of the links of this chain is the house-drainage system—in other words, the plumbing. Its importance is enhanced by the fact that it is in far closer contact with the everyday life of the citizen than is the common sewer or sewage treatment plant. The sewage which the plumbing system carries is potentially dangerous in that it frequently contains disease-producing bacteria. Leakage in plumbing systems, therefore, is a menace to health, whether it occurs in the house, where infection of food is possible, or in the ground outside the house, where well-water supplies may be contaminated. In either case an offensive condition will result. Even more important is the danger that defective plumbing may allow wastes to enter the water-supply pipes. A further danger is the possible entrance into the house of insects and rats from the drainage system, possibly bearing upon their feet and bodies the germs of disease. Sewer air may also make its way into buildings through defective plumbing. A further discussion as to the nature of sewer air will be given below.

A knowledge of good practice in plumbing is valuable in many ways to the sanitarian and also to the city engineer. In municipalities which require licenses for plumbers, one or both may be members of the examining board. In smaller cities very frequently the city engineer or sanitarian is the plumbing inspector. He encounters defective plumbing in the investigation of nuisances and occasionally in the study of epidemics.

6-2. Legal Control. The public regulation of plumbing is based upon the police power of government. This is based upon the principle that government has the right to provide for the safety, health, and morals of the people. Plumbing codes, therefore, are or should be designed to protect, with reasonable provisions, the health, welfare, and comfort of the public. The police power is delegated to the individual states, but not all of them have yet attempted to apply it to plumbing. Some states have no laws regulating plumbing, although there may be local municipal codes. Others have laws that prescribe state-wide regulations. Some have laws that are applicable only to cities of a certain size, while still others require the licensing of plumbers with or without making it obligatory for cities to adopt plumbing ordinances. Uniformity of codes, throughout a state at least, is desirable.

6-3. Plumbing Codes. As may be imagined, there is little or no uniformity as to principles or practice in plumbing codes. Furthermore, there is a regrettable tendency on the part of officials, particularly in the smaller cities, to neglect the enforcement of regulations. Occasionally the attitude is encountered that the only purpose of codes is to make plumbing more elaborate, to the greater profit of the plumber. The price of plumbing may be increased insofar as plumbing codes eliminate the incompetent workman who is competing with responsible master plumbers. The work of the incompetent, however, is expensive at any price. Well-designed plumbing regulations, properly enforced, result in no increase of plumbing costs when the work is done by conscientious and skilled plumbers. In general, however, plumbing codes make provision for the examination and licensing of plumbers; regulate the sizes and kinds of pipes and fittings, placing of traps and vents, and grades of horizontal lines; and require inspections and tests of new work before approval. As space does not allow discussion of all details of a comprehensive plumbing code, the following articles emphasize only the points in which sanitation is particularly involved and the more important matters concerned with adequacy and good workmanship.

In 1951, the Coordinating Committee for a National Plumbing Code published its report[1] which represents a consensus of the members of the Coordinating Committee and of its advisory committee. This report reflects the experience and conclusions reached from research in the field of plumbing conducted by laboratories, including those of the National Bureau of Standards, the University of Iowa, the University of Illinois, and the U.S. Public Health Service. It is an attempt to attain national uniformity, and to this end, it is certain to be soundly conceived and suitable for general acceptance. The American Standards Association accepted the recommendations of this committee in publishing the American Standard Plumbing Code[2]. Plumbing practice, as outlined in this chapter, follows in general the recommended requirements contained in these two publications for plumbing in dwellings and similar buildings.

6-4. Enforcement. In the smaller cities, enforcement of plumbing regulations may present some difficulties. Two possibilities present themselves: placing enforcement within the jurisdiction of either the city engineer or the waterworks division. The city engineer, if one is retained by the city, is probably the logical enforcement officer, as he has the maps showing sewer locations and is also concerned with street openings. If no city engineer is available, some qualified member of the waterworks staff may be selected for this work. The employment of a plumber on a part-time basis is unsatisfactory, since he must inspect and pass upon work of his competitors. In the larger cities, full-time plumbing inspectors are essential. Practice varies as to the placing of the plumbing division within the city government. In some cities it is a division of the health department; in others, of the bureau of building inspection or the public works department. If the health department has a division of sanitary engineering, plumbing inspection should be placed in it.

Plumbers are required to obtain permits to make sewer connections or to install or construct plumbing fixtures. Fees are charged according to the number of fixtures placed. Permits for opening streets or alleys to make connections with sewers are also required. Before the work is approved, two tests are applied: the first, after the "roughing in" is completed; the final, after all fixtures have been placed and trap seals filled. No work is covered before the inspector has seen it. Certificates of approval are issued, and in many cities the certificate must be presented by the property owner or agent when application is made for turning on the city water.

6-5. Scope of Plumbing. Plumbing has two objects: (1) to furnish water to the various parts of a building, (2) to remove the liquid wastes and discharge them into the sewer or private disposal plant.

The water system must accomplish two objects: (1) there must be provided a sufficient amount of water to serve each fixture; (2) there must be no opportunity for backflow of used water into the water pipes. The waste system must also accomplish several objects: (1) quick removal of the wastes with minimum chance for stoppage of drains, (2) prevention of entrance into the house of vermin and "sewer gas" or foul-smelling air from the plumbing system or sewer.

6-6. Sewer Gas. A few words as to the character of the so-called "sewer gas" will be appropriate here. Strictly, it is not a gas of definite chemical composition but air that has come into contact with decomposing organic matter. The sewer air may contain some of the gases which are the results of decomposition, such as hydrogen sulfide and carbon dioxide, and which, under some circumstances, as in unventilated sewers or in sewer manholes, may overcome workmen. Numerous bacteriological tests have shown that sewer air is as free from bacteria as ordinary air, so that no disease infection need be feared from sewage bacteria floating into houses with sewer gas. The matter should not be dismissed so lightly, however. No one can say with certainty that long exposure to sewer air will not have some harmful physiological effect other than the causing of some specific disease. Hence, safe practice and

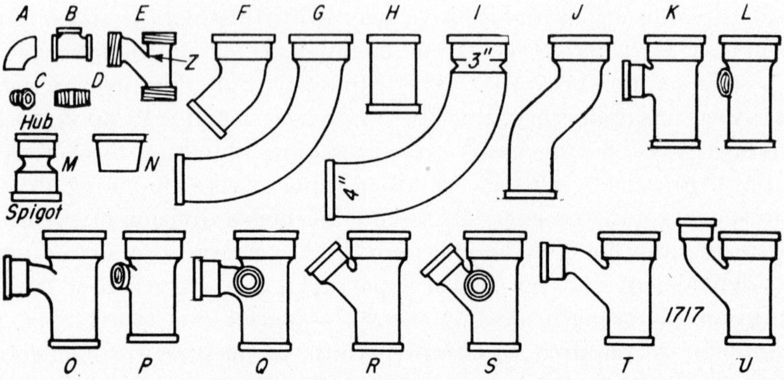

FIG. 6-1. Fittings: *A*, plain elbow or ell, turns one-quarter of a circle or 90 degrees; *B*, beaded tee branch; *C*, shoulder bushing; *D*, shoulder nipple; these four are typical wrought water-pipe fittings; *E*, section of 90-degree long-turn Y-branch or TY drainage fitting recessed and threaded for wrought pipe; note that the point Z is below the center line of the inlet pipe, an important feature in soil and waste lines; *F*, eighth or 45-degree bend, cast-iron, hub, and spigot type; *G*, long-sweep quarter bend; *H*, sleeve, sometimes used for joining two spigot ends on repair work; *I*, long-sweep reducing quarter bend, 4-inch spigot, 3-inch hub, often used at the bottom of 3-inch soil stacks; *J*, offset; *K*, T-branch; *L*, T-branch tapped for wrought pipe; *M*, reducer; an increaser has the spigot on the smaller end; *N*, plug; *O*, sanitary T-branch; *P*, sanitary T-branch tapped for wrought pipe; Q, sanitary T-branch with right-hand side inlet; *R*, Y-branch; *S*, Y-branch with right-hand side inlet; *T*, combination Y and eighth bend or TY fitting; *U*, upright Y-branch. (*Courtesy of U.S. Department of Agriculture.*)

good sense dictate that sewer air be prevented from entering buildings. On the other hand, since it is established that occasional small amounts of sewer air are not dangerous, heavy expense is uncalled for in cases where possible entrance of offensive air is problematical and where such entrance would be likely to occur only at widely spaced intervals.

6-7. Definition of Terms. Definitions of the more important terms used in plumbing are given below[1].

The *plumbing system* includes the water-supply and distribution pipes; plumbing fixtures and traps; soil, waste, and vent pipes; building drains and building sewers, including their respective connections, devices, and appurtenances within the property lines of the premises; and water-treating or water-using equipment.

Plumbing fixtures are installed receptacles, devices, or appliances which are supplied with water or which receive or discharge liquids or liquid-borne wastes, with or without discharge into the drainage system with which they may be directly or indirectly connected.

A *fixture unit* is a quantity in terms of which the load-producing effects on the plumbing system of different kinds of plumbing fixtures are expressed on some arbitrarily chosen scale.

A *trap* is a fitting or device so designed and constructed as to provide, when properly vented, a liquid seal which will prevent the back passage of air without materially affecting the flow of sewage or waste water through it.

The *trap seal* is the maximum vertical depth of liquid that a trap will retain, measured between the crown weir and the top of the dip of the trap.

A *vent pipe* or *vent system* is a pipe or pipes installed to provide a flow of air to or from a drainage system or to provide a circulation of air within such a system to protect trap seals from siphonage and back pressure.

A *local ventilating pipe* is a pipe on the fixture side of the trap through which vapor or foul air is removed from a room or fixture.

A *soil pipe* is any pipe which conveys the discharge of water closets, urinals, or fixtures having similar functions, with or without the discharge from other fixtures, to the building drain or building sewer.

A *waste pipe* is a pipe which conveys only liquid waste, free of fecal matter.

The *main* of any system of continuous piping is the principal artery of the system, to which branches may be connected.

A *branch* is any part of the piping system other than a main, riser, or stack.

A *branch interval* is a length of soil or waste stack corresponding in general to a story height, but in no case less than 8 feet, within which the horizontal branches from one floor, or story, of a building are connected to the stack.

Public fixtures, in the classification of plumbing fixtures, are those in general toilet rooms of schools, gymnasiums, hotels, railroad stations, public buildings, bars, public comfort stations, or places to which the public is invited or which are frequented by the public without special permission or special invitation, and other installations (whether pay or free) where a number of fixtures are installed so that their use is similarly unrestricted.

A *horizontal branch* is a drain pipe extending laterally from a soil or waste stack or building drain, with or without vertical sections or branches, which receives the discharge from one or more fixture drains and conducts it to the soil or waste stack or to the building (house) drain.

A *stack* is the vertical main of a system of soil, waste, or vent piping.

The *building (house) drain* is that part of the lowest piping of a drainage system which receives the discharge from soil, waste, and other drainage pipes inside the walls of the building and conveys it to the building (house) sewer beginning 3 feet outside the building wall.

The *building (house) sewer* is that part of the horizontal piping of a drainage system which extends from the end of the building drain and which receives the discharge of the building drain and conveys it to a

TABLE 6-1. FIXTURE UNITS PER FIXTURE OR GROUP

Fixture type	Fixture-unit value as load factors	Minimum size of trap, inches	
1 bathroom group consisting of water closet, lavatory, and bathtub or shower stall			
Tank water closet	6		
Flush-valve water closet	8		
Bathtub* (with or without overhead shower)	2		1½
Bidet	3	(nominal)	1½
Combination sink-and-tray	3		1½
Combination sink-and-tray with food-disposal unit	4	separate traps	1½
Dental unit or cuspidor	1		1¼
Dental lavatory	1		1¼
Drinking fountain	½		1
Dishwasher, domestic	2		1½
Floor drains†	1		2
Kitchen sink, domestic	2		1½
Kitchen sink, domestic, with food-disposal unit	3		1½
Lavatory‡	1	small P.O.	1¼
Lavatory	2	large P.O.	1½
Lavatory, barber, beauty parlor	2		1½
Lavatory, surgeon's	2		1½
Laundry tray (1 or 2 compartments)	2		1½
Shower stall, domestic	2		2
Showers (group) per head	3		
Sinks:			
Surgeon's	3		1½
Flushing rim (with valve)	8		3
Service (trap standard)	3		3
Service (P-trap)	2		2
Pot, scullery, etc.	4		1½
Urinal, pedestal, syphon jet, blowout	8	(nominal)	3
Urinal, wall lip	4		1½
Urinal stall, washout	4		2
Urinal trough (each 2-foot section)	2		1½
Wash sink (circular or multiple), each set of faucets	2	(nominal)	1½
Water closet:			
Tank-operated	4	(nominal)	3
Valve-operated	8		3

* A shower head over a bathtub does not increase the fixture value.

† Size of floor drain shall be determined by the area of surface water to be drained.

‡ Lavatories with 1¼- or 1½-inch traps have the same load value; larger P.O. (pipe-outlet) plugs have greater flow rate.

SOURCE: "Report of the Coordinating Committee for a National Plumbing Code," U.S. Department of Commerce, Domestic Commerce Series, No. 28.

public sewer, private sewer, individual sewage disposal system, or other point of disposal.

A *dead end* is a branch leading from a soil, waste, or vent pipe, building drain, or building sewer, which is terminated at a developed distance of 2 feet or more by means of a plug or other closed fitting.

6-8. Water Supply. The water-service pipe of any building should be of sufficient size to permit a continuous ample flow of water at any time and never less than ¾ inch. If flush valves or other devices requiring high flow rates are used, the water-service pipe must be designed to meet this flow.

TABLE 6-2. MINIMUM SIZE OF FIXTURE-SUPPLY PIPE

Type of fixture or device	*Pipe size, inch*
Bathtub	½
Combination sink-and-tray	½
Drinking fountain	⅜
Dishwasher, domestic	½
Kitchen sink, residential	½
Kitchen sink, commercial	¾
Lavatory	⅜
Laundry tray, 1, 2, or 3 compartments	½
Shower, single head	½
Sinks, service slop	½
Sinks, flushing rim	¾
Urinal, flush tank	½
Urinal, direct-flush valve	¾
Water closet, tank type	⅜
Water closet, flush-valve type	1
Hose bibs	½
Wall hydrant	½

SOURCE: "Report of the Coordinating Committee for a National Plumbing Code," U.S. Department of Commerce," Domestic Commerce Series, No. 28.

The plumbing fixtures should be provided with a sufficient supply of water for flushing purposes. This will be at least 4 gallons per flush for water closets and at least 2 gallons for urinals. Also, waste water should not be placed in flush tanks for flushing purposes when the city water is cut off because the waste water may pollute the water-supply system. Water closets or urinal bowls should not be supplied directly from the water system through a flushometer or other valve unless such valve has an approved vacuum breaker that will prevent siphonage of water back into the water pipes. This requirement applies to all fixtures having underrim water inlets. Backflow preventers should also be provided with lawn sprinkler systems and fixtures with hose attachments. A cutoff in the water-service pipe should be provided at the curb and, if the building is divided into apartments, cutoffs should also be placed in the individual supply lines just inside the foundation walls. Good practice also calls for cutoffs for each closet, lawn sprinkler, and hot-water tank. A check valve, to prevent the backing up of hot water, should be placed in the cold-water pipe which supplies the hot-water tank. This will also necessitate a relief valve in the hot-water system. The entire water distribution system should be protected against freezing. (See Table 6-2 for recommended minimum sizes of water-supply pipes.)

6-9. Building Sewer. The line from the public sewer to within 3 feet of the foundation wall of the building is known as the building sewer and is of cast iron, vitrified clay, concrete, bituminized fiber, or asbestos cement. The required size of the building sewer will vary according to the number of fixtures drained by it. Some ordinances prescribe a minimum of 6 inches. However, 4 inches will probably be sufficient for the ordinary residence having one closet and the usual number of other fixtures, provided that a slope of ⅛ to ¼ inch per lineal foot can be obtained. This pipe is laid in the same manner as are public sewers. The spigot of the pipe is the downstream end of each length. Care must be taken that the bottom of the trench is hollowed at each joint sufficiently to allow for the excess diameter caused by the bell and also that the trench bottom is shaped to the pipe so that one-third of the pipe surface will have a bearing area. In backfilling the trench, fine earth must be carefully tamped around the pipe until it is covered. In completing the backfilling, no heavy stones should be dropped in the trench until the pipe is covered to a depth of at least 1 foot. The method of making joints is described in Art. 6-13. Table 6-3 gives recommended size of house sewers and drains in column 1 together with the slope required and the number of fixture units connected.

6-10. Building Drains and Branches. The building drain is that part of the lowest horizontal piping of a house-drainage system which receives the discharges from soil, waste, and other drainage pipes inside the walls of any building and conveys the same to the building sewer. The building drain is of cast-iron pipe of a size conforming to the specifications given in Table 6-3. It should be laid or supported so that there will be no sags. Special precautions should be taken where it runs through the foundation wall. It is common practice to leave an opening around the pipe. This may be justified by the fact that settlement of the foundation wall may damage the pipe. It is felt, however, that protection from this possible damage is more than offset by the certainty that rats and mice will find easy entrance through such an opening. The "Report of the Coordinating Committee"[1] recommends that all exterior openings provided for the passage of piping be properly sealed with snugly fitting collars of metal or other ratproof material securely fastened in place. Interior openings should likewise be ratproofed.

TABLE 6-3. SIZES OF HOUSE SEWERS, DRAINS, HORIZONTAL BRANCHES, VERTICAL SOIL, OR WASTE STACKS IN TERMS OF MAXIMUM NUMBER OF FIXTURE UNITS CONNECTED TO THEM

Required diameter of pipe, inches	Building drains or sewers: Inch fall per foot				Any horizontal fixture	One stack, three stories in height, or three intervals	More than three stories in height	
	1/16	1/8	1/4	1/2			One branch interval	Total for stack
(1)	(2)	(3)	(4)	(5)	(6)	(7)	(8)	(9)
1¼	.....	.....	.....	.....	1	2	1	2
1½	.....	.....	.....	.....	3	4	2	8
2	.....	.....	21	26	6	10	6	24
2½	.....	.....	24	31	12	20	9	42
3	.....	.....	27*	36*	20*	30†	16*	60†
4	.....	180	216	250	160	240	90	500
5	.....	390	480	575	360	540	200	1,100
6	.....	700	840	1,000	620	960	350	1,900
8	1,400	1,600	1,920	2,300	1,400	2,200	660	3,600
10	2,500	2,900	3,500	4,200	2,500	3,800	1,000	5,600
12	3,900	4,600	5,600	6,700	3,900	6,000	1,500	8,400

* Not over two water closets.

† Not over six water closets.

SOURCE: "Report of the Coordinating Committee for a National Plumbing Code," U.S. Department of Commerce, Domestic Commerce Series, No. 28.

Horizontal branch drains carrying waste from a toilet must be not less than 3 inches in size. All horizontal branch drains should be laid on a uniform grade and at no lesser slopes than as follows:

Diameter of pipe, inches..........	1½ to 3	4 to 8	10 and 12
Slope per foot, inches.............	1/4	1/8	1/16

Soil and waste pipes for drainage in a building shall be of cast iron, galvanized wrought iron, galvanized open-hearth iron, galvanized steel, brass, copper, or lead. All drains which are underground shall be of extra-heavy cast-iron soil pipe.

6-11. The Building Trap. The building trap, if used, is placed in the building drain just within the foundation walls. It is a running trap and should have at least one cleanout hole. The purpose of this trap is to isolate the house-drainage system from the sewer, particularly to prevent passage of sewer air into the house system. If it is used, a fresh-air inlet is necessary, running from the house side of the building trap to the outer air. The fresh-air inlet allows circulation of air through the building drain into the stacks and vent pipes.

There has been much controversy over the use of the building trap. That there are advantages has already been noted, but it is doubtful whether such isolation is necessary. It is undoubtedly an advantage to have the sewer system freely ventilated through the house systems, and there should be no excessive amount of odorous sewer air at any particular point if the sewer system is properly designed and constructed. The building trap is likely to stop up and in cold weather may freeze, particularly if the fresh-air inlet is close to the trap. Considering the necessity of simplifying the plumbing system, the general opinion at present is that the building trap can be safely dispensed with. The "Report of the Coordinating Committee"[1] recommends that building traps not be installed except where specifically required by the administrative authority. The place of this trap in rural plumbing is discussed in a later article.

6-12. Changes of Direction. Changes in direction are made by the use of 45-degree wyes, short- or long-sweep quarter bends, sixth, eighth, or sixteenth bends or combinations of same or equivalent fittings. Single and double sanitary tees may be used on vertical stacks, and short quarter bends may be used in soil and waste lines when the change in direction of flow is from the horizontal to the vertical. Tees, crosses, and short quarter bends may be used in the vent pipes.

6-13. Joints. Joints in cast-iron soil pipe known as caulked joints are made by firmly packing the opening between the bell and spigot with oakum or hemp and then filling with molten lead in a single pouring to a depth of not less than 1 inch. The lead is then tamped or caulked so that the joint will be tight. No paint, varnish, or putty is permitted until after the joint is tested. In joining wrought iron, steel, or brass to cast iron, either screwed or caulked joints are used. When joining lead pipe to cast iron, steel, or wrought iron, the joint should be made by means of a ferrule, soldered nipple, or bushing (see Fig. 6-2). Joints in lead pipe, or between lead pipe and ferrules, or with brass or copper pipe should be wiped joints, with an exposed surface of the solder to each side of the joint of not less than ¾ inch and the minimum thickness at the thickest part of the joint of not less than ⅜ inch.

Threaded joints should have all burrs removed, and pipe ends should be reamed or filed so that the interior of the pipe is unobstructed. Pipe-joint cement and paint are permitted only on the male threads. For soft copper tubing, flared joints are permissible when made with proper fittings. The tubing must be expanded with a proper flaring tool. When such joints are concealed either in a building or underground, they should also be soldered. Soldered or sweat joints are used for joints between tubing and appropriate types of brass fittings. If slip joints are used, they should be installed only on the inlet side of a trap, or in the trap seal, and on the exposed fixture supply. In making hot poured joints for clay or concrete sewer pipe, all surfaces joined must be cleaned and dried, or a suitable primer should be applied. Approximately 25 per cent of the joint space in the base of the socket should be filled with jute or hemp. A pouring collar rope or other device should be used to hold the hot compound during the pouring. If cement joints are used, a layer

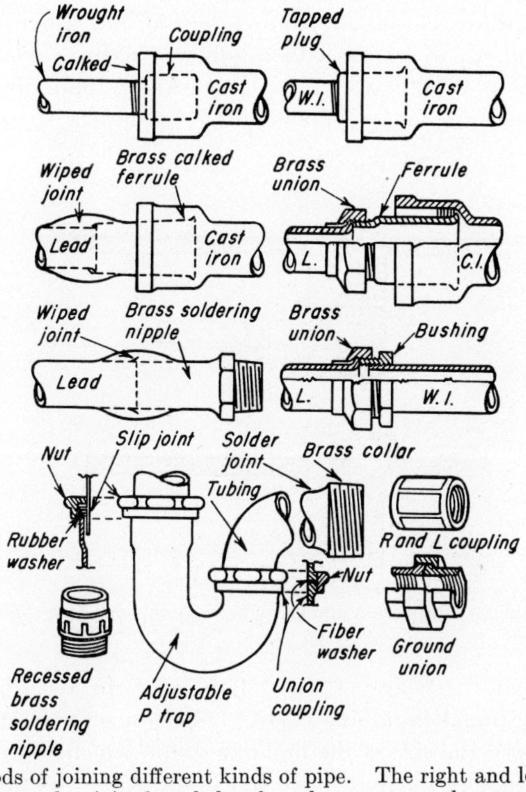

Fig. 6-2. Methods of joining different kinds of pipe. The right and left coupling and ground union are used to join threaded male ends on water and vent pipes. (*Courtesy of U.S. Department of Agriculture.*)

of jute or hemp should be inserted into the base of the joint space with the jute or hemp dipped in a slurry suspension of Portland cement prior to insertion in the bell. The remaining space is filled with a mixed mortar composed of 1 part cement and 2 parts sand. After a half-hour of setting, the joint should be rammed around the entire periphery with a blunt tool. Additional mortar is then troweled so as to form a 45-degree taper with the barrel of the pipe. Asbestos cement pipe joints are made with sleeve couplings of the same composition as the pipe sealed with rubber rings. Bituminized-fiber pipe joints are made with tapered-type couplings of the same material as the pipe.

6-14. Stacks. At least one of the stacks of the plumbing system must extend full size through the roof for the following purposes: to ventilate and carry off the sewer air above the roof; to prevent the siphoning of the traps by suction; to prevent the possibility of a back pressure forcing the seals of the fixture traps. Stacks that receive wastes from fixtures only are known as waste stacks. Those receiving wastes from fixtures and also from water closets are known as soil and waste stacks. The sizes of soil and waste stacks with number of fixtures contributing are given in Table 6-3, columns (7) to (9). Many plumbing ordinances require that no water closet should discharge into a stack less than 4

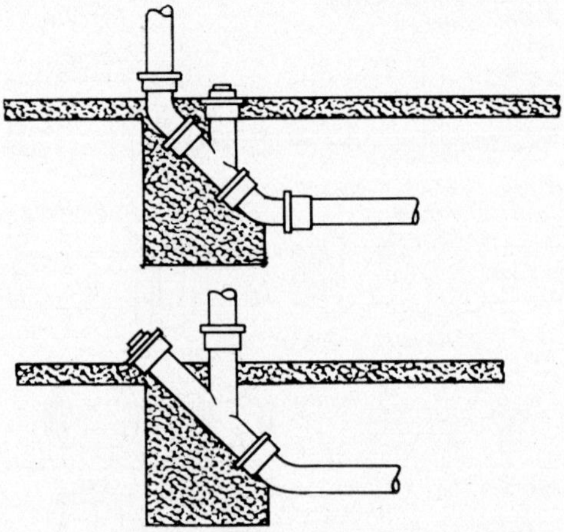

FIG. 6-3. Methods of supporting stacks. (*From New York State Standard Plumbing Code.*)

inches in diameter. However, the "Report of the Coordinating Committee for a National Plumbing Code"[1] recommends a minimum stack size of 3 inches or the size of the building drain, whichever is the smaller. The roof extension of soil and waste stacks should be run full size at least 6 inches above the roof. When the roof is used for purposes other than weather protection, the extension should be not less than 5 feet above the roof.

6-15. Pipe Supports. Since cast-iron stacks and soil pipes are jointed with lead, it is important that they be properly supported; otherwise changes in alignment may occur that will cause leaks. Vertical stacks should be supported at their bases by brick or concrete piers and at each floor a wrought-iron strap should be placed just below the bell of the joint or branch of a fitting securely fastening the pipe to a rafter or vertical timber. Wherever possible, the stack support should be built integrally with the foundation so there will be uniform settlement. Unequal settlement may cause breakage of branch waste pipes and even raising of fixtures off the floors. Each joint of a horizontal line should be supported in some way: if overhead, by straps; if close to the floor or ground, by piers or special supporting fittings.

6-16. Fixture Traps and Trap Venting. The pipes that carry off the waste from various plumbing fixtures would allow the entrance of air from the plumbing system into rooms if traps were not placed in the waste-pipe lines. The trap seal should be not less than 2 or more than 4 inches. There are several varieties of plain traps. These are known as the S-, ¾S-, and ½S- or P-traps. The plain traps are subject to siphonage, which results in the removal of the water in the trap, thereby allowing free passage of sewer air. This may be prevented by venting the trap. Nonsiphoning traps have been devised which are supposed to

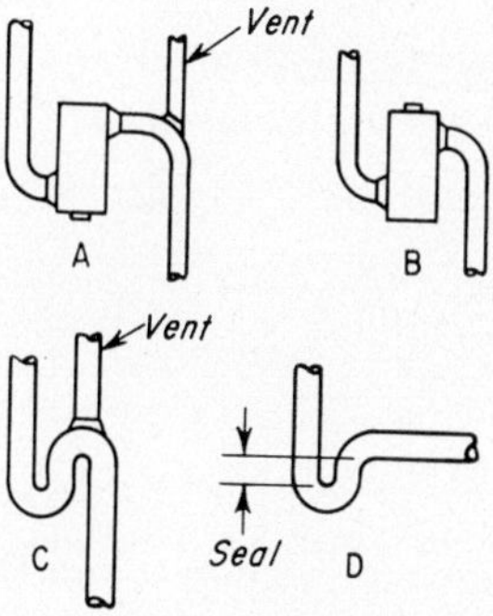

FIG. 6-4. A, drum trap with crown vent; B, drum trap as usually placed, allowing easy cleaning but possible leakage of sewer air at cleanout; C, the S-trap with a crown vent; D, the P-trap.

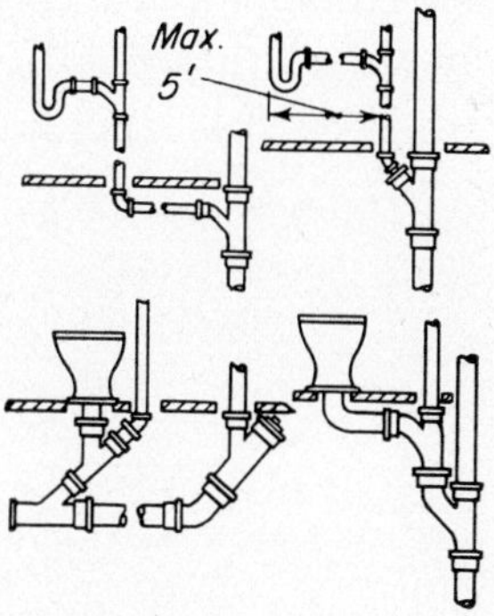

FIG. 6-5. Approved forms of venting single fixtures. (*From New York State Standard Plumbing Code.*)

resist siphoning without the necessity of venting. These traps usually depend upon some form of ball within the trap or some mechanical device to prevent loss of the seal. They do not usually have the same scouring power, however, as the plain traps, and also, in the course of time, the division wall or mechanical device may become so corroded that the seal can no longer be held. The unrestricted use of nonsiphoning traps without vents is, therefore, recommended only under exceptional conditions, and many codes forbid them.

Ordinary traps are vented in various ways as indicated in Figs. 6-4 and 6-5. S-traps must be vented from the upper part of the curve. This is known as crown venting, prohibited by most codes. A particular danger arises in crown venting which may also be present in the venting of other trap fixtures. This is the accumulation of lint and grease in the vent pipe, particularly if, as the waste water is drained from the fixture, the water level rises into the vent pipe during the early periods of flow. This in time will surely cause stoppage; consequently the trap will be unvented and siphonage may result. For this reason the P-trap is probably the best trap for all-round use for washbowls, sinks, and similar fixtures. The P-trap may be used safely without a vent if it is within permissible distance (Table 6-4) of the waste stack into which the waste pipe discharges and if the nominally horizontal waste pipe does not join the stack at a point lower than the dip of the trap. Some codes allow venting by a stack or otherwise if the trap is not over 5 feet from the vent or stack used as a vent. This is permissible only if no fixture or only a minor fixture discharges into the stack used as a vent. According to the "Report of the Coordinating Committee," a combination waste-and-vent system should be permitted only where structural conditions preclude the installation of a conventional system, and then only for floor drains and sinks.

TABLE 6-4. PERMISSIBLE DISTANCE OF TRAP FROM VENT

Size of fixture drain, inches	*Distance from trap to vent, feet*
1¼	2½
1½	3½
2	5
3	6
4	10

SOURCE: "Report of the Coordinating Committee for a National Plumbing Code," U.S. Department of Commerce, Domestic Commerce Series, No. 28.

Drum traps have been widely used, particularly in connection with the waste pipes from bathtubs. They are somewhat more resistant to siphonage than S- or P-traps but do not give so good a scouring velocity. When used, they should be placed as shown in the figure so that the clean-out at the bottom will be covered by the trap seal; otherwise leakage around the opening may allow the escape of sewer air. The vents of drum traps are subject to the same dangers of stoppage as those of S-traps. There is no reason why P-traps should not be used in place of drum traps.

Trap seals may be broken by back pressure resulting from a large mass of liquid compressing air as it moves down a near-by stack, by evaporation of the water in the trap, by capillary attraction working through lint or threads partly in the trap. The first-named can be prevented by venting, the last two by ensuring that there will always be enough water passing through to keep the seal intact. Vents should join the waste lines within certain prescribed distances from the traps (see Table 6-4).

TABLE 6-5. SIZE AND LENGTH OF VENTS FOR SOIL AND WASTE STACKS

Size of soil or waste stack, inches	Fixture units connected	Diameter of vent required, inches								
		1¼	1½	2	2½	3	4	5	6	8
		Maximum length of vent, feet								
1¼	2	30	...	...	...	...	.....	.....	.....	.....
1½	8	50	150	...	...	...	.....	.....	.....	.....
1½	10	30	100	...	...	...	.....	.....	.....	.....
2	12	30	75	200	...	...	.....	.....	.....	.....
2	20	26	50	150	...	...	.....	.....	.....	.....
2½	42	..	30	100	300	...	.....	.....	.....	.....
3	10	..	30	100	200	600	.....	.....	.....	.....
3	30	..	...	60	200	500	.....	.....	.....	.....
3	60	..	...	50	80	400	.....	.....	.....	.....
4	100	..	...	35	100	260	1,000	.....	.....	.....
4	200	..	...	30	90	250	900	.....	.....	.....
4	500	..	...	20	70	180	700	.....	.....	.....
5	200	..	...	...	35	80	350	1,000	.....	.....
5	500	..	...	...	30	70	300	900	.....	.....
5	1,100	..	...	...	20	50	200	700	.....	.....
6	350	..	...	...	25	50	200	400	1,300	.....
6	620	..	...	...	15	30	125	300	1,100	.....
6	960	..	...	...	...	24	100	250	1,000	.....
6	1,900	..	...	...	...	20	70	200	700	.....
8	600	..	...	...	...	...	50	150	500	1,300
8	1,400	..	...	...	...	...	40	100	40	1,200
8	2,200	..	...	...	...	...	30	80	350	1,100
8	3,600	..	...	...	...	...	25	60	250	800
10	1,000	..	...	...	...	...	.....	75	125	1,000
10	2,500	..	...	...	...	...	.....	50	100	500
10	3,800	..	...	...	...	...	.....	30	80	350
10	5,600	..	...	...	...	...	.....	25	60	250

SOURCE: "Report of the Coordinating Committee for a National Plumbing Code," U.S. Department of Commerce, Domestic Commerce Series, No. 28.

6-17. Venting Systems. Trap venting is necessary to supply air to the trap, thereby preventing siphonage. The trap vent must connect with the vent stack or main stack in such a manner that there will be no stoppage of circulation of air and, in addition, no danger of backing up of wastes into the vent pipes. No vents are less than 1¼ inches in diameter.

For 1¼- and 1½-inch waste stacks the vents are of the same diameters as the waste pipes. Branch vents or main vents should never be less than half the diameter of the soil or waste stack they are venting. As to permitted lengths, branch vents are restricted in the same manner as main vents. The size of vents is based upon the size of the waste or soil stack, the number of fixtures or closets connected, and the actual length of the vent or vent stack (see Table 6-5). Vent pipes should have uniform grades without sags or depressions so that moisture will drip back to the soil or waste pipe. If it is necessary to run horizontal vents, they should be kept clear by having a minor fixture empty into them. Vent pipes that are connected to horizontal soil and waste pipes should branch off above the center line of the pipe and extend vertically or at an angle of 45 degrees to the vertical for at least 6 inches above the fixtures they are venting before changing to a horizontal direction or connecting with a branch vent. This latter precaution is necessary to prevent flow through the vent pipe due to stoppage in the waste line.

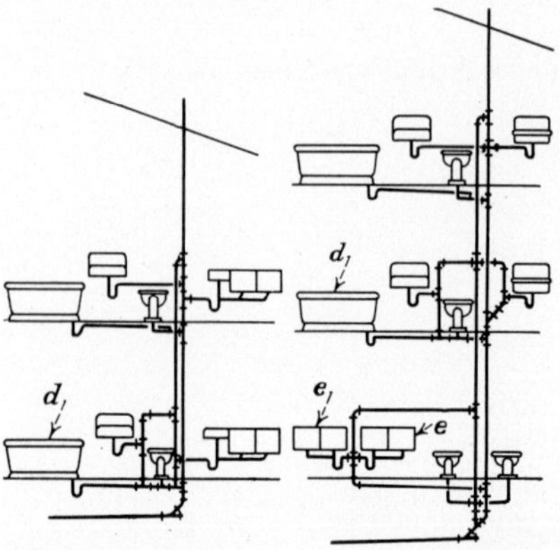

FIG. 6-6. Continuous venting in buildings of two or more stories. Bathtubs *d*, wet vents. The fixtures marked *e* have a common vent.

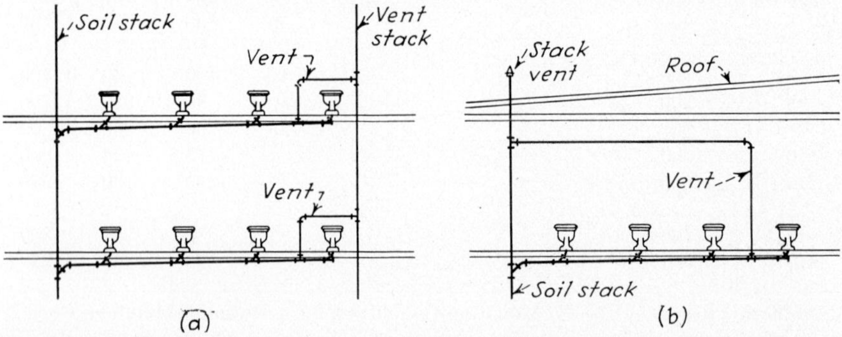

FIG. 6-7. (*a*) Circuit venting of a group of toilets; (*b*) loop venting, which is permitted if there are no other fixtures discharging into the stack above where the vent joins.

In houses of two or more floors *continuous venting* is adopted. This is illustrated by the figures. In this connection it should be noted that the vent stack should connect with the main stack at the bottom at an acute angle. This prevents clogging of the bottom with rust and scale. The top of the vent stack may go through the roof in the same manner as the main stack but is usually connected with the main stack. This connection, of course, must be made above the highest fixture.

A *stack vent* is the extension of a soil or waste stack above the highest horizontal drain connected with it.

A *vent stack* is a vertical vent pipe installed primarily for the purpose of providing circulation of air to and from any part of the drainage system.

A *circuit vent* is a branch vent that serves two or more traps and extends from in front of the last fixture connection of a horizontal branch to the vent stack (Fig. 6-7).

A *loop vent* is the same as a circuit vent except that it loops back and connects with a stack vent instead of the vent stack (Fig. 6-7).

A *wet vent* is any waste pipe which also serves as a vent. This is permitted only on the waste pipes from lavatories, kitchen sinks, or a combination fixture. It is also used to vent a bathtub or shower trap. The wet vent connects with the drain pipe in a vertical plane or not more than 6 inches therefrom, provided also that not more than one fixture unit discharges into a 1½-inch wet vent and not more than four fixture units into a 2-inch wet vent and that the wet vent is within the required distance of the trap it is venting (Table 6-4).

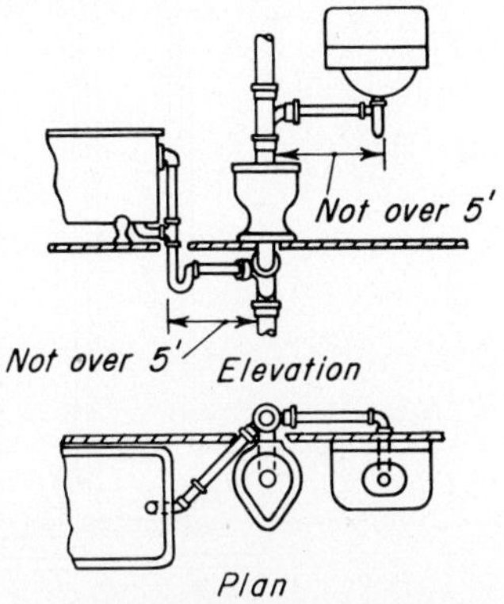

Fig. 6-8. Approved design for a stack-vented bathroom group of fixtures. (*From Report of Subcommittee on Plumbing, U.S. Department of Commerce.*)

A *common vent* is a vent connected at the junction of two fixture drains which serves as a vent for both fixtures.

Where *crown venting* is used, the vent pipes are run from the crowns of the individual traps to the vent stack. Owing to the possibility of stoppage of the vents in this case, most plumbing codes prohibit this practice.

A *local ventilating pipe* is a pipe on the fixture side of the trap through which vapor or foul air is removed from a room or fixture. These are sometimes attached to closet bowls. In some instances their outlets are in the chimney of the house in order to obtain a good draft.

Venting may be dispensed with in the case of rain-leader traps, floor drains, and subsoil drains. Individual fixture vents may be dispensed with for a group of fixtures consisting of one bathroom group and a kitchen sink in a one-story building, or on the top floor of a building, provided that each fixture drain connects independently to the stack and that each enters the stack at the same level.

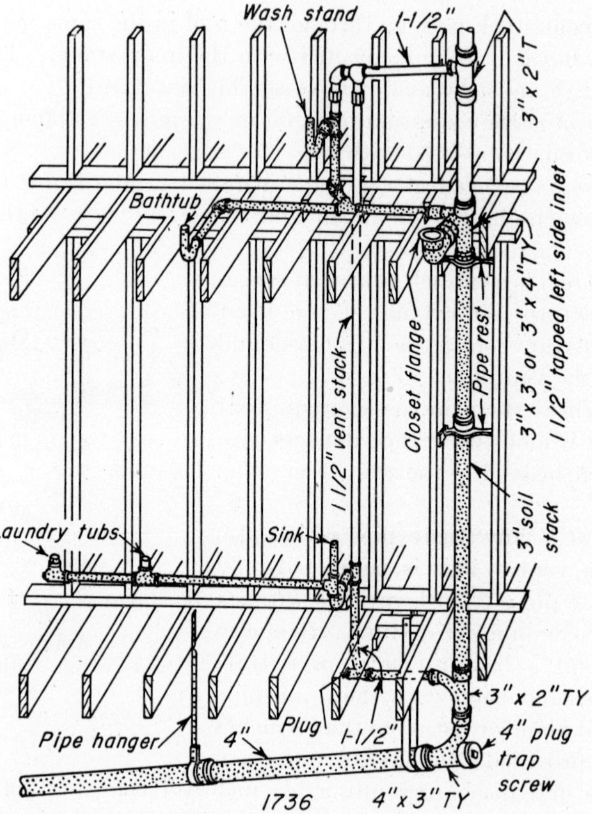

FIG. 6-9. A job roughed in. Waste and soil pipes are stippled and vent pipes are outlined. (*Courtesy of U.S. Department of Agriculture.*)

6-18. Horizontal Piping. All horizontal piping should run at not less than a uniform grade of ⅛ inch per foot and should be supported or anchored as indicated in Art. 6-15. Dead ends are prohibited. Waste-pipe sizes are shown in Table 6-3.

6-19. Inspection. The first inspection of a drainage and vent system is made after the roughing in. Plumbing work is said to be roughed in when all the work has been done up to the setting of the fixtures and with all piping open to view. Usually at this time the water test is given. All the openings except the top of the stack are closed by caps, soldering, or special plugs, and the complete system is filled until water flows from the top of the stack. The water is then allowed to stand in the pipes for a period of at least 15 minutes. Every part of the system should be tested with at least a 10-foot head of water, except the top 10 feet. All joints should then be examined for leakage. The air test is made by attaching an air compressor or testing machine to any suitable opening, closing all other openings, and forcing in air until there is a gauge pressure of 5 pounds per square inch. This pressure is held for a period of at least 15 minutes. Joints are sometimes tested by applying soapsuds to them with a brush. In the case of a very high building it may be necessary to test the system in 75-foot sections of stack.

Smoke or peppermint is used for the final test, which is made after the work is completed and the traps have their seals. When smoke is used, a machine for generating it and producing a small air pressure is connected to the system and smoke is forced in. After smoke appears at stack openings, they are closed and a pressure equivalent to 1 inch of water column is reached and maintained for 15 minutes before inspection starts.

The peppermint test is an old favorite, but because of its disadvantages it is falling into disuse. A mixture of 2 ounces of oil of peppermint to 1 gallon of hot water, sufficient for testing the plumbing of an ordinary house, is poured down the stack from the roof. The man who does the pouring must then efface himself until the joints have been inspected, as the odor of peppermint may cling to his clothes sufficiently to make it impossible to detect a leak. There is also the possibility of one leak in the system causing sufficient odor to conceal other leaks.

It is possible to make simple tests to discover whether traps are sealed. If knocking on the pipe at the trap results in a hollow sound, it will probably mean that the trap seal has been lost. A still better method is to hold a match at the entrance to the waste pipe. Flickering will indicate a loss of the trap seal.

The water system is tested by filling it with water from the source of supply at a pressure not less than the normal working pressure.

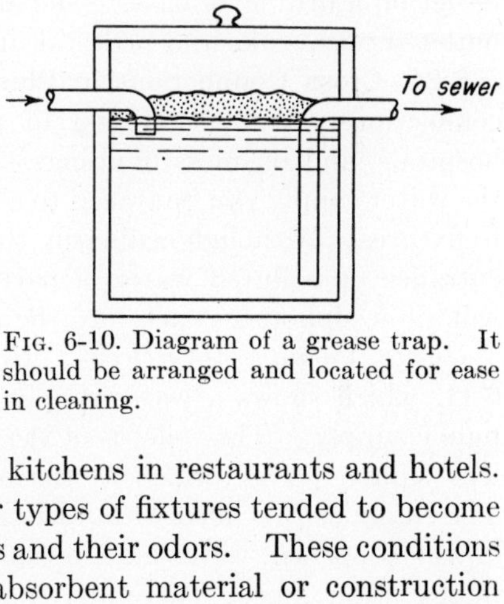

FIG. 6-10. Diagram of a grease trap. It should be arranged and located for ease in cleaning.

6-20. Grease Traps. Traps are installed for the purpose of removing grease from waste water. They should be placed as near as possible to the fixture which they are serving. Also they should be frequently cleaned. They are especially desirable in waste lines from the sinks of kitchens in restaurants and hotels.

6-21. Fixtures. Many of the older types of fixtures tended to become offensive because of their unsightliness and their odors. These conditions were frequently due to the use of absorbent material or construction which resulted in joints that tended to accumulate organic matter. For this reason modern plumbing codes require that porcelain or vitrified earthenware, white-enameled cast iron, or hard natural stone be used in fixtures for excreta disposal. Closets are required to be molded in one piece to hold sufficient water between flushes so that surfaces will not be fouled and to have a flushing rim that will ensure complete cleansing of the inside of the bowl. Closets of the pan type or of the long hopper and washout varieties are no longer considered desirable.

All fixtures should be so installed as to allow ease of cleaning. The overflows from washbowls, bathtubs, and similar fixtures should enter the waste pipes on the inlet side of the trap and should be arranged for ease of cleaning. Good practice requires that all fixture pipes run directly into the wall and that no lead pipes or traps be within 12 inches of the floor unless protected. Strong metal strainers are required at the outlets of all fixtures except closets and pedestal urinals.

6-22. Fixture Wastes. Requirements as to waste-pipe sizes vary somewhat in plumbing codes. For instance, the minimum size of pipe for one kitchen sink may be 2 inches in one city, while another code may specify $1\frac{1}{2}$ inches. Table 6-3 gives the recommendations of the Coordinating Committee for a National Plumbing Code.

6-23. Closet Floor Connections. A joint which is frequently made in an unsatisfactory manner is the connection at the floor between a water closet and its soil pipe. The connection should be made by means of a flange of cast iron, at least $\frac{3}{16}$ inch thick, or a brass flange at least $\frac{1}{8}$ inch thick. The flange is bolted to the earthenware of the closet base with a gasket or a setting compound placed between to effect a tight joint, and is screwed, caulked, or soldered to the drain pipe. The floor flange must be set on a firm level base. The above requirements also apply to floor-outlet service sinks and pedestal urinals.

6-24. Cross Connections in Plumbing. This article deals with cross connections commonly found in plumbing systems of homes, hotels, hospitals, and business buildings. In each case the danger of polluting the water supply can be traced to a faulty arrangement of the water pipes to fixtures. Although ordinarily the pressure in water pipes prevents the entrance of polluted water, a partial vacuum may be generated which will allow siphonage back into the pipes.

How a Vacuum May Occur. How this may happen is shown in Fig. 6-11, which shows a water-supply system that is fed upward from the public supply. The toilet is of the siphon-jet type and has a flush valve. The siphon jet is formed at the opening C when the toilet is flushed. The chamber D is filled with water at all times. With valve A closed and faucet B opened, water may be siphoned back from the toilet bowl down in the water pipe. There are small openings in the flushing rim of the bowl, and these may prevent a vacuum from forming between D and the flushometer, but they are likely to clog and even when open may not furnish sufficient air to break the vacuum. If there is a stoppage at E, water will rise to the rim of the toilet bowl, and siphonage is even more likely. A stoppage in the drain of washbowl *F* will cause the faucet outlets to be submerged, and siphonage may again occur. With valve *A* open, a heavy usage at *B* or a fire demand outside the building may cause a partial vacuum in the riser pipe and cause siphonage.

FIG. 6-11. Diagram showing how back siphonage occurs in water-supply pipes.

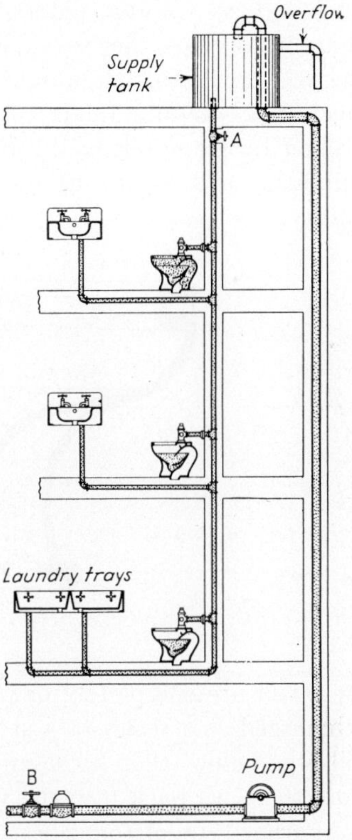

FIG. 6-12. Diagram showing how back siphonage occurs in water-supply pipes. Downfeed layout. (*Courtesy of Wisconsin State Board of Health.*)

Figure 6-12 shows how a vacuum may occur in a downfeed layout of the water-supply system. This method is used in large buildings where the pressure in the public supply is insufficient to raise water to the upper floors. A pump is installed to raise the water to the supply tank. The supply pipe should terminate above the overflow or preferably above the top of the tank; otherwise it would constitute a cross connection. From Fig. 6-12 it is seen that, if valve *A* is closed and the toilet on the upper floor is clogged and if any fixture below is opened, the toilet-bowl contents will be back-siphoned into the water pipe. If valve *A* is open and a very heavy draft occurs in the lower floors, a vacuum may occur in the upper part of the downfeed pipe and the closet-bowl contents will be back-siphoned.

Water Closets. Water closets of certain types are dangerous. Figure 6-13 is a cross section of the ordinary jet type of closet generally used with flush valves. Water enters the bowl at the top and in the rear-top chamber divides, one part going to the flushing rim through port *A* and the rest going to the submerged jet *B*. With the water at the normal level, if a vacuum tends to occur in the water-supply line, it will be broken by air entering through the rim ports and port *A* and no back siphonage will occur. If the port *A* and the rim ports are too small, if

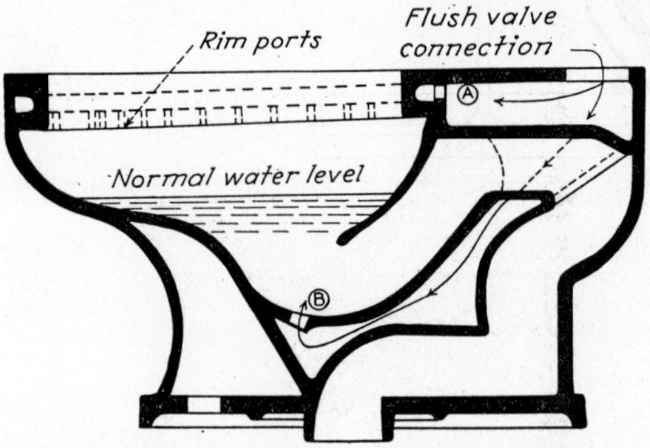

FIG. 6-13. Cross section of jet-type closet. (*Courtesy of Wisconsin State Board of Health.*)

the latter are completely or partly clogged or "limed up," or if they are submerged as a result of a stoppage in the toilet or at some point in the soil pipe below, then air cannot enter and the vacuum will siphon water from the bowl back into the water-supply line.

Another type of toilet bowl has the flush valve connection on the side instead of the top. In most such cases, the connection is partly submerged in the normal water seal of the bowl. With such bowls, back siphonage can take place with almost any degree of vacuum in the water-supply pipe. They are dangerous and should never be installed. Many plumbing codes prohibit them.

Flush valves should be protected[1] by placing the valve about 6 inches above the overflow rim of the bowl and using a vacuum breaker between the flush valve and the bowl and at least 4 inches above the bowl top.

[1] For an excellent discussion of cross connections in general and also of flush valves and vacuum breakers, the reader is referred to "Cross-connections in Plumbing and Water Supply Systems," published by the Wisconsin State Board of Health, Madison, Wis.

A check valve may be combined with the stop valve to the toilet as an added protection.

There is no danger of water contamination from the commonly used closet tank with a water-supply float valve if the tank is high above the toilet bowl or is elevated only a short distance. This statement does not apply, however, to the integral closet bowl and tank combination. In this fixture the bowl rim is above the bottom of the flush tank, and in case of stoppage the bowl contents will mingle with water in the tank. Should a vacuum occur, the mixture will be back-siphoned into the water-supply line.

Other Dangerous Fixtures. These are of two classes. In one class are those having inlets constantly submerged below the normal water level. Examples are bidet fixtures, steam tables, water baths, laundry washing machines, swimming pools, hydraulic lifts, tanks used in industrial processes, water jet ejectors for pumping sewage from cellar sumps, filters, softeners, boilers, stock watering troughs, and such hospital fixtures as instrument sterilizers and bedpan sterilizers. The other class of dangerous fixtures allows water openings to be submerged through carelessness or clogging of drains. Examples are flushing rim openings in water closets, urinals and slop sinks, lavatories, bathtubs, drinking fountains, and dishwashing machines.

Direct connections from a water-supply pipe to a waste pipe or sewer are also dangerous, for in case of stoppage or heavy storms, they may allow sewage to back up into the water. Instances are drains from water filters and softeners, water coolers, refrigerators, water stills, and water sterilizers. Different but also dangerous are priming connections to pumps handling sewage or other polluted material.

The remedy will depend upon the type of hazard. So far as possible, submerged inlets into fixtures must be abolished by bringing them in at an elevation above the overflow rim of the fixture. The air break or gap required between the faucet or pipe outlet and the rim will depend upon the effective size of the opening of the inlet pipe or faucet and the presence of vertical walls or ribs near the pipe or faucet. The minimum gap is specified because a vacuum or strong suction in the pipe or open faucet sets up air currents which carry water from a full bowl or tank for a short distance vertically into the opening. Near-by walls which will channelize the air flow tend to increase this effect. Table 6-6 gives the air gaps required for safety. The "effective opening" in the case of faucets is the smallest opening, which may be in the seat of the faucet. A "near" wall or rib is one that is within three times the effective opening if it is only one wall, or four times the effective opening when there are two walls. The effect of three or more walls is unknown, but it is suggested that in this case the gap should extend from the top of the wall.

TABLE 6-6. MINIMUM AIR GAPS FOR COMMON PLUMBING FIXTURES

Fixture	Minimum air gap, inches	
	When not affected by near wall	When affected by near wall
Lavatories with effective openings not greater than ½ inch diameter	1.0	1.50
Sink, laundry trays, and gooseneck bath faucets with effective openings not greater than ¾ inch diameter	1.5	2.25
Over-rim bath fillers with effective openings not greater than 1 inch diameter	2.0	3.00
Effective openings greater than 1 inch	2 × effective opening	3 × effective opening

SOURCE: "Report of the Coordinating Committee for a National Plumbing Code," U.S. Department of Commerce, Domestic Commerce Series, No. 28.

For tanks with under-rim inlets, overflows may be used if the vertical distance between the inlet and the overflow is 1½ times the distance required in Table 6-6 for a corresponding effective opening. The overflow pipe must, however, be large enough to carry off all the water which may enter and itself have a break of the type indicated in Fig. 6-14.

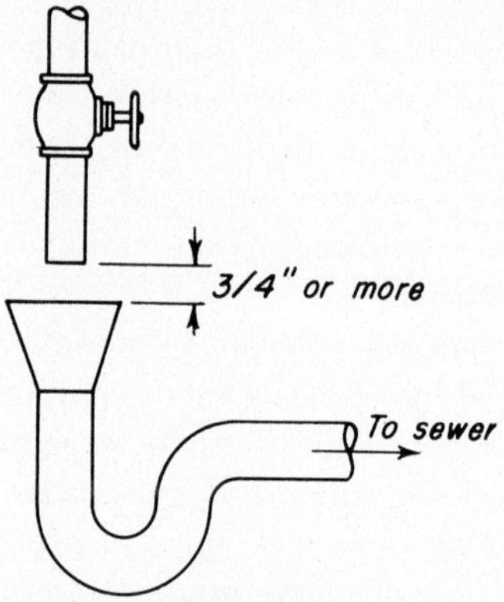

FIG. 6-14. Method of placing an air break in lines draining water systems, refrigerators, etc.

Toilet flush valves must discharge under the bowl rim, and the safeguards are vacuum breakers in the valves. Careful specifications as to flush valves and vacuum breakers are needed in plumbing codes, for not all give satisfaction.

Direct water connections to waste pipes should be cut off and the water discharged into a funnel or pipe that is properly trapped, with the discharge point above the funnel rim. This applies also to drains of refrigerators and potable water systems (see Fig. 6-14).

6-25. Durham or Screw-joint System. Owing to the possibility of damage to caulked lead joints by settlement or other movement, it is obvious that a plumbing system which includes them has many potential leaks and weaknesses. The Durham system overcomes this fault by substituting wrought-iron threaded pipe for the cast-iron soil pipe with lead joints. Screwed cast-iron fittings are used with the wrought-iron pipe, so the screw joint is as strong as the pipe itself. This gives a very strong and rigid system.

Several precautions are necessary in the use of screwed pipe. The fittings must be recessed so that the inside surfaces of pipe and fitting will be continuous. Also, as the pipe is cut and threaded, there is a possibility of a rough burr at the end of the pipe that may catch lint and other solids. Therefore burrs should be carefully removed. It should also be remembered that the life of wrought-iron pipe is much shorter than that of cast-iron pipe, particularly if underground. Some codes prescribe, therefore, that the underground soil pipes must always be of cast iron. The substitution of steel for wrought-iron pipe will further shorten the life of the system. In making the threaded joints, red or white lead is used to give a tight seal. The lead is applied only to the male thread to prevent its being squeezed into the pipe and forming an obstruction.

6-26. Storm-water Drainage. Storm water from roofs and paved areas should not be discharged into a sewer system designed for domestic sewage only. Connection should be made with the storm sewers if available. If the storm-water drains are discharged into a combined sewer system, *i.e.*, one designed to carry both domestic and storm water, the pipes should be trapped unless the roof gutter or opening is more than 12 feet from a door, window, or air shaft. No soil, waste, or vent pipes should be used as storm-water conductors, nor should vent connections to the conductors be permitted.

BIBLIOGRAPHY

1. "Report of the Coordinating Committee for a National Plumbing Code," U.S. Department of Commerce, Domestic Commerce Series, no. 28, 1951.
2. "American Standard Plumbing Code," American Standards Association, New York.
3. Babbitt, H. E.: "Plumbing," 2d ed., McGraw-Hill Book Company, Inc., New York, 1950.
4. Day, L. J.: "Standard Plumbing Details," John Wiley & Sons, Inc., New York.
5. Plum, S.: "Plumbing Practice and Design," John Wiley & Sons, Inc., New York.
6. "Cross-connections in Plumbing and Water Supply Systems," Wisconsin State Board of Health, Madison, Wis.

CHAPTER 7

PUBLIC BATHING-PLACE SANITATION

7-1. Swimming pools and bathing places are acquiring ever-increasing popularity as recreational media. Since World War II, a new type of professional individual has invaded this field, the swimming-pool contractor. Equipment and designs are becoming so standardized that a plan can be found to fit any given set of variables. This is especially true when the only variables are prospective bathing load and money available. Swimming pools were formerly regarded in the category of a municipal, Y.M.C.A., institutional, or country-club installation. They are now becoming essential features of motels, hotels, and even apartment houses and subdivisions. The technology of plastics has been utilized in this field to make more widespread the installation of a personal swimming pool for the average back yard. Not only have pools been built of concrete, Fiberglas, and steel, but a vinyl plastic liner has been developed which can be laid over a basin formed or constructed of almost any material.

The supervision of these greatly increased numbers and types of pools, from a public health standpoint, is attaining increased importance, although the problem is primarily one of public health education and training. Municipal pools are usually operated by the city park or recreation department, and cooperation between it and the health department will be necessary to maintain sanitary standards. The close association of many persons, with the water as an effective vehicle of infection, has resulted in an important problem for the sanitarian. There is no reason, however, that the public need fear to patronize the swimming pool at which the available sanitary precautions are applied. Sanitary control of pools may be applied by city ordinances or by regulations of the state health departments.

7-2. Bathing Waters and Health. Disease may be transmitted to bathers from waters which have been contaminated by sewage or from one bather to another. The diseases which have been associated with bathing are the intestinal disorders, such as typhoid and paratyphoid fevers, dysentery, and gastrointestinal upsets; eye, ear, nose, and throat infections, including respiratory diseases; skin diseases, such as ringworm, scabies, impetigo, and "swimmer's itch"; and the venereal diseases. Since it has been discovered that the virus of poliomyelitis can be found in sewage, there has been renewed fear that this disease may be contracted in swimming pools, but there is no epidemiological evidence to this effect. In fact there is little confirmed epidemiological evidence of any kind incriminating pools, except a few instances of outbreaks of intestinal disease and definite evidence of contraction of swimmer's itch (see Art. 7-12). However, despite the absence of any great danger, decency

FIG. 7-1. Well-constructed, beautifully appointed semipublic swimming pool. (*Photograph courtesy of Shamrock-Hilton Hotel, Houston, Tex.*)

requires that the water of public bathing places be kept as clean as possible and as free as is practical from organisms causing disease.

Some of the dangerous bacteria, particularly those causing respiratory diseases, are frail and do not survive long in the unfavorable environment afforded by the water. Hence the greatest danger of contracting such disease should be during periods when the pool is crowded. The intestinal bacteria are able to survive for a much longer period. As in the testing of water supplied for public use, therefore, the presence of the coliform group of organisms is ascertained in investigating the quality of the pool water. If the coliforms have been removed or killed, it is considered good evidence that all disease bacteria have been eliminated. Some authorities believe that examination of the water for the presence of hemolytic streptococci is also helpful in gauging the sanitary condition of a swimming pool. The bacterial standards of bathing-pool water are similar to but not quite so stringent as those governing drinking water. By the regulation of bathing loads, or the proportioning of the allowable number of patrons to size of pool, an attempt is made to eliminate the hazards caused by overcrowding.

Certain skin infections are associated with swimming pools, the commonest being a form of ringworm or fungus infection known as "toe itch" or "athlete's foot." This disease is not spread by the pool water, however, but by contact with the floor surface of dressing rooms, locker rooms, runways, etc. The infection may also be contracted at gymnasiums and other places where persons go barefoot over damp wood or other surfaces which are favorable to growth of the organism.

The natural bathing beaches at lakes, streams, or the seashore are somewhat more difficult to control than artificial pools. The most important consideration is that the beaches be located where there is no possibility of pollution by sewer outlets or otherwise.

Another matter to be borne in mind in connection with pools and beaches is protection of bathers from drowning and mechanical injury. This calls for such measures as the stationing of lifeguards, avoidance of overcrowding, and the placing of the deep portion of the pool on the opposite side to the entrance.

7-3. Bathing-place Standards. Standards for the sanitation of swimming pools have been developed by the Conference of State Sanitary Engineers and the Public Health Engineering Section of the American Public Health Association. The latest joint report of these two bodies was made in 1957, and the information given in this chapter is largely based upon the standards recommended in it. Certain important portions are directly quoted as follows:

24. CHEMICAL AND PHYSICAL QUALITY OF SWIMMING POOL WATER

A. *Excess Chlorine*—Whenever chlorine, calcium hypochlorite, or other chlorine compounds, without the use of ammonia, are used for swimming pool disinfection, the amount of available or excess chlorine in the water at all times when the pool is in use shall not be less than 0.4 ppm or more than 1.0 ppm except where high-free residual chlorine is used as described below. Available data indicate that for most effective results this should be present as free available residual chlorine. Whenever chlorine or chlorine compounds are used with ammonia effective results have been reported where the amount of available or excess chloramine is between 0.7 ppm and 1.0 ppm, but recent reports suggest the desirability of operating with higher chloramine residuals such as 2.0 ppm and there is a trend away from chlorine and ammonia disinfection in properly designed pools, inasmuch as less reliable disinfection is accomplished. Attention is directed to the possibility of interference by nitrites with the orthotolidine test particularly when chlorine-ammonia disinfection is employed. If readings are made on the water to be tested within 5 to 10 minutes after the orthotolidine is added, and samples are kept away from the light during this period, the nitrite interference will be decidedly lessened. Standards for determining chlorine residuals shall be prepared and used according to the recommendations in *Standard Methods for the Examination of Water, Sewage, and Industrial Wastes* of the American Public Health Association. Standardized color discs and comparators may be used.

B. *High-Free Residual Chlorine*—A new development in the United States, "High-Free Residual Chlorine," has been based on successful English practice whereby advantages have been cited in maintenance of relatively high concentrations of free available chlorine (1.0 ppm or above) with accompanying high alkalinity (usually pH 8.0 to 8.9), as compared with lower chlorine residuals and pH of 7.0 to 7.5 as generally practiced in the United States. Advantages claimed are: more consistent satisfactory bacteriologic conditions, especially in outdoor pools, clearer pool water, and less irritation of the eyes of swimmers. A disadvantage is the higher cost of chlorine. This development is looked upon with considerable favor by some who have observed it in the United States and its progress will merit watching.

C. *Acidity-Alkalinity*—Whenever alum or sulfate of alumina is used during purification or repurification of swimming pool waters, the water at all times when pool is in use shall show an alkaline reaction. This means that the hydrogen ion content of the pool water shall not fall below 7.0.

D. *Clearness*—At all times when the pool is in use the water shall be sufficiently clear to permit a black disc 6 inches in diameter on a white field, when placed on the bottom of the pool at the deepest point, to be clearly visible from the side walks of the pool at all distances up to 10 yards measured from a line drawn across the pool through said disc. This is a minimum standard and most pools with modern filtration systems produce water far clearer than this minimum safety standard. Accident prevention is an important reason for maintaining clear water, and very clear water adds greatly to the pool attractiveness.

E. *Temperatures*—The water in any swimming pool should not be artificially heated to a temperature above 78°F. The temperature of the air at any artificially heated swimming pool must not be permitted to become more than 8°F warmer nor more than 2°F colder than the water in the pool at any time when the pool is in use. For best results it is desirable that air temperatures shall be about 5°F warmer than the pool temperature.

25. Bacterial Quality of Swimming Pool Waters

A. *Bacteria Count on Standard Nutrient Agar—24 Hours—37°C—and Confirmed Test*—Not more than 15 per cent of the samples covering any considerable period of time shall contain more than 200 bacteria per ml or shall show positive test (confirmed test) in any of five 10 ml portions of water at times when the pool is in use. All primary fermentation tubes showing gas should be confirmed.

B. All chemical and bacterial analyses should be made in accordance with the procedures recommended in the *Standard Methods for the Examination of Water,*

Sewage, and Industrial Wastes of the American Public Health Association in so far as these methods are applicable to swimming pool waters. In order to secure a true picture of the condition of the swimming pool water at the time of sampling, it is recommended that sodium thiosulfate be employed to neutralize the chlorine residual in the water sample bottle during transportation to the laboratory.

C. The part played by the various strains of streptococci in the respiratory diseases and their prevalence in the intestinal, buccal, and nasal discharges make the presence of streptococci in bathing waters very undesirable. Yet to eliminate them from swimming pools would mean decidedly smaller bathing loads and decided increases in chlorine residuals, either or both of which would hamper the usefulness of the pool. The committee calls attention to the fact that streptococci tests are of value in passing on the conditions of swimming pool water but does not recommend any uniform standard limit for their presence.

D. *1. Preparation of bottle for sampling*—

All samples of chlorinated swimming pool water shall be collected in bottles treated with sodium thiosulfate. The purpose of using water sample bottles containing sodium thiosulfate is to reduce the chlorine present in a treated water at the moment the sample is collected to prevent a continuance of the killing action of the chlorine on the bacteria while the sample is being transported to the laboratory. The bacteriological examination then shows the true sanitary quality of the water at the time the sample was collected.

2. Several procedures for preparing the bottles are presented.

For moist heat sterilization—

Option 1—The sodium thiosulfate solution is prepared by dissolving 1.5 gm of sodium thiosulfate in 100 ml of distilled water. One-half ml of this solution is placed in each clean bottle. (This amount has been found sufficient to reduce completely residual chlorine in an amount up to 2.0 ppm in a sample of 130 ml of water.) After the introduction of the sodium thiosulfate solution, the bottle is stoppered and capped. The bottles are then placed in an autoclave and sterilized for 15 minutes at a pressure of 20 pounds per square inch.

Option 2—Into clean wet bottles, add approximately 0.02 to 0.05 gm of powdered sodium thiosulfate. The amount need not be weighed. An estimated amount on the tip of a spatula is sufficiently accurate. The bottles are sterilized as in *Option 1*.

For dry heat sterilization—

Into clean dry bottles is added from 0.02 to 0.05 gm of powdered sodium thiosulfate as in *Option 2*. The bottles are stoppered, capped, and sterilized at 180°C for 10 minutes. The temperature of sterilization must not approach 220°C as sodium thiosulfate decomposes at this temperature.

E. *Collection of Samples*—The samples should be collected by plunging the open bottle beneath the surface, sweeping the bottle forward until filled. The bottle should not be rinsed in the pool or the sodium thiosulfate will be removed. Samples should be collected only when the pool is in use and preferably during periods of heaviest bathing loads during the day. The hour of the day, the day of the week, frequency of collection, and the location of the point of sampling shall be varied in order to obtain over a period of time a representative cross-section of the sanitary quality of the pool. It is desirable wherever facilities permit, to collect one or more samples weekly from swimming pools.

26. Cleaning Pool

A. Visible dirt on the bottom of a swimming pool shall not be permitted to remain more than 24 hours.

B. Any visible scum or floating matter on the surface of pool shall be removed within 24 hours by flushing or other effective means.

28. Operating Control

A. *Trained Operators*—Each swimming pool should be operated under the close supervision of a well-trained operator with common sense and good judgment. Operator training courses have been of aid in promoting good operation.

B. *Tests for Excess Chlorine*—At any pool where chlorine, hypochlorite of lime or other chlorine compound is used for disinfection, the operator must be supplied with a proper outfit for making the orthotolidine test for excess chlorine and with permanent standards showing maximum and minimum permissible chlorine in the water.

Tests for excess chlorine in the water shall be made as frequently as experience proves to be necessary to maintain adequate residuals.

C. *Tests for Acidity*—At any pool where alum or sulphate of alumina is used or where artificial alkalinity is added to the water, the pool operator must be equipped with a hydrogen ion testing outfit and must take hydrogen ion tests on the water every day that the pool is in use, and more often if necessary.

D. *Operating Records*—Every pool operator must be supplied with a proper note book or with blank forms on which shall be recorded every day the number of persons using the pool, peak bathing loads handled, the volume of new water added, the temperature of the water, and the temperature of the air. Wherever a pool is used by both males and females the number of each and whether adults or children should also be recorded. At all pools where artificial circulation, filtration, or any chemical treatment is used, a full daily record must also be kept of the actual time pumps and filters are in operation, of the time each filter is washed or cleaned, of the time and amount of each chemical used or added, of the time the bottom and sides of pool are cleaned, and the results of all hydrogen ion, excess chlorine, or other tests.

7-4. Bathing Loads. Pools are classified according to the manner in which they are operated. Fill-and-draw pools are filled with fresh water, used, drained, cleaned, and refilled. Other pools operate with a continuous flow of water passing through them, either fresh water from the source of supply or water which has been filtered and recirculated. Discussion of the area-load requirement will be found in Art. 7-15, "Safety Provisions."

The purpose of recirculation of water is to remove suspended material and to carry chlorine into the pool and thus maintain the required chlorine residual. The presence of much suspended material will reflect upon the safety of the pool since it will reduce the efficiency of the chlorine residual. Experience indicates that the rate of turnover should be at least three times daily and preferably four times where the recirculation system is kept operating continuously, as it should be. Also, the chlorine residual should be maintained at all times.

Fill-and-draw pools are not recommended by the Joint Committee, since they are more difficult to keep clean and to disinfect. Where used, however, they should supply at least 500 gallons of water per person between complete changes of pool water without disinfection. Where intermittent disinfection is employed, the number of bathers using the pool will be governed by the area requirement per person and by bacteriological analyses of the pool water. Chlorine residuals must be maintained within the limits already specified.

For outdoor pools which are partly artificial and partly natural, such as a pool created by building a dam across a stream and making other improvements, and for other situations where dependence is placed upon a continuous flow of water from a clean, unpolluted stream, a safe well, or a spring, the 500-gallon requirement should be applied, although bacteriological conditions should rule. If cleansing baths are not required prior to using such pools, reductions in bathing loads will be found necessary to maintain safe bacteriological conditions, even with high chlorine residuals. Cleansing baths should, of course, be required at all pools.

7-5. Bacteriological Control. The swimming-pool standards given above require that the total bacteria count shall be no more than 200 per milliliter after incubation for twenty-four hours at 37°C in at least 85 per cent of the samples and that not more than 15 per cent of the standard samples for determination of coliform organisms shall show gas in any of the five 10-milliliter portions. These standards are less severe than drinking water requirements.

To maintain proper conditions, frequent bacteriological tests are necessary, and steps should be taken by pool owners to have them made at a laboratory. If no commercial laboratory is available, arrangements can sometimes be made with instructors at schools or colleges who have the necessary technical training. Daily testing should be the rule in addition to the occasional check tests made by the public health authorities.

7-6. Recirculation of Water. Fill-and-draw pools are now considered obsolete. The continuous-flow system is more popular and, since the large amount of water required for the fill-and-draw type results in high operating costs if the water must be purchased from a city, filtration and recirculation of the water are very widely practiced. Proper equipment of this sort will allow the same water to be used for months and still satisfy the standard requirements.

The slow sand type of filter, described elsewhere, is seldom used in connection with swimming pools. Rapid sand filters are generally used, and 80 per cent of these are of the pressure variety. Open gravity rapid filters are used at some large outdoor pools and are preferred by some authorities for very hard waters where cementation of the sand may occur. A pressure-filter installation requires little space and, since the

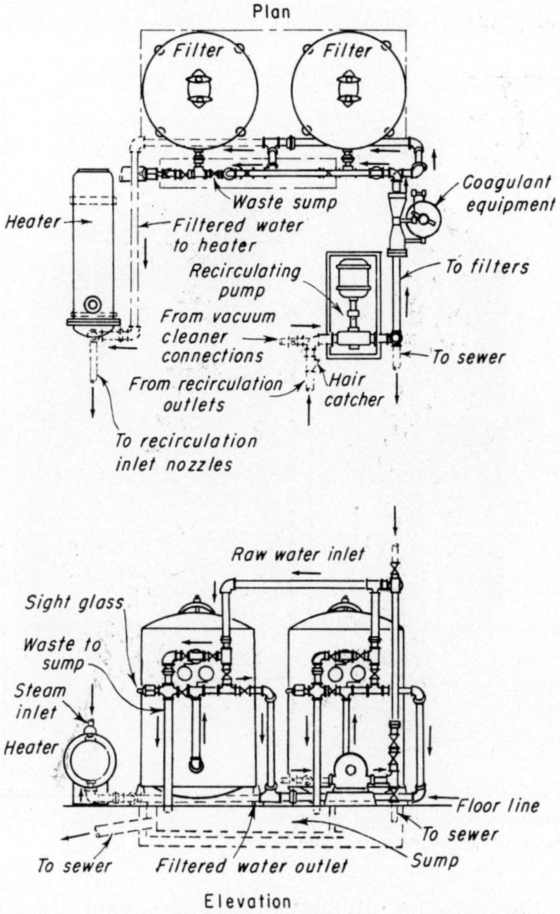

FIG. 7-2. Typical arrangement of pressure filters used in recirculating water of swimming pools.

filters are enclosed in steel tanks, one recirculating pump can force the water through the whole system. Figure 7-2 is a typical layout. Preferably two or more filters are used in parallel with the cylinders placed vertically, as shown, or horizontally. The water is pumped from the pool to the filter. Prior to entering the filter a small portion is bypassed through a coagulating apparatus to return laden with enough chemical to form a cloudy gelatinous floc which coats the upper layers of sand grains and aids materially in filtering out sediment and bacteria. The pot type of chemical-feeding apparatus is used in most small installations. One can be seen in the plan view of Fig. 7-2, and details are shown in Fig. 7-4. It is charged with the chemical in lump or crystal form, and a flow of water is passed through it. The flow of water into the pot is caused by the pressure difference on each side of an orifice or Venturi

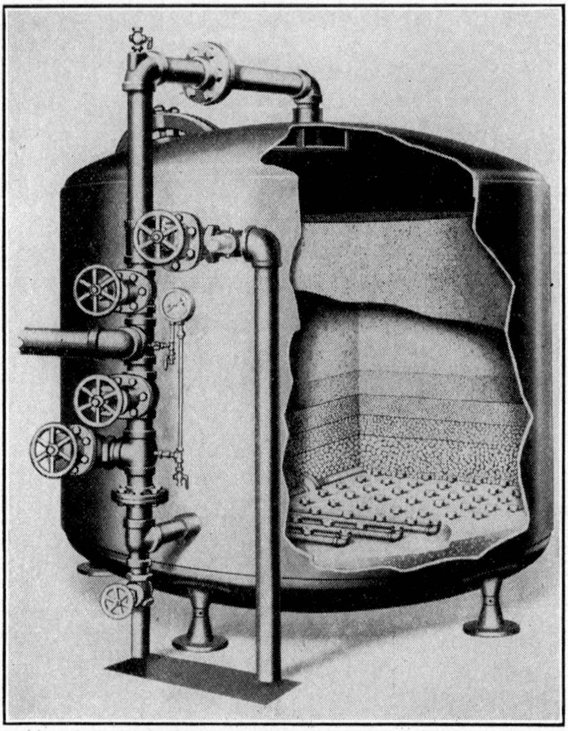

FIG. 7-3. Sectional view of vertical pressure filter. (*Courtesy of Infilco Inc., Tucson, Ariz., and Public Works Magazine.*)

tube. Since the pressure difference depends upon the rate of flow through the orifice or tube, the amount of water, and hence the amount of chemical dissolved by the water, is automatically proportioned to the amount of water passing through the filters. The desired dosage is set by the regulating valve. Potash alum or ammonia alum as the coagulant and sal-soda as the alkaline agent, both in lump or crystal form, must be used with pots.

Many operators dislike the pots and consider them inefficient. Feed can be controlled better by open tanks which are obtainable commercially, and feeding is done either into a surge tank, if there is one, or into the suction side of the recirculation pump. These tanks allow use of the cheaper filter alum (aluminum sulfate) and sodium carbonate. The operator must recognize that the water must be sufficiently alkaline in reaction to produce a proper floc. Even though the original water carries the requisite alkalinity, which is not always the case, it is used up in the recirculation process and generally must be replaced by the addition of sodium carbonate or some other chemical. This is why the acidity test mentioned in the Standards is made. Determination of the pH is a simple test.

After passing through the filter where all the floc and sediment, together with most of the bacteria, are removed, the water is forced back to the pool, being heated on the way if temperature conditions require it. After heating, the water is disinfected.

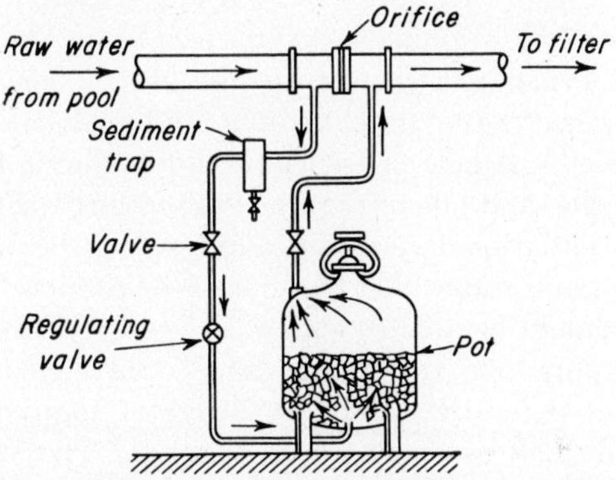

FIG. 7-4. Flow diagram of pot-type feeder for crystal alum or sal-soda.

The filters are cleaned by the simple process of reversing the flow through the filter. This can be accomplished by manipulating various valves. The wash water, carrying with it the floc, sediment, and bacteria which have accumulated in the filter, is run into the sewer. If the installation is a large one and consists of a battery of filters, one is washed at a time and filtered water from the others is used. In a one-filter layout it is necessary to wash with water from the original source of supply. Pool water may also be used, but this, of course, is undesirable unless the first water filtered after washing is wasted. Where less than four pressure filters are used, the Joint Committee has pointed out that a special wash water pump may be a desirable provision to ensure an adequate backwash rate. Rate controllers, devices that keep the filtration rate constant between washings, are highly desirable but are not usually installed in small filtering systems because of their cost. For large pools, those with 100,000 gallons or more, such equipment should be used. Rate-of-flow gauges can be provided in most instances as an aid to control.

Recirculation systems have a hair catcher in the return line before the water reaches the pump. This is a metal strainer which catches hair, lint, and other solids which may clog the pump and form masses in the filter. It is arranged so that removing a plug allows the accumulated material to flow out.

In general, swimming-pool filters are operated at about 3 gallons per square foot of filter area per minute.

7-7. Maintenance of the Pressure Sand and Gravel Filters. Some operating difficulties may appear in recirculating systems. The sand grains of the filters may cement together or mud balls may form to the extent that filtration is ineffective. These effects may be due to backwashing with an insufficient amount of water or overdosing with alum. Filters should be inspected once each bathing season. This is done by backwashing the filter, draining the water well below the top of the sand, and removing the manhole cover from the filter. The sand should be level, with no pools of water standing on it, and no cracks or pulling away from the filter shell. A hole or trench should be dug in the sand at least 1 foot deep, and the sand taken from the various levels should be carefully examined. The situation may require a redesign of the washing system in order to obtain more water. If there are four or more filters, the recirculation pump should be able to backwash properly; otherwise a special pump will be required, or Anthrafilt, which is pulverized anthracite coal, may be substituted for the sand. It is lighter than sand and can be washed with only half as much water as sand. The standard washing rate is a 24-inch rise of the water per minute through the sand.

If backwashing a filter does not remedy the clogging, organic matter may be removed by using lye or sodium hydroxide. This is done as follows: Draw the water level by means of the drain valve down to within 4 inches of the sand and add 1 pound of the chemical for each square foot of the filter. Allow this to act on the bed for several hours. Then draw the water down part way through the bed and repeat the process. Follow this with a thorough backwashing. Care must be taken in handling the lye and also the wash water containing it, or burns may result. The above treatment will not clear clogged nozzles or perforations in the underdrain system. When these occur, the manufacturer of the filter should be consulted. Certain acids can be used to clear the openings, but skill is required in using them.

Some operators wash filters only after they note a reduction in the rate of filtration. It is better, however, to wash when the pressure difference reaches a certain amount, such as 5 pounds per square inch or about 10 feet, as shown by the pressure gauges.

7-8. Vacuum-septum Filters. During World War II, the Army adopted filtering systems previously in use in petroleum and chemical industries for the treatment of water for drinking purposes in the field. This vacuum-septum type of filter, which involves the application of a filter aid, has since become widely used in swimming pools. It has found

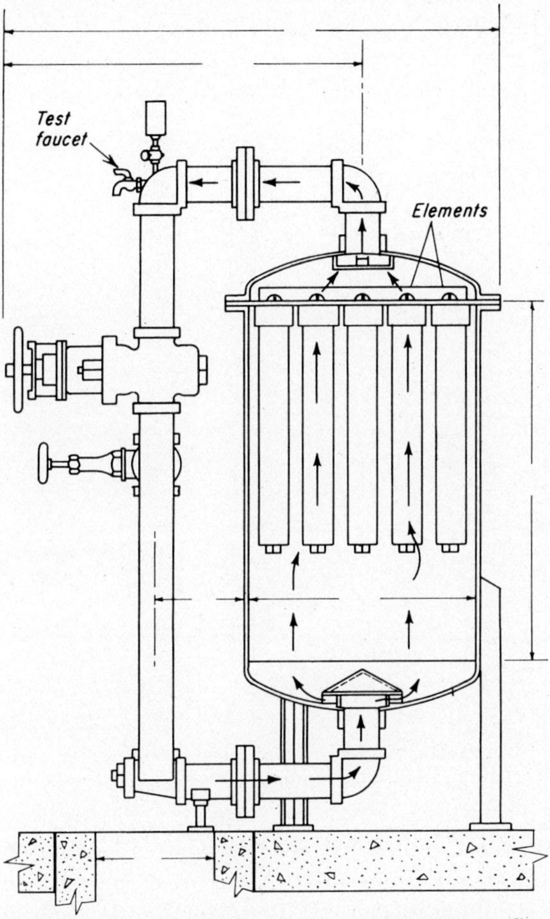

FIG. 7-5. Section through diatomite filter. (*Courtesy of Waterite Co., Omaha, Neb.*)

adaptation peculiar to this field in that, generally speaking, relatively nonturbid water can be applied to the filter. While the filter design and construction take many different forms, the principle embodied involves a tank in which the water is introduced under pressure, a filter septum which acts as a base to which the filter aid may cling, and a channel for the discharge of the filtered water. The septum is a metallic or ceramic cylinder, porous in nature, usually with its exterior (upstream side) wound with small-diameter monel or stainless-steel wire. A number of these cylindrical elements may be placed within a single filter shell, and, of course, the filter surface is the sum of the surface of all of the elements. This makes possible a considerable space saving as compared with the use of pressure or gravity sand filters. Diatomaceous earth is most commonly used as the filter aid, although other finely divided materials have been proposed and used. By means of a slurry feeder, the filter aid is fed at first in a relatively large amount to form a precoat and thereafter in a small amount to raw water entering the filter

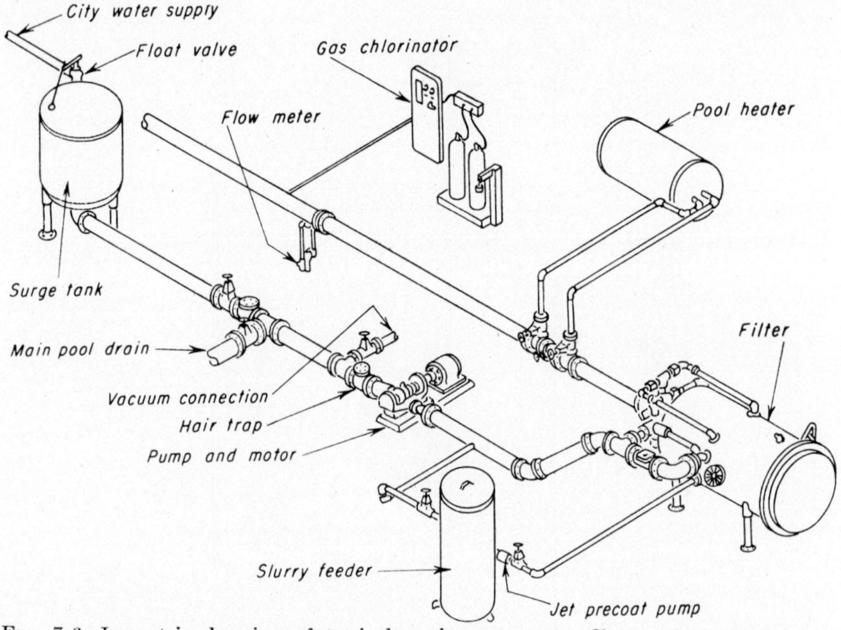

FIG. 7-6. Isometric drawing of typical equipment room: filter and precoat pump, heater, chlorinator, surge tank, and piping. (*Courtesy of Kinetrol Company, Dallas, Tex.*)

shell. As the water containing the filter aid passes through the filter element, the filter aid clings to the exterior of the element, forming a very effective straining surface. Filtering action proceeds in this manner until a high loss of head develops, with consequent reduced efficiency. The unit is then backwashed; in the process the filter cake is removed from the elements. The filter aid is subsequently discarded, and the cycle repeated. Tray filters have made their appearance in this field where the filtering septum or element is composed of layers of sand. Diatomaceous earth, or filter aid, is fed in this case also, and as with the other types, backwashing consists of the discarding of the filter aid through a flow-reversal procedure. The vacuum-septum filter is capable of producing a high filtering efficiency and has numerous other advantages. Some of these may be listed as follows[2]: eliminating the need for coagulants if filters are not overloaded, permitting variation by as much as 100 per cent in filtration rates, allowing a greater latitude in efficiency of filtration at high head losses, and providing a high degree of compactness, resulting in space saving.

There are some disadvantages which have interfered with wholehearted acceptance of this method as a substitute for the sand and gravel filters. Levin and Cary[3] found that both wire-wound and screen-mesh elements are subject to galvanic corrosion, which is particularly disadvantageous in the case of the former because complete unwinding of the wire surrounding the filter element may occur through failure of the wire at any one point. This can be corrected to some extent by avoiding the use of dissimilar materials in contact with each other in the construction of the filter unit. The same investigators also observed that it is difficult to clean the elements adequately with the backwash means available. Experimental tests conducted by the Army, using mechanical air compressors, show that air-bump backwashing is successful in cleaning the filter units if instantaneous rates of 100 to 200 times maximum filter rates are used. Another disadvantage is the fact that successful filtration depends entirely upon the operator at all times. In other words, failure to feed filter aid can result in very ineffective filtration. Kiker[4] states that the number of septum-filter installations is likely to increase in the near future, primarily for economic reasons, but that, compared with sand filters, they are in a rather early stage of development and that sand and gravel filters are still to be preferred where conditions permit.

7-9. Disinfection of Pools. While filtration of the swimming-pool water removes all ordinary suspended matter, it does not remove all bacteria. Hence some means of disinfection must be applied. Disinfection processes are much more effective in clear water than in turbid water carrying much organic matter.

The hypochlorites, either of calcium (chlorinated lime) or sodium, have been extensively used to disinfect swimming-pool water. Solutions of hypochlorites can be pumped or injected into the recirculation system of a pool by the use of appropriate commercial apparatus. For fill-and-draw pools intermittent dosage is accomplished by sprinkling a solution of the chemical over the surface of the water or by dragging a cloth bag containing the proper amount through the water. The objection to applying the disinfectant at the surface is the greater likelihood that bathers may notice the odor of chlorine. This often results in complaints of more or less imaginary smarting of the eyes. One method of intermittent hypochlorite application is weighting the bag sufficiently so that the chlorine will be released near the bottom rather than near the surface.

It should be well diffused by dragging around in all parts of the pool near the bottom. Vertical diffusion can be depended upon to take place naturally.

Liquid chlorine is generally used in connection with recirculation equipment. Liquid chlorine is actually chlorine gas under pressure in storage. Several manufacturers furnish apparatus which feeds controlled amounts of chlorine gas wherever desired. If water is recirculated, the chlorine is added to the water just before it reenters the pool. The advantage of chlorine gas over chlorinated lime is that it does not lose strength, as does the latter, and is in general more convenient to handle and apply.

The most satisfactory method of controlling disinfection is by retaining a slight excess of chlorine over and above that required to satisfy the demand of the organic matter in the water. The excess can be determined by the use of the orthotolidine test, described in Art. 5-19. The standards mentioned above recommend an excess of 0.4 to 1.0 part per million. The dosage necessary to retain this must be learned by experiment. Methods of calculating dosages are the same as used for treating drinking water and are given in Art. 5-20. Dosages tried are, of course, somewhat in excess of the residual required. After the desired excess has been obtained, frequent tests are necessary so that it may be retained. If water is being recirculated, the excess can be retained by means of proper setting of the chlorinator which is feeding into the recirculating water. During periods of heavy patronage, the water should be tested at frequent intervals throughout the day for excess chlorine, the samples being taken from both the shallow and the deep ends of the pool.

The addition of chlorine so that free chlorine residuals are obtained provides a distinct advantage as far as disinfection is concerned, and the pool operator should strive to maintain free chlorine residuals to the exclusion of combined chlorine residuals. Experience in maintaining high chlorine residuals (equal to or greater than 1 part per million) indicates that a greater margin of safety is produced than through the use of residuals on the order of 0.4 to 0.6 part per million. Mood[5] states that high free-residual chlorination of swimming-pool water reduces the amount of irritation to the eyes of swimmers as compared to marginal chlorination. He found that optimum conditions of the swimming pool exist where the pH of the water is 8 to 8.9 and there is a residual chlorine concentration of 1 to 3.99.

Chlorine, either as a gas or in hypochlorite form, when used as a disinfectant has the advantage, if proper dosage is used, of giving a residual bactericidal effect which lasts for some time. Other methods of disinfection, such as the ultraviolet ray, do not have this residual effect—or, at best, have it only in an uncertain or negligible amount. As a result, chlorine is favored by health authorities for swimming-pool use for it is available to kill bacteria immediately after they are contributed by the bather. Because no chemicals are used in connection with sterilization by ultraviolet ray, with no possibility of odors, and also because of its popular appeal, this method has been installed at many pools. The Joint Committee recommends that, since there is no demonstrated residual effect, it not be used or, if it is, that chlorine be used also.

Ozone has been used for swimming-pool water. Its residual effect is very uncertain, and, accordingly, it is little better than ultraviolet ray. Chlorine, therefore, is to be preferred.

Ionized silver has been used for swimming-pool disinfection abroad and to a slight extent in the United States. The process is costly, and the action of silver is slow. Some substances, such as ammonium salts, interfere with the silver and, in general, the disinfection is rather poor. Silver is not recommended by the Committee.

During the war the use of bromine was introduced, particularly in Illinois, where 44 pools were reported as using it. It is a dark-brown liquid which vaporizes rapidly at room temperature. As the liquid will cause a burn in contact with the skin, caution is required in handling it. It is mixed with water in glass containers and is then fed into the recirculation system. The dosages used varied from slightly under 1 part per million to over 4 parts per million, with the preferred residuals from 0.2 to 0.5 part per million. Pool operators gave the following reasons for using it: it was hard to obtain chlorine during the war; bromine was easier to apply than chlorine; equipment was simpler and less costly; it was easier to maintain a residual; there were fewer complaints from patrons as to eye and skin irritations; there were better bacteriological results. The disadvantage given was the greater cost of bromine, although nearly half the pool operators thought otherwise. One Y.M.C.A. pool operator thought that the bromine was more dangerous to store and that the glass feeding equipment was too delicate.

7-10. Natural Bathing Places. In artificial pools the most important consideration with respect to the water is that it not be contaminated after it enters the pool. At the natural bathing places, which may be beaches, lakes, or slightly improved pools in streams, the original condition of the water must also be considered. Here bacteriological tests of the water do not tell the full story, for the total count and tests for coliforms do not differentiate between harmless pollution from animals and cultivated fields, and the dangerous contamination caused by sewage from dwellings, hotels, factories, municipal sewerage works, and the bathers themselves. The tests must therefore be supplemented by a sanitary survey covering sources and possibilities of dangerous contamination. Little has been accomplished with regard to water standards for natural bathing places. One state has rated ocean bathing places at various depths and tide levels on the basis of analyses as follows:

	Average coliforms per 100 milliliters
Class A	0–50
Class B	51–500
Class C	501–1,000
Class D	Over 1,000

At the same time a sanitary survey was made of the same areas, covering such matters as sewer outlets and shore currents which would spread pollution, and a similar letter rating was adopted on this basis. A close correlation was found between the survey and the analysis rating. The letter ratings may be interpreted as good, doubtful, poor, and very poor.

The bacterial limits for natural bathing waters recommended by West Virginia, Great Lakes and Upper Mississippi River Boards, T.V.A., and New York State are indicated in Table 7-1.

TABLE 7-1. BACTERIAL LIMITS FOR NATURAL BATHING WATERS AS RECOMMENDED BY FOUR AGENCIES

Water classification	Coliform density per 100 milliliters			
	West Virginia	Great Lakes and Upper Mississippi River Boards	Tennessee Valley Authority	New York State
Satisfactory for bathing	0–1,000	100–500	0–50	0–1,000
Satisfactory with reservations	....	501–1,000	51–500	1,000–2,400
Use doubtful; not recommended	....	1,001–10,000	501–1,000	50 per cent of samples, over 2,400
Do not use	....	10,001–100,000	Over 1,000	Evidence of infection from area

SOURCE: Eugene L. Lehr and Charles C. Johnson, Jr., Water Quality of Swimming Places, *Public Health Repts.*, vol. 69, no. 8, 1954.

In this connection the action of Los Angeles in relation to beach pollution is interesting. The criterion for safe water at its bathing beaches is that less than 30 per cent of the samples taken over a period of time shall have 1,000 or more coliforms per 100 milliliters. The beaches were endangered by the discharge of untreated Los Angeles sewage, and 11.52 miles in the proximity of the outlet was closed to bathing. The sewage was then chlorinated, with a reduction of coliforms in the water to the extent that 4.52 miles of beach could be reopened for bathing.

7-11. Disinfection and Bathing Loads for Natural Bathing Places. Whether or not disinfection is employed, efforts should be made to eliminate sources of sewage pollution of small ponds or streams used for bathing, and sanitary surveys of watersheds are recommended. Chlorine can be applied to the inlet water continuously, or several applications may be made over the area during bathing periods, with the same residuals as recommended for artificial pools.

Disinfection of large bodies of water by the so-called "chloroboat" has been successfully used in a few cases. The chloroboat is a boat from which gaseous chlorine is fed as it is being rowed over the water. Bathing areas several acres in extent have been chlorinated by use of pipe systems laid on the bottom, through which chlorine solution or chlorinated water is applied by means of what is, in effect, a recirculation system. Whether disinfection should be applied to natural bathing areas will depend not only upon the safety of the water but also upon the amount of water available and its changes by action of tides and currents.

In small natural pools it is possible to correlate the amount of water with the bathing load. It should probably never be less than 500 gallons per bather without disinfection. New York State uses the Becker formula in relating the load to the volume of diluting water. This formula is $Q = 6.25T^2$, where Q is the quantity of water per bather in gallons and T is the replacement period in hours. For example, if the flow is such as to replace the pool volume in 8 hours, then Q will be 400 gallons, and the number of bathers permitted in 8 hours would be the capacity of the pool divided by 400.

7-12. Swimmer's Itch. A disease contracted by bathing in natural waters, particularly in weedy lakes and ponds, is schistosome dermatitis. Most cases have been reported from Minnesota and Wisconsin. It is caused by a small parasite, derived from birds, that spends a part of its life cycle in certain species of water snails, which release the larval organisms in the water. In their search for a second host, they enter the skin of human bathers where they cause a rash and intense itching which may last for several weeks until the organisms die. They do not produce any other ill effects. Prevention methods have been directed against the snails. Application of 2 pounds of copper sulfate and 1 pound of copper carbonate per 1,000 square feet of beach area will kill the snails and eliminate the danger for a season or longer. The treatment should be given to at least 1,000 feet of continuous shore line. A solution of the two chemicals is made and applied by means of a garden hose which is dragged on the bottom from a boat. Two hoses may be used, one suspended from each side of the boat. Sodium arsenite has been used to kill the rooted aquatic plants to which the snails attach themselves. In any area used for swimming, however, this chemical must be used with extreme caution because of its very high toxicity. It is difficult to secure uniform distribution of the chemical in natural waters; consequently, after its application, tests for arsenic should be conducted throughout the area at varying depths to ascertain, before swimming is permitted in the area, that at no point does there exist a lethal concentration. Sampling might also include bottom sediments. It is reported that BHC, or Gammexane, is very effective against snails when applied as a dust to water containing them to produce a concentration of 5 to 6 parts per million.

7-13. Pool Construction. Pools are of various shapes and dimensions. Outdoor pools are frequently oval, with the shallow water at the edges and the deep water in the middle. The usual swimming pool, however, is rectangular, shallow at one end and deep at the other. Pools which are to be used for athletic contests must have a minimum length of 60 feet. For racing it is also necessary that each contestant have a free lane 5 feet wide. For these reasons it is quite common for the dimensions of the smaller swimming pools to be set at 60 feet in length with the width a multiple of 5 feet, the most popular size for indoor pools being 30 by 60 feet.

The depth of a pool should receive careful consideration during its design, particularly the proportion of the shallow and deep parts. If it is to be a public pool, a large number of the patrons will be unable to swim and, therefore, too small an area of shallow water may result in an undesirable crowding. In college or association pools the deep-water area may be large, although shallow water must be provided for beginners' classes. Hinman[6] states that in the largest public pools at least 95 per cent of the pool area should be less than 5 feet deep. As the pools considered become smaller, the proportion of shallow area will become smaller, for the space for diving will remain constant. Deep water for diving should extend a distance of 10 to 15 feet beyond the end of the springboard to minimize the chance of accidents. In parks where many children may be expected, unless special wading pools are provided, it may be advisable to slope the shallow portion of the pool to the water surface. Usually, however, the minimum depth of water is 3 feet with a maximum depth of 9 feet. The maximum depth probably need not be as much as 9 feet unless towers are provided for diving from heights. Depths should be clearly marked by tile inlays, figures painted at the pool edges, or by conspicuous signs.

The bottom slopes of pools should be gradual enough to prevent slipping. A fall of 1 foot in 15 feet or 1 foot in 20 feet will be safe in the shallow area. Where the water is over 5.5 feet deep, steeper slopes are permissible. There should, of course, never be sudden drops.

Pools are usually constructed of reinforced concrete, sometimes with a tile surface. They should be impervious, smooth of surface, and easy to clean. Concrete polished with carborundum bricks immediately after removal of the forms makes an excellent surface. The rounding of corners and the avoidance of recesses also facilitate cleaning. A light-colored finish, when accompanied by clear water, makes a more attractive pool and also allows lifeguards or attendants to discover submerged bodies easily.

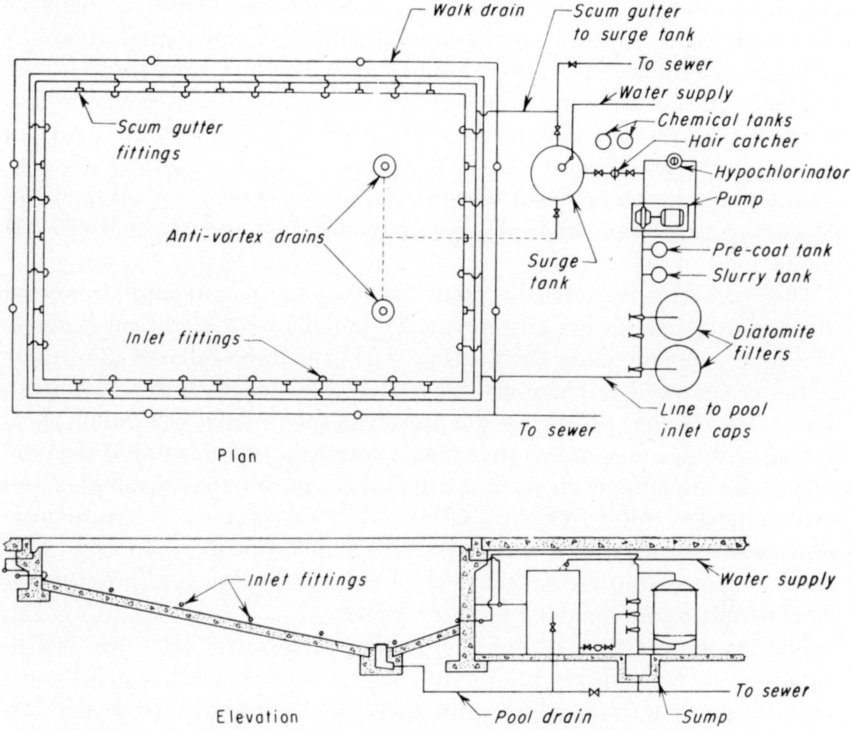

FIG. 7-7. Layout of typical pool. (*Courtesy of Waterite Co., Omaha, Neb.*)

If concrete curbing and runways are used, they should be given a wood-float surface that will prevent slipping. The walks or runways around the pool should slope gently away or be otherwise arranged so that no drainage will enter the pool from them.

Runways should be not less than 4 feet wide. It is not advisable to have grass plots within the pool enclosure, as grass will be carried into the pool on the feet of bathers and result in unsightly water. Entrance to the pool should be at the shallow end.

Scum gutters are recesses in the pool wall extending completely around the water edge at the water level. They receive overflow, scum, and floating matter and act as expectoration troughs. There is no objection to their being arranged to receive drainage from runways, in which case the latter are sloped slightly to the pool. The gutters may drain to the pump in the case of recirculation pools or directly to the sewer. They should have drainage outlets at not more than 15-foot intervals and should slope to the outlets. They are sometimes molded to form the liferail, in which case they should be deep enough so that the hand will not touch bottom. More frequently, however, the liferail is made of pipe fastened to the wall of the pool by brackets and placed about 10 inches above the water. It has become quite common practice to utilize the scum gutters as part of the recirculation system. In other words, a percentage of the swimming-pool water is returned via the scum gutters to the purification equipment. Advantages in this method are (1) maintaining the water level constantly at the overflow point and (2) improving circulation efficiency by increasing the number of withdrawal points.

There is a growing tendency to utilize mechanical skimmers to replace the more expensive scum-gutter construction, particularly in small pools. The skimmers may be of the floating type or may be recessed at various points in the walls. These are generally connected with the pump suction. The city of Los Angeles has approved their use on semipublic pools having a surface area of less than 800 square feet. It is required that the devices be adjustable up to at least 50 per cent of the capacity of the swimming-pool filter system. Other features specified are automatic adjustment to variations in the water level over a range of 3 inches, provision of a device to prevent air lock in the suction line, and provision of a removable and cleanable basket or screen.

The "water-level deck type" of swimming pool has been installed in a number of cases in recent years. Here the water level is maintained with the peripheral overflow, and there are no scum gutters as such. Water is flushed over the walls onto a floor which is sloped to deck drains, spaced at about the same distance as scum-gutter outlets would have been. This type of construction also requires the use of a balancing tank to maintain the pool level.

Diving boards should be covered with corrugated sheet rubber or some other rough material to prevent slipping. In indoor pools, 13 feet of headroom is required above a springboard. No diving tower greater than 10 feet in height should be used in public pools. The minimum safe depth of water is 8 feet; if diving platforms are 9 to 10 feet above the water, the minimum depth should be increased to 10 feet. Lifeguards should be instructed to prevent congestion of swimmers in the water near the boards in order to minimize the chance of accident.

The inlets and outlets of continuous-flow pools must be carefully placed to ensure a complete change of water and the absence of stagnant portions. It is recommended that inlets be installed, at least in the shallow portion of the pool, so that each serves 15 linear feet. The main drains are usually placed at the deepest point of the pool and vary in number according to the width. In general, the drains should not be placed farther than 10 feet from a side wall.

If steps are used rather than ladders, they should be recessed and not allowed to extend into the pool. Indoor pools require adequate ventilation but should be so arranged that no drafts will strike the bathers.

7-14. Cleaning Pools. Cleaning of pools is necessitated by heavy sediment or by accumulations of vegetable growth (algae) on the bottom and side walls. Cleaning can be accomplished by draining the pool and scrubbing the sides and bottom. This causes a considerable expense in

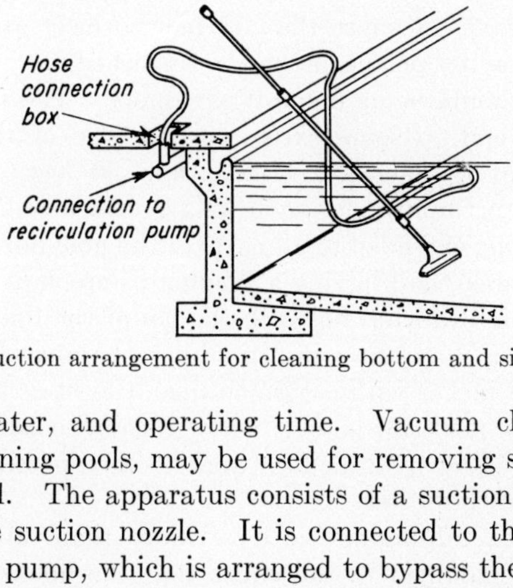

FIG. 7-8. Suction arrangement for cleaning bottom and sides of pool.

labor, loss of water, and operating time. Vacuum cleaners, specially designed for cleaning pools, may be used for removing sediment without draining the pool. The apparatus consists of a suction tube with a stiff brush within the suction nozzle. It is connected to the suction side of the recirculation pump, which is arranged to bypass the mingled foreign matter and water to the sewer or to conduct it to the filter. Special inlet connections for the suction hose must be placed at intervals around the pool. About 6 inches of water is removed from the pool during the operation of cleaning.

Algae growths, though harmless, are unsightly and are likely to discolor the water and give it an unpleasant odor. Their development can be prevented by dosing with copper sulfate at the rate of 10 to 20 pounds per million gallons. It can be applied in the same manner as chlorinated lime, either by dragging the chemical through the water in bags or by adding it continuously to recirculated water. Chlorination also tends to prevent algae growths. A very important factor in algae control is the maintenance of pH at a proper level. The range generally recommended is 7.0 to 8.0. Once pool walls have become discolored and slimy with algae, chemical treatment may have but little effect in their removal, particularly if the walls are rough. Emptying and scrubbing will then be necessary. Scrubbing with a solution of caustic soda has been found effective in completely removing the slime. Where algae troubles are expected, continuous but light treatments with copper sulfate are commonly applied as a preventive measure. This is especially likely to be necessary in outdoor pools, as exposure of the water to sunlight promotes heavy growth of algae; indoor pools may also have trouble at times.

7-15. Safety Provisions. Attendants should be stationed at all pools for lifesaving purposes. They should be expert swimmers, skilled in lifesaving and resuscitation. A certificate in lifesaving, as awarded by the Red Cross, is a logical requirement. If the pool is large, it is of advantage to place the guard on an elevated platform where he can easily survey the whole pool. Hinman suggests that lifeguards be so placed that they need travel no more than 75 feet to meet an emergency and that one guard per 100 people should be furnished.

A first-aid kit should be on hand at each pool. The safety equipment required will depend to some extent on the size of the pool. If the minimum horizontal dimension is less than 30 feet, there should be provided (1) one or more poles each longer than one-half of the width and capable of being extended to all parts of the pool bottom, constructed preferably of bamboo, and having a shepherd's crook at the end with an opening of at least 18 inches between the tip of the hook and the tip of the pole; (2) one or more throwing ring buoys having a maximum diameter of at least 18 inches with a $\frac{1}{4}$-inch line at least as long as the maximum width of the pool; (3) one or more "flutter boards," each approximately 1 foot by 3 feet by 2 inches, capable of supporting a weight of at least 20 pounds in the water.

At pools with a minimum width of more than 30 feet, the above requirements are modified to the effect that the hooked poles must be at least 15 feet long, that two or more of the other pieces of apparatus are required, and that the ring buoys must be attached to at least 60 feet of line.

Liferails along the pool and the allowance of space around the diving boards have already been mentioned. Fewer injuries will occur if the pool is not overcrowded. A minimum of 27 square feet per person is considered necessary, except within a radius of 10 feet of a diving board, which may be considered as serving only 12 persons, including those waiting to dive. Not more than two or three persons should be allowed in the diving area at one time while diving is in progress. This diving area must be subtracted from the total pool area before applying the 27-square-feet rule. If the runways are narrow, less than 4 feet, a rail around the pool is advisable.

7-16. Control of Bathers. Of great importance is supervision of the bathers. The entrance into the pool of persons with communicable diseases or with open wounds or bandages should be prohibited. This is necessary, not only to prevent contamination of the water, but also to protect the bathers themselves. Serious sinus trouble has been attributed to infectious material being forced by the water into the interior cavities of the head when bathers are suffering from ear discharges, colds, or respiratory infections. This prohibition with the other instructions mentioned below should be made plain by means of placards displayed at the entrance to the dressing rooms and inside them.

The need for requiring swimmers to take shower baths before entering the pool is recognized, but not always enforced. The quality of the pool water reflects, to a very great extent, the degree to which this requirement is complied with. The showers, to be effective, must be taken before the bathing suit is put on; soap should be used, and the water should be warm. Inspection is necessary to enforce the rule. Here firmness and tact are necessary, for many persons feel that their personal cleanliness is being questioned when they are required to take a shower, hence the need of placards fully setting out its value. It is difficult for the inspector to be certain that a cleansing shower has been taken. It is sometimes apparent by glancing at the feet back of the ankle bones. If those parts are still dry, the shower has been too brief to be of any value.

At many pools foot baths are provided for patrons to pass through on returning to the pool after leaving the enclosure. Eating and smoking in the pool enclosure are also prohibited in order that foreign material shall not be thrown into the water. In general, it is good practice to segregate spectators in street clothes in such a manner that they do not have access to the pool enclosure.

7-17. Suits and Towels. Swimming suits, unless properly treated, are likely to harbor many bacteria. Although at most pools it is the practice to allow patrons to bring their own suits, it would probably be better to require that all use suits furnished by the pool management, so that they may be washed and sterilized after each use. Cleaning and practical sterilization of suits and towels is accomplished by thorough washing with hot water and soap, followed by complete drying. Cold-water washing and air drying should be prohibited. A further valuable requirement is that the stock of suits and towels be large enough to allow storage of the clean supply for twenty-four hours, thus reducing the danger of the patron being issued a dirty suit at rush times.

Clean suits and towels should never be allowed to come in contact with unwashed stock or be stored on shelves or in baskets which have held it. The issuing of clean suits and towels at the same counters where dirty suits and towels are turned in is dangerous. Hinman mentions several epidemics of skin disease caused by towels handled in this manner.

7-18. The Bathhouse. Of the bathhouse equipment the toilets and showers are the most important. The usual minimum requirements are one shower for each 30 dressing rooms or lockers, one toilet for each 30 dressing rooms on the women's side of the house, and one toilet for each 40 dressing rooms, with one urinal for each 20 dressing rooms on the men's side. Danger of pollution of the pool with urine will be reduced if a notice is displayed urging patrons to make use of toilets before entering the water. In this connection it will be advantageous to route the bathers from the dressing rooms to the toilets and then to the showers before they can leave the bathhouse for the pool entrance.

The shower-bath heads should preferably be of the shoulder-high, slanting-jet type. This will allow use without wetting the hair, which is desirable if rubber bathing caps are worn. Precautions should be taken with showers, by means of check valves and other apparatus, to prevent hot water from entering the cold-water pipes and to ensure proper mixing of the hot and cold water.

The locker room must be well ventilated and, if possible, separated from the shower rooms in order to prevent excessive moisture. The lockers themselves are usually ventilated by means of expanded metal or screen doors, slots, or perforations. While ventilation of the lockers is much needed, the possibility of stealing from the stored clothing by means of wire hooks should be considered. The presence of an attendant would lessen this danger.

Drinking fountains are a necessity. No common drinking cups, towels, combs, brushes, or toilet articles of any kind should be furnished.

7-19. Prevention of Athlete's Foot. Cases of athlete's foot, which is a disease caused by a fungus and sometimes called "ringworm" of the foot, have been attributed to infection obtained from the floors of showers and dressing rooms of swimming pools. At some pools bathers are required to rinse their feet in foot baths containing a solution of 0.3 to 0.6 per cent available chlorine to prevent, or at least greatly reduce, the danger of infection. At other pools a 15 per cent sodium thiosulfate solution has been used with varying success. This chemical will reduce the chlorine residual in a pool; therefore, bathers should use it only after leaving the pool. Some authorities do not favor the use of disinfectant foot baths because of the difficulty of getting bathers to use them and securing control of disinfectant strength. General sanitation and floor cleanliness are of more importance than foot baths. Floors and walkways should be constructed so that they drain readily, and they should be scrubbed daily. Good ventilation of dressing rooms is desirable, for dry floors are of value in preventing athlete's foot.

7-20. Small Pools. Particularly in the Southern states, the construction of small pools of a semipublic nature is growing in popularity.

Motels, for example, frequently provide them for use by their customers. They are also being constructed to serve apartment houses and even subdivisions. Quite often their size invites departure from accepted standards which were written primarily for the municipal type of pool. Examples of such departure are failure to maintain the 1-in-15 slope of the floor in the nonswimming section, nonobservance of recommended recirculation rates, utilization of skimming devices rather than scum gutters, and utilization of substitutes for the generally accepted masonry construction. These bear watching on the part of health departments, not only because of substandard features, but because trained and qualified operation is just as important in these installations as in the larger community pools, if not more so.

BIBLIOGRAPHY

1. "Recommended Practice for Design, Equipment and Operation of Swimming Pools and Other Public Bathing Places," American Public Health Association, 1957.
2. Lehr, Eugene L., and Charles C. Johnson, Jr.: Water Quality of Swimming Places, *Public Health Repts.*, vol. 69, no. 8, 1954.
3. Levin, Gilbert V., and William H. Cary, Jr.: "Diatomaceous Earth Filters for Swimming Pools," Proceedings of the Twenty-sixth Annual Conference of the Maryland-Delaware Water and Sewage Association, 1953.
4. Kiker, J. E., Jr.: Septum Filters for Swimming Pools, *Eng. Progr. Univ. Florida*, vol. 7, pp. 47–49, September, 1953.
5. Mood, E. W.: Development and Application of High–Free Residual Chlorination in the Treatment of Swimming Pool Water, *Am. J. Public Health*, vol. 43, pp. 1258–1264, 1953.
6. Hinman, Jack J., Jr.: The Swimming Pool and Its Sanitation, *Iowa Health Bull.*, vol. I, no. 4.

CHAPTER 8

REFUSE SANITATION

8-1. While the problem of collection and disposal of refuse was for many years left to the ever-changing whims of the individual, public recognition of the implications for health, together with a general desire for more sanitary surroundings, is forcing municipal authorities to accept responsibility for this vital phase of the community environmental sanitation program. Modern conceptions of municipal refuse sanitation have justly elevated the refuse removal and disposal service to a position similar to that accorded other public utilities. A sound basis for this new respect for refuse sanitation is seen in the fact that the service in larger cities necessitates expenditures of about 5 per cent of the total city budget and approximately 25 per cent of that portion of the entire budget which is allotted to all public works.

The primary consideration of the problem is sanitation, which must be adequate if the over-all environmental sanitation program is to be efficient in the protection of public health. The secondary consideration is the procurement of satisfactory results with a minimum expenditure of funds. The attainment of both of these objectives will require close study of local conditions, technical assistance with regard to the initiation and operation of the program, and the close cooperation of health authorities in the regulation of the program in its three phases: storage, collection, and disposal.

8-2. Refuse. The materials that are collected and disposed of under the term *refuse* include many different substances from a multitude of sources. The amounts and characteristics of the various types of refuse may differ with the time of year, geographical location, and the habits of the contributing population. Table 8-1 illustrates seasonal fluctuations in quantities of municipal refuse. Recent attempts to establish uniform terminology regarding the various components of refuse are not well recognized by the general public; however, most writers and other technical persons associated with refuse programs have recognized the need for uniform terms for maximum understanding by those working together in the same field. Generally accepted components of refuse include all putrescible and nonputrescible solid wastes, with the exception of body wastes. Such wastes include garbage, rubbish, ashes, street sweepings, dead animals, and solid market and industrial wastes.

Some collection and disposal systems enable the collection of all solid wastes from a common receptacle for removal to the same disposal site. The term *mixed refuse* denotes combinations of all components. It weighs 500 to 1,000 pounds per cubic yard.

From an over-all standpoint, the collection and removal of refuse from the environment of man in a sanitary manner is of importance in effecting vector control, nuisance abatement, aesthetics improvement, and fire protection.

8-3. Garbage. The term *garbage* is used to designate those putrescible wastes resulting from the growing, handling, preparation, cooking, and

TABLE 8-1. REPORTED QUANTITY RANGE OF MUNICIPAL REFUSE COLLECTED
Pounds per Capita per Day

Type of Refuse	Summer*		Winter†		Yearly average
	Minimum	Maximum	Minimum	Maximum	
Garbage	0.2	2.2	0.1	1.4	0.6
Rubbish	0.5	1.8	0.4	1.4	0.9
Ashes	0.1	1.5	1.4	3.0	1.1
Garbage and combustible rubbish	0.4	3.7	0.3	2.6	1.2
Ashes and noncombustible rubbish	0.2	3.5	0.4	5.4	1.5
All refuse combined	1.4	4.6	1.6	5.1	2.2

* Summer season: May 1–October 31.
† Winter season: November 1–April 30.
SOURCE: "Sanitary Refuse Practices," pt. I, U.S. Public Health Service, 1953.

consumption of food. Quantities of garbage vary throughout the year, being greatest in amount during summer months when vegetable wastes are more abundant. It weighs 800 to 1,500 pounds per cubic yard. Garbage requires careful handling with frequent removal and adequate disposal because it attracts and breeds flies and other insects, supplies food for rats, and rapidly ferments, resulting in the production of unpleasant odors. Garbage is probably the most valuable component of refuse in that it yields grease and fertilizer through reduction and composting processes and is utilized as hog feed.

8-4. Rubbish. *Rubbish* denotes all nonputrescible wastes except ashes. It consists of both combustible and noncombustible substances, such as cans, paper, brush, glass, cardboard, wood, scrap metals, bedding, yard clippings, crockery, etc. It weighs 100 to 700 pounds per cubic yard. Garbage and rubbish are difficult to separate entirely because those materials classed as rubbish are often used to package food or food products and various amounts of garbage are seen to remain attached to paper, boxes, cans, etc. Rubbish is frequently responsible for the creation of nuisances when it becomes scattered by the wind and careless handling.

8-5. Ashes. *Ashes* are the waste products of coal and other fuels which have been used for industrial purposes and in homes for cooking and heating. Ashes weigh 1,150 to 1,400 pounds per cubic yard. Ash production varies greatly with geographical location and, of course, the time of year.

Table 8-2 illustrates comparative quantities of refuse produced in the United States in the years 1921 and 1941. It is noteworthy that quantities of rubbish and garbage increased during the twenty-year period while ash production was reduced to almost one-half the original volume. This decrease, a direct result of the increased use of oil and natural gas for heating and other purposes, has undoubtedly become even more pronounced since 1941. Ashes are of no particular sanitary significance unless collection and disposal methods result in the creation of dust nuisances.

8-6. Dead Animals. The problem of the removal and disposal of large dead animals, *i.e.*, cows, horses, mules, hogs, etc., in many cities is handled by privately owned rendering plants. However, these concerns do not collect small animals in most cities, and their collection is usually left to the municipal collection system. Some municipalities have solved the small-animal disposal problem by providing collection and delivery of these animals to a local rendering plant where disposal is accomplished, often without charge to the city. Other satisfactory small-animal disposal methods include incineration and deep burial in *specified locations.*

8-7. Street Sweepings. These consist principally of materials worn from street surfaces, dirt and other materials dropped or worn away from vehicles, leaves, sweepings from sidewalks, and bits of wastepaper. Street sweepings are not usually putrescible enough to cause concern as a possible source of fly breeding or odors, and may frequently be used for fill, although some dust nuisance may be created. They usually weigh 1,150 to 1,400 pounds per cubic yard.

8-8. Industrial Wastes. The solid wastes resulting from many manufacturing processes are often a cause for concern to public health authorities. Some wastes, if not properly handled, will produce aesthetically obnoxious odors, and in the case of putrescible wastes health hazards will be created. Most municipalities require that industrial concerns maintain their own waste collection and disposal facilities, although many producers of industrial wastes arrange for the use of municipal disposal facilities.

REFUSE STORAGE

8-9. The maintenance of adequate sanitary facilities for temporarily storing refuse on the premises is usually considered a responsibility of the individual householder or businessman. Not only is the proper premises storage of refuse essential from a sanitation viewpoint, but the general efficiency of the entire collection and disposal system is partially dependent upon the degree of individual cooperation accorded the storage phase. While many cities have enacted ordinances regulating the refuse-sanitation program which contains specifications for home storage, the most desirable approach in improving home-storage conditions lies in public education. Although a suitable ordinance is necessary, legal enforcement should have a minor role, with dependence placed on the willingness of individuals to cooperate when they are made aware of the hazards and nuisances associated with insanitary practices.

8-10. Separation of Refuse. The separation required depends very largely upon the method of disposal to be utilized. Where no separation

TABLE 8-2. QUANTITIES OF REFUSE REPORTED, AVERAGE
(Pounds per Capita per Day)

Type of refuse	Collection and disposal of municipal refuse, 1921	Refuse collection practices, 1941
Garbage	0.46	0.64
Rubbish	0.23	0.90
Ashes	2.00	1.10

SOURCE: "Sanitary Refuse Practices," pt. I, U.S. Public Health Service, 1953.

is required and frequent collection service is provided, a single container may be utilized for storing the mixed refuse. All sanitary landfill operations and some systems using incinerators allow common collection and disposal of mixed refuse. Garbage may be segregated from ashes and rubbish to allow its utilization as hog feed. Some systems using incinerators require the separation of combustible from noncombustible materials, and in a few instances a three-can system is utilized, wherein separate receptacles are provided for garbage, rubbish, and ashes. Although separation has the advantage of facilitating the disposal method, it has the disadvantage of increasing the cost of collection, for special equipment and workers are necessary to collect each type of material and each pickup route must be traveled more than once.

8-11. Storage Containers. Receptacles for the temporary storage of refuse should be specifically designed for the waste to be stored. Since the loaded container must be hoisted into the collection vehicle, often by one man, the size should be given consideration and should be limited in the regulatory ordinance. Containers for mixed refuse should not exceed 30 to 32 gallons in capacity and should be equipped with side handles to facilitate handling. Those containers utilized for garbage storage, whether separate or in combination with other refuse, should be constructed of 26- to 30-gauge galvanized metal and be equipped with tight-fitting lids. Cans used expressly for garbage storage should not exceed 12 to 20 gallons in capacity and should preferably be equipped with a lock-type cover. To avoid odors and the accumulation of fly-supporting materials, garbage containers should be washed at frequent intervals.

Ashes should be placed in strongly constructed fireproof receptacles, and covers should be provided to prevent dust and the possible scattering of embers. Again, the container should not be so large that convenient handling by one person is impossible.

Where disposal methods allow the collection of mixed refuse, rubbish as well as garbage should be stored in a well-covered galvanized container of convenient handling size. Some cities allow the separate storage of tree limbs, lawn clippings, etc.; however, these materials should be stored in such a manner that scattering is limited and ease in handling is provided. Storage will be facilitated by cutting limbs in convenient lengths and bundling them, placing lawn clippings in disposable bags, etc.

8-12. Point of Collection. The location of the refuse containers for collection can have an important bearing on the speed—and, therefore, the cost—of the collection service. Many cities require that the individual householder transport the container to the curb or, in the case of alleys, to the rear property line. Curb collections require a rigidly scheduled collection service since nuisances are likely to be created if containers are left in the front yards of homes for long periods. Where traffic conditions permit, curb collections probably allow the most rapid pickup service. An additional service is provided in a number of cities where the pickup men enter the yard for backdoor collections. Usually refuse is dumped into a transfer can, which is then carried to the collection vehicle. This procedure is considerably more expensive than either alley or street collections.

Extensive studies at the University of California[2] reveal significant conclusions with respect to the location of storage containers for collection.

The approximate manpower requirements for the pickup operation (time required to load the refuse on the collection vehicle) varied rather consistently from an average of 100 man-minutes per ton for 100 per cent alley or curb collection to 165 man-minutes per ton for 100 per cent rear-of-house (backdoor) collection. Approximately 28 per cent of the pickup time is spent walking on private property for 100 per cent rear-of-house collection.

If program economy is essential, the individual must undoubtedly be called upon to assist collection personnel by placing containers in a convenient location.

8-13. Special Treatment. The requirement that garbage be drained and wrapped prior to being placed in containers is stressed in some cities. Draining and wrapping have a tendency to assist in drying the garbage, thus slowing down its fermentation. This procedure also partially prevents the exposure of garbage to flies and the build-up of organic accumulations within containers which can support fly breeding. Where garbage is utilized as hog feed or as raw materials in reduction plants, wrapping cannot be allowed.

A few municipalities require that garbage and rubbish containers be placed on racks or other suitable platforms above ground level. Such racks, usually constructed of wood or metal tubing, serve to lengthen the useful life of metal containers, since corrosion is reduced, to permit the cleaning of spilled wastes around the container, and to prevent the spillage of container contents by dogs. Racks are especially well-suited where alley or backdoor collections are made.

8-14. Public Education. The regulations governing the individual treatment of refuse must be brought to the attention of the householder to ensure compliance with them. Cards giving instructions as to the degree of separation required, location of containers for collection, and the collection schedule should be distributed to each resident, together with information concerning changes in established schedules. Very often, however, it will be found that regulations have been violated for various reasons. In this respect, tags on which various violations may be designated and attached to the container have proved helpful. Householders are usually willing to comply with the various recommendations or directions on the tag, but some follow-up activity is necessary to ensure compliance in a few instances.

REFUSE COLLECTION

8-15. In many cities, the refuse collection system furnishes the most intimate contact between the taxpayer and the municipal administration. Therefore, any deficiencies in the system are very likely to be subject to criticism. Furthermore, the collection phase is almost always the most expensive portion of the refuse-sanitation program because of equipment and labor requirements. To satisfy the demands of public approval, municipal economy, and public health, careful consideration must be given to organizing the collection system, selecting and training labor, purchasing equipment, and planning collection routes.

8-16. Organization for Collection. Several possibilities for establishing the collection system are available to cities. These include contractual operations, municipally administered programs, and a scavenger system in which private individuals are licensed to collect refuse in certain defined areas.

A number of cities have attempted to operate the refuse collection system by contract. Some advantages are inherent in this method in that the system can remain free of the influence of local politics and the private contractor is more likely to apply business methods to the operation. In most contracted operations a known and definite sum is fixed in advance of the work, with the contractor usually being paid from general fund revenues or from revenue received from refuse service charges. There are several disadvantages in contractual services, particularly in view of the fact that profit, and not service or the welfare of the public, is often the predominant concern. Sanitary control of the program is not easily obtained, and the response to unforeseen emergencies is often slower than in the case of municipally operated systems.

Those systems operated directly under an agency of the municipal administration are usually in a better position to care for the sanitary needs of the public than is a private concern. Modern trends in municipally administered programs include the designation of a responsible and qualified person as head of a sanitation division which operates within the authority of the public works department or some other comparable organizational unit. The over-all responsibility for the entire refuse program might appropriately be divided into two general areas: (1) the direction of personnel and operation and maintenance of equipment; and (2) the development and enforcement of desirable sanitation standards in the program. Frequently, responsibility in the latter area is delegated to public health agencies.

Scavenger operations are rarely suitable in large cities and must be rigidly controlled by health authorities wherever practiced. Scavengers are often interested in limiting their collections to garbage and, for this reason, must be forced to comply with the necessary sanitary regulations concerning the removal, handling, and disposal of putrescible wastes. In some instances scavengers will be interested in the collection of scrap metals, rags, paper, etc. Sanitary regulations for the handling of these materials should also be rigidly enforced.

8-17. Collection Personnel. The selection and training of the proper type of labor are important factors in the efficient operation of the collection system. With shorter working hours, clothes provided by employers, and generally improved labor-employer relations, the lot of collection personnel has improved during recent years. However, improved labor conditions have also resulted in increased operational costs. Frequent labor turnover is costly, and some cities have found that economies can be effected by rewarding attendance and meritorious work. Some cities have placed the collection personnel on an incentive basis, whereby the working day can be completed when a fairly allotted number of collections are made.

8-18. Time of Collection. A majority of the refuse collections in most cities are made during the regular working day. However, night collections in business areas are sometimes favored in larger cities to avoid the difficulty of maneuvering the large collection trucks in heavy traffic. Residential collections during night hours are ruled out in almost all cities because of noise nuisances and difficulty in locating storage containers in the dark.

8-19. Frequency of Collection. For best results, from both the aesthetic and the sanitation viewpoint, garbage should be collected at least two times weekly in residential sections in summer and winter. Most commercial establishments should be accorded daily collection service throughout the year. Rubbish is generally collected weekly in residential areas and daily in business sections. Mixed refuse should be collected twice weekly from residential areas and daily from most commercial concerns. An important consideration in providing frequent collection service is the prevention of fly breeding in garbage. Since the time required for the development of flies from eggs to mature larvae may be less than one week, weekly collections do not remove the larvae prior to their migration from the garbage in order to pupate in the surrounding soil. The provision of frequent collection services can also be an important asset in the premises storage of wastes. Householders cannot be expected to provide storage capacity greater than their minimum requirements, and irregular collections can contribute to the nuisances and hazards which result under poor storage conditions.

8-20. Collection Equipment. The equipment used by various cities for the collection of refuse differs considerably in size and character. To achieve sanitation requirements, equipment should include a suitable cover to prevent the exposure of contents, except during loading and unloading. The vehicle should be of watertight construction, preferably metal, to prevent leakage and facilitate thorough cleaning. Other considerations in equipment selection include truck capacity; type of waste collected; loading height; specific problems associated with alley, curb, or carry-out pickup service; and manpower requirements, which are all-important in their relation to the over-all cost of the collection operation.

Some municipalities utilize open-body trucks with capacities of 2 to 20 cubic yards or more for collection vehicles, although many cities are replacing open equipment with the more modern enclosed, packer-type collection vehicles. Tarpaulin covers and special construction which reduces loading height enable open trucks to perform certain collection jobs adequately, and such equipment is sometimes superior where bulky rubbish is collected separately.

Mixed refuse can be satisfactorily handled by the enclosed, packer-type vehicles. Several types have been produced, utilizing different mechanical devices for performing the loading, unloading, and packing operations. One type is equipped with a loading bucket at the rear

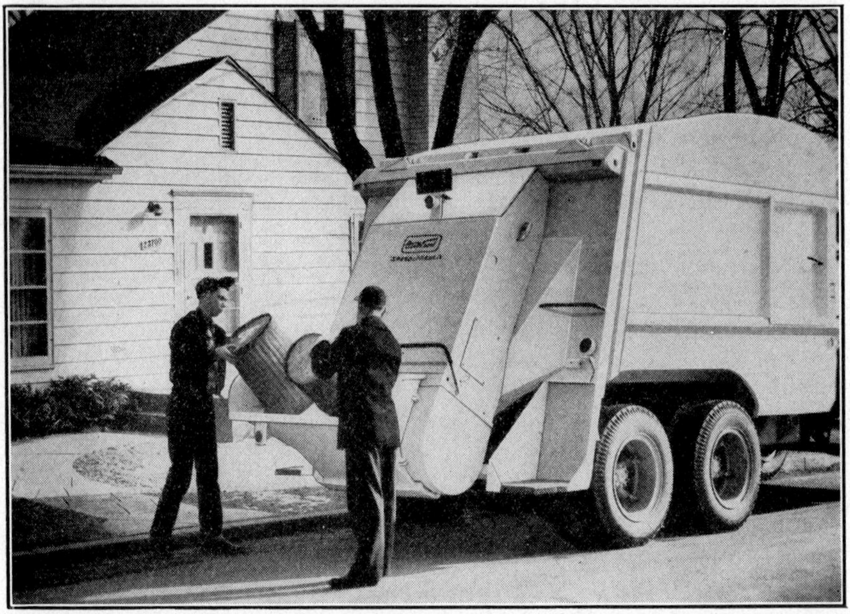

FIG. 8-1. A packer-type truck, in which the hopper loader is filled at the rear of the truck, with the refuse crushed into fragments and then fed into the truck body. (*Photograph courtesy of Gar Wood Industries, Inc., Wayne, Mich.*)

which, when filled, is raised and dumped mechanically into a door in the top of the body, which opens as the bucket moves into position to empty into the garbage compartment of the truck. In another type, the batch or hopper loader is also loaded at the rear of the body, and the refuse is pushed by means of a hydraulic mechanism directly into the body. The truck is unloaded by hydraulically elevating the front of the body. A vehicle of this type is illustrated in Fig. 8-1. A variation of the rear-loading type utilizes an escalator device to transport refuse from the loading port to the interior of the truck. Still another recent variation includes equipment for shredding refuse prior to escalator-type loading into the packing compartment. Figure 8-2 pictures a refuse collection vehicle which is loaded through sliding doors situated at the front of the body. A plate is utilized to push and compact the refuse against the rear of the bed and to unload the vehicle.

Dempster-Dumpster and others have produced equipment for refuse storage and collection that is applicable to large apartment houses, housing projects, some commercial areas, and other places where large amounts of refuse are produced. Refuse is placed in a closed steel container. A specially designed truck hoisting unit makes routine rounds to each container, hoists it on the truck, hauls it to the disposal area, dumps it, and returns it to the original location. An empty container

FIG. 8-2. A packer-type collection vehicle in which refuse is loaded through sliding doors at the front of the truck body and is compacted. (*Photograph courtesy of Pak-Mor Manufacturing Co.*)

may replace the full one. Only the truck and a driver are required in this collection scheme.

8-21. Factors Affecting Collection. The time required for collection may be divided into productive and nonproductive periods. Productive time is that in which collections are actually being made, and nonproductive time is that employed in traveling to and from the disposal point, the unloading period, and the time lost by pickup personnel in waiting during the compaction cycle of packer-type trucks.

The number of workmen used per truck, location of containers, collection frequency, and population density are other factors in the organization of the collection phase. In a densely populated district where cans are placed at the property line or curb by householders, one workman should handle about 500 cans per day. On the other hand, if rear-door collection of cans is practiced, one man could probably handle no more than 200 to 300 cans per day. While twice-weekly collections of refuse are recommended for residential areas, it has been observed that two collections per week result in a considerable increase in refuse produced when compared with once-weekly collection. Economies will llkely result if one man in the crew is designated as full-time vehicle operator in densely populated areas. Where stops are less frequent, the driver may assist with the collection procedure.

8-22. Laying Out a Collection System. Collection routes should be arranged so that the haul distance for loaded trucks is as short as practicable. Economies will also be realized if each truck is loaded to capacity prior to the trip to the disposal site.

Tentative routes may be mapped and adjusted permanently after the accumulation of the following information: (1) the number of premises served and average density per block or mile, (2) the length of time required to service various portions of the route, (3) whether the truck is fully loaded when the route is completed, and (4) location of route origination and termination points with respect to travel distance from headquarters and to the disposal site.

Such information will enable the adjustment of routes to facilitate economical use of equipment and labor and will permit the establishment of a time schedule which is necessary in those cities where householders are required to place containers at their front or rear property lines. Some administrators use the survey information as a basis for assigning specific, permanent routes for each crew. The designation of a specific area serves to fix responsibility among the various crews for service performed.

8-23. Records. Appropriate records form the basis upon which financial and operational controls may be developed. Fundamental data are the daily refuse collections, expressed in both tonnage and cubic yardage, personnel records, financial data, and operational reports.

While it is impractical to weigh all loads, it is very important to make routine check weighings to keep abreast of any changes in the quantity of refuse produced in any particular district or in the city as a whole. Personnel records should provide data indicating the performance of each employee, including attendance, conduct, and payroll information. Financial reports from the various supervisors, of course, enable the administrator to evaluate his financial status with respect to his budget. Reporting should permit a ready interpretation of the unit-cost status for each of the principal operations in the department.

The daily operational report made by the collecting unit should include the following: the vehicle number, its capacity, and miles traveled; number of loads collected, their volume and, if known, their weight; the number of collections made; the number of premises from which no collection was made and the reason therefor; complaints and their disposition; and payroll data for workmen. Additional operational reports in the departmental office should include expenses for repairs and maintenance and other equipment costs. The "Manual of Public Works Records and Administration," published by the Public Administration Service, Chicago, Ill., and the "Manual of Public Works Records and Accounting," prepared by the Committee on Street and Sanitation Records, Chicago, Ill., provide useful information on records.

8-24. Cost of Collection. Because of variations in labor costs, frequency and type of service provided, disposal methods, terrain, and other local factors, it is difficult to arrive at an average unit cost for the collection service. For purposes of comparison, some engineers recommend the ton-mile as a unit. This enables consideration of not only the quantity of wastes collected but also the number of miles the load must be hauled. Sometimes collection costs are expressed in terms of per capita costs. Such estimates may be reliable only in cities of comparable size and with similar collection practices. The range \$2.50 to \$3.50 per capita per year has been suggested as an approximate cost of the collection service. An accurate estimate of refuse-sanitation costs in any city can be made only after a study of the individual conditions in that city.

REFUSE DISPOSAL

8-25. The refuse-sanitation program cannot be satisfactorily completed until necessary measures have been taken to ensure the inoffensive disposal of these wastes. In primitive times, solid wastes were merely thrown upon the ground. Unfortunately, some municipalities have refined this procedure only by stipulating that the materials be deposited at a single location. The establishment of a point of disposal is an advantage in itself, as it prevents unauthorized and promiscuous dumping, which would probably produce objectionable conditions. Rapidly expanding modern urban areas, however, have surrounded areas which were originally intended as isolated disposal sites. This expansion necessitates a thorough evaluation of disposal methods suitable for semipopulated areas, since isolated sites are now beyond convenient access for most large cities. Methods have been developed wherein the final disposition of refuse can be accomplished without the creation of undue nuisance. It is the purpose of this section to review several disposal methods that are available to municipalities and to discuss in some detail the advantages and disadvantages associated with each method.

8-26. Dumping. Some components of refuse are suitable for open dumping. These include street sweepings, ashes, and some rubbish. However, serious nuisances and hazards will result if garbage or mixed refuse is disposed of in this manner. Low areas which may be brought up to grade by filling are generally chosen for the dump. Ashes and street sweepings, though dusty, enable the construction of a fairly stable fill. Carefully selected rubbish may also be utilized, although fires often occur and some settling of the filled areas will result. Dump locations must be carefully chosen, so that there will be a minimum chance of complaint from near-by residents.

While some municipal ordinances prohibit the placing of garbage and some rubbish, *i.e.*, paper, food cartons, cans, etc., on open dumps, most dumps invariably receive some of these materials because the difficulties of inspection make rigid enforcement impossible. This, together with lack of adequate supervision of open dumps, has resulted in unsatisfactory conditions in many cities.

8-27. Individual Incineration. In an effort to reduce the volume of refuse to be collected, some municipalities encourage or condone the incineration of rubbish by individuals. Such practices usually result in smoke and odor nuisances and fire hazards and when widespread in the community, have often been implicated in air-pollution problems. The temperature produced in most home incinerators is not sufficient for complete combustion of garbage; therefore, separate storage facilities are required for this material. In sparsely populated rural or suburban areas the disposal of garbage in home incinerators is sometimes practiced, although final disposal by burial is generally recommended to prevent the accumulation of media for fly propagation and sources of food supply for rodents.

Various types of commercial incinerators have been designed to meet the needs of business establishments that produce large volumes of refuse. Such incinerators usually incorporate the basic features of the large municipal incinerators, including provision for an auxiliary fuel supply and mechanisms for the production of draft through the furnace.

8-28. Hog Feeding. The feeding of garbage to hogs has been practiced for many years. U.S. Public Health Service surveys indicate that 30 per cent of the cities questioned disposed of all or a part of their garbage in this way. A survey by the Committee on Refuse Collection and Disposal of the American Society of Civil Engineers indicates that some 848 communities in 25 states practice this method of disposal. That it is profitable if properly handled is shown by the fact that most hotels and restaurants can easily dispose of their garbage to farmers who are willing to collect it themselves. While garbage is the most potentially valuable element of refuse, it is most difficult to handle in a sanitary manner and is responsible for the majority of the nuisances and health hazards associated with the refuse program. Hog feeding, like other methods of garbage utilization, still involves the necessity of providing for the proper disposal of other refuse.

Garbage-fed Hogs and Health. In recent years health authorities have recognized the danger of contracting trichinosis from the consumption of improperly cooked pork products. This disease is caused by trichina worms. The larval worms are encysted in the muscle tissue of the hog, and if the pork is not properly cooked, a dangerous infection may result. Garbage-fed hogs have been found to harbor up to five times as much trichina infestation as grain-fed hogs, and trichinosis in humans is reported most frequently where large numbers of garbage-fed hogs are raised.

Prior to 1952, health and agricultural agencies were generally unsuccessful in stimulating hog feeders to cook garbage preliminary to feeding. However, in 1952, a new swine disease, vesicular exanthema, occurred in this country, and its rapid spread through 41 states during that year brought about a drastic change in the attitude of garbage feeders. It was soon determined that vesicular exanthema among hogs was chiefly due to the feeding of uncooked garbage. By October, 1955, all but two states, New Jersey and Connecticut, had adopted legislation or regulations to control the feeding of raw garbage to animals. U.S. Public Health Service studies reveal that the subjection of raw garbage to a temperature of 212°F for thirty minutes is necessary to remove the threat of vesicular exanthema and trichinosis. These recommendations, together with the various state regulations, have caused several municipalities to discontinue the feeding of garbage to animals and to change to other methods of garbage disposal. However, equipment has been developed which does afford a convenient means for cooking garbage[3].

Organization. Disposal of garbage by feeding it to animals may be controlled in various ways. The garbage may be collected by the hog owners under city license or regulation. The city may collect the garbage and give or sell it to hog feeders. Or, the city may wish to establish a farm and control the entire program under municipal direction. In any event, rigid specifications should be adopted and enforced concerning frequency of collection, type of collection vehicle, cooking of garbage, and, where possible, regulation of the animal-feeding area. Some cities realize an appreciable revenue from garbage sold to farmers and at the same time find a saving in the final disposal of their solid wastes, since volume is somewhat reduced.

Sanitary Consideration. Hog farms are frequently the cause of complaints of odors, flies, rats, and other nuisances and sanitation hazards. With proper operation and supervision many of these conditions can be eliminated or minimized. Impervious, easily cleaned feeding platforms should be provided to prevent the trampling of garbage into the ground, a condition that is especially favorable for the production of flies and odors. A well-designed feeding platform may be constructed of reinforced concrete poured as dry as possible and cured to assure long service. Feeding areas should also be equipped with properly located drains to facilitate cleaning. Manure and uneaten garbage may be collected daily and placed in a compost pit. Each daily accumulation of the material is covered with dry earth. The compost produced in such pits is an excellent fertilizer.

8-29. Incineration. Well-designed and properly operated incineration plants efficiently handle the disposal of combustible refuse. Bacteria and insects are destroyed in the process, and the noncombustibles—ashes, metal, etc.—cause only minor sanitation problems if properly handled. On the credit side also is the fact that by proper design the incinerator may produce steam that can be sold to near-by industries or utilized in some other municipal enterprise requiring steam.

Cost. At the present time high construction and operating costs limit wide utilization of municipal incinerators, although a number of larger cities, where landfill sites are not conveniently available, are formulating long-range plans for the construction of increased incinerator capacity. Incinerators cost $1,800 to $4,500 per ton of rated daily capacity. Mechanized procedures[4] being incorporated in newer installations should bring about a reduction in operation costs. The cost of operation, including fixed charges, should range between $1.50 and $4 per ton of refuse burned. Operational costs will, of course, fluctuate according to the per cent of total daily capacity utilized, being lower per ton as total capacity is approached. Also, the sale of steam and salvageable materials partially offsets operational costs at some installations.

Principal Features of an Incinerator. Various types of incinerators have been used, and no two will be exactly alike, not even when designed by the same engineer. It is possible, however, to describe certain features that will be included in any well-designed incinerator. They are as follows:

1. CHARGING APPARATUS. The simplest charging procedure consists of manually pushing refuse through a circular opening located over the furnace. These openings are usually covered by a heavy metal door which can be raised or lowered by means of a chain hoist. Large furnaces may have two or more charging doors. Collection vehicles may dump at or near the charging door or, in some instances, directly into the furnace. Sometimes refuse is dumped near the doors and a small dozer- or bucket-equipped tractor performs the charging. Charging by this method, called the "direct method," is considered undesirable because of the necessity for rehandling the refuse.

Other installations are equipped with charging compartments or hoppers which have two doors, one for receiving the dumped wastes and another for discharging them by gravity to the furnaces. This permits charging with less heat loss than occurs when charging is done directly. A variation of this method utilizes a mechanical conveyor to move materials from the unloading compartment to furnace openings.

The modern method, particularly for large incinerators, is to dump into a large storage pit and convey the materials to furnaces by means of a power-driven crane. In this, as in other phases of refuse handling,

FIG. 8-3. Exterior view of rear of Kelly Street Incinerator, Houston, Tex. (*Photograph courtesy of City of Houston, Tex.*)

the knowledge and skill of manufacturers of materials handling equipment should be utilized to the fullest extent.

2. THE FURNACE, OR PRIMARY, CHAMBER. This chamber should be designed to facilitate the rapid desiccation of moist wastes and the complete combustion of solid refuse and volatile gases arising from the burning material. Some furnaces are equipped with a ledge, or hearth, upon which wet materials are deposited so that hot gases will surround and dry them. Following drying, the unconsumed solids are lowered to

the grates for further burning. Not all designers favor the use of a drying hearth. The alternative is to charge all refuse directly into the burning fire. The primary chamber should not only provide ample grate area but must also supply the volume necessary for the bulky materials contained in mixed refuse. University of California investigations[5] indicate that, in presently operating incinerators, primary chambers have been designed to consume 3 to 12 pounds of refuse per hour per cubic foot of volume. Grate design should allow for 40 to 150 pounds of refuse to be consumed per square foot of grate area in a one-hour period.

The total required furnace capacity is often divided into units or cells of a size convenient for a stoker to care for, although some modern plants are utilizing mechanical stokers to reduce labor costs. Cell or unit construction of the primary chamber enables separate discharges to a common secondary chamber and a separate charging door. This has the advantage of allowing a uniform temperature in the secondary chamber, since only one cell is charged at one time with a consequent cooling that will be overcome by the undisturbed cells.

3. THE COMBUSTION, OR SECONDARY, CHAMBER. The combustion chamber is between the furnace and the stack, and its purpose is to permit mixing of burning and unburned gases and to allow time for combustion to take place. Some plants also provide for the disposal of dead animals in the secondary chamber. Another important function of this chamber is to complete the burning of fly ash which would otherwise be emitted from the chimney to present a fire hazard. A temperature of not less than 1250°F is necessary for complete consumption of combustible gases. Properly designed combustion chambers call for the provision of 10 to 15 cubic feet of volume per ton of rated daily capacity. In addition, the design should include facilities for convenient removal of settled particles and might also provide for recirculation of hot secondary chamber gases to be mixed with fresh air and introduced as forced draft into the primary chamber.

Large incinerators sometimes have an expansion chamber between the combustion chamber and the stack. Its purpose is to reduce turbulence and allow settlement of dust and ash.

4. THE CHIMNEY, OR STACK. The incinerator stack serves as an exhaust medium to discharge the gases into the atmosphere and also as a means for providing air movement or "stack draft" through the incinerator system. The wide use of forced-draft systems has had the effect of lowering chimney heights; however, the chimney height should be designed to enable adequate dilution of gases with air and to minimize fly-ash problems. Most designers feel that stacks should provide for gas velocities of 25 to 50 feet per second. Well-designed chimneys might

also include convenient access for ash removal and interior repairs, an exterior ladder for safe access to the top, protection against lightning, and aircraft warning lights.

5. REFRACTORIES. Because of the intense heat, the primary and secondary chambers and the chimney must be protected with suitable refractory materials. Firebrick and plastic materials have been developed for this purpose. The furnace and combustion chambers are usually lined with 9 inches of refractory material enclosed in 4 inches of a suitable insulation substance. Stacks, while basically constructed of brick or reinforced concrete, should also include an interior lining of refractory material. Much care must be exercised in estimating refractory needs and installing the chosen materials.

6. MISCELLANEOUS FEATURES. Provision must be made for temporary storage and removal of ashes. Most plants utilize a system of *ash pits* which receive the noncombustible wastes and are equipped with a water-spray system or other quenching device. Many ash pits are hopper-shaped and located so that removal trucks may be loaded by gravity. *Forced-draft apparatus* consists of a fan, or blower, and the necessary ducts to force air below the grates and up through the bed of burning material, but no farther. The chimney should then supply the remainder of the necessary draft. Not all incinerators employ forced draft, but the practice of including it is increasing. *Preheating of the air supply* is also an operational practice that is considered economical in plants of more than 75 tons capacity. The air discharged below the grates is preheated by passing it through ducts where it may absorb heat from the chimney gases. *Steam-generating apparatus* has been installed at some plants. It usually consists of a water-tube boiler placed between the combustion chamber and the chimney. Steam generation requires a higher temperature in the combustion chamber than is otherwise necessary, 1800 to 1900°F as compared with 1250°F. *Control apparatus* should include thermometers for checking temperatures of the burning chambers, the preheated air, and the stack gases. Scales for weighing the refuse are a necessity, and provision for weighing ashes is desirable. Special fly-ash removal apparatus to complement expansion-chamber action is sometimes desirable. Filters, baffle devices, centrifugal or cyclonic separators, water-spray chambers, and electrostatic devices have been developed for this purpose.

General Considerations in the Design of Incinerators. Certain factors necessary to proper incinerator operation must be understood if incinerator design is to be successful. Most important are the characteristics of the refuse to be burned. It is important also to recognize that refuse is a low-grade fuel and that proper design depends upon its analysis. Two types of analysis are used. The proximate analysis shows the percentages by weight of ash, moisture, and combustible material, the latter being subdivided into fixed carbon and volatile matter. The ultimate analysis is more useful, and it shows the percentages by weight of carbon, nitrogen, oxygen, sulfur, ash, and moisture. From this analysis the calorific value of the refuse, the required air supply, the composition of the products of combustion, and the critical temperature to be maintained in the furnace can be computed. The temperature should be 1250°F, slightly above the ignition points of carbon monoxide and the hydrocarbons to assure complete combustion and to prevent odors. As previously mentioned, temperatures of 1800 to 1900°F will be necessary if steam is generated, but temperatures exceeding this figure will exert considerable structural stress.

Knowledge of the amounts of carbon and hydrogen in the refuse, which are the elements that combine with oxygen in combustion, permits calculation of the amount of air that must be supplied. The number of heat units in the combustible portion of the refuse can be calculated, and also the number required to evaporate the moisture and to raise the air supplied to the critical temperature (1250°F or more). If the refuse will not supply sufficient heat, either the air supply must be preheated or an auxiliary fuel must be supplied.

Refuse storage and collection practices, together with present and future capacity demands, should be thoroughly studied in formulating a suitable design. Practical experience indicates that mixtures of 80 per cent garbage and 20 per cent rubbish, by weight, will burn without auxiliary fuel if the air supply is preheated to 300°F. Mixtures of 60 per cent garbage and 40 per cent rubbish and down to 50 per cent of each will burn satisfactorily without preheated air. If the garbage is less than 50 per cent, a "flashy" fire results and operation is usually unsatisfactory. Wetting of rubbish to overcome this difficulty has not proved satisfactory. The design can incorporate provision of over-fire cooling air to facilitate keeping down excessive temperatures. Provision for auxiliary fuels is usually incorporated in modern plant construction, coal, gas, and oil being the most common fuels. Auxiliary fuel is necessary when garbage is incinerated alone or the rubbish content of the refuse is low. Also, auxiliary fuel is necessary in small plants not operating twenty-four hours per day to preheat furnaces and to afford a constant heat supply if waste heat is utilized for other purposes.

Incinerator Operation. The quality of operation and maintenance received by an incinerator will determine its success or failure. Care in charging will prevent reduction of furnace temperature and thereby avoid excessive smoke, odors, and escape of unburned material. It is important that moisture and volatiles be driven off and burned in the combustion chamber while solid materials are being consumed in the primary chamber. To ensure this, and to avoid a flashy fire, firing should not be infrequent and at long intervals, but rather as continuous as furnace construction permits.

Removal of clinkers, which are large fused masses of incombustible material, must be done by raking the bed frequently enough to ensure proper operation of the furnace. Ash removal and disposal also require considerable effort, and routine procedures should be inaugurated for handling the material. Some attention to the appearance of the plant and grounds is also desirable.

Purchase of Incinerators. In contracting for the construction of an incinerator, definite specifications should be formulated, and certain requirements should be established in detail. The kind and condition of the refuse to be destroyed should be specified as definitely as possible, or facilities for prospective bidders to review local operations should be provided. Various operating conditions should also be specified. These include furnace temperature desired, amount of refuse to be destroyed within a certain time, amount of fuel, if any, that is required, and quality and quantity of ashes and clinkers. It should also be recognized that forced draft, preheaters, top-quality refractory materials, and automatic temperature and air-valve controls are all requirements for good incinerator operation and not merely "frills." Contracts should not be awarded on the basis of price if any of the above has been omitted.

Contracts should also guarantee a satisfactory test run of several days duration under the supervision of the contractor. Some municipalities require the builder to supervise the operation of the incinerator for a month or longer with the city paying all expenses and furnishing materials but assuming no responsibility and accepting the plant only after a twenty-four- or forty-eight-hour test run at the end of that time.

8-30. Sanitary Landfill. Sanitary landfill differs from ordinary dumping in that the material is placed in a trench or other prepared area and adequately compacted and covered with earth at the end of the working day. The procedure has been defined as a method of disposal wherein each day's accumulation of refuse is thoroughly compacted and covered. The term "modified sanitary landfill" has been applied to those operations where compaction and covering are accomplished once or twice each week.

General Considerations. As in other methods of disposal, satisfactory sanitary landfill operation demands careful preliminary evaluation of local conditions. As opposed to other methods, sanitary landfills are designed to care for the complete disposal of all refuse produced, with the possible exception of bulky building wastes and the like. For this reason, sanitary landfill capacities usually are designed for the total refuse produced. Where compacted refuse is placed in the fill to a depth of 6 feet, it is estimated that 1 acre of land per year will be required per 10,000 population.

Prospective landfill sites should be evaluated with respect to type of soil available, drainage, prevailing winds, availability of access roads, the underground water situation, and the haul distance involved. Sandy loam is considered the most ideally suited landfill soil, although other soils can be utilized. Poor surface drainage may hinder the operation, and care should be exercised to prevent interception of an underground water stratum in constructing the fill. Other considerations governing the planning of sanitary landfill sites are contained in a publication of the Texas State Department of Health[6]. They are as follows:

1. Scavenging materially interferes with the over-all efficiency of the operation, and should be discouraged. If it is permitted, strict regulations should be formulated and rigidly enforced.

2. Provisions should be made for temporarily fencing the leeward side of the landfill so that the nuisance of blowing papers will be held to a minimum. This is economically accomplished with light chicken wire.

3. Regulations governing the operation and maintenance of the landfill should be predetermined and publicized. Printed instructions should be distributed to all concerned. This is particularly significant if private hauling is permitted.

4. Signs should be erected at the disposal ground which clearly indicate the correct procedure for depositing refuse. The entrance sign should have something similar to "Sanitary Landfill Refuse Disposal Area" clearly labeled.

5. The landfill disposal area should be fenced and have an entrance gate. The gate should be locked during non-operating hours to discourage indiscriminate dumping of refuse.

6. A responsible attendant should be at the disposal site during the operating hours.

Operational Techniques. Methods of landfill operation are largely determined by the information obtained during the preliminary evaluation of prospective sites. Also, the population to be served and the type of equipment available will influence the choice of methods. Adverse climatic conditions sometimes require special operational techniques[7]. Three broad classifications of operational methods have been developed: the trench method, the area-ramp method, and the area-fill method. The three methods are similar in many respects, and the principles of each can often be combined to serve specific local conditions. Figure 8-4 is a cross section of the working face or slope of a typical landfill. No matter what operational method is chosen, the working face should be maintained at about a 30-degree slope and kept as narrow as practicable. Dumped refuse is spread over the slope, compacted, and covered as a part of the daily operational routine. Six inches of earth are placed over the compacted refuse on the slope, and at least 2 feet of earth should be placed on that portion of the fill that is completed each day.

Where level terrain is available, the trench method is usually chosen. The trench may be completely excavated prior to beginning the operation, or it may be excavated progressively as the work proceeds. Trenches are usually 6 to 10 feet in depth and, depending on local conditions, 12 to 36 feet in width. Figures 8-5 and 8-6 illustrate two methods of trench landfill operation.

The area-ramp method is well suited for moderately sloping terrain. Actually, this method can be utilized to bring a sloping area to grade by an operation similar to that depicted in Fig. 8-7. Some excavation is done to secure cover materials and side ramps. Refuse is placed in the excavation to the desired height above the original ground level.

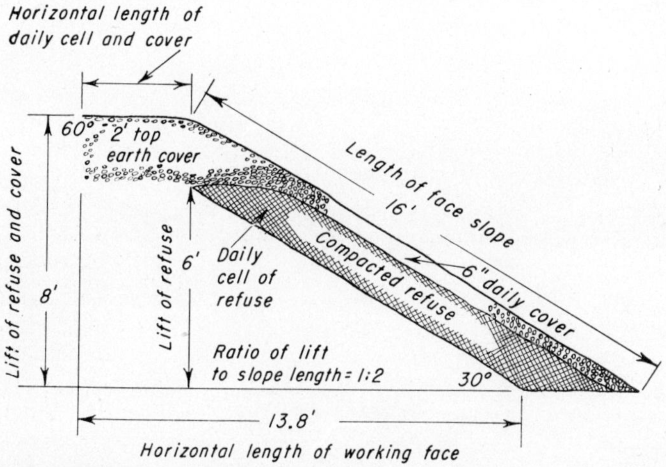

FIG. 8-4. The working face of a sanitary landfill. (*From "Refuse Collection and Sanitary Landfill Operational Methods," Texas State Department of Health, Division of Sanitary Engineering, Austin, Tex.*, 1954.)

Figure 8-8 depicts a typical area-fill operation where two separate fills are utilized to bring a deep depression to grade. This method often has the disadvantage of requiring supplemental earth from outside sources.

Suitable equipment has been developed to perform the complete landfill operation—excavation, spreading and compacting refuse, and moving earth to serve as cover material. Track-type equipment fitted with an appropriate bucket, clamshell, or blade can easily accomplish the landfill operation in smaller cities. Larger cities sometimes prefer the use of power shovels or draglines for the excavation of trenches, with tractors being freed for the other operational phases.

A portable wire fence is used at some fills to reduce the nuisance of blowing paper from the face of the fill. The addition of moisture to dry refuse is said to reduce blowing paper and to aid in compaction of bulky boxes and the like.

Characteristics of the Fill. Little is known of the chemical, bacteriological, and physical changes that occur in buried refuse. In about four days after placement and at about 3 feet below the surface, temperatures rise rapidly to 130 to 150°F. They remain at this point for about sixty days, then fall gradually for about ten months to near air temperatures. It appears from observation of deposited materials that decomposition proceeds very slowly. The composition of landfill materials,

FIG. 8-5. The progressive-slope method of trench landfill operation. (*Photograph courtesy of "Refuse Collection and Sanitary Landfill Operational Methods," Texas State Department of Health, Division of Sanitary Engineering, Austin, Tex.*, 1954.)

which include only about 15 per cent garbage, is probably responsible for this slow decomposition. An important factor in the development of temperatures is the type of material incorporated in the fill. In some cases cells containing "mixed" refuse do not attain temperatures much higher than 100°F.

Some settlement of the fill should be expected, and if the desired elevation of the finished fill is known, allowance for settling can be made during construction. Most of the final settlement will probably occur within the first twelve months and by the end of two years most fills have completed settlement. The actual amount will vary with the character of the wastes, compaction given, and the depth of the fill. Uneven settlement may be caused by improper placement of bulky rubbish and no provision for a well-mixed refuse. An ultimate settlement of between 10 to 30 per cent is to be expected at most fills.

Use of Filled Land. The potential use of filled land should receive careful consideration during the planning stage of landfill construction. Sanitary landfills have been used to improve eroded areas, marshes, and other marginal lands. Following the settling period, such filled areas

FIG. 8-6. Trench method by disposal in a prepared trench with earth cover obtained by excavating an adjacent trench. (*Photograph courtesy of "Refuse Collection and Sanitary Landfill Operational Methods," Texas State Department of Health, Division of Sanitary Engineering, Austin, Tex.,* 1954.)

have been used for parks, golf courses and other recreational areas, parking lots, and small construction. It is usually recommended that construction be limited to single-story buildings, although heavier buildings may be constructed if foundations are carried through the fill to undisturbed earth or if reinforced concrete mat foundations are utilized. Water pipes and sewers passing through the fill will probably require special precautions against corrosion, contamination, and settlement. Methane gas is produced in the decomposition process. Consequently any construction which might allow seepage into areas that are restricted in air movement, such as a basement, should receive very careful attention with respect to mechanical ventilation facilities.

Advantages and Disadvantages of Sanitary Fill. As compared with the ordinary dump, sanitary fill has the advantage of minimizing odor and fire nuisances and such health hazards as insect and rodent breeding. Over such other disposal methods as incineration, reduction, and hog

Fig. 8-7. The trench-ramp method with side-earth ramps. (*Photograph courtesy of "Refuse Collection and Sanitary Landfill Operational Methods," Texas State Department of Health, Division of Sanitary Engineering, Austin, Tex.*, 1954.)

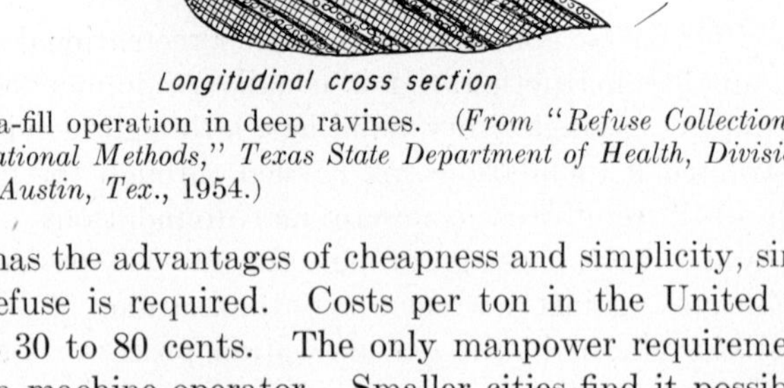

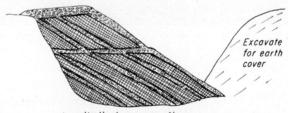

Fig. 8-8. Area-fill operation in deep ravines. (*From "Refuse Collection and Sanitary Landfill Operational Methods," Texas State Department of Health, Division of Sanitary Engineering, Austin, Tex.*, 1954.)

feeding, it has the advantages of cheapness and simplicity, since no separation of refuse is required. Costs per ton in the United States vary from about 30 to 80 cents. The only manpower requirement at many landfills is a machine operator. Smaller cities find it possible to utilize landfill equipment for other municipal activities, although allowance must be made for the daily use of the equipment at the landfill. Landfill operations are usually elastic enough to care for unusual quantities of refuse caused by expanding populations. Properly operated fills can be located in such a way that collection trucks have convenient access. Finally, marginal land can often be reclaimed for profitable resale.

The principal disadvantage is that unless careful and continuous supervision is given, the fill may deteriorate into an ordinary dump. A sanitary fill of any size should preferably be under the supervision of a sanitary engineer. Since land requirements for sanitary landfill operations approximate 1 acre per year per 10,000 population, larger cities sometimes experience difficulty in obtaining suitable sites at reasonable prices.

8-31. Composting. During recent years, considerable interest has been developed in the composting of municipal refuse as a method of waste disposal. Europeans recognize the process as one of waste recovery since composted refuse is considered an excellent organic additive for agricultural soils, and composting operations are common in European countries. Because of the availability of cheap, inorganic fertilizers in this country, a widespread demand for compost has not yet materialized. Composting should, however, be considered by the engineer in evaluating the various methods of refuse disposal.

The Compost Process. While the biochemical processes which occur during composting are fairly well understood, very little is known of the economic aspects of a commercial refuse operation. Anaerobic processes have been tried in this country without success, but trial of aerobic methods indicates that decomposition in the presence of oxygen is much more rapid and affords freedom from odors and other nuisances associated with the older anaerobic method. Operations fundamental to the composting of municipal refuse may be listed as follows:

1. REMOVAL OF NONCOMPOSTABLES. Several components of mixed municipal refuse are of no value in the compost process. Some of these, cans and other metals and glass, can sometimes be recovered for sale. While magnetic devices will remove a majority of the metal materials, some provision must be also made for hand-picking the wastes. California studies[8] indicate that, after initial segregation, the refuse from a number of California cities is 66 per cent compostable. These studies also indicate that it may be desirable to remove some of the paper found in modern refuse because of the desirability of maintaining a carbon-nitrogen ratio of 30:1 to 35:1 in the composting materials. Carbon-nitrogen ratios greater than 50:1 retard the process and necessitate the removal of some paper.

2. GRINDING OR SHREDDING. Most authorities agree that bacterial decomposition is speeded up if raw refuse is shredded prior to placement in stacks, piles, or bins for decomposition. One of the major problems

facing manufacturers of compost equipment is the development of a grinder suitable for handling the abrasive refuse produced in this country.

3. PLACEMENT FOR DECOMPOSITION. Various enclosed mechanisms or digesters have been developed in which raw materials may be placed for the compost process. Most of the manufactured types are equipped with agitation devices, vents to allow aerobic action, temperature gauges, and devices for the regulation of moisture content. The California study reports that a moisture content of 40 to 65 per cent is most desirable for rapid decomposition. Where rainfall is moderate and ground temperatures are generally high, open-air composting has been practiced. One of the major problems in this regard is the development of satisfactory techniques for aerating the piled or windrowed materials.

While some authorities feel that the addition of special strains of organisms is necessary to start and speed up the compost procedure, California investigations indicate that the raw refuse contains ample organisms to accomplish decomposition without the addition of the various inoculants. Some operators have utilized a mixture of refuse and digested-sewage sludge to obtain a higher nitrogen content in the finished product. The amount of sludge added must depend on the initial moisture content of the raw refuse.

4. REGRINDING AND MARKETING. Finished compost should have a dark-brown color, an earthy odor, and a carbon-nitrogen ratio of 20:1 or less. The time required for the various aerobic compost operations in the United States varies from two days to six weeks for the complete process[9].

When decomposition is complete, regrinding, drying, and bagging can be accomplished to improve the marketability of the compost. At present, compost is sold principally to small users for relatively high prices. The future of refuse composting in this country lies, in part, upon the development of a market among large-scale users of fertilizers.

8-32. Reduction. The recognition of the value of certain organic elements of garbage has resulted in the use of various methods for extracting them. *Reduction* is the term applied to the procedure wherein garbage is processed to produce grease and a solid residue called tankage, which is utilized in some fertilizers. Reduction processes can be applied economically only in large cities where sufficient garbage is collected and where a favorable market for finished products is available. Populations of 100,000 to 200,000 are said to be the minimum for an adequate supply of garbage.

A gradual decline in the utilization of this method of disposal is apparent from the fact that in 1918 there were 24 plants in the United States; in 1942, this number was reduced to 8 plants, and in 1953, only 3 cities utilized the method[10]. Several disadvantages of the process have contributed to its decline in favor, including the production of odors at most installations, the high cost of separate refuse collection, fire hazards involved in the extraction of grease with solvents, cost of plants and equipment, and the unreliable market for finished products.

Two general methods of reduction have been used. The simpler is the drying method, whereby garbage is crushed, ground, and dried with heat. The dry solids are then treated with a solvent (naphtha or gasoline) to extract the grease. The solvent is distilled off for re-use, and the grease is thus separated. In the cooking method, raw materials are placed in vats and heated. The cooked mass is pressed to recover grease, and

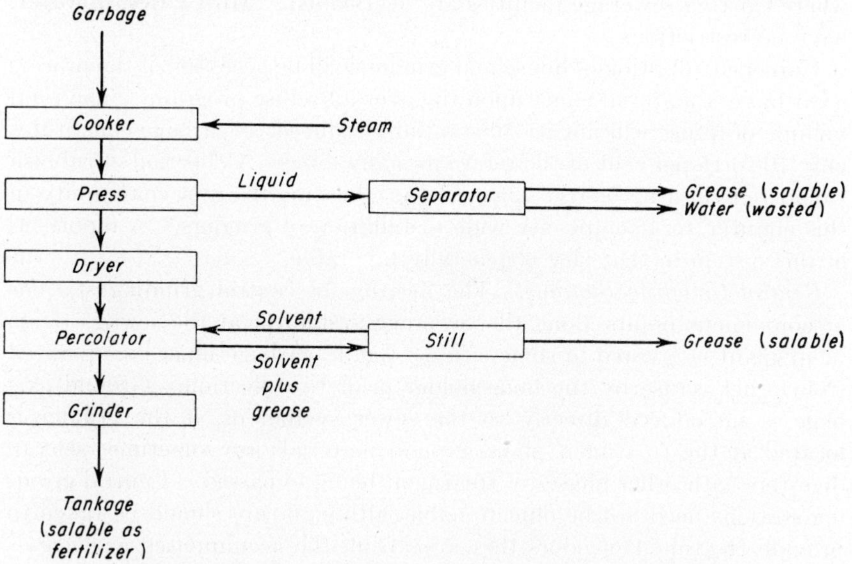

FIG. 8-9. Flow diagram of typical garbage-reduction process.

solid residues are dried and ground for sale as fertilizer. The cooking method results in fewer odors, and the physical condition of the products is better. However, the first cost of the plant and its operation is higher than the drying process.

Greases obtained from the reduction process are brown, low-grade fat and are suitable for the manufacture of glycerines, candles, and soaps. Dry solids are usually sold as a base or filler for fertilizers or as a supplement for stock and poultry feed. Figure 8-9 is a flow diagram of the typical reduction plant.

8-33. Grinding. As opposed to reduction, garbage grinding with discharge to sewers is increasing in this country. The use of home grinders had increased from 50,000 before 1940 to 1,500,000 in 1954. Commercial grinders show a similar increase. Three methods for the disposal of garbage with sewage have been advanced in the United States: the use of individual grinders in homes and commercial establishments; the installation of municipally operated, centrally located grinding stations; and the installation of grinders at sewage treatment plants and discharge of the ground materials directly into incoming raw sewage or to the digestion tanks.

Household Grinders. Household grinders contribute no difficulties in sewer collection systems. At the sewage treatment plant, the load of solids is increased by 0.15 to 0.30 pound per person on the dry basis. A few cities have forbidden grinders, and this restriction is justified where existing sewerage facilities are overloaded. Most cities, however, have no restrictions.

Universal adoption of household grinders will be necessary if the process is to have a material effect upon the over-all refuse program. The total volume of refuse will not be substantially reduced, as garbage constitutes only 10 to 15 per cent of the refuse in many cities. Collection of rubbish would remain a necessity. Jasper, Ind., became the first community in this country to attempt city-wide installation of grinders. A report[11] of the system in that city is generally favorable.

Central Grinding Stations. The location of central grinding stations at convenient points along the sewerage system or at the sewage treatment plant is favored in some cities. Again, garbage must be separated from other refuse by the householder prior to collection. Ground garbage is introduced directly to the sewer system or, if the grinder is located at the treatment plant, ground materials are sometimes sent to digesters with other phases of treatment being bypassed. Central grinding stations need not be objectionable, although care should be taken to provide treatment of odors that arise from the accumulated garbage.

With respect to the effect of ground garbage on the sewer system and sewage treatment facilities, Tolman[12] gives the following information:

1. Facilities should be provided for removal of garbage grit before this material is sent to the digesters.

2. When all of a city's garbage is added to the raw sewage, the increase in suspended solids will be approximately 25 to 35 per cent, and in B.O.D., 18 to 26 per cent, depending upon the solids in the raw garbage.

3. The increase in strength of primary settled sewage after 2.0 hours settling will be approximately 10 to 14 per cent in suspended solids and 11 to 16 per cent in B.O.D.

4. Garbage matter is oxidized by activated sludge and probably by all secondary processes as efficiently as is sewage material; therefore, increased plant secondary units must be based upon the increased garbage load in the primary effluent.

5. For digestion of primary solids and garbage, 5 cu. ft. per capita of digester

capacity is needed, while the capacity for primary and secondary sewage solids, plus garbage, should be 9 cu. ft.

6. The most economical means of dual disposal appears to be by direct addition of garbage to the digesters, unless central grinding stations are used.

7. The cost of disposal of garbage at the sewage plant will be between $0.10 and $0.50 per ton. [This excludes interest and depreciation on the first cost of the added plant, and includes a credit for excess garbage gas.]

8-34. Salvaging. Such disposal methods as hog feeding, composting, and reduction produce valuable products from materials that would otherwise be wasted. Although objectionable and often economically unsound, salvage operations are sometimes practiced in connection with other disposal methods. Salvaged materials must also be properly stored, pending their utilization, or nuisances will result. If householders are required to segregate and store refuse separately for salvage purposes, the revenue from salvaged goods must be weighed against the additional costs entailed by multiple-collection systems.

Paper, glass, metals, rags, garbage, and miscellaneous commercial wastes are the principal elements of refuse having marketable value from time to time, although this market is subject to wide fluctuation. If clean paper can be reclaimed, it can be re-used in the manufacture of some paperboard or cardboard. Glass has some value, especially if it can be hand-sorted according to size and color. Broken glass is quite limited in value. Cans and other metals have some salvageable value, but considerable equipment and skill are needed in handling metal wastes. Commercial areas are often the source of such salvageable refuse as cloth and leather trimmings, some wood materials, and, of course, cardboard cartons and garbage. Careful evaluation of potential local markets for salvageable goods should precede municipal salvage activities.

THE REFUSE PROBLEM IN SMALL TOWNS AND ON THE FARM [13]

8-35. In many of the smaller cities and towns there are no organized efforts to collect and dispose of refuse. Business establishments and some householders may make private arrangements for collection, usually at irregular intervals. This may result in unsightly and offensive accumulations between collections and is uniformly unsatisfactory so far as disposal is concerned. The piles of cans and other refuse, even dead animals, so frequently found in highway ditches at the outskirts of the town and in vacant lots testify to the irresponsibility of the casual collector. It has also been seen that the payments made to private collectors who serve only a fraction of the city total nearly enough to give regular service to all the city. Annual clean-ups are substituted for regular collection in some small cities. This practice results in some temporary betterment and considerable civic complacency, which is not justified. Cleaning should be a continual process, not just an annual affair.

In general it is recommended that the small city collect refuse itself rather than by contract. In any event, municipal authority should adopt a suitable ordinance regulating the entire program and specifying the storage, collection, and disposal procedures to be observed. Technical assistance in financing, organization, and operational methods should be sought.

Many small cities have found that a complete refuse collection and disposal system can be operated for approximately $1 per month per resident and $3 per month per commercial establishment. Some municipalities prefer a fee system by which bills are mailed monthly or quarterly for the refuse service. Other cities prefer tax-supported systems, with revenue being taken from general funds.

Residents of sparsely populated rural and suburban areas usually find the solution to refuse problems through a combination of incineration and burial. The farmer or suburbanite usually must find a safe, convenient method of disposal within the confines of his own property. Since open burning will not achieve complete combustion of all refuse, the removal and burial of ashes and noncombustibles are necessary for adequate disposal. For the small organized communities, sanitary landfill probably is the best disposal method.

BIBLIOGRAPHY

1. "Sanitary Refuse Practices," pt. I, U.S. Public Health Service, 1953.
2. An Analysis of Refuse Collection and Sanitary Landfill Disposal, *Univ. Calif. Sanitary Eng. Research Center Tech. Bull.* 8, 1952.
3. "Equipment for the Heat Treatment of Garbage to Be Used for Hog Feed," U.S. Agricultural Research Service and the U.S. Public Health Service.
4. Eliassen, R.: Incinerator Mechanization Wins Increasing Favor, *Civil Eng.*, vol. 19, no. 4, 1949.
5. Municipal Incineration, *Univ. Calif. Sanitary Eng. Research Center Tech. Bulls.* 5, 6.
6. "Refuse Collection and Sanitary Landfill Operational Methods," Texas State Department of Health, Division of Sanitary Engineering, Austin, Tex., 1954.
7. "The Sanitary Landfill in Northern States," U.S. Public Health Service, 1952.
8. Reclamation of Municipal Refuse by Composting, *Univ. Calif. Sanitary Eng. Research Center Tech. Bull.* 9, 1953.
9. Ludwig, Gordon W.: "Recent Advances in Composting of Organic Wastes," Public Health Service, Communicable Disease Center, Technology Branch, Vector Control Section, Atlanta, Ga., September, 1953.
10. "Garbage Reduction," American Society of Civil Engineers, Subcommittee on Refuse Collection and Disposal, September, 1954.

11. Community-wide Installation of Household Garbage-grinders, *U.S. Public Health Service Pub.* no. 224, 1952.
12. Tolman, S. L.: Ground Garbage: Its Effect upon the Sewer System and Sewage Treatment Plant, *Sewage Works J.*, vol. 19, no. 5, p. 441, 1947.
13. "Refuse Collection and Disposal for the Small Community," Joint Study of the U.S. Public Health Service and the American Public Works Association, Chicago, November, 1953.
14. "Manual of Public Works Records and Administration," Public Administration Service, Chicago.
15. "Manual of Public Works Records and Accounting," Committee on Street and Sanitation Records, Chicago.

CHAPTER 9

INSECT VECTOR AND RODENT CONTROL

9-1. By definition[1], *vectors*, in communicable-disease terminology, are "arthropods or other invertebrates which transmit infection by inoculation into or through the skin or mucous membrane by biting, or by deposit of infective materials on the skin or on food or other objects." The vector may be infected itself or may act only as a passive or mechanical carrier of the agent. The *vector* is distinguished from the *vehicle* in disease transmission by the fact that the intermediary is animate and is generally an insect. Insect vectors have been, at times in man's history, the scourge of humanity, being responsible for the great pestilences in the Old World and the New—the "Black Death," "yellow jack," and "chills and fever." Fortunately for our modern era, techniques have been developed which have eliminated or minimized the disease potential of the insect vector. In some cases wholesale attack has been unleashed on the insect itself—mosquitoes, in the case of yellow fever and malaria, and fleas, in the case of endemic typhus. In the latter situation, the animal host, the rat, has also been subjected to control efforts.

With the passing of the importance of insect and rodent vectors in disease transmission, in the United States at least, the techniques developed in destroying more insects and rats have made us aware of one phase of a new concept of public health—comfort, physical efficiency, and a sense of well-being. Mosquitoes of the harmless varieties are being destroyed because they interfere with human comfort. While flies remain significant to some extent in disease transmission, fly-control measures are employed largely because flies annoy people. The same may be said of rats. Thus, while their place in disease transmission in the United States is a minor one, insect and rodent vectors may be said to remain of importance in the public health picture.

MOSQUITOES AND THEIR CHARACTERISTICS

9-2. Mosquitoes are arthropods of world-wide distribution. They are important to man as transmitting agents of disease-producing organisms and as pests which may have sufficient significance to influence seriously the comfort and general welfare of an affected population.

Mosquitoes are the most significant of all insects as vectors of disease, although not all species carry disease. Malaria is carried by various species of the genus *Anopheles*. Certain species of the genus *Aedes*, particularly *aegypti*, are vectors of dengue fever and yellow fever; infectious encephalitis is carried by species of the genus *Culex* and possibly others; and species of the *Aedes*, *Culex*, and *Anopheles* genera have been incriminated in the transmission of filariasis.

The ability of certain species within a genus to transmit human pathogens varies considerably. Some species may serve as hosts for the infecting organisms and still become inefficient vectors of human disease. On the other hand, other species may prove to be very efficient vectors of a particular disease, either through their intimate association with man or other circumstances in nature which enhance their ability to transmit the infection to man.

Malaria remains the most important mosquito-borne disease in the world. Although the significance of the disease in the United States has been greatly reduced, its toll of sickness and death retards all social and economic progress in several regions of the world. The development of control programs, made possible by the availability of funds and technical personnel, will effect further reduction of the problem.

Yellow fever, of importance in tropical America prior to 1900, no longer occurs in major epidemic form; however, some minor outbreaks have been recorded in recent years. The United States has recorded numerous epidemics; however, the most recent outbreak occurred in New Orleans in 1905. It is known that sylvatic yellow fever is present among certain monkey and other animal populations in the jungles of South and Central America, and may be brought into urban areas where the *Aedes aegypti* mosquito may pick up the infection and transmit the disease to humans. Since little is known of control measures which will eliminate the disease in the vast jungle areas of the Americas, attention has been focused on the total elimination of the urban *Aedes aegypti* throughout the Americas as a safeguard against future outbreaks of this disease.

During World War II there were outbreaks of dengue fever in the Gulf Coastal area; however, the last major epidemic occurred in the southern part of the United States in 1922. This disease is usually nonfatal and is characterized by an illness of short duration.

Infectious encephalitis, as distinguished from other types of the disease syndrome, is known to occur in all sections of the United States. The Western and Eastern equine types are recognized as human infections in the United States, Canada, and some Central and South American countries. The Venezuelan equine type is encountered in South America and the Japanese B type in Japan, Korea, and China. The St. Louis type occurred in epidemic form in St. Louis and a number of other areas in 1933 and 1937 and in Hidalgo County, Tex., during 1954. The *Culex* genera of mosquito are generally considered to be responsible for this transmission of the virus disease, with the *Culex tarsalis* as the principal vector of the Western equine type.

Filariasis, also known as "elephantiasis," is widespread over the tropical areas of the world. It formerly existed endemically in an area in the vicinity of Charleston, S.C.

9-3. Life Cycle of the Mosquito. The life cycle of the mosquito is characterized by complete metamorphosis, having four stages—the egg, the larva, the pupa, and the adult winged insect. The adult female lays eggs in batches ranging in number from less than 50 to more than 200, and one female may deposit several batches in her lifetime. The eggs of some species are glued together in a mass which floats on the water; others are deposited on the soil at the edge of the water or in depressions where water will collect; and still others are deposited singly on the water. The eggs of the *Anopheles*, the malaria mosquito, which are in the last group, have structures or floats on the sides which keep them afloat. The yellow fever mosquito, *Aedes aegypti*, prefers to lay its eggs on wet surfaces contiguous to water in artificial containers. The incubation period is usually two to three days in warm weather; however, the eggs of many species can withstand long periods of drying or cold. The eggs of some of the salt-marsh mosquitoes may remain dormant for years.

The eggs hatch into the larvae, which are popularly known as "wigglers" or "wiggletails." The larvae of all mosquitoes are aquatic; however, they are air breathers and must renew their air supply occasionally through a breathing tube situated at the tail. During this period of development, usually four to ten days, the larvae pass through four successive stages of growth in which the skin is shed four times. Most mosquito larvae are free-swimming and feed by straining minute plants, animals, or particles of debris from the water through action of the mouth parts.

The pupae, commonly called "tumblers," appear with the fourth molt. They are comma-shaped, appearing to be all head and tail, and are still aquatic and air-breathing but do not feed. The adult winged insect is formed during this period of development and usually emerges in about two days. Upon emerging, the adult rests on the surface of the water until its wings dry and harden; it is then capable of flight.

It will be noted that the first three stages of the life cycle require about seven days. This, for most species, is the minimum period under the most favorable conditions; colder weather lengthens the time. The life span of the adult mosquito in nature is difficult to determine, but probably is only a few weeks during the summer months. A large reduction in broods of certain species of *Anopheles* and *Aedes* have been noted within two weeks while the yellow fever mosquito, *Aedes aegypti*, may live, on an average, a month or more with a maximum of several months. Some adult mosquitoes hibernate and pass the winter in sheltered spots; a few species survive as larvae, and many others remain in the egg stage.

9-4. Habits of Adult Mosquitoes. Only the female mosquito is able to bite humans or animals, the mouth parts of the male not being adapted

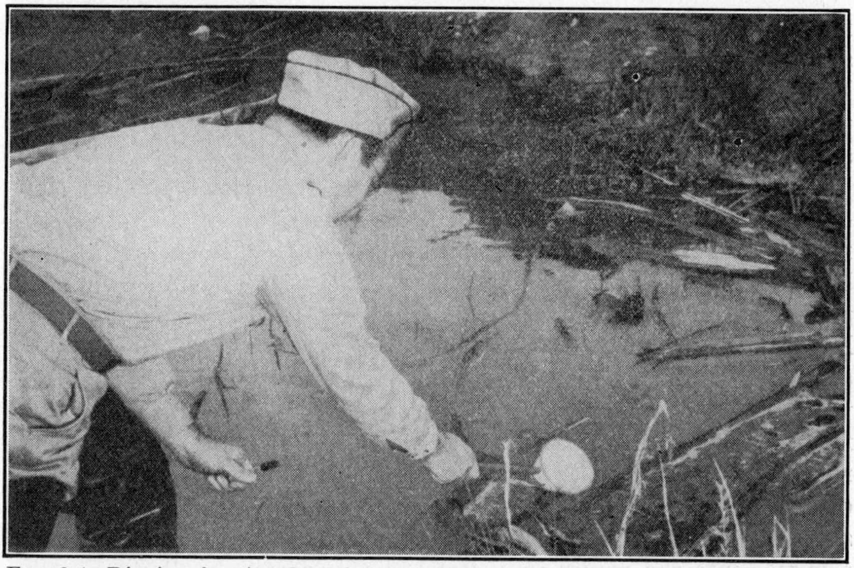

FIG. 9-1. Dipping for *Anopheles* larvae. Note that collection is made in floating debris. (*Courtesy of U.S. Public Health Service.*)

to piercing human or animal skin. The male lives upon plant juices, which also support the female in the absence of a blood supply. The female usually must obtain a blood meal prior to the development of viable eggs. Many species of mosquitoes never bite humans and are, therefore, inconspicuous, while others, mainly swamp and sylvan types, never leave their native haunts and may attack any humans or other animals that come their way. Certain mosquitoes are night biters and spend the daylight hours in dark corners of structures and in high grass, weeds, vines, and shrubbery, where they are sheltered from the sun, wind, and rain. The discomfort that results from mosquito bites is caused by the small amount of liquid which is injected by the mosquito as soon as she has penetrated the skin.

As a rule mosquitoes do not travel long distances. *Anopheles* are likely to travel a half-mile, and occasionally more than a mile, from their breeding places to obtain a blood meal. The common mosquitoes, so numerous around dwellings, are usually produced in the immediate neighborhood. When, however, a breeding place is producing large numbers of mosquitoes, a small percentage of them may travel much farther than a mile; even though the percentage is small, the numbers may be so large that a considerable infestation will result in the locality to which they have migrated. This has been particularly noted in the case of streams that receive sewage. Such a locality is a favored breeding place of several of the *Culex* mosquitoes and produces such enormous numbers that they are noticeably present at dwellings a mile or more away. Other exceptions to the general rule are salt-marsh mosquitoes. With favorable winds, these mosquitoes will travel long distances, sometimes as far as 30 or 40 miles, while other mosquitoes are more likely to avoid winds of any great strength.

9-5. Evaluation of Mosquito Populations. In order to control mosquito populations and thus reduce their menace to man and other animals, it is important to determine the amount and kind of mosquito breeding that is occurring in an area. All water in which breeding may take place must be examined; a container of water near a house or a tree hole may be a source; or the mosquitoes may be flying in from a more distant area. In general, the edges of bodies of water where there is vegetation or floating debris are the points where larvae or pupae will be found. In most cases the water in which mosquitoes breed is easy to reach, and larvae can be picked up in a long-handled dipper. For the collection of anopheline larvae, the lip of the dipper may be quickly swept along the surface of the water in such a manner that water is skimmed into the dipper or, if vegetation is dense, the dipper may be submerged so that water flows into it. The aquatic stages of some culicine mosquitoes require a quicker, deeper dip (Fig. 9-2). Mosquito larvae and pupae are very wary and will dive when alarmed; therefore, it may require many dips before any are captured, particularly if the breeding is not very heavy. Skilled taxonomists can determine the species of mosquitoes by examining larvae, and specimens should be submitted for identification where possible.

The quickest indication of the mosquito species present and the type of control that may be required can be secured by capturing adult specimens in traps or by hand. Hand collection of adults from their resting places in dark corners of dwellings, barns, privies, and chicken houses and under bridges and culverts can be accomplished with a flashlight and a "killing tube." A satisfactory killing tube can be made from a test tube or similar container fitted with a cork stopper. Rubber bands or wads of cotton saturated in chloroform and placed in the bottom of the

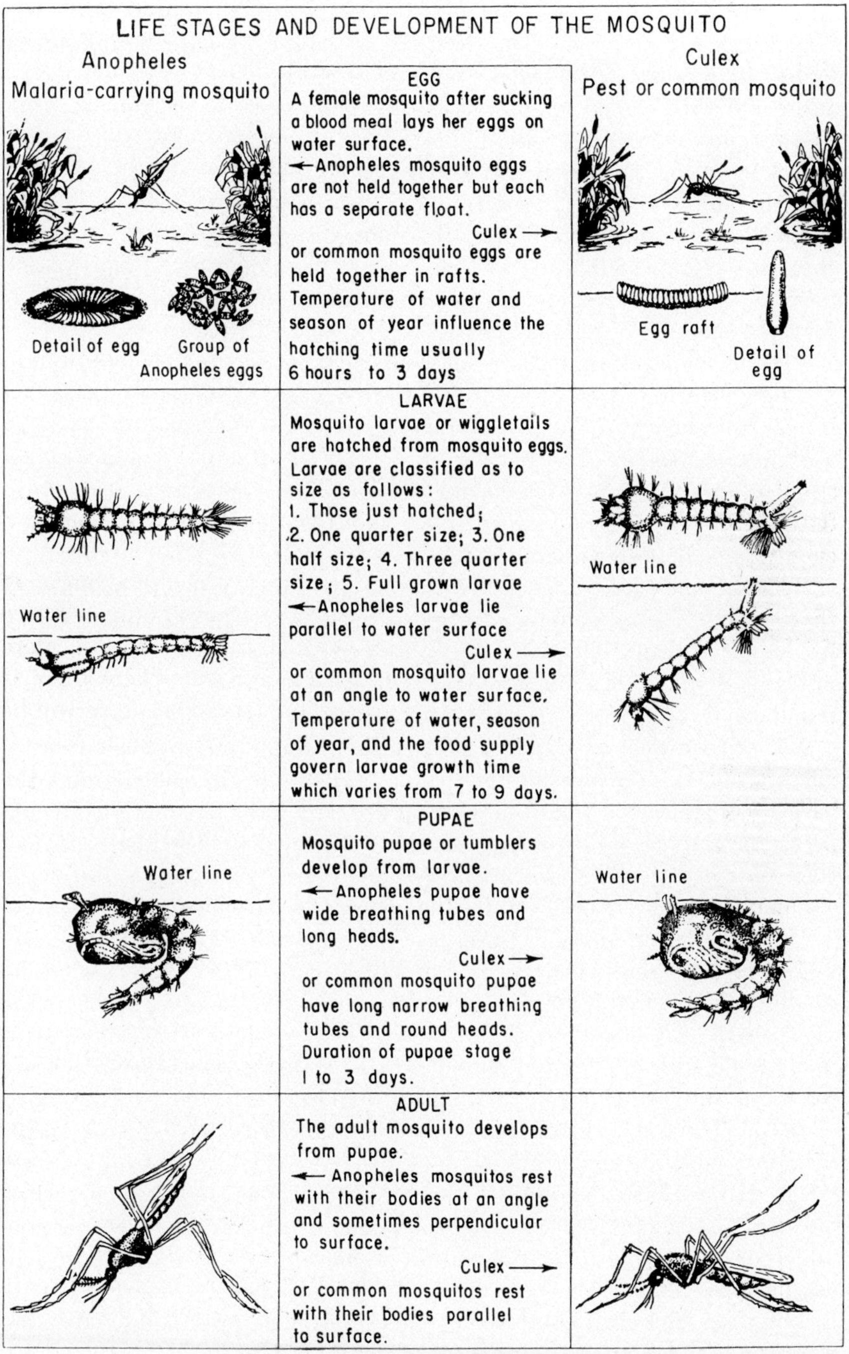

FIG. 9-2. Life cycles of the *Anopheles* and *Culex* mosquitoes. (*Courtesy of Texas State Department of Health.*)

tube under wadding cut from blotting paper kill the specimens. The tube is placed under or over the resting mosquito, and the chloroform causes it to fall into the tube. Specimens are removed to pill boxes and protected with cotton for submission to the laboratory for identification.

The most commonly used light trap is the New Jersey type. This trap consists of a vertical metal cylinder covered by a metal roof. An electric light under the roof attracts the mosquito to the cylinder, and a small electric fan draws it into the cylinder where it strikes a funnel-shaped screen which diverts it downward to a jar containing poison, usually calcium cyanide. Light traps are not particularly appropriate for the collection of anophelines.

Another type of trap has been used with success in the tropics, but has not been found of value in the United States. A donkey is placed in a small shed with large screened windows on the sides so arranged that mosquitoes are diverted to slits in the sceen wire or louvered areas situated just below the screened area which allow them to enter. After feeding, the mosquitoes are unable to escape and can be captured and counted on the following morning.

Because of the difference in their habits, the proportions of the different species of mosquitoes present in an area cannot be determined exactly by hand or trap collections, but thorough collecting by one or both methods should give a fairly reliable indication of changes in the mosquito populations.

9-6. Mosquitoes as Carriers of Disease. Some mosquitoes are very efficient in the transmission of disease. The mosquito first obtains the parasite or causative organism while feeding upon the blood of an infected person or animal and then injects it into a susceptible individual. Effective control of mosquito-borne disease, therefore, most often calls for the elimination of the middle link of the chain, the mosquito.

Malaria is caused by certain parasitic animals of microscopic size, known as protozoa, which live in the blood of the infected person. The mosquito is infected by ingesting some of the sexual forms of the parasite along with the blood of an infected person. These organisms, after undergoing a developmental period varying from ten to twenty-one days, reach the salivary gland of the mosquito and are injected into the blood of the next victim. Until this developmental period has elapsed, therefore, the mosquito is not infective.

The *Aedes aegypti* mosquito, the urban vector of yellow fever, when biting a victim of the disease imbibes some of the virus, which perhaps undergoes some transformation within the mosquito, as ten to twenty-one days elapse (four or five days if kept at 37°C or 98.6°F) before it is able to infect a susceptible person. This mosquito presumably remains infective throughout its lifetime.

At least two strains of the causative organisms of dengue fever have been identified. The *Aedes aegypti*, which is the vector, becomes infective in eight to eleven days after biting an infected person and can then transmit the organisms while biting a susceptible individual.

Each form of infectious encephalitis is caused by a specific virus. Birds, wild and domestic, are probably the principal reservoir of mosquito infection for those types occurring in the United States—Eastern

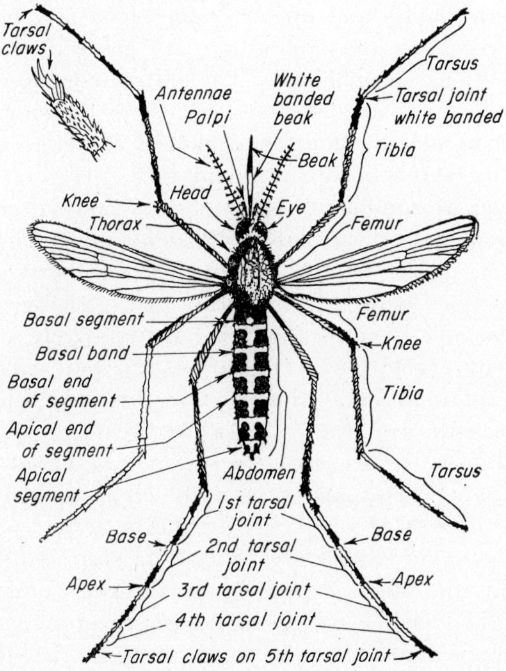

FIG. 9-3. Adult mosquito (*Aedes solicitans* Wlk.) with parts named. (*After John B. Smith, New Jersey Agricultural Experiment Station.*)

equine, Western equine, and St. Louis. Man and horses apparently are not important as sources of mosquito infection in the United States.

Filariasis is caused by filarial worms which lodge themselves in the lymphatics, causing a stoppage which results in swelling of the limbs or other body parts. The mosquito, in biting a person whose blood contains the immature worms, takes some of the larval worms into her stomach, where they develop into infective larvae in fourteen to twenty-one days. Then the larvae are transmitted to another person when the mosquito feeds. Mosquitoes of the *Culex*, *Aedes*, *Anopheles*, and *Mansonia* genera have been incriminated as vectors in various sections of the world.

9-7. Mosquitoes of the United States. The mosquito descriptions given in the following articles follow Dyar[6] and cover only the more common of the 100 or more species of mosquito that occur in the United States. Of those described, the most important to the sanitarian are the *Anopheles*, which is represented by one or more species in all parts of the country and may carry and transmit malaria; *Aedes aegypti*, which is found in communities and municipalities of the South and may transmit yellow fever and dengue; and several of the genus *Culex*, which, because of their domestic habits and appetites for blood and because of their efficiency as vectors in the laboratory, are generally regarded as the carriers of infectious encephalitis. The salt-marsh mosquitoes assume importance in certain coastal regions because of the enormous numbers produced under favorable conditions and their ability to move relatively long distances to centers of human population.

9-8. *Anopheles* Mosquitoes. Although these mosquitoes are of world-wide distribution in tropical and warm temperate regions, only those species occurring in the United States and of importance in carrying malaria are described here. The eggs are laid in the permanent waters of ponds, lakes, and swamps that are comparatively unpolluted and contain emergent vegetation. The larvae can be easily distinguished from other mosquito larvae by the fact that they take a position at, and parallel to, the surface of the water while breathing and feeding and, when disturbed, usually dart along the surface and do not dive as readily as do the larvae of *Culex* and practically all other mosquitoes. The larva breathes through an opening near the posterior end of the body; there is no tube. The adults are of medium size, usually bite only at dusk or at night, and take a "standing on the head" position when resting or biting. The wing markings of *Anopheles* adults give the wings a dusky or dark appearance and vary in pattern with the species (for wing markings see Fig. 9-4).

Anopheles quadrimaculatus is a medium-sized blackish mosquito with four well-defined spots on its wings. It frequents houses more than do the other *Anopheles* and is the most dangerous of the malaria carriers. It breeds in fresh water, particularly permanent pools, lakes, or swamps, and is distributed east of the Rocky Mountains from Mexico to New England.

Anopheles freeborni is medium-sized and blackish, with wings resembling those of *A. quadrimaculatus*. It is the most dangerous malaria carrier of the West Coast, besides being something of a pest. It breeds in puddles, preferring permanent water. Its habitat is the Western United States and Canada.

Anopheles punctipennis has white-spotted wings with two conspicuous pale yellow spots, with the fringe dark. It breeds in all sorts of water pools, both temporary and permanent, and is distributed over the whole of the United States except the dry central region.

Anopheles pseudopunctipennis is not considered an important malaria carrier in the United States. Its wings are white-spotted and the fringe is white-spotted at the end of each vein. It occurs in the Southwestern United States, where it breeds mainly at the edges of streams.

Anopheles crucians seldom enters houses but will bite on porches and in yards and will occasionally bite in the daytime. The wings are white-spotted with the front margins of the wings dark except for a white spot

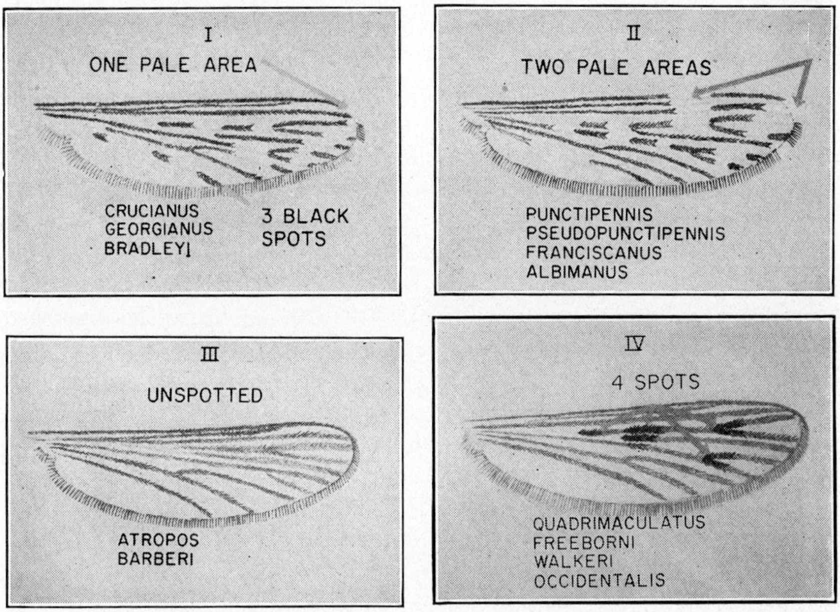

FIG. 9-4. Wing markings of the more common *Anopheles*. (*Photographs by the U.S. Public Health Service.*)

at the tip of the first vein and with three characteristic dark spots on the anal vein. Breeding places include both fresh and brackish water, coastal marshes, and swamps.

Anopheles albimanus has legs conspicuously marked with white and wings white-spotted with the fringe white-spotted at the end of each vein. It breeds in shallow, sunlit marshy areas, seepage areas overgrown with moss, and frequently in artificial containers close to habitations. This is one of the principal malaria carriers of tropical America, but at the present time is known to occur in the United States only in the Lower Rio Grande Valley of Texas.

9-9. *Aedes aegypti* Mosquitoes. This mosquito is the carrier of dengue and yellow fever. It has had many names during its nefarious career, the commonest one being *Stegomyia*. The adult is medium-sized and gives the impression of being gray. When closely examined, the gray color is found to be due to silvery markings on the legs, abdomen, and thorax. The markings on the thorax have some resemblance to a lyre. The wings are clear. This mosquito bites only in daytime or by artificial light, and its favorite point of attack is the ankles. Probably this mosquito was originally a tree-hole breeder but has since become domesticated, for it breeds only in artificial containers in the immediate vicinity of human habitations or business buildings. It does not fly very far but seeks its food within a few hundred feet of its breeding place. As the adult is quickly killed by frost, it survives the winter in the egg stage in the Northern states within its range. It is a warm-climate mosquito and usually is not found any farther north than the latitude of Kentucky.

9-10. *Culex* Mosquitoes. *Culex pipiens* is a small, brown, night-biting mosquito. The abdomen is blackish with whitish bands connected to the spots on the sides. The wings are clear. It breeds principally in artificial containers but will also breed in ground pools and has a predilection for sewage as a breeding place. This is the common house mosquito of Europe, introduced into the United States through commerce and now one of the most important pestiferous mosquitoes in this country from Virginia to Canada on the Atlantic Coast and California to British Columbia on the Pacific Coast.

Culex quinquefasciatus sometimes resembles *C. pipiens* in habits and also in appearance, except that the bands of the abdomen are not connected to the spots at the sides. It breeds in artificial containers but also likes ground pools and sewage. It is the common house mosquito of the tropics and in the United States ranges as far north as Kentucky.

Culex territans is a medium-sized, reddish-brown mosquito, with proboscis and legs all dark, or the tarsi may have faint pale-brownish rings at the ends of the joints. The thorax is bronze-brown, sometimes ornamented with light patches of yellowish scales on each side of the middle. The abdomen is blackish-brown above and evenly banded with white. It breeds in ground puddles and is likely to take to artificial containers. The adults enter houses, so that this is the common house mosquito of northern New York and New England. It is widely distributed, however, over eastern North America.

Culex tarsalis is a medium-sized mosquito with a bronze-brown thorax, frequently adorned with a few narrow silver-white lines. The proboscis is dark, with a white ring near the middle; the legs are bronze—the femora are white beneath, and the tarsi have white rings at both sides of the joints. The distinctive silvery longitudinal lines on the legs separate this species from *C. stigmatosoma*. The larvae are commonly found in grassy ponds or marshes, in escaping irrigation water, and in well-treated sewage effluent. They do not breed in artificial containers. This mosquito may enter houses and become a nuisance in the western part of the country and is the generally accepted vector of Western equine encephalitis. It is distributed over the Mississippi Valley and western prairies to the Pacific Ocean.

Culex salinarius is a medium-sized brown mosquito with brown thorax; the abdomen is blackish with or without narrow whitish bands. The legs are blackish; femora pale beneath. It breeds in permanent pools and marshes containing vegetation. While it is frequently very abundant on the seashore, it also occurs inland and occasionally in water barrels. Its habitat is the United States east of the Great Plains.

9-11. The Salt-marsh Mosquitoes. The salt-marsh mosquitoes are usually ferocious biters, but carry no human disease, so far as is known. Of these mosquitoes, one of the most important is *Aedes sollicitans*. It is a medium-sized-to-large blackish mosquito with conspicuously ringed legs. The thorax is bronze-yellow, dark-bronze at the sides. The abdomen is black with crossbands of pale yellow and a longitudinal band down the middle. The proboscis has a white ring. The larvae occur in salt tidal pools on the coast but sometimes develop inland in association with salt-water wastes from industrial processes. The adult is a strong flier and in many instances travels long distances inland. It is distributed over the Gulf states and over the Atlantic Coast to New England.

Aedes taeniorhynchus is the small salt-marsh mosquito. It is rather blackish in color; the thorax is dark brown, and the abdomen is black with narrow white bands and white spots at the sides. The legs are black, but the femora are white beneath, and the tarsi have narrow white rings which are wider on the hind legs. The proboscis has a narrow white ring. It breeds in saline or slightly saline pools near the seacoast. It is very abundant in the Gulf states and Florida, but also occurs in the North Atlantic states and along the Pacific Coast.

Aedes cantator is a medium-sized brown mosquito with a reddish-brown thorax and a black abdomen with dull-white bands. The legs are black, but the femora are white below, and the tarsi have very narrow white rings. It breeds in salt-marsh pools along the northern Atlantic Coast. The females frequently travel many miles inland.

9-12. Malaria Trends. Until the last quarter of the nineteenth century, malaria was prevalent in the eastern two-thirds of the United States, with the exception of the highlands of the Appalachians. There was also an endemic area in central California. Since then the incidence has regularly declined, with limited sporadic outbreaks occurring at irregular intervals.

There has been much speculation as to the causes of the virtual disappearance of malaria from the United States, since observations of malariologists have proved that it has not resulted from any decrease in the efficiency of mosquito vectors to transmit the disease. The prosperity of the country has resulted in homes that have better mosquito-proofing, an important factor since the malaria vectors of this country prefer to bite at night when people are most likely to be in their homes. Prosperity has also ensured better medical treatment and a consequent reduction in the number of acute and fatal attacks of malaria.

In rural areas not only prosperity but a balanced farm program resulted in an increase of cattle raising, possibly a factor in malaria reduction since *Anopheles quadrimaculatus* will readily attack domestic animals as a source of blood. The actual size of the rural population has decreased because of a general migration of farm workers to industrial areas from the marginal or poorer farms.

In the long fight against malaria a number of methods have been tried. The potential number of mosquitoes has been reduced in certain areas by means of drainage and the use of efficient larvicides. If the number of vector mosquitoes is sufficiently reduced, transmission of malaria is sharply curtailed. This method first proved its worth in Panama in connection with the construction of the Panama Canal, and similar but less spectacular successes have been obtained in many areas of the United States, and elsewhere. The difficulty with this method is that it cannot be applied to large areas that include sparsely populated rural regions, since it presents many technical and operational problems and requires considerable capital.

A second plan of attack is the use of medical agents to reduce the parasites in the human population of a specific region. This calls for a malaria survey which usually includes blood tests of the population and regular supervised dosage of those persons who are infected. In many instances, this method has not had any important effect in checking transmission; the failure is due in part to the limitations of the available medicines and in part to the difficulty of giving effective mass treatments.

Both of the above methods have been supplemented by educational campaigns which attempt to impress upon people the facts of malaria—how it is transmitted by mosquitoes, what precautions to take, and how to obtain skilled medical treatment. Frequently this is accomplished by a more or less intensive campaign to obtain improved housing with good screening. The most important shortcomings of these methods are the difficulty in reaching all the people with the information and, after instruction, their proneness to postpone translating knowledge into action.

A fourth method, a combination which is inexpensive and applicable both to populous areas and to large areas having relatively small populations, has been applied by the U.S. Public Health Service in cooperation with state and local health organizations. It consists of keeping both the infected vector population and the parasitic infection in humans at levels so low that transmission will be interrupted. The first part of this method has been accomplished by the use of DDT as a residual spray in inhabited buildings to destroy the mosquitoes which have entered homes and have bitten infected persons. This control was accompanied by epidemiological measures encouraging local physicians to use better diagnostic methods, to report all cases, and to use the best antimalaria drugs available for treatment. Work of this nature serves to focus attention upon areas where malaria is most prevalent, and efforts can then be concentrated upon points of residual infection.

A similar campaign was carried on by Venezuela, in cooperation with the Pan American Sanitary Bureau and the Technical Assistance Program of the United Nations, on a country-wide basis with marked success. Spraying crews were organized in the malarious sections of the country; the more populous regions were worked first, and when malaria was checked there, the less populous areas were treated. Argentina, the United States, and Chile, as well as Venezuela, now report that malaria has been to a great extent eradicated.

The decisive factor in these antimalaria campaigns has been the use of residual insecticides. While DDT has been the most widely used material for spraying, such others as BHC (benzene hexachloride), dieldrin, and chlordane have also been successfully employed.

While prospects are favorable for eventual control of malaria throughout the malarious sections of the world by the type of campaign described, more or less continuous work will be required. The epidemiological forces must be on guard for a resurgence of infection which will require residual spraying to be resumed. If this is done, there is basis for hope that malaria may eventually disappear from those parts of the world where it has taken toll so long.

9-13. Yellow Fever Control. Sylvatic yellow fever, it is now known, is endemic among certain of the animals in the jungles of Africa, South America, and at least as far north in Central America as Guatemala. Fortunately, although they are the same disease, jungle yellow fever is transmitted by forest mosquitoes that do not enter towns, whereas urban yellow fever is transmitted only by *Aedes aegypti*, a species of mosquito that breeds only in artificial containers near human habitations. Urban areas that are free of *A. aegypti* are not endangered by the jungle infection.

In 1947 the Pan American Sanitary Bureau was entrusted with the responsibility of coordinating programs required to eradicate *A. aegypti* from the American continent. All infested countries have accepted the responsibility for eradication campaigns except the United States. In the Latin American countries, under the auspices of the P.A.S.B., the perifocal or preferential method of eradication is employed, a program wherein DDT is applied to the outside and inside of containers that hold or may hold water, and also to a small area of the near-by walls. This is a very effective method, since the female rests near the oviposition site before depositing her eggs. In those areas where malaria is a problem, the two programs are combined by the addition of intradomicile spraying; that is, DDT is applied to the inside walls of houses and outbuildings.

The rapid travel now possible by airplanes can easily allow an infected person to enter the United States. If he is not discovered and isolated by the inspection given to passengers at the point of entry, an outbreak may result in a city of the United States. Also, infected mosquitoes may enter the United States in airplanes or other convenient means of transportation, although rigid inspection programs and the efficient use of insecticidal sprays will minimize this danger.

Because of the deadliness of yellow fever, an epidemic calls for prompt and energetic measures. Infected persons should be placed in mosquito-proof rooms, preferably in hospitals. Persons who live in the same house or near-by, or who have worked in the same or near-by buildings, should be vaccinated against yellow fever. Measures to be taken against the mosquito vector should consist of the following:

1. A force of sanitary inspectors should be immediately organized and given technical instructions.

2. The city should be divided into convenient districts, and an inspector assigned to each one. Each district should be of such size that the inspector can make a round in one week. If time permits, cards should be printed and filled out for each piece of property having buildings located on it. Each card should have a printed list of possible breeding places, and those actually found would be checked.

3. The inspectors should look for such breeding places as sagging roof gutters which hold water after rains, flower vases in houses, discarded automobile tires, barrels, open cisterns, cans and tubs and, if possible, should have them corrected immediately. If this cannot be done, a warning notice should be given that the correction is to be made within a prescribed number of days, and all uncorrected potential breeding places immediately treated with DDT residual spray. Follow-up inspections should be made at the end of the allowed time, and if appropriate corrections have not been made, action should be taken as prescribed by the state laws and city ordinances, which may allow the levying of fines against property owners or tenants who permit mosquito breeding. In an emergency, such as a yellow fever epidemic, the city should have authority to make an improvement on private property.

4. Supervisors should make check inspections of the work of inspectors. If the inspection is continued for any length of time, inspectors should be shifted from district to district.

5. Residual spraying with DDT should be applied by control crews to all buildings within the immediate vicinity of houses or buildings where yellow fever cases have been confined. Spraying should not be confined to houses, stores, and offices, but should be applied also to outhouses, garages, etc.

6. Vacant lots should be cleared of cans and other possible water containers. Dump grounds should be given attention.

7. Educational methods should be given a prominent place in the control program. Householders should be encouraged to use insecticidal sprays in their homes and insect repellents on their persons.

9-14. Dengue Fever Control. Dengue fever is not a fatal disease and, therefore, does not arouse so much public alarm as yellow fever. An extensive epidemic, however, may justify many, if not all of the measures recommended for yellow fever control. Movement of all patients to hospitals or into specially mosquitoproofed rooms may not be considered necessary, and there is no vaccination against the disease. More dependence might be placed upon educational measures. Doctors should be encouraged to report all cases so that inspections can be made at points where infection occurs.

9-15. Control Methods against the Mosquito. From Art. 9-12 it is apparent that malaria control involves a complex organization requiring the services of physicians who are malariologists, entomologists who obtain information of the vectors and their habits, public health nurses who make contacts with the infected persons and the public in general, and local practicing physicians, whose cooperation is essential. Not the least important is the work of the sanitary engineer and sanitarian in controlling the mosquito vector.

Mosquito control is applied against the aquatic forms by means of drainage, filling, and the use of larvicidal agents. These procedures may be grouped under the term *larvicidal methods.* Other methods, which we may call *adulticidal methods,* are directed against the mature, winged mosquito and include the use of sprays under various circumstances and mosquitoproofing of occupied buildings. Each of these methods has its field of usefulness, and a choice of the appropriate method or methods must be made to meet any situation.

Species control is also possible and economical if systematic and skilled observation is given to breeding places. For example, an extensive breeding area may be producing *Anopheles,* but if they are of the nondangerous type, control will not be required. Should dangerous anophelines appear later, control can then be started.

LARVICIDAL METHODS

9-16. Drainage. Drainage improvement includes installation of open ditches, subsurface drains, vertical drains, filling low areas, the cleaning and draining of natural streams, and control of impounding reservoirs. In tidal areas it may also include construction of dykes and tide gates. Drainage frequently makes it possible to eliminate permanently not only small pools, but also such large breeding areas as swamps. It has some disadvantages, however. The ditches, if not carefully constructed and properly maintained, may themselves breed mosquitoes. This applies particularly to unlined earth ditches. Usually it is not possible to eliminate all natural waters. The streams which drain the area will provide mosquito breeding places unless they are carefully observed and cleared. Heavy rains will cause overflows and temporary pools, which may be very expensive or impossible to drain. The same applies to ponds and lakes.

Major drainage is costly and must be carefully evaluated in terms of human population densities and other factors. In general, highly populous areas are seldom found to be malarious, and the expense of drainage will have to be justified from the standpoint of physical comfort and the reclamation of waste areas.

Drainage for mosquito control differs in some of its details from ordinary drainage. Storm-water drainage, for instance, requires immediate carrying away of large volumes of water, while drainage of water for mosquito control requires only that the water be carried off in less time than the period necessary to produce mosquitoes. Ordinary drainage of agricultural land is concerned only with keeping the land sufficiently dry to produce crops, and little or no consideration is given to small amounts of water retained in the ditches. On the other hand, such small accumulations are more favorable for mosquito breeding than are larger bodies of water. Hence, antimosquito drainage must be so arranged that no water is allowed to stand for appreciable lengths of time in the drainage ditches or elsewhere.

9-17. Ditching. The first step in drainage is to make a tentative layout of the system of ditches. If the problem is to drain a swampy area formed by seepage at the bottom of a hill, the main ditch should parallel the bottom of the hill and be deep enough to intersect all the ground-water flow before it appears on the ground surface. Flat, swampy areas and ponds will require a main ditch leading from the deepest point of the area. The main ditch should always be dug first and drainage allowed to occur. After a few days the lateral ditches may be dug, and it may be discovered that not so many will be required as was first supposed. Frequently there will be smaller ditches connecting low areas with the main ditch.

Ditches should have clean sides sloped as steeply as the earth, or other material, will permit. The bottoms should be as narrow as possible in order to confine the stream to a small area. Wide ditches are undesirable since they permit pools of water to stand and breed mosquitoes. Where a very wide ditch is essential, this problem may be eliminated by constructing a small ditch in the bottom of the large one so that small flows will be concentrated and kept moving. Sharp bends should be avoided when making changes of direction, and branch ditches should join the main ditch at acute angles, or with a curve. The grade of an unlined ditch should be great enough to give a cleaning velocity, but not so great that erosion will occur. A grade or fall of 0.05 foot per 100 feet is the minimum for an unlined ditch, and 0.6 to 0.8 foot per 100 feet is the maximum. When steeper grades are necessary, spillways or check dams of concrete, rock, brush, or poles are used to reduce the velocity.

Side slopes of earth ditches are usually 1 horizontal to 1 vertical in firm loam or sand clay. In soft, loose soil it should be 1.5 horizontal to 1 vertical. In hard, rocky material, it may be steeper than 1 to 1.

Where sharp curves are necessary and the grade is near the upper limit suggested above, it may be necessary to place some type of lining at the outer side of the curve to avoid excessive erosion. This can be done by laying stone or concrete blocks on the ditch side or by driving small logs into the ditch bottom at the same angle as the ditch side. This may also be necessary where a lateral ditch enters a main ditch, both in the lateral where it is curved and in the main ditch opposite to the junction. The lateral should have an increased grade just before it enters the main ditch, and its bottom at the point of junction should be slightly higher than that of the main ditch.

The natural watercourses of cities and towns carry off large amounts of storm water and need maintenance because of the damage done by the frequent high flows. This generally results in water standing permanently in pools in the streams and adjacent flooded low areas, and thus in a great production of mosquitoes. Frequent straightening and clearing of such streams will temporarily remedy matters, but the best solution is to line them. Not only will lining save the cost of continual maintenance, but it will also pay for itself by reducing the cost of larviciding the standing water.

Figure 9-5 shows the ditch lining originated at Panama. It consists of a curved section, or invert, which ensures that small flows will be concentrated and good hydraulic conditions will prevail. Side slabs are placed so that the lined portion extends as far up the ditch sides as the flows may require. For small ditches the inverts alone may be sufficient. The Panama invert is flat on the bottom, as it is easier to trim the earth of a ditch bottom to fit it. Frequently, however, the inverts are merely half-sections of concrete pipe, or third-sections, if the ditch is to be very wide and the diameter of the invert section is over 24 inches. The concrete is usually a 1:3:5 mix. The lining here illustrated is precast, but monolithic linings, *i.e.*, those laid continuously in place, have also been used. Cement mortar reinforced with chicken wire gunited in place is occasionally used. Side walls, and sometimes the inverts also, have been constructed of rough stones, or riprap, laid to grade, and carefully grouted. In locations where there is not room for ditches that are wide at the top, the sides are made of rock carefully laid vertically with mortar joints, the bottom being sloped to form an invert at the middle.

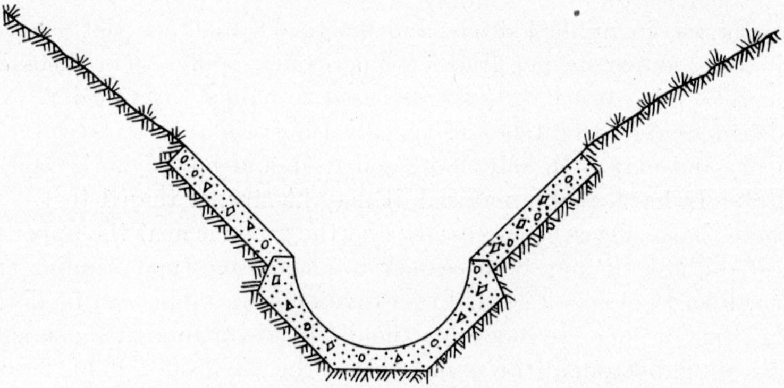

FIG. 9-5. Cross section of a lined ditch.

If a ditch has a small flow with occasional large flows, the invert may be a half-round channel with the rest of the bottom sloped slightly to obtain proper width, and more steeply sloping sides rising higher. For very infrequent heavy flows a ditch may be widened still more on a slope of 1½ horizontal to 1 vertical, which is sodded. Bermuda grass sod 1 inch in thickness is satisfactory. Sod bonds more rapidly to the earth if it is thinner than 2 inches. The sod should be carefully tamped with shovels for quick bonding. The lower edge of the sod must rest upon the upper edge of the ditch lining.

Junctions of branch ditches coming into lined main ditches should be carefully designed so that no injury will be done to the lining of either ditch. If lined ditches are to pass through muck, it may be necessary to remove the soft material and replace it with sand, gravel, or other available satisfactory material. If the ditch is to traverse a seepy area, it may be advisable to lay open-jointed tile drains that will intercept or collect the water and discharge it into the ditch through openings that pierce the ditch lining. If the grade of the ditch is steep, there is a tendency for water to run beneath the lining. This can be prevented by placing cutoff or key walls at intervals of 200 feet. If the velocity in the ditch will be more than 4 feet per second, some authorities recommend that the grade be flattened and that spillways or drops from one elevation to another be constructed. Precautions should be taken at the point of abrupt elevation change so that the falling water will do no damage. Velocities should be more than 2 feet per second to ensure cleaning, and grades should be increased slightly on curves to prevent deposition of silt.

Ditching in swamps where the earth is saturated with water and perhaps filled with roots is a difficult and expensive undertaking. Under these conditions, ditching with dynamite has been very effectively carried out. This method should not be attempted without an experienced

FIG. 9-6. Widening ditches which checkerboard the salt marshes at Baldwin Harbor in Nassau County, N.Y. (*Courtesy H. O. Penn Machinery Co. and Public Works Magazine.*)

blaster on the job. It is usually cheaper than ditching by hand and much faster, since ditching at the rate of 100 to 200 feet per hour is possible. Dynamite manufacturers furnish instruction booklets giving the details of this method of swamp drainage.

9-18. Ditch Maintenance. Ditches should be carefully maintained or they may themselves become breeders of mosquitoes. This is particularly true where cattle have access to unlined ditches. It is usually necessary to give the ditches a thorough working-over each spring. They may or may not require further cleaning in the middle of the summer.

Extensive improvements are sometimes necessary. Regrading will be needed when ditches have become eroded in some sections and silted in others. Brush and vegetation must be removed. Excessive erosion may be prevented by placing in the ditch key walls of concrete 3 inches wide, 18 inches deep, and 12 to 24 inches longer than the ditch width. The upper edge is set at the permanent grade elevation desired. Eroded banks are protected by log stakes. If the ditch has widened, it may be necessary to dig a small ditch in the bottom to confine small flows. Lined ditches need occasional inspections to locate and reset dislodged slabs.

9-19. Vertical Drainage. Pools and swamps are sometimes due not only to insufficient surface drainage but also to the fact that an impervious stratum sometimes occurs immediately below the ground surface. It happens at times that beneath the impervious stratum there is one that is very open and porous, such as sand or gravel, or fissured, such as limestone. If surface drainage in such a case is impracticable or too costly, vertical drainage may be employed. This requires the sinking of one or more shafts or wells through the impervious stratum to the porous or fissured one. In the case of fissured rock, a hole may be drilled in it at the bottom of the shaft and one or more sticks of dynamite exploded to open up the seams. Inlet ditches may be required to carry the water to the shafts. Such shafts or wells may be lined with tile pipe or sheeted with timber to prevent caving. If of large diameter, they are sometimes filled with large stones. In the case of small shafts, a drain head is often placed at the top. This is, in effect, a wooden box with screened entrances for the water. The box also has a screened opening at the bottom, which is placed over the end of the shaft. This arrangement will serve to keep out coarse sediment and floating matter that may clog the openings through which the water is escaping into the porous or fissured stratum.

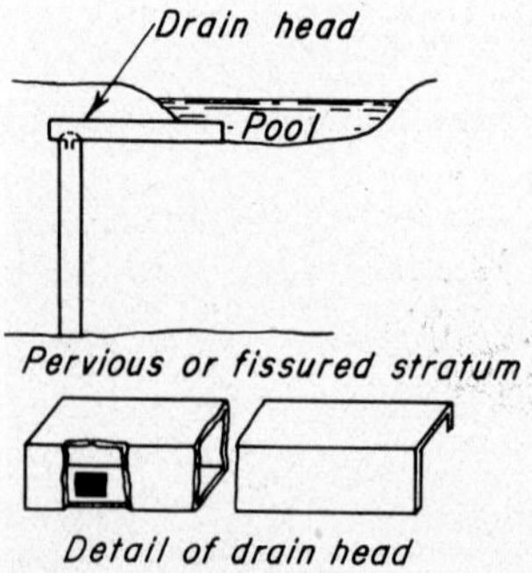

FIG. 9-7. Vertical drainage, showing detail of drain head. (*After Metz, U.S. Public Health Service.*)

9-20. Improvement and Maintenance of Streams. Mosquitoes do not breed in swiftly running water. This, however, does not eliminate the running stream as a mosquito producer, as there will frequently be found deep pools, obstructions, or vegetation which will retard the flow of the stream sufficiently to allow breeding in such favorable places. Conditions in the streams may be materially improved by clearing it of vegetation and other obstructions. It will sometimes be possible to eliminate deep holes by rechanneling or filling. Swampy areas can often be eliminated by straightening the channel of a slow, winding stream. Before this is done, levels should be run to make sure that enough slope is available. Many streams cease flowing in dry periods, and no water remains except in isolated pools. These should be connected by ditches. Clearing and maintaining streams will materially aid minnows and other predators to keep down mosquito production. The spring work of an antimosquito campaign should include the careful working over of streams in the area under control.

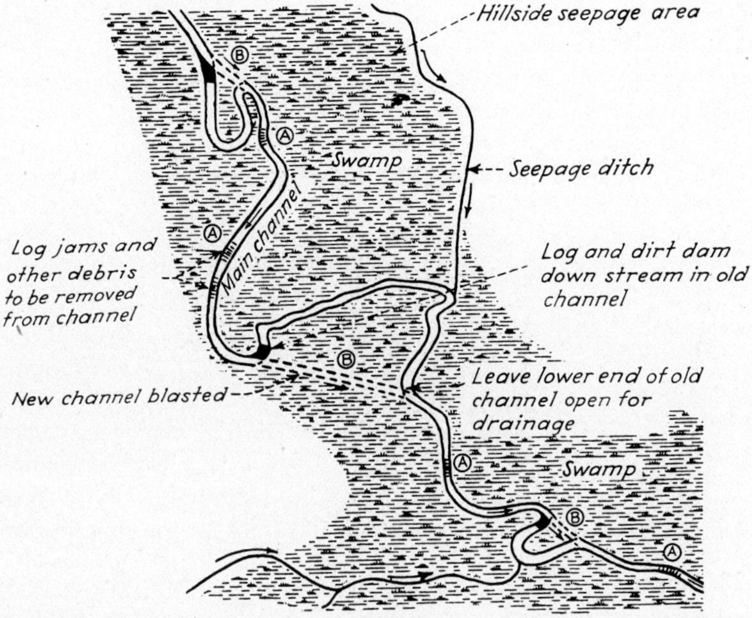

FIG. 9-8. Stream rechanneling to eliminate a swamp. *A*, points where stream clearing may be needed; *B*, points where new channels may be dug or blasted. Upper ends of old channels are blocked with earth and log dams. Note intercepting ditch for hillside seepage area. (*Courtesy of U.S. Public Health Service.*)

9-21. Street Drainage. Mosquito control in cities and towns will be greatly facilitated by giving proper attention to street drainage. All side ditches of unpaved streets should be brought to grade, cleaned, and freed of weeds. Culverts are frequently silted up at the lower end and consequently hold water for weeks if not cleared. Storm-water catch basins, particularly the trap type, may be mosquito breeders. The usual spring work that is done on streets should be carried out with mosquito control in view. This calls for cooperation between the street department and the health authorities.

9-22. Subsurface Drainage. Underground tile drainage has been used to advantage in mosquito-control work. It is advantageous in swampy areas where open ditches quickly become choked with vegetation or trampled by cattle. It also eliminates possible breeding in the ditches themselves and reduces maintenance costs. Tiling of marshy property, in addition to eliminating mosquito breeding, may be profitable as a matter of land reclamation.

The tile used varies from 3 inches in diameter upward. Under average soil conditions the laterals may be appropriately spaced and the pipe laid at a depth of 2 to 4 feet. The tile, which is of the plain-ended, porous variety, is laid with close joints, which may be covered with straw or sacks to prevent entrance of sand. The usual fall given is not less than 2 inches to 100 feet, and care must be taken that the tile is laid carefully to grade.

A less expensive drain can be made by using logs, as shown in Fig. 9-9. Such drains should slope from 0.2 to 1.0 foot per 100 feet of ditch length.

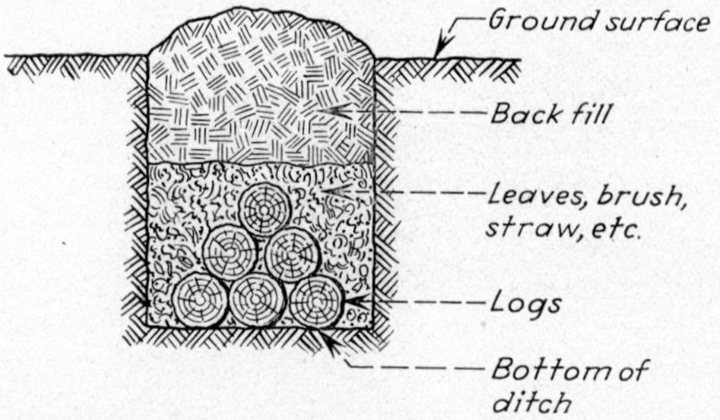

FIG. 9-9. Log drain. Backfill is mounded to allow for settlement.

9-23. Impounded Waters. The impounding of waters has proved advantageous in some instances and in others has created problems of greater magnitude than existed previously. Marshy areas in stream beds have been controlled by erecting a dam and flooding the areas. Under such conditions, particularly if the edges can be kept clear, some degree of control may be anticipated through the natural predators having access to the mosquito larvae.

Waters impounded in reservoirs for flood control, power, irrigation, water supply, or other purposes frequently become producers of large numbers of mosquitoes. Prevention of mosquito breeding should start with the interested individuals, groups, and official agencies recognizing and accepting their legal and moral responsibility toward protecting the human population in the area from mosquito hazards. When this responsibility has been accepted, mosquito-control principles will be incorporated into reservoir design, construction, and operation.

It should be recognized that mosquito breeding does not occur in the open water of reservoirs where the larvae would be exposed to injury by wave action and destruction by fish, but usually occurs in the shallow water along the edges, where there is vegetation and floating matter to give protection and concealment to the larvae. Reservoir design for mosquito control should place emphasis on obtaining a maximum of vegetation-free water surface by "building out" the most favorable mosquito-producing areas through shoreline alterations—by deepening and filling or by dyking and dewatering.

Shoreline improvement may not always be practicable, in which case water-level management may be carried on to reduce mosquito production. Effective supplements to water-level management include drift removal, marginal-drainage maintenance, and plant-growth control. Reservoir construction should, therefore, include clearing of the land which will be the margin of the reservoir to prevent protrusion of stumps, branches, etc., which, in turn, would give protection to larvae. Clearing should also be extended a sufficient distance above the high water level so that falling trees will not extend into the water. Wherever erosion may be expected to extend the reservoir margin, such potential extensions should also be cleared. Depressions in the marginal area between high and low water levels should be drained or filled.

It is advisable to fill the reservoir for the first time when vegetation is not in the growing season, so that floating leaves and other organic materials which encourage and conceal heavy mosquito breeding will be at a minimum. If possible, the reservoir should first be filled above the normal level, so that much of the floating material will be stranded. Thereafter, mosquito control will be greatly aided or perhaps obtained by systematically varying the water level. Whether this can be done will depend upon the continuity of the supply of water to the reservoir and the demand for water. The Tennessee Valley Authority at the Wilson Reservoir obtained good results by lowering the water level a distance of 1 foot in one-half week and refilling 0.9 foot in the rest of the week. This resulted in a gradual net drawdown during the six months of the breeding season.

Water-level variations are beneficial in several ways. They strand mosquito eggs and protective floating matter. They discourage both land and aquatic marginal vegetation, making the reservoir edge an unsuitable environment for larvae by giving no protection against wave action or fish. Some types of vegetation, however, are resistant to water fluctuations, and clearing or larvicidal measures may be required.

Clearing of land plants may be accomplished by cutting or hoeing. Certain species of willows will sprout persistently after cutting, and these may require special treatment. Girdling the stump just above the ground so that a trough is formed completely around and through the bark and cambium and filling the trough with Diesel oil has been found fairly effective in killing trees. A 12.5 per cent solution of sodium arsenite in water applied to the trough girdle by means of a knapsack sprayer is more effective, but this chemical is dangerous to workmen and cattle and, of course, should not be used if the reservoir is to be used as a water supply.

Small ponds that have a slight but continual flow of water into them have been controlled by installation of a siphon that will automatically go into operation every three or four days and lower the water level 3 or 4 feet in a few hours. This procedure will not only control mosquito breeding in the pond but also flush the stream below the outlet, thereby washing downstream, or destroying, larvae which have developed since the last flushing.

The sanitarian who is concerned with malaria control in a rural county should investigate the many fish and stock ponds constructed as a part of conservation work. These, unless precautionary measures are taken, may result in an increase of mosquito vectors and the introduction of mosquito-borne diseases into regions formerly free of these maladies.

9-24. Other Man-made Mosquito Breeding Places. Careless construction work has been responsible for a large amount of mosquito breeding. Culverts beneath highways and railroads are frequently placed so high that a pool is formed on the upstream side which cannot be drained. In other cases the culvert is placed too low, with the consequence that it is continually filled with water. Borrow pits, left without any means of drainage, become filled with water and contribute mosquitoes to the countryside. It is important that engineers and construction men realize the danger of such conditions and take measures to prevent them by inserting sound drainage requirements into specifications and by locating culverts, spoil banks, and borrow pits properly.

Irrigation of agricultural lands has caused an increased incidence of mosquito-transmitted diseases. This consequence can be traced to carelessness in the design and operation of irrigation systems, particularly the latter. Poor maintenance of irrigation ditches may allow mosquito breeding, but the greatest danger can usually be attributed to waste water and lack of facilities to care for this excess water. Waterlogged soil with excess water standing in low areas, standing pools formed by overflows from irrigated lands, and leaky ditches are the common faults seen in irrigated sections. Good operating methods and proper drainage are essential if mosquito control is to be considered.

Rice fields are frequently flooded soon after planting and may be more or less continuously flooded. Control by larvicides is not always practicable, and fish have not proved effective. The most promising method of preventing breeding of anophelines in the rice fields is by draining periodically at such intervals that the life cycle of the mosquito cannot be completed. Attention should be given, however, to the irrigation and drainage ditches. Intermittent irrigation has been found to increase the yield of some varieties of rice without injuring its quality.

9-25. Salt-marsh Drainage. Control of salt-marsh mosquitoes requires knowledge of the breeding habits of the mosquitoes involved, tidal fluctuations, and the nature of the soil in the marsh. As previously indicated, the eggs are laid on the mud in depressions at the edges of the marsh which will be filled by rain water or flooded by exceptionally high tides. Hatching occurs rapidly, and adults may emerge, under favorable conditions, within seven days. Not all eggs will hatch at the first, second, or even later wettings. This helps the mosquito to survive in an area even though the pools may dry up before the first-hatched larvae have had time to emerge. To determine the area to be controlled, it is necessary to determine the highest tidal elevation. The so-called spring tides, which occur several times a month, are the highest. Their heights may be obtained from government records. To this height, an addition must be made for onshore winds, which may force the water even higher. Under some conditions it may also be necessary to make a further addition for waves, although this is of more importance in connection with the design of dykes. Soil conditions are important for several reasons. If the soil is principally peat, it is advisable to draw the water level only below the grass roots. Too great a drawdown will permit shrinkage to such an extent that drainage is interfered with, or fires may occur. Either of these difficulties may require flooding of the area by pumping or otherwise. Some marshy regions are of claylike silt. This may crack when it dries, and the cracks may hold water and breed mosquitoes. The remedial measures are larviciding or plowing of the ground, followed by disking to fill the cracks.

Open-marsh drainage is used in narrow marshes where the longest length of drain to outlet is not in excess of 2,000 feet, or where settling may be a problem. Two methods of open-marsh drainage are used. In one, parallel ditches are run at regular intervals, either to a main ditch or directly to the main body of water. A more economical approach is to construct a ditch leading from all low spots holding water to the main body of water or to the natural sloughs or waterways in the marsh. These ditches may be curved somewhat to take in a number of the low spots or pools. Areas that are merely wet are not drained at first, as construction of the first drains frequently lowers the ground-water table sufficiently to dry up many of them. Free circulation of water through the drainage ditches permits the various predators to consume mosquito larvae. The top-water minnow (*Gambusia affinis*), which is discussed in Art. 9-34, is efficient for this purpose, but the stocking of salt water or brackish marshes should be done with specimens that have been accustomed to salt water, and this species is primarily a fresh-water fish.

There are species of small salt-water fish that are common to many sections of the country, and these may be depended upon as an aid in keeping ditches clear of larvae.

The closed-drainage system is also known as the "reclamation method." It is used for large marshes and has the advantage of making the land usable for agricultural or other purposes. It has the disadvantage of allowing cracks and shrinkage, which require expensive remedies. In this method the tide is prevented from entering the area by means of a dyke or levee, and the surface water is allowed to escape in one or more outlets through the dyke. The outlets must, of course, be provided with flap gates of some type that will prevent water from entering the area during high tide. It may be necessary or advisable to pump the water into the sea or bay rather than to depend upon free drainage.

The dyke is usually constructed with a slope of 3 horizontal to 1 vertical if the height is not more than 6 feet, and the construction of a berm may be advisable. Frequently the top is made wide enough to provide a roadway for vehicles. The borrow pit, which provides earth for the dyke, is inside but far enough away so that there is no danger of a slide. The ground surface on which the dyke is to be placed should be scarified, or, better still, a cutoff trench should be dug to prevent leakage. The height must be great enough to protect against the highest tides—wave height and some freeboard. If the dyke fronts on the open sea, local inquiries must be made to determine wave heights to be expected. If the dyke is on a bay or harbor front, the following formula will give the wave height to be expected:

$$H = 1.5\sqrt{R} + (2.5 - \sqrt[4]{R})$$

where H is the wave height in feet and R is the reach in miles of the longest straight line that can be drawn from the dyke across the water surface of the bay or harbor.

If excessive wave action is expected, the front of the dyke may be protected with riprap or other facing materials.

The drainage gates, if 8 feet in width or less, are usually of the metal type. If they must be larger, wooden flap gates may be used. They should preferably be creosoted and suspended by 1½- or 2-inch galvanized pipe threaded through galvanized iron or bronze U-bolts. A channel of wood or concrete through the dyke will be necessary. This will require wing walls and an apron on the outlet side and may have to be supported on piling. The capacity must be great enough to carry off the runoff expected during the time the gates are discharging. The "rational" method of computing runoff of rainfall may be followed, as outlined in works dealing with hydrology or storm-sewer design. Runoff need only be rapid enough, however, to prevent the development of a crop of mosquitoes. If the outlets discharge into the open sea, protective works may be necessary to prevent damage by waves. These may take the form of timber structures supported by piles extending beyond the outlets to break the force of the waves.

The ditches used in salt-marsh drainage are often deep and narrow. Sometimes vertical sides are possible, particularly if there is a heavy mat of grass roots. In some cases the top foot is sloped 1:1, and the rest of the ditch has vertical sides. Long-handled, square-pointed shovels have been found satisfactory for this work. The cutting edge of the shovel

Fig. 9-10. Armco flap gate discharging at low tide.

should be kept sharp. Each laborer should be furnished with a 10-inch mill file. Large ditches are excavated with machinery. In recent years excavating machinery has been developed which has its weight distributed over a large bearing so that it can operate on soft ground. Ditches must be maintained so that fish can circulate and the water can move out freely.

In areas adjacent to salt water there may be marshes containing fresh or slightly brackish water in which *Anopheles* mosquitoes may be breeding. It is sometimes practical and economical to construct ditches that will permit salt water to enter the marshy areas, and this will make the water unsuitable for *Anopheles* mosquito breeding. This may be accomplished by placing flap gates so that salt water flows into the area at high tide at one point and out of the area at low tide at another point. This will provide circulation of salt water. Care must be taken that other species of dangerous mosquitoes do not begin breeding in the salt water. This may require clearing of vegetation and careful maintenance of the ditches.

9-26. Filling. Areas that cannot be drained can sometimes be economically and adequately kept from breeding mosquitoes by filling. Large fills along water fronts may be accomplished with hydraulic dredges. In some cases it is possible to fill low areas on the outskirts of towns with rubbish. This, if properly done, is satisfactory, but care should be taken that cans, buckets, and other containers are covered with earth, ashes, or cinders so that they will not hold water and breed mosquitoes or cause other nuisances. The sanitary fill described in Chap. 8 is applicable to this type of situation. Street sweepings are also of value for filling purposes.

9-27. Larviciding. The larvae and pupae of the common varieties of mosquitoes are air breathers and must come to the water surface to renew their air supply by means of their breathing tubes. Oil, when applied to the water, forms a film over the water surface, and when larvae return to the surface, some of it will enter the breathing tubes. The oils used have a poisoning effect rather than mere clogging or choking. Experiments have shown that if mosquito larvae are exposed to kerosene and then are removed to clear water they will die in about fifteen minutes, practically the same length of time as required to kill those remaining beneath a kerosene film. With the heavier crude oils, three hours may be required before the larvae die. Pupae are somewhat more resistant than larvae.

9-28. Oils Used. As mentioned above, kerosene is a very rapid destroyer of mosquito larvae. It also has the advantage of good spreading ability. Its disadvantages are its higher cost, compared with some other oils; quick evaporation from the surface of the water, particularly in hot weather; and a lack of color, which makes it difficult for the oiler to be certain that he has adequately covered the surface of the water.

Crude and fuel oils vary somewhat in toxic power and spreading ability. The latter quality is usually the governing factor. Proper spreading can be obtained by diluting the heavy oil with a sufficient amount of kerosene, or a small amount of spreader. The crude oils have the advantage of being easily inspected for continuous film, and in addition, will remain on the water surface for several days, thereby increasing the intervals between applications. What is known to the oil trade as a No. 2 Diesel oil will be satisfactory. Dilution of the heavier oils will not ordinarily be so economical as purchasing oil under proper specifications. Specifications recommended by Ginsburg[1] are as follows: type, distillate fuel; gravity (A.P.I.), 27 to 33; flash, 130°F or higher; viscosity, Saybolt Universal at 100°F, 35 to 40; odor, none offensive; distillation, 10 per cent at

430 to 450°F, 50 per cent at 510 to 550°F, and 90 per cent at 630°F and higher. The low-boiling fractions cause a quick kill, while the high-boiling fraction ensures a lasting film. Spreading power and toxicity may be increased by adding up to 5 per cent of cresol or cresylic acid to the oil.

Objections are sometimes raised to the oiling of some waters, such as ornamental ponds and areas where fish and waterfowl are raised or encouraged to congregate. An oil-pyrethrum larvicide has been developed by Ginsburg[1] that will be reasonably efficient wherever oil is objectionable. It is primarily an oil emulsion of the following composition: 66 per cent kerosene or similar light petroleum distillate, 0.07 per cent pyrethrins, 33.5 per cent water, 0.5 per cent sodium lauryl sulfate. This stock emulsion can be made by the user, but it is preferable to purchase it from manufacturers, who sell it under the name of the New Jersey Larvicide. In the field it is diluted with 10 parts of water before spraying. The film produced is not lasting, but there is no injury to waterfowl, fish, or plants. It is more costly than oil.

9-29. Oil Application. Oil is applied by means of spraying apparatus that will produce an even thin film over the water surface. Hand and power equipment of various sizes is used for this purpose. The conventional hand sprayer consists of a tank to hold the liquid, a nozzle for regulating the size of droplets and rate of discharge, and an internal or external liquid pump or built-in air pump to supply the force for moving the liquid through a flexible hose to the nozzle. A typical power sprayer consists of a tank with an agitator to hold the liquid, an engine to supply power, a pressure regulator and relief valve, and a flexible line to carry the liquid to the discharge system, consisting of a hand-operated shutoff valve and nozzle. A relatively new type of power unit, the mist-blower machine, has been found to have wide application in mosquito-control work. The unit consists essentially of an engine-driven blower added to a low-pressure and low-volume power sprayer. The spray material is discharged through nozzles or a shear plate into the air stream produced by the blower. This principle gives the machine a range effective to several hundred feet, depending on the amount of foliage, the direction and velocity of the wind, and the terrain.

Where large areas are to be covered, power sprayers may be used if it is possible to bring the power equipment to the water that is to be sprayed. Under these conditions, power spraying may be more economical. Plunger pumps which force the oil through a high-pressure hose at 300 pounds per square inch through a special nozzle have been found satisfactory. Application of oil under high pressure has the advantage of giving better penetration through vegetation on the water.

The edges of reservoirs have been oiled by the Tennessee Valley Authority in the following manner. Flat-bottomed boats 4 to 5 feet wide, 24 feet long, 2 feet deep with a draft of 10 inches are used. They are square and shallow at the ends so that approach to mud banks is easy. Either outboard or inboard motors are installed for locomotion. If an inboard motor is used, a spray pump is powered from a friction wheel connected to the motor flywheel; otherwise, the spray pump must have a separate motor of its own. The former method is more desirable. The pump draws water from a 6-inch pipe well and also draws oil from a tank, the mixture, which contains 95 per cent or more of water, being thrown through a hose for a distance of 30 to 50 feet. The oil used is 80 per cent kerosene and 20 per cent crude black oil.

Tank trucks with pumps for spraying the oil have also been used where it is possible to approach the water. In softer soils, trucks mounted on very large tires or caterpillar tractors have been used instead of standard trucks.

The amount of oil required will depend upon conditions. If the oil spreads well and there are no obstructions, it is possible to cover an acre of water surface with 10 gallons of oil. In actual practice, however, losses caused by vegetation and uneven application are likely to result in application figures of 20 to 60 gallons of oil per acre of water surface covered. The amount of oil applied by one man, using a hand sprayer, in an eight-hour day is also variable, but it should be within the limits of 40 to 80 gallons per day.

In large bodies of water, oiling is necessary only along the edges or in patches of vegetation where the larvae are protected from wave action and natural enemies. In ornamental pools, where there may be objection to the use of heavy oils, kerosene or the New Jersey Larvicide (Art. 9-28) is useful and is not injurious to vegetation. Oiling should be done at frequent enough intervals to prevent emergence of a crop of mosquitoes. The interval will depend upon the type of mosquito and the weather. Inspectors in charge of oiling should check the work of oilers to ensure their efficiency.

A simple yet convenient arrangement to prevent the dissipation of the oil film on small running streams is to place, at intervals across the stream, planks fastened in a vertical position at the water surface to act as a dam to hold back the oil as it floats down. This results in a continuous film for some distance upstream.

9-30. Usefulness of Oiling. Oiling must be done on water that cannot be drained or on streams where there is a continuous supply of water, particularly when the current is not uniform, where there are overhanging banks and quiet pools, and where control by minnows cannot be obtained. Oiling should not be depended upon too greatly in streams or pools that are overgrown with vegetation which will prevent access of oil to all parts. Such sheltering vegetation must be cleared from the stream if good control is to be obtained. Poorly maintained side ditches of unpaved streets need much attention from the oiler. The practice of allowing the discharge of waste water from residences into street ditches results in unnecessary oiling work. A permanent remedy, either sewer connection or subsurface drainage, should be required.

It should be pointed out that oiling should not be done indiscriminately. For instance, in rain-water pools there is no chance of a mosquito crop emerging until five to seven days after the pool is filled. Therefore, it is not necessary to oil such pools immediately after a rain but only in sufficient time to prevent a crop from developing. Precaution should be taken, however, to start an oiling round in time to have all water treated within the time required to produce a crop. Proper attention to weather conditions and observation of actual breeding conditions enable the sanitarian to cut down the oiling expense.

Storm sewers will sometimes hold water in the sewer itself or in catch basins. Such breeding may be prevented by pouring oil into the water of the catch basin, but frequently it will be found of advantage to use one of the other larvicides mentioned later.

9-31. DDT as a Larvicide. This insecticide (Art. 10-24) is also a good mosquito larvicide. It is effective against both the culicine and anopheline mosquitoes as a solution in petroleum oils, as a concentrate for use in water emulsions, and as a dust (for methods of preparation, see Art. 10-24).

Oil Solution. The oil solution is generally used in a 1.0 per cent concentration and applied by means of a sprayer. The ordinary 3- or 4-gallon garden sprayer with a nozzle which produces a very fine spray or mist at a low application rate is satisfactory. Even better results will be obtained by using a power sprayer with pressures to 50 pounds per square inch. For initial control, *i.e.*, a kill of existing larvae and pupae, only 0.1 pound of DDT is required per acre of water surface. With a 1 per cent solution, this will require 5 quarts of solution per acre. Where there is much vegetation, additional quantities may be advisable. Precautions should be taken to see that even coverage is obtained. For residual toxicity, *i.e.*, a killing effect which will last for several generations of mosquitoes, 1.0 pound of DDT is used per acre. This is done only where wind and waves do not agitate the water surface. This dosage would require 2½ gallons of 5 per cent DDT solution. The stronger solutions have the advantage of easier transportation, but require a finer spray, or even a mist, in order to obtain proper coverage. For very small areas where economy of materials is not important, use of the 5 per cent solution with sprayers of the ordinary flit-gun type is satisfactory (for application over large areas by aircraft, see Art. 9-40).

Emulsion. In the water emulsion the same amount of DDT is required as with oil. The 35 per cent emulsion concentrate mentioned in Art. 10-24 would be mixed with six times its volume of water to obtain a 5 per cent emulsion, or 34 parts of water to obtain a 1 per cent emulsion. Five quarts of the 1 per cent emulsion would be required for 1 acre. At a dosage of 0.1 pound per acre only 1 pint of concentrate will suffice to treat 3.5 acres of water surface. Fine sprays should be used for emulsions also. Since there is a tendency for the emulsion to mix with the water, there may be a residual action. Therefore, dipping for larvae should be the rule before each application of the emulsion.

FIG. 9-11. Applying DDT larvicide with a hand sprayer. (*Courtesy of U.S. Public Health Service.*)

If the emulsion in sufficient concentration is well dispersed through the water, breeding will be prevented for several weeks. Dosages for this purpose are calculated on a parts per million basis, with 1 part per million of DDT as the dose. This requires about 8 pints of the 35 per cent concentrate per acre of water 1 foot deep. The concentrate after dilution should be applied as a coarse spray. Since fish may be killed by doses of DDT of over 1 part in 10 million parts of water, this method is applicable only to temporary pools, borrow pits, and other situations where fish are not present. The heavy application of DDT here will reduce the frequency of application.

Dust. DDT as a dust is 25 times as toxic as Paris green to *Anopheles quadrimaculatus.* The usual dosage of 0.1 pound per acre is used. A

10 per cent dust can be applied at a rate of 1 pound of dust per acre, but a larger quantity will usually be necessary to get effective coverage. A 2 per cent dust applied at the rate of 5 pounds per acre will be more satisfactory. The rotary hand duster used in agriculture is suitable. Residual effect can be obtained with 1 pound of DDT per acre. If this is desired, it is unnecessary to dilute the 10 per cent dust. Attempts to obtain a residual effect with dust should be confined to sheltered areas, usually with considerable vegetation, since the surface dust film drifts about.

FIG. 9-12. Applying oil solution of DDT with a power sprayer. (*Courtesy of U.S. Public Health Service.*)

9-32. Effect of DDT on Aquatic Life. Investigations made by the U.S. Public Health Service[2,3] indicate that DDT must be used with caution where fish life is of importance. The undesirable effects of DDT may be indirect; by killing large and small water organisms which are food for fish, it upsets the biological balance of a body of water.

The application of 0.4 pound or more of DDT per acre in shallow water is detrimental to fish life. Single applications of 0.1 pound per acre or less cause no fish mortality. Repeated treatment at this dosage will cause some fish mortality between the third and tenth applications, and after 11 to 18 applications, the fish population will be significantly reduced.

It is suggested that, where fish must be conserved, routine treatment be at a rate not exceeding 0.05 pound per acre. Complete treatment of a shallow pond, if repeated at this low rate, will cause some mortality. It is believed that mortality will be negligible if only the margins, where the mosquito breeding normally occurs, are treated. In areas similarly treated at 0.025 pound per acre, no mortality was observed.

Surface organisms, such as large beetles, are killed, and accordingly fish food is reduced, but not significantly. The effect upon plankton is so slight that the biological balance is not affected. Birds are not affected, nor are such mammals as rabbits, cotton rats, and raccoons.

DDD or TDE (Art. 10-27) is an effective larvicide, and may be substituted for DDT where aquatic life is of importance.

9-33. Comparison of Larvicides. All the larvicides discussed are equally efficient when used in proper quantities and properly applied. Cost, therefore, becomes the important consideration. Oiling may be estimated as costing, for oil and hand labor, $4 to $7 per acre per application. This may be reduced 30 to 50 per cent by the use of power equipment on a truck or boat. Use of the pyrethrum or New Jersey Larvicide costs nearly the same. DDT with hand application costs not more than half as much as oil either by hand or by power application. These costs include foremen and transportation but not higher overhead expenses.

9-34. Natural Enemies. The mosquito, like most animals and insects, has its natural enemies. Dragonflies, birds, and bats prey upon the winged mosquito. Dragonfly larvae and other aquatic insects feed upon the larvae and pupae of the mosquito. However, of the natural enemies, only fish appear to be useful from a practical standpoint.

The most important fish are several species of minnows. While the top-feeding minnows, and the other fish discussed later, are not naturally present in all parts of the country, close observation will probably result in the discovery of some local fish that is effective as a larvae destroyer. It is also possible to import top-feeding minnows from more favored localities for the purpose of stocking mosquito breeding places. Goldfish are of little value in keeping ornamental pools clean of larvae. Small catfish have been used to keep open wells free of larvae, but they are of no value in open water.

Mosquito control by means of fish is the cheapest method that has been discovered so far. The possibility of using this agency should never be overlooked by the sanitarian. Fish, however, have their limitations under natural conditions, and too much reliance must not be placed upon their unaided efforts.

Top-water minnow. The top-water minnow, also known as the pot-bellied minnow, whose scientific name is *Gambusia affinis*, is naturally distributed along the Atlantic coast from Delaware to Mexico, in the Mississippi Valley from Louisiana to Illinois, and in Texas. It grows to a maximum length of approximately 3 inches. Because it feeds voraciously upon larvae and pupae and multiplies rapidly, it is a particularly valuable fish to be used in stocking mosquito breeding waters. It bears its young alive in successive broods numbering up to 50 or more throughout the spring and summer. It is very hardy and is able to live equally well in brackish water, fresh water, or water with some pollution. It gets its name of "top-water minnow" from its habit of surface feeding. One specimen was observed to eat 165 mosquito larvae in one day. The young minnows will start feeding on the larvae immediately after they are born.

Use of fish. The larvae have well-developed instincts which lead them to seek protection from fish in floating debris and in vegetation.

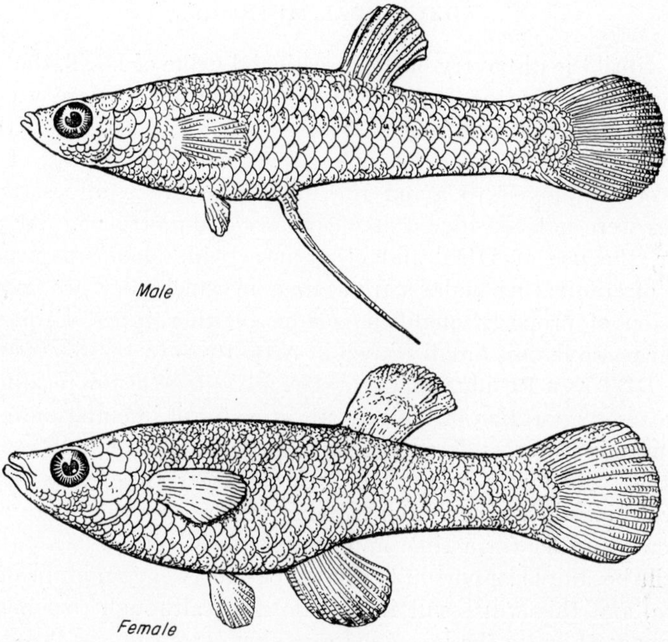

FIG. 9-13. The top-water minnow, *Gambusia affinis.* (*After U.S. Bureau of Fisheries.*)

Therefore, clearing the edges of bodies of standing water will be necessary. In impounded waters, fluctuations of the water level tend to discourage marginal growths, and such fluctuations are sometimes induced expressly for that purpose. It is difficult to say how many fish will be necessary to prevent mosquito breeding. Few may be needed in a clean-edged pool, while great numbers may be unable to obtain control where the shores are heavily lined with vegetation. Observations must be made to determine whether control has been established or whether assistance to the fish, in the form of clearing, may be necessary. In many instances chemical larviciding will have to be utilized as an additional control measure.

Hatcheries. As before mentioned, *Gambusia* is a prolific breeder, which makes it easy to establish hatcheries that will provide a supply of minnows for stocking such water as accumulates under deep culverts, watering troughs, wells, rain barrels, ponds, and streams which occasionally dry up. When these fish are not naturally present, it is frequently possible to have them shipped long distances in order to start a hatchery in the locality in which they are needed. The same precautions should be taken in shipping as are necessary in the transportation of live fish by government hatcheries, *i.e.*, keeping the water cool in transit.

ADULTICIDAL METHODS

9-35. Until the discovery of the insecticidal value of DDT, the destruction of adult mosquitoes as a means of preventing disease was not in general practice. Fumigation of homes and other buildings with insecticides was used as a means of yellow fever control. Sprays of various kinds were employed to avoid the nuisance of mosquitoes, but such measures were not considered as of any great importance. At present, however, the use of DDT and other insecticides looms as a potential method of eradicating malaria from areas in which they are used under supervision of properly qualified persons. Other types of insecticides and their possible uses are discussed in Arts. 10-25 to 10-35.

9-36. DDT as a Residual Spray. The advantage of the residual spray is that after evaporation of the solvent, or water, if in emulsion form, the remaining minute crystals on the surfaces of walls, etc., will poison the mosquitoes which rest upon them. Mosquitoes frequently rest upon walls or ceilings after they enter a room. They are even more likely to rest upon a surface for a time immediately after biting. In either case there will be ample opportunity for a ten- to twenty-minute or longer exposure, and this will result in a toxic dose, although the mosquitoes may manage to leave the house before dying.

While spraying has been conducted as a malaria-control measure, other effects have been noted. Diarrhea and other enteric diseases, especially among children, have decreased, probably as a result of the effect upon houseflies. Medical costs to the families have been lowered. Household insects, such as roaches, have been reduced, and the comfort of the people has been improved.

When temperatures are above 60°F, a 35 per cent DDT concentrate is used. At lower temperatures, a 25 per cent strength is used (see Art. 10-24). In each case the concentrate is diluted with water to a strength of 5 per cent DDT. The emulsion is applied at such a rate that there will be 200 milligrams of DDT per square foot or 4 milliliters of 5 per cent emulsion per square foot, or about 1 gallon per 1,000 square feet.

For hand spraying, the compressed-air type of spray can is recommended. A satisfactory sprayer holds 4 gallons and has a pump by which air pressure may be built up to 100 pounds per square inch. The sprayer should have a pressure gauge attached. The insides of lids of new sprayers should be examined, and paint, if any, should be scraped off; otherwise it will come off as flakes in the emulsion. The tank should be tested at 100 pounds per square inch and any leaks soldered. The tank should be marked inside by soldering a short piece of wire inside at the 12-pint water level. When ready to use, the 12 pints of water is placed in the tank, and to this is added 2 pints of 35 per cent DDT concentrate. The pump is replaced and screwed down tightly. The tank

FIG. 9-14. Residual spraying of the interior of a house. (*Courtesy of U.S. Public Health Service.*)

is then inverted several times to mix water and concentrate. The pump is given 60 strokes to obtain the proper operating pressure of 50 pounds per square inch. The spray is then applied for about four minutes, after which 30 more strokes are given to regain lost pressure, and spraying is resumed until the tank is empty. The most effective spray-nozzle produces a flat spray with an angle of 50 to 80 degrees. When this nozzle is used and the above procedure followed, the spraying time is eight to nine minutes. Before being refilled, the nozzle tip should always be cleaned with a fine brush.

It is important that the spray be applied at the proper rate in order to obtain the required amount of DDT per square foot, *i.e.*, 200 milligrams. In order to accomplish this with the hand sprayer described above, 190 square feet should be covered in one minute; *i.e.*, about 1,650 square feet should be covered in the eight to nine minutes of spraying.

The spray operator should practice with plain water until he can cover close to 190 square feet of surface per minute with the hand sprayer. Whether in practice or actual spraying, the work is done on walls by starting at one corner and working from floor to ceiling and then back in steady up-and-down movements. The nozzle is held about 18 inches from the surface. For ceilings it may be necessary to add extension pipes so that the nozzles will be at the proper distance. The spray is not applied directly overhead but at a slight angle, and strips are sprayed from one side to the other. Interiors of closets should be sprayed. Washable work clothes may be sprayed also. Porches and screens should be treated. Respirators and goggles should be worn by workmen while spraying.

Power sprayers are also used and are of particular value where houses are close together. They have two outlets, a large tank, and two 100-foot lengths of xylene-resistant hose with two nozzles, of the same type as used with the hand sprayer.

9-37. Frequency and Extent of Spraying. Within certain limits, the greater the dosage of DDT, the longer the toxic effect lasts. It appears, however, that there is little advantage in applying DDT at over 200 milligrams per square foot. There is a belief on the part of some workers that an emulsion strength of 7.5 per cent is desirable as insurance that the 200-milligram application will be attained. Application at 100 milligrams is quite effective, but observation indicates that in the United States one application at the 200-milligram rate is sufficient to give protection for one mosquito breeding season, particularly if the backs and undersides of furniture are treated as well as walls, ceilings of rooms and porches, unscreened or not, and screens. If a case of malaria is known to exist in a house, not only are the surfaces of the house sprayed but also privies, stables, and other outbuildings.

9-38. Organization and Cost of Residual Spraying. A DDT-spraying crew generally consists of two or three men and perhaps a foreman. For transportation, a half-ton pickup truck is useful. It is desirable to have boxes to hold containers of concentrate, several sprayers, hose, measuring cans, and a fire extinguisher. A special box will be needed to hold tools, spare parts and hoses for sprayers, lubricants, rubber gloves, etc.

One member of the spraying crew should, if possible, give notice to householders that the spraying will be done soon, and he should instruct them and perhaps aid them in getting the house ready. All furniture is moved away from walls into the center of the room and covered, since the solvent will affect varnish. Bed covers may be used to cover furniture and varnished floors may be covered with newspapers. Dishes and food should be put away or covered, and all open flames should be extinguished. When the spraying is over, the occupants may reenter immediately if they wish, but it is advisable to wait half an hour to permit the odor of the solvent to disappear. They should be warned that if a surface is touched while still wet, a streak will result.

The cost of spraying is not very great. Only 1 quart of a 35 per cent concentrate or 1.8 gallons of 5 per cent DDT spray will be needed for a small tenant house with 1,700 square feet to be sprayed. As an average, taking into account the larger houses and the fact that occupants vary in the amount of preparation already made, about 1.6 man-hours and about 1 pound of DDT will be required per spraying.

FIG. 9-15. "Fogging" with DDT for control of adult mosquitoes.

9-39. Space Sprays. The ingredients of the aerosol space sprays are discussed in Art. 10-24. They are very efficient in destroying mosquitoes and other winged insects in enclosed spaces. Another type of space spray is an oil solution, usually in deodorized kerosene, of pyrethrin and DDT. This is the popular commercial fly spray. It is effective when used in sprays of the Flit-gun type. The spray of the oil solution or aerosol must actually come in contact with the insect if a kill is to be effected. Some residual action can be obtained by holding the oil-solution sprayer close to surfaces so that they are obviously dampened, but this is not very efficient, and it is wasteful of insecticide.

9-40. Outdoor Control of Mosquitoes. Most culicine and many anopheline mosquitoes rest in areas with much vegetation and enter buildings only to obtain blood. Residual treatment of 1 to 2 pounds of DDT per acre, although the dosage actually depends on the amount of surface to be treated, applied to vegetation and ground litter where mosquitoes rest reduces mosquitoes 80 to 95 per cent for several weeks after treatment. The applied spray should be as fine as possible and well distributed on the lower 8 to 10 feet of vegetation. DDT wettable powders or emulsions are most desirable as oil solutions may cause injury to foliage. To

FIG. 9-16. Spraying from an airplane with DDT thermol aerosol for control of adult and larvae mosquitoes. (*Courtesy of U.S. Public Health Service.*)

obtain adequate surface coverage the sprays are diluted to 1 per cent concentration and are applied at the rate of 10 to 25 gallons per acre.

For the temporary control of adult mosquitoes a number of formulations may be used in the form of mists and fogs. The usual formulations for this purpose contain from 5 to 10 per cent of DDT, which is applied at the rate of 0.1 to 0.2 pound of DDT per acre. The fog- or mist-producing machines are transported on vehicles which are operated at approximately 4 miles per hour. Swath width will vary, depending upon atmospheric conditions, density of vegetation, etc., but 200 to 300 feet is usually considered average. Sufficient residue to provide some lasting effect is deposited by mist machines, especially the mist blowers. However, fogs applied at the rate of 0.1 to 0.2 pound of DDT per acre are considered space treatments.

Some of the mist-producing machines are provided with attachments so that dusts may be dispersed either separately or at the same time as mist sprays. Dusts containing 10 per cent DDT or 3 per cent gamma isomer of BHC have been used as an adulticide in a number of community and other mosquito-abatement programs, reportedly with good success.

Airplanes have been used successfully to apply DDT and other chlorinated hydrocarbons for the control of both larvae and adult mosquitoes. The insecticide has been used in various forms and distributed with various types of spraying equipment and planes. The skill of the airplane pilot is the most important factor in obtaining best results with the minimum amount of material. He must know the pattern of spray emitted by his plane and must be able to cover the area evenly.

It is desirable to use a solution containing as much DDT as is practical to handle and to select a solvent with relatively low volatility and a relatively high flash point. Certain high-boiling methylated naphthalenes have proved very satisfactory and permit the use of concentrates containing 20 to 30 per cent of DDT. An application of ½ to 1 pint of a 20 per cent solution (0.1 to 0.2 pound of DDT) per acre will give satisfactory results. In Panama effective control was obtained at dosages of 0.3 to 0.8 pound per acre. No better results were observed from the greater doses. Emulsions of 5 per cent strength have also been distributed by airplanes. Dusts are more difficult to apply from aircraft than are sprays, but good control is obtainable by their use. A 5 per cent dust is recommended.

Application of DDT by airplanes is possible over large areas, such as extensive swamps and the edges of large reservoirs. Since there is a heavy kill of adults as well as larvae, the mosquito population may be practically absent for an indefinite period although there may be rapid migration of adults into the area.

CONTROL OF HOUSE MOSQUITOES

9-41. The Most Pestiferous Mosquitoes. *Culex pipiens*, *C. quinquefasciatus*, and *Aedes aegypti*, it will be remembered, frequently find their breeding places in water containers in the immediate vicinity of homes, occasionally actually within residences. Since *A. aegypti* is the carrier of dengue and yellow fever, it is evident that health authorities should consider the presence of domestic mosquitoes of this type as more than a mere nuisance. As a general rule, the mosquitoes mentioned do not travel long distances. Their presence, therefore, in appreciable numbers about a home usually indicates that they are being produced in the immediate neighborhood, and a search for the water producing them will usually result in the discovery of a container thickly populated with larvae and pupae. The breeding places of these mosquitoes may be found not only in the more sparsely inhabited residential sections of the city or in the country but will also be encountered in the densely populated and business districts. For instance, *A. aegypti* has been observed breeding in a five-and-ten-cent store of a large city in a bowl of water in which lily bulbs had been placed. Fire buckets under the counters of department stores have been discovered breeding both *Culex* and *Aedes* mosquitoes, much to the discomfort of the store employees and customers.

9-42. Breeding Places. Possible water containers which may produce mosquitoes around residences and places of business are, of course, numerous. A few which may be mentioned without requiring special discussion as to safeguarding are as follows: leaky water cutoffs; other leaks in pipes; sagging roof gutters, which hold water after rains; choked downspouts, which have the same effect; flower vases in houses, water pitchers in guest rooms, discarded tire casings, which frequently hold rain water; chicken watering troughs; and unused flush toilets.

9-43. Methods of Control. Shallow-dug wells are frequently producers of the domestic mosquitoes. The larvae may be present in the well without the user suspecting it, for as the bucket is lowered both larvae and pupae dive. Of course, wells of this type are of highly questionable safety from a drinking water standpoint. The mosquito-control sanitarian could render additional service by pointing out to the owner or tenant methods of correction to minimize contamination of the water. The best method of control is to cover the well tightly and install a pump, as illustrated in Chap. 5. As a temporary expedient, three or four top-water minnows may be placed in the well. Catfish have also been used with good results. The fish improve the quality of the well water as they consume, in addition to the mosquito larvae, other insects and worms which are usually present in uncovered shallow wells. An unused well should be promptly filled. If this is impracticable, it may be sealed, or if no better method can be used, several gallons of heavy crude oil poured into the well will make it mosquitoproof for several months.

Cisterns of the underground type can be treated in the same manner as wells. Overground cisterns require tight covering. The overflow spout should be screened with 16-mesh wire screen, and the inlet pipe should be treated in the same manner. A coarse filter in the inlet pipe will have the same effect as screening. Any openings in an overground cistern will almost invariably result in mosquito breeding.

Rain barrels and water barrels, in general, are heavy producers of mosquitoes, and this situation is somewhat difficult to control, particularly when the water is caught and kept for laundering purposes. The barrels need continuous attention. Breeding may be prevented by keeping a film of kerosene upon the water surface, by keeping a few minnows in each barrel, or by covering. The last method is the least satisfactory of the three, as the cover will be left off for a longer or shorter time, which may result in a female mosquito gaining access to the water and laying eggs.

Fire barrels can be easily controlled by the use of larvicides. A small amount of creosote, half a pint to the fire barrel, will poison the water against mosquito breeding for an indefinite length of time. Some of the antifreezing compounds which are used in fire barrels in warehouses have the same effect. One milliliter of 35 per cent DDT emulsion concentrate (Art. 10-24) mixed with the water will permanently prevent breeding in barrels holding up to 50 gallons of water.

Cans holding rain water in which mosquitoes are breeding are frequently found in the vicinity of homes. They present a difficult problem not only at the homes but also at the dumps to which they may be conveyed. Persuading the householder to punch holes in the bottom of the cans immediately after emptying does very little good; a better method is to hammer them flat. It will sometimes be necessary to use a 5 per cent DDT oil solution on the face of a dump after a rain to prevent breeding in water held by cans.

Waste water from sinks and outdoor faucets is often allowed to trickle into the grass, forming pools which may breed not only *Culex* but *Anopheles* mosquitoes. Such water should be drained into a sewer or into an underground septic tank if available. If no other method can be applied, the water should be confined to a ditch or gutter and oiled or treated with a DDT preparation at the proper intervals.

Septic-tank effluent should never be allowed to run upon the ground surface but should be disposed of as illustrated in Chap. 4. If the effluent accidentally reaches the surface, it should be confined to a clean-edged ditch and oiled or treated with a DDT preparation. The tank itself should have a mosquitoproof cover. The same precaution applies to cesspools. The practice of covering cesspools with a few boards or logs banked with earth usually results in holes through which an adult mosquito can find entrance, and the consequence is a neighborhood infested with *Culex pipiens* or *C. quinquefasciatus*.

Watering troughs for cattle and horses are frequently found to be mosquito producers. They should be completely emptied and cleaned at least once a week. Merely emptying will not always give control, as the small amount of water that remains in the bottom frequently contains many larvae and pupae. A few minnows in the trough will keep it clear of larvae, provided that the trough does not have too many of them when the minnows are introduced. There are limits even to the capacity of a minnow, and a few of them should not be expected to clean out a watering trough that is alive with larvae. A little kerosene on the water will not deter animals from drinking.

The practice of allowing refrigerator drippings to run through a hole in the floor to collect in a pool under the house is a dangerous one, so far as mosquitoes are concerned. It is better to collect the water in a pan, which is emptied when full. Another solution is to excavate a hole about 3 feet in diameter and 8 to 10 inches deep. This, when filled with sand, gravel, or cinders, will allow seepage into the ground without forming a pool, provided that the earth is sufficiently porous.

Ornamental pools and fountains must be carefully watched, particularly if aquatic plants are growing in them. Minnows in sufficient number may be the best solution. Goldfish should not be depended upon.

SCREENING

9-44. The malaria-carrying mosquitoes are primarily night biters. Also they are shy and easily alarmed by any movement. A sleeping person, therefore, is much more likely to be bitten by an *Anopheles* mosquito than is a person who is awake. It follows that sleeping in a well-screened house is one of the best ways to avoid malaria. This means of malaria control is particularly useful in rural sections. For this reason it is the duty of the sanitarian to encourage proper screening in homes and elsewhere. Many railroads running through malarial regions pay particular attention to the screening of their bunk cars and section houses, finding a real economy in the prevention of malaria and of the loss which the disease entails to the company. Though many buildings are screened, the fact is that very few of them are properly screened.

9-45. Screen Mesh. Apparently much present-day screening is based upon the idea of keeping out flies only, and the wire cloth that is used is of 12-mesh material, *i.e.*, having 12 openings to the inch each way. This is entirely too large an opening, and will allow a very large percentage of mosquitoes to find entrance to the building. Wire of 14-mesh is some improvement, but no mesh with fewer than 16 openings to the inch gives good protection against mosquitoes. Even a 16-mesh screen will allow some smaller specimens of the common *Culex* to enter. The sanitarian, therefore, should constantly exert himself to the end that hardware dealers stock and that customers buy wire cloth of at least 16-mesh for the purpose of house screening. Screens of 12- to 14-mesh which are already in place may be improved somewhat by giving the wire one or more coats of special screen paint. This has the effect of making the mesh openings somewhat smaller.

9-46. Screening Material. Most screening is made of iron wire, generally galvanized. The life of this material depends upon the climatic conditions and the usage given to it. Wire of other metals, such as bronze and copper, has a longer life. The latter is most satisfactory, for bronze, being an alloy, may vary somewhat in character, so that certain parts of the screen may corrode much more quickly than the rest. It is important that copper tacks be used to fasten the copper screening, as steel or iron tacks set up an electrolytic action which results in speedy

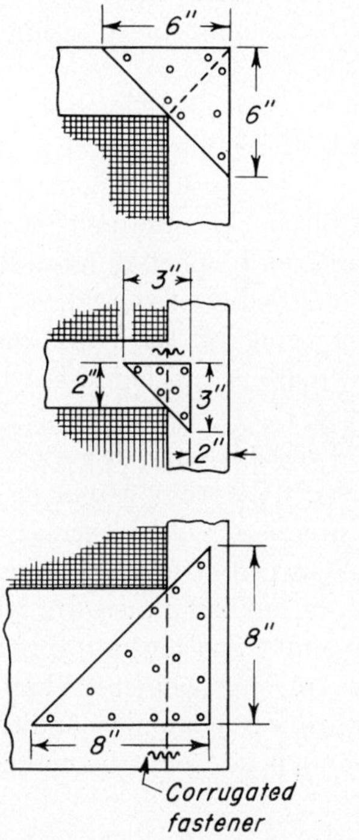

FIG. 9-17. Detail of joints showing 24-gauge galvanized iron triangles.

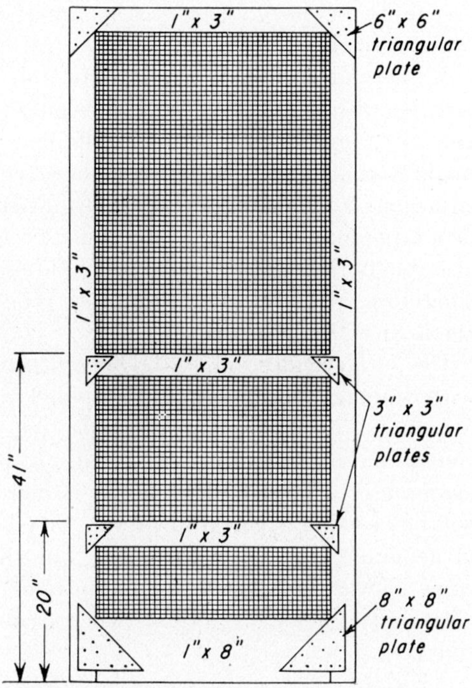

FIG. 9-18. Inside of door after completion.

corrosion at the contact points. On the seacoast, copper screening is imperative, as iron wire may last only a few months.

Plastic screen cloth, now available, is corrosion-resistent and hence longer-lived than metal. The plastic strands are thicker than the metal wire, and accordingly the openings for the same number mesh are smaller. The rule should be to have openings equivalent in size to those of the 16-mesh metal screen cloth.

9-47. Mosquito Bars. Where screening is impracticable, mosquito bars may be used in combating malaria. They should be made of bobbinet rather than of the ordinary netting. When in use over beds they should be tucked in around the mattress and not allowed to hang loosely to the floor. Care should also be taken that no part of the bar comes in contact with the sleeper. A spray of 5 per cent DDT solution applied to the bar occasionally would add greatly to its efficiency.

9-48. Considerations in Choice of Control Methods. Mosquito control is practiced either for nuisance prevention or disease prevention. In either case the control director must know the species of mosquitoes to be controlled, their flight range, and the breeding places which are producing the mosquitoes to be eliminated. This may necessitate the assistance of entomologists who are specialists in mosquito studies or other specialists.

If the end desired is malaria control, the nuisance mosquitoes can be ignored, although this is sometimes puzzling to the public, for the average person cannot understand the difference between mosquito control and malaria control. Permanent malaria control can be obtained in some situations by draining a few important sources of anopheline mosquitoes or a large number of small mosquito-producing bodies of water. It may also be obtained by organized residual spraying of DDT in homes. Therefore, although the mosquitoes remain, malaria can be absent from the area without spraying.

Use of larvicides, oil, or DDT will usually be necessary in connection with drainage for malaria, or these may be used alone; they will be needed for elimination of nuisance. Inspection of premises will be necessary to control nuisance mosquitoes and also to prevent yellow fever and dengue epidemics. The use of minnows is merely an auxiliary measure which will be of value in certain waters. Good screening and mosquitoproofing in general should be encouraged, but they are improvements that will come slowly with better education and improved economic conditions. The actual choice of methods will, of course, depend upon the comparative cost.

FLY CONTROL

9-49. Of the many species of flies in the United States, only the common domestic flies are significant in the carriage of disease. Flies spread diseases either mechanically or by inoculation through biting. The former is the method of the housefly (*Musca domestica*), and the latter is used by the tsetse fly of Africa, which transmits sleeping sickness through its bite. The biting stable fly (*Stomoxys calcitrans*) is often found among the house-frequenting flies in America.

Although the presence of houseflies is annoying and distasteful (90 to 95 per cent of the flies collected in houses belong to this species), their importance as health menaces would be appreciably reduced if human excreta were disposed of properly and if flies were excluded from sick-rooms and prevented from coming in contact with infectious discharges. Until such conditions have been attained, however, the housefly should be included among the enemies of man.

9-50. The Housefly as a Disease Carrier. All species of the common domestic fly, except the stable fly, have sponging mouth parts and, therefore, cannot inoculate a person by biting. Structurally, the housefly is well suited for the role of a mechanical carrier of disease. Its hairy body and legs become covered with the filth on which it delights to crawl and feed. The housefly can easily transfer this material, which may contain large numbers of pathogenic organisms, to human beings by resting on

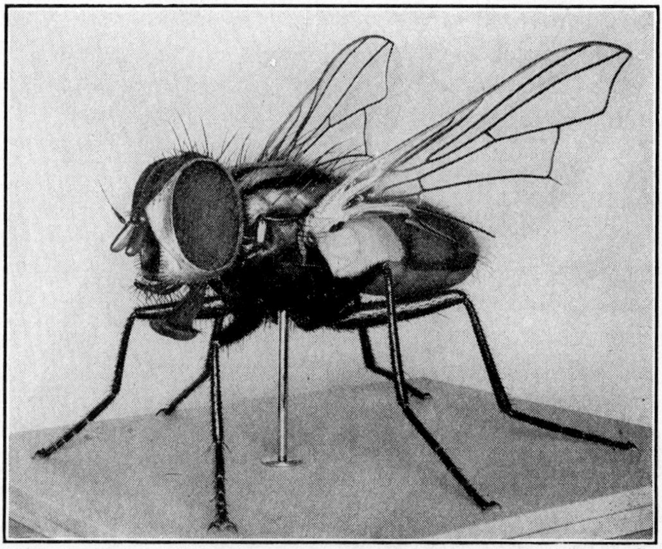

FIG. 9-19. The housefly. (*Photograph courtesy of Communicable Disease Center, U.S. Public Health Service.*)

the individual or by crawling across something which he consumes or handles. Furthermore, bacteria can live unharmed in the fly's alimentary canal until they are discharged in the excrement, the familiar "fly specks," or regurgitated in small drops known as "vomit spots." When it is considered that the flies which are on the dinner table may have been feeding upon the discharges of tubercular patients or upon human excreta which possibly contained typhoid and dysentery germs, it is apparent that fly control is a matter of importance.

Houseflies are also implicated in the spread of typhoid, ophthalmia, and parasitic worms, in addition to the intestinal diseases—enteritis, cholera, and infantile diarrhea. At one time or another, flies have been involved in cases of human myiasis, the invasion of living tissue by fly larvae. In the United States the flesh flies (*Sarcophaga*) have been the principal offenders in cases of myiasis.

In addition to their significance as transmitters of human diseases, flies cause an annual loss of several million dollars to the livestock and dairy industries.

9-51. Life History of the Housefly. The life cycle of all flies includes four developmental stages: egg, larva, pupa, and adult. Eggs are

FIG. 9-20. Fly pupae. (*Photograph courtesy of Communicable Disease Center, U.S. Public Health Service.*)

deposited upon the organic medium in which future development will take place. Only the flesh flies deviate from this procedure by hatching the eggs within the body of the female and then depositing the living larvae.

The female housefly starts laying eggs at the age of 2¼ to 23 days, depending to a large extent upon temperature and the character of her food. She lays 100 to 150 eggs at one batch and will lay two to four such batches, depositing the eggs in cracks and crevices of the breeding medium. Favorite breeding media include animal manure, human feces, garbage, decaying fruit, cannery wastes, and spilled animal feed.

Any moist, warm organic matter is a potential source of housefly breeding. After a period of eight to thirty hours, the eggs hatch, producing the larvae, or maggots, which feed upon the surrounding organic matter and grow rapidly for three to fourteen days. When the larva attains full growth it migrates to a drier part of the breeding medium, forms a dark-brown barrel-shaped case, and enters the pupa stage, the nonfeeding stage in which the larva develops into the adult fly. If the breeding medium is excessively moist, the larva may pupate in the surface of the soil or under boards, dry straw, or other adjacent shelter. After a period of three to ten days the full-grown fly emerges from the pupa case, works its way to the surface, moves about for a short time until its wings have extended and hardened, and then flies off. The minimum time from egg to adult is eight to ten days, but unfavorable food, moisture, and temperature conditions can extend this to a period of several months.

9-52. Habits of the Housefly. Long flights are not characteristic of the housefly, although marked specimens have been recovered at a distance of 13 miles from the point where liberated. Normally, houseflies remain close (200 to 300 yards) to their breeding places. However, depletion of the breeding source or excessively high densities may force a wider dispersal of the fly populations, depending upon the accessibility of new breeding or feeding sites.

Houseflies are not long-lived, having an average adult life span of thirty days with a possible maximum of sixty days. During the winter, in colder regions of the United States, this period may be extended well beyond sixty days. In warmer climates the housefly breeds throughout the year, and under favorable conditions, such as within a warm stable, continuous breeding has been observed even in northern areas. However, available evidence is contradictory on the question of how the housefly overwinters outdoors in colder regions.

9-53. Other Common Flies. The so-called "lesser housefly," or "little housefly," is frequently mistaken for an immature housefly. Although it resembles the common housefly, except that it is smaller, the little housefly is an entirely different species. Flies do not grow after they have left the pupa case. This species has larval habitats that are similar to those of the common housefly, and it enters houses freely in the early summer months. In development and activity, the latrine fly, a closely related species, is similar to the little housefly.

The stable fly is a fierce "biter," attacking man as well as animals. The favored breeding media are manure mixed with straw or silage and large accumulations of waste organic matter, such as peanut litter, marine grasses, and vegetable wastes. Attacks commonly ascribed to the "biting" housefly are often made, instead, by the stable fly.

There are other flies which are frequently seen, but they are not usually as numerous as the housefly, at least not in homes. These are the green bottle fly, the blue bottle fly, the black blowfly, and the secondary screwworm fly—shiny, metallic-looking flies colored green, blue or black—and the flesh fly, a grayish fly, usually large, with a checkerboard pattern on the abdomen. These flies breed primarily in decaying animal matter, and two species, the black blowfly and the secondary screwworm fly, are frequently important in domestic fly control, particularly in areas around abattoirs.

The fruit flies, or vinegar flies, are the small insects that make their appearance around over-ripe fruits or where the pickling of vegetables is in process. They use such material as food and as places to deposit eggs, although they may also feed on more dangerous materials.

Whereas the varied larval habitat of the green bottle fly, the black blowfly, and the flesh flies includes wounds of animals and man, the larva of the primary screwworm fly is found only in open wounds of living animals. The maggots of these flies bore through flesh and may cause the death of the animal.

9-54. Antifly Measures. The measures applied against the housefly are of several kinds, but no single one of them affords complete protection. An economically sound blending of the methods available in each situation is essential to effective antifly operations. First, and most important, is the application of measures that prevent the breeding of flies, whether protection is desired in an individual industry, farm, or household or throughout the community. The second measure is the prevention of the access of flies to human excreta, thus decreasing the danger of flies, becoming infected with disease bacteria. The third measure is the protection of food from flies, and the fourth is the destruction of those flies which have emerged.

9-55. Prevention of Breeding. The removal or elimination of potential fly-breeding materials and attractants is still the most feasible method of fly control. These sources include improperly handled garbage, spilled animal feed, manure, human feces, and industrial wastes produced by fruit- and vegetable-packing houses, rendering plants, and grain elevators and mills. In residential areas where other fly-breeding materials are scarce, the fecal droppings of dogs may be of significance as a minor source of fly breeding, particularly of flesh flies.

9-56. Prevention of Access to Human Excreta. This involves the proper disposal of human excreta. The exclusion of flies from the infectious discharges of an individual ill with a communicable disease is of prime importance. Of the various means of disposal, the water-carried sewage system is the best and gives the most complete protection from the possibility of flies carrying disease. The sanitary pit privy is effective in this respect when properly constructed and maintained. Experience has shown, however, that under practical operating conditions this type of privy is almost never kept flyproof. The open-back surface toilet, of course, gives the fly its best opportunity to contact human feces. The use of various disinfectants on the accumulations in surface toilets is of no particular value. Any slight effect the usual disinfectant might have on fly larvae is lost almost immediately by reacting with the organic matter of the excreta.

9-57. Protection of Foods. There are usually a few flies seeking entrance to homes and other buildings where food is prepared. Therefore, where flies are not excluded by other means, screens should be provided for all homes, restaurants, food markets, and similar establishments to reduce possible contact between flies and food. The practice of displaying on tables or in stalls open to flies vegetables and other foods that will be eaten uncooked is to be discouraged. Such food should be placed in glass cases.

9-58. Destruction of Adult Flies. Prevention of breeding is the most efficient and economical method of controlling flies. Other measures directed against the adult fly are not only expensive but also temporary, and thus do not replace fundamental sanitary measures. They may be necessary in case of an epidemic, in an area where some disaster has occurred, or at some point or area of a city which is especially attractive to, or productive of, flies. Control of adult flies, as demonstrated by making stool tests and noting attack rates, markedly reduced diarrheal diseases in an experiment in the Rio Grande Valley of Texas.

9-59. Garbage Handling for Fly Control. Widespread sources of fly breeding usually develop where facilities for the storage, collection, and disposal of garbage are inadequate. Covered, watertight metal containers should be provided where garbage is stored before collection or disposal. The wrapping of garbage prior to placement in the container is to be encouraged, and the container should be kept clean with frequent washing. To reduce attractants and the possibility of larvae development in storage containers, garbage collection should be on a twice-weekly schedule, particularly during the summer months. The use of covered, leakproof collection and transport vehicles should be encouraged.

The maintenance of an open garbage dump permits the completion of larvae development begun in garbage storage containers, and if the dump is located within flight range the emerging flies may return to the inhabited areas. The burning of refuse on an open dump may consume a portion of the organic matter present but does not provide a significant reduction in fly potential. Incinerators and sanitary landfills are two acceptable methods of disposal, the choice between them being dependent upon economic factors. Combined sewage and garbage disposal is another acceptable method subject to available local facilities.

On the farm, when kitchen wastes are not fed to animals, the same principles apply. Garbage should be buried, and since a 24-inch earth cover is necessary, storage is needed until a sufficient amount is accumulated to warrant burial.

9-60. Animal Feed and Manure. Stock feed and manure require constant attention to prevent fly breeding. Moist, finely ground stock feed can produce innumerable flies. Therefore, it is essential that such feed be kept completely dry and that spilled feed be removed frequently.

It is practically impossible to prevent all fly breeding in manure that is held to be used as fertilizer. When conditions permit, manure should be spread on the fields daily, or at least not less than two or three times weekly, depending on climatic conditions. In handling manures it is well to remember that a completely dry material is unfavorable for fly development and that dry surfaces are not attractive to flies. When animal droppings are to be held, heaps should be located where surface waters do not continuously wet them, preferably indoors. The outer surface may be made less attractive to flies by compacting. Some urban communities have solved this problem by collecting license fees, based upon the number of animals maintained on the premises, from the owners of the animals. In return for the fee, the city makes regular collections of the manure. Under such a program, it is advisable that the owner be required to gather the manure daily and store it in a flytight container and that collection be made at least once every seven days. Fly breeding in heaps or containers can be effectively reduced by treating the manure with larvicides, provided that the larvicides, as used, will not damage the land or crops fertilized with the manure. The most desirable and effective practice, however, is the frequent and complete removal of animal droppings.

9-61. Industrial Wastes. Wastes from fruit- and vegetable-packing houses, slaughterhouses, rendering plants, grain mills, and many similar establishments can provide sources of heavy fly breeding, whether located in urban or rural areas. Satisfactory disposal of most industrial wastes in which flies might breed can be accomplished by complete incineration or sanitary landfill. When such disposal facilities have not been available or the volume of wastes has been too great, many industries have converted these wastes into marketable products or have provided their own disposal systems when forced to by law.

9-62. Human Excreta. Human body wastes serve, when left exposed, not only as a reservoir of contamination from which filth-bearing flies may spread disease organisms, but also as a source of fly breeding. A water-carried sewage system, as mentioned before, provides the most complete protection from this source of flies and from disease transmission by flies. These facilities, however, if inadequate or improperly maintained or operated, can provide sources capable of prolific fly production. Fly breeding has been found in bar-screen wastes, grit-chamber wastes, open sludge digesters, sludge-drying beds, scum on Imhoff-tank vents, and lagooned raw sludge. The provision of adequate facilities and competent maintenance personnel will eliminate these hazards, the only practicable solution.

9-63. Chemical Treatments. On individual premises or on a community-wide basis, larvicides, residual sprays, poison baits, and space sprays are valuable in reducing fly populations when judiciously blended with a sound program of environmental sanitation.

FIG. 9-21. Treating an accumulation of refuse with a Buffalo turbine. *(Photograph courtesy of Communicable Disease Center, U.S. Public Health Service.)*

For killing flies which have entered buildings, interior space sprays of pyrethrum and combinations thereof with synergists or other insecticides are recommended. Residual applications of 5 per cent DDT water emulsions or solutions can be made on interiors in areas where houseflies are still susceptible to this chemical, except in dairy barns or other situations where it may contaminate milk or food. Lindane or methoxychlor may be used in dairy barns at rates of 25 and 200 milligrams per square foot.

In areas where houseflies have become resistant to DDT, a number of chemicals can be substituted, although resistance to these substitutes may also develop. The residual spraying of porches, sheds, small barns, and other outbuildings with chlordane as a 5 per cent emulsion, dieldrin as a 0.625 to 1.25 per cent emulsion, or lindane with application rates of about 1 gallon per 1,000 square feet has proved effective. Applications may be made with a common compressed-air spray can of 2- to 4-gallon capacity.

A residual bait spray, formulated with malathion at a rate of 2.5 parts of sugar to 1 part of malathion, applied at a rate of approximately 1 gallon per 100 square feet, is effective against DDT-resistant houseflies. The toxicity level of this compound permits safe usage as a residual spray

FIG. 9-22. "Fogging" for fly control. *(Photograph courtesy of Communicable Disease Center, U.S. Public Health Service.)*

at strengths of 1 to 2.5 per cent. Malathion or Diazinon may also be used in dairy barns as a residual treatment.

Malathion and Bayer L 13/59 are organophosphorus compounds extensively used in the formulation of poison baits. Liquid bait formulations generally contain 0.1 per cent of one of these compounds and 10 per cent sugar, molasses, or other attractant. The bait is applied at the rate of 1 gallon per 1,000 square feet of floor area. When an impervious floor surface is not present, the bait may be sprinkled on sacks or on metal or wooden sheets with an ordinary garden-sprinkling can. Dry baits generally are composed of 1 to 2 per cent toxicant and an attractant. The dry baits are placed at points of greatest fly concentration at the rate of 2 to 4 ounces per 1,000 square feet.

The use of dieldrin, chlordane, lindane, or BHC (benzene hexachloride) as a larvicide can be an effective fly-control measure and in certain situations, as in the treatment of manure or other concentrations of fly breeding media, may be advantageous. The wide use of these chemicals as fly larvicides may speed up the development of resistance in fly populations, particularly if the same chemical is used also as an adulticide. Saturation of the surface of the breeding material with a 1 per cent emulsion of these chemicals will kill some of the fly larvae and many of the emerging adults. Good results have been obtained by covering the surface of the material with a 3 per cent BHC dust or a 5 per cent chlordane dust. Borax is an effective larvicide for treatment of manure. It can be applied in solution, or it can be sprinkled over the manure in the powdered form, after which the manure is wetted down with water. If the manure is to be used as fertilizer, it is important that not more than 1 pound of borax to every 16 cubic feet of manure be used and that not more than 15 tons of such manure be applied to 1 acre.

Spraying large areas with mists or fogs, called "space spraying," is the only alternative for chemical control in a community program in areas where houseflies are no longer susceptible to residual or larvicidal applications. Specially designed machines which break up liquids into tiny air-borne droplets are used to disperse space sprays. The machines are all essentially the same in principle, consisting of a pump to introduce the liquid under pressure, a device to break the liquid into small droplets, and a fan to supply an air blast for initial carriage of the mist in a certain direction. Combustion chambers have been added to some machines to provide a heated air blast, thus creating a "fog" instead of a mist. Under good operating conditions, the effective distance of these machines in fly-control work is 100 to 200 feet.

Equipment using heat to create fogs or smokes by breaking up liquids into very small droplet sizes is dependent upon favorable atmospheric conditions for efficient operation. Wind velocities in excess of 5 miles per hour or the presence of thermal air currents may so quickly disperse the fogs that most of the effectiveness of the treatment is lost. Favorable conditions for use of thermal-type fog machines are most likely to prevail for short periods late in the afternoon, early in the morning, or at night.

The mist-blower type of machine, because of the larger droplet size, can operate efficiently with wind velocities up to 15 miles per hour. The adverse effects of high temperatures and low humidity are minimized by the larger droplet sizes and the initial velocity given the mist by the blower. Some machines of this type can be equipped with a duster attachment so that the machine can be used to disperse dusts, as well as water-wettable suspensions, water emulsions, and oil solutions. Because of their versatility, mist-blower machines are usually more adaptable in fly-control operations.

For outdoor space spraying the most generally used insecticides include 5 per cent DDT or chlordane emulsions or oil solutions, 5 per cent BHC emulsion, and 2 per cent lindane emulsion or solution. For effective results these emulsions or solutions are applied at a rate of 1 gallon per acre.

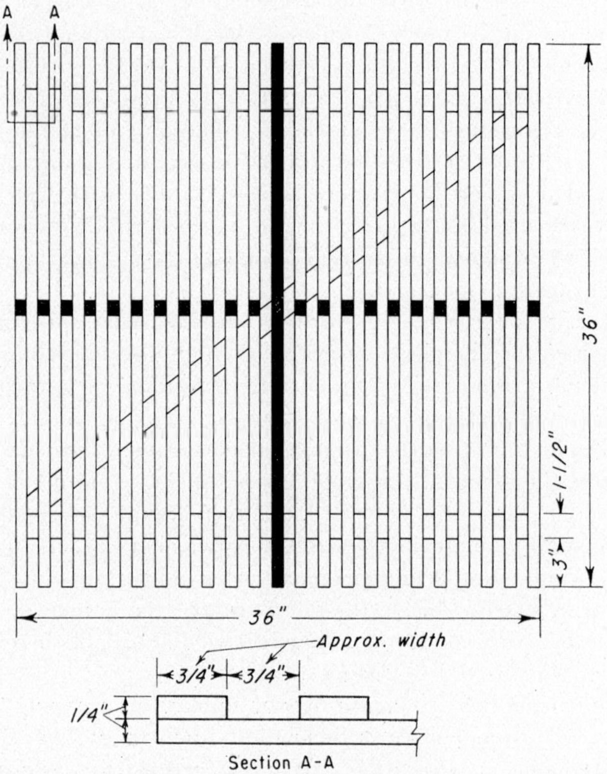

FIG. 9-23. Fly-counting grill.

9-64. The Community Fly-control Program. The success of a community fly-control program is dependent upon both effectiveness and economy. Therefore, the program must be carefully planned and made into a cooperative endeavor, since individual sanitary measures are of small value unless similar action is taken throughout the area. An initial survey of the community should be made to locate potential breeding areas and principal fly densities and to determine the extent and kind of control measures to be applied. Sanitary measures should be depended upon to secure any major reductions in fly populations since application of chemicals is not a substitute for sanitation.

The operation of a community-wide program should include routine checks of fly-population densities on regular schedules to determine the effectiveness of the control measures being applied and to indicate where and when operations are needed. The use of the same means for each check of fly densities will provide comparable data. This may be accomplished by using the Scudder grill (see Fig. 9-23). It is made of unplaned

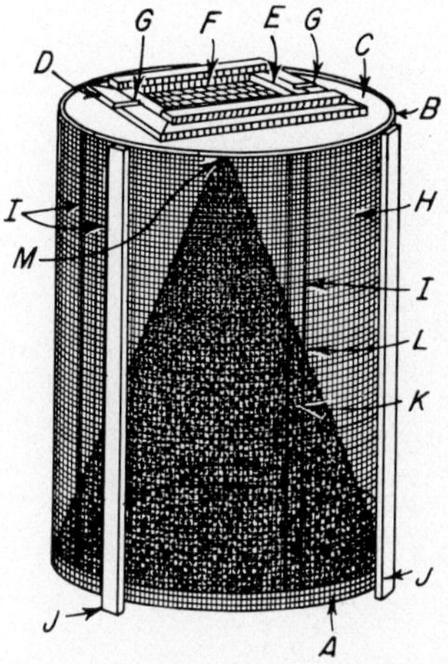

FIG. 9-24

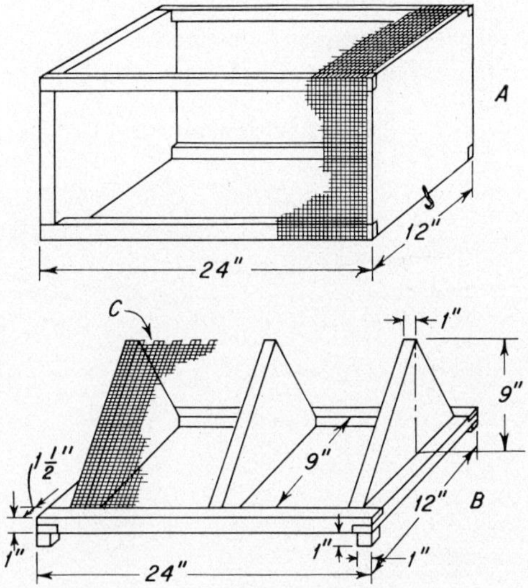

FIG. 9-25

FIG. 9-24. Conical fly trap, side view. *A*, hoops forming frame at bottom; *B*, hoops forming frame at top; *C*, top of trap made of barrel head; *D*, strips around door; *E*, door frame; *F*, screen on door; *G*, buttons holding door; *H*, screen on outside of trap; *I*, strips on side of trap between hoops; *J*, tips of these strips projecting to form legs; *K*, cone; *L*, united edges of screen forming cone; *M*, aperture at apex of cone. (*After Bishopp. Courtesy of U.S. Department of Agriculture.*)
FIG. 9-25. Tent fly trap. When the trap is set up, the screen box *A* fits on the base *B*, and two pans of bait are placed beneath the tent. *C*, holes in screen at apex of tent. (*Courtesy of U.S. Department of Agriculture.*)

boards ¾ inch wide, ¼ inch thick, and 36 inches long, spaced ¾ inch apart on a light "z" frame. In making a count, the grill is placed over an attractant, such as garbage or manure, disturbing the flies. The number that return and alight on the slats are then counted. Grill counts are made on a block rating. Fly traps may be used when it is desired to make surveys for species determination.

In many communities the fly-control program is operated by the local health department, since this department is in constant contact with many establishments in regard to sanitary conditions and is also aware of areas where the transmission of disease by flies is most likely. However, to be successful, the program must be a cooperative effort of all municipal departments and all individuals in the community.

RODENT CONTROL AND RAT FLEAS

9-65. There are numerous wild rodents in the United States, and many of them are actual or potential reservoirs of disease. However, the most dangerous and destructive rodents to be dealt with are three introduced species of domestic rodents: *Rattus norvegicus* (Norway rat), *Rattus rattus* (roof rat), and *Mus musculus* (house mouse). Naturalists disagree

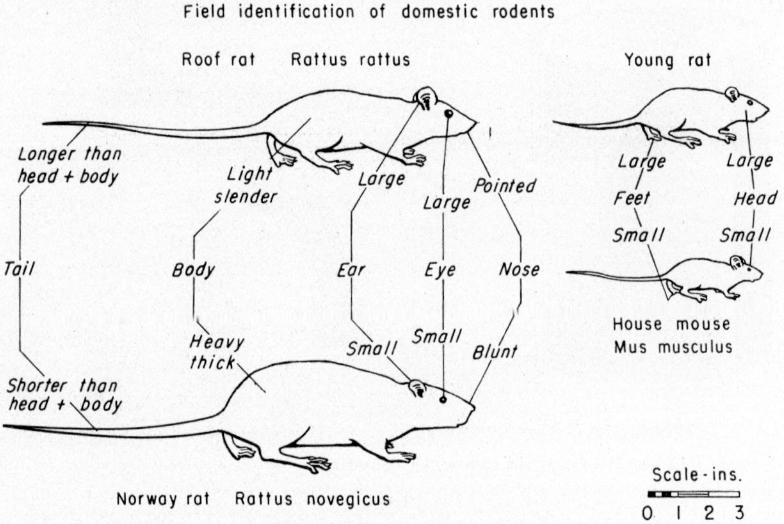

FIG. 9-26. Characteristics of rats. (*From "Training Guide," U.S. Public Health Service, Communicable Disease Center, Rodent Control Series, Atlanta, Ga.*)

rather sharply in their opinions concerning the origination and dissemination of the domestic species. The Norway rat, also called the brown rat, apparently originated in western China and first appeared in Europe in about 1727. By the latter part of the eighteenth century, this species had gained a strong foothold in Europe and had migrated to America. Because of its ferocity and greater size, it is generally supposed that this species rapidly exterminates all other species with which it comes in contact. There appear to be exceptions to this rule, however, since Norway rats are occasionally seen to frequent the same buildings as roof rats. The Norway rat, whatever the reason, is the most numerous in cities, where it is sometimes referred to as the "sewer rat" or "wharf rat." It is grayish-brown and has a short tail and ears and a comparatively stocky body. It burrows and nests in the ground or under buildings and piles of rubbish. An omnivorous feeder, it consumes garbage, grain, vegetables, meat, or any food used for human consumption. Where food supplies and harborages are ample, the Norway rat breeds rapidly, producing litters of eight to twelve young four to seven times per year. Young females breed at the age of three or four months, and the gestation period averages twenty-two days.

The roof rat existed in Europe as early as the eleventh century and became widespread until the advent of the Norway rat curbed its further increase. It is lighter in weight than the Norway rat and has longer ears and tail. The roof rat, as the name implies, is often found to infest the upper portions of buildings, as it climbs adroitly and can easily gain entrance to buildings through ventilators, open windows, skylights, etc.,

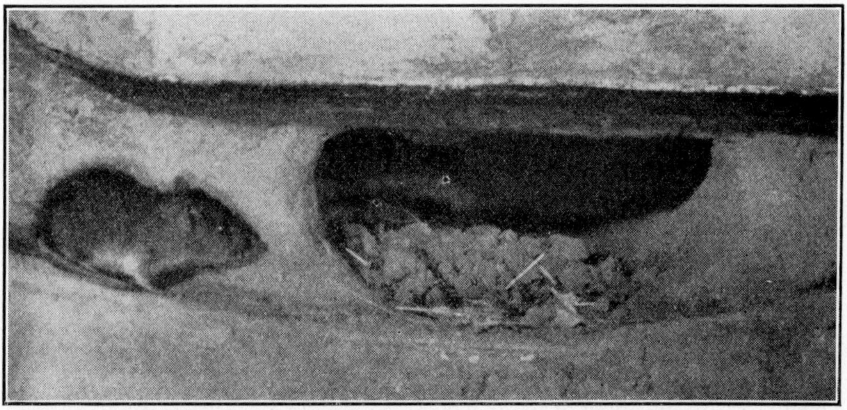

Fig. 9-27. Harborage of a Norway rat. (*Photograph courtesy of U.S. Public Health Service, Communicable Disease Center.*)

after having reached the building by traveling on overhanging trees, power lines, and the like. *Rattus rattus* (roof rat) includes three subspecies: *Rattus rattus alexandrinus* (alex or gray rat), *Rattus rattus frugivorus* (fruit or tree rat), and *Rattus rattus rattus* (black rat). The three subspecies have interbred to some extent and are all commonly referred to as roof rats. Since the coloring of the roof rat varies from black to brown to gray, it is somewhat unreliable for purposes of identification. Roof rats appear to prefer grain and grain products as food, but will eat other foods when grain is not available. Breeding habits are quite similar to those of the Norway rat, although roof rat litters tend to be somewhat smaller. Whereas Norway rats predominate in urban areas, roof rats are, in general, more commonly observed in rural areas.

9-66. Rodents and Public Health. Domestic rats and other rodents, because of their wide distribution and close association with man, provide potential reservoirs of a number of important diseases. The afflictions for which rats are responsible range from purely local discomforts caused by rodent bites to the more serious *murine typhus fever* and the often fatal *bubonic plague*. *Ratbite fever*, as the name indicates, is transmitted to humans by the bite of an infected animal. While only a small percentage of rat bites result in *ratbite fever*, the disease itself often becomes important in some urban areas where several hundred persons are bitten by rodents each year. Infected rats excrete the causative organism of *salmonellosis* in their urine and feces. The disease is transmitted to man from food contaminated with infected excreta. *Weil's disease*, or *hemorrhagic jaundice*, may also be transmitted to humans who ingest food contaminated with urine and feces from infected rats, who bathe in contaminated water, or who handle infected rats or excreta from infected rats. Rats have been incriminated as contributing to the transmission of various other diseases, including *amoebic dysentery*, *tapeworm*, and *trichinosis*. The house mouse (*Mus musculus*) has been identified as the reservoir of *rickettsialpox* in the Northeastern United States and is also known to be capable of serving as a reservoir for plague. The more important rodent-borne diseases are discussed in greater detail.

9-67. Plague. Plague is an acute infection running a rapid, severe course. The flea is the principal vehicle of infection from rat to rat and from rat to man. The plague organism causes a mechanical stoppage in the esophagus of the flea which makes the flea regurgitate when feeding. Thus, when the flea takes blood from a host animal, the victim's blood is mixed with the plague organism within the body of the flea, which—unable to swallow normally—regurgitates the mixture back into the victim. Bubonic plague is derived from rodents in this fashion, but an especially deadly type, transmitted from man to man by nose and throat discharges, is known as *pneumonic plague*. This infection, however, is still bubonic plague; it has simply become localized in the lungs of human victims. A third term, *sylvatic plague*, is used to denote the disease in wild rodents. This infection also manifests itself as bubonic plague when transmitted to humans.

Bubonic plague in humans is essentially a disease of warm, moist climates and, having been introduced into such climates, tends to persist indefinitely. Geographically, plague is widespread and has occurred at sporadic intervals in most of the principal seaport cities of the world. With the spread of rats by ship-borne commerce, plague infections have occurred in several United States seaports. Two epidemics of flea-transmitted bubonic plague in San Francisco resulted in 281 cases, with 191 deaths, during the years 1900 and 1907. There have been a number of such outbreaks in California and elsewhere since 1900. Unfortunately, the disease in California apparently became endemic in local domestic rats and thereafter spread by means of fleas to wild rodents and other small mammals. The small mammals that have become infected include ground squirrels, meadow mice, deer mice, pack rats, rice rats, marmots, prairie dogs, kangaroo rats, pine squirrels, cottontail rabbits, and jack rabbits. House mice have also been found to be infected.

Plague among colonies of wild rodents has moved gradually eastward in the years since it was first introduced into California. It has now been observed in wild rodents in several Midwestern states. A few cases of bubonic plague in humans have been traced to contact of the victims with infected wild rodents, usually during hunting or trapping expeditions. However, a more significant possibility of human infection would result should fleas from infected wild rodents transmit the disease to the domestic rat species in heavily populated Midwestern and Eastern states.

In general, an outbreak of bubonic plague requires an abundance of infected rats, an abundance of the proper type of fleas in the rat population, and sufficient contact between the infected animals and man. Although other fleas are possible vectors of plague, the oriental rat flea (*Xenopsylla cheopis*), which is prevalent on domestic rats throughout most of the world plague belt, is accorded major responsibility for the transmission of plague from rat to rat and from rat to man. Such other fleas as *Nosopsyllus fasciatus*, the northern rat flea, and *Pulex irritans*, the human flea, are considered of secondary importance in the infection of humans.

Although plague is a dangerous disease and usually has a high fatality rate, a vaccine has been developed that provides some immunity from the disease. It is supposed, on good evidence, to be the disease which was called the Black Death and which nearly depopulated Europe in the fifteenth century. At the present time the disease remains endemic in many areas of Asia, particularly India and Arabia, and in Africa.

9-68. Typhus Fever. Two types of typhus fever have played important roles in history: *epidemic*, or the Old World type, which is transmitted from man to man by lice, and *endemic*, or the murine type, of which the rat is the reservoir and the flea is the vehicle of infection. A rather obscure ailment, which originally was erroneously called Brill's disease and supposed to be confined largely to Mexico, was identified only a few decades ago as murine or flea-borne typhus. Although milder, the clinical symptoms of murine typhus resemble the epidemic form, and the two diseases are caused by a variety of the same organism. Subsequent investigations have revealed that murine typhus is widespread in the rat populations of the Southern states and Texas. Approximately 90 per cent of the cases in the United States occur south of a line drawn from El Paso, Tex., to Norfolk, Va.

Murine typhus is far less fatal than plague, but its incidence in many sections of the Southern United States justifies the use of preventive measures against both the rat and the vector, the flea. As in the case of plague, the principal vector is the oriental rat flea (*Xenopsylla cheopis*). However, in contrast to the anterior or oral transmission of plague, typhus is transmitted posteriorly as the infected *X. cheopis* deposits feces while feeding on its victim, who then scratches a portion of the infected feces into the bite or other abraded part of his skin. The flea serves as the vehicle of disease transfer from rat to rat and from rat to man. Murine typhus is not known to be transmissible from man to man.

FIG. 9-28. Bleeding a rat, for specimen to be tested for typhus fever. (*Photograph courtesy of Texas State Department of Health.*)

9-69. Rodents as an Economic Factor. The toll taken by rats is enormous. Conservative estimates reveal that the rat population equals the human population in the United States and that each rat can be expected to consume at least 1 ounce of food per day. Rodents may eat practically anything used as food by humans or livestock. If the rat population lived only on wheat, they would need a daily food supply of almost 5,000 tons, which would amount to an annual food bill of over $100,000,000.

Other rat damages and resulting economic losses occur in food-processing establishments. State and Federal food inspectors are giving increased attention to food contaminated by rats, and they can recognize hair, droppings, and urine stains which necessitate the condemnation and disposal of food supplies. It has been estimated that rats and mice waste or render unfit for human consumption several times as much food as they actually eat. Gnawing damage, fires, and poultry losses are other losses attributed to domestic rat populations. With these indictments of the rat, it is difficult to account for the tolerance with which its depredations are regarded.

9-70. Rodent-survey Techniques. The presence of rats may be detected in a number of ways, the most common being the discovery of damaged materials. Reasonably accurate determinations of the severity of rat infestations can be obtained by observing feeding or nesting activity

FIG. 9-29. Interior of a building showing marks left by rats running along the ceiling beams. Rat runs are used in determining the location of traps. (*Photograph courtesy of U.S. Public Health Service, Communicable Disease Center.*)

and signs of movement between nesting and feeding areas. Although rats will nest as close as possible to the food supply so as to minimize exposure to predators, it is not unusual for the rat to range up to approximately 100 feet from its nest. In contrast, the house mouse is normally limited to a range of not more than 30 feet.

The following signs can be observed in evaluating the extent of rat infestations:

1. Gnawing. Rats gnaw continually during active hours so that their rapidly growing front teeth can be kept short. In order that food supplies may be obtained, rats gnaw doors, boxes, bags, and other storage containers.

2. Burrows. Norway rats prefer underground nesting places. Burrows will frequently be observed along fences, near foundations, near

garbage containers, and under concrete slabs or walks. Fresh burrows will have a clean, slick appearance.

3. Droppings. Rat droppings will be noticed along runways, near food and water sources, and in harborages. Rat droppings are up to three-fourths of an inch long and may be easily distinguished from mice droppings, which are about the size of a grain of wheat.

4. Runways. Rats follow a specific pathway time after time in their movements from burrows or nests to sources of food and water. Active runways have a shiny, slick, dust-free appearance and, if outside, will be almost free of vegetation.

5. Footprints and tail marks. Tracks will often be noticed in dust, mud, and in some food products, such as flour.

6. Rub marks. Roof rats commonly climb posts and studs leading to a ceiling, then travel along the plate where the rafters and joists join. When rats travel these routes, they usually have to swing under the rafters on joists. Grease and dirt from the body of the rat will soon begin to accumulate on the rubbed surfaces to form black "swing" marks. Such marks are also noticed on pipes and ducts which have been utilized for runways.

7. Miscellaneous signs. Rat odor, urine stains, live rats, dead rats, nests, and stored food may also be encountered in the course of rat-infestation inspections.

9-71. General Methods of Control. The principal means of rodent control are poisoning; trapping; fumigation; ratproofing; the elimination of food, water, and harborages; and to some extent, destruction by natural enemies. Rodent-control activities are more effective when coordinated into organized community-wide campaigns. Natural enemies of rodents, among which may be counted cats, dogs, snakes, and birds of prey, while helping to reduce the number of rats and mice, will not usually prove sufficiently effective to exterminate these pests from a given area without human aid. Cats are sometimes effective mousers, but most of them are too well fed and lazy and have too wholesome a dread for the fighting qualities of the Norway rat to care to come to close quarters with him. Dogs, especially the small fox terriers and similar breeds, are of some value in reducing the rat population, but too often rat nests and other harborages are impenetrable for dogs. Hawks, owls, and other birds of prey destroy some rodents, but because of the popular misconception that all these birds are injurious to the interests of man and the consequent war on them, this method of control cannot be relied upon to any great extent. The important methods are discussed in the following paragraphs.

9-72. Sanitation and Rat Control. Proper sanitation with principal emphasis on adequate refuse storage, collection, and disposal is considered the most effective rat-control measure available. In any given rat-infested area there is a more or less constant population of rats whose number is determined largely by the amount of food, water, and harborage available. As more food becomes available, the rat population increases very rapidly. As the food supply diminishes, the rat population very rapidly decreases. To a lesser degree, rat-population fluctuations are dependent upon the availability of suitable harborage or nesting places. Rats require three things for propagation: food, water, and harborage. If insanitary conditions which provide the rat with these necessities can be eliminated, the problem of rat control can likewise be eliminated.

9-73. Poisoning. In general, poisoning, where it can be used without danger to man or domestic animals, has proved one of the most efficient methods of destroying rats. The poisons commonly used in the past were arsenic, strychnine, phosphorus, red squill, barium carbonate, or compounds containing one or more of these. In ordinary use, these rodenticides did not always give satisfactory results. However, during and immediately following World War II, several new rodenticides were developed which considerably enhanced rodent-control efforts. Included among the comparatively newer poisons are 1080, Antu, Warfarin, and Pival. A brief discussion of some of the more satisfactory rodenticides follows.

Warfarin and Pival. The two most recently developed rodenticides are Warfarin and Pival, which may be formulated into solid food baits, and Warficide and Pivalyn, which may be formulated into liquid baits with identical toxic effects on rodents. These rodenticides are anticoagulants which, when ingested at intervals for a period of several days, cause sufficient internal bleeding to result in death. Continuous feeding from a constant supply of poison bait is necessary to produce the desired results. For this reason, it is recommended that frequent checks be made of bait containers during the first few days the poison is made available to ensure that adequate supplies of bait are kept accessible. Occasionally dead rats are noticed within four to seven days after the baits have been established. However, in some instances rats die in their nests, and bait effectiveness becomes apparent only by the odor produced by dead rats or the continued absence of rats from bait locations.

The toxic action of Warfarin and Pival is considerably slower than that of 1080, Antu, red squill, and other rodenticides; however, an advantage of the retarded action is that rats never develop an aversion to these materials and will continue to feed from both liquid and solid baits until they die or until the baits are exhausted. While the anticoagulant action of Warfarin and Pival is also effective in other warm-blooded animals and humans, these poisons are not considered as hazardous as other types because an efficient antidote, vitamin D, is readily available and because repeated feedings in liberal quantity of the concentration recommended for rodent control are necessary to endanger human beings. Both Warfarin and Pival are usually purchased in concentrates of 0.5 per cent. This material is diluted 1 part poison to 19 to 49 parts bait for Norway rats, and 1 part poison to 19 parts bait for roof rats and house mice. Common bait materials include cornmeal, rolled oats, bread crumbs, nut crumbs, sugar, and corn or peanut oil. Warficide and Pivalyn are obtainable in preformulated units, with each unit containing sufficient toxicant to produce an effective bait when mixed with 1 quart of water. Effective bait stations utilizing the liquid baits have been prepared by inverting a quart or pint jar containing the poison into chick fountains and placing them where accessible to rats.

The development of anticoagulant poisons has enabled a new approach to rodent control in that complete control in a given building is possible and reinfestation can be limited by making the baits constantly available. The relative safety and convenience of the materials enable them to be used by individuals not trained in rodent control, thus making possible community-wide efforts in rodent control. While safety precautions are inherent in both liquid- and solid-bait formulations, it is recommended that the poisoned baits be considered hazardous to humans and warm-blooded animals and that steps be taken to prevent exposure of the materials to accidental ingestion.

Red Squill. Powdered red squill has proved a useful rodenticide and is commonly used in the proportion of 1 part squill to 9 parts bait. While red squill was one of the earliest poisons utilized in organized rodent-control activities, its popularity has remained, chiefly because it has the advantage of being relatively safe for human beings, cats, dogs, and fowls. The substance is a natural emetic which, when taken by most warm-blooded animals, results in immediate regurgitation and evacuation of the poisonous material. The emetic action of red squill provides an almost specific poison for Norway rats, since they are unable to regurgitate. Squill baits are bitter and have the disadvantage of creating an aversion in rat populations, and some rats appear always to avoid baits containing red squill, especially if they have observed its poisonous effects on other rodents.

1080. This is the common name for sodium fluoroacetate, a very efficient poison for rodents. Its great disadvantage is that it is highly poisonous to man and domestic animals, and there is no known antidote for the material. It is, therefore, recommended for use only by qualified responsible persons who are obligated to protect poisoned premises and to remove unused baits, bait containers, and poisoned rodents prior to public admittance. Water is probably the most effective bait, and the use of ½ ounce of 1080 in 1 gallon of water is the recommended formulation.

Antu. This poison, which has the chemical name alpha naphthylthiourea, is an effective poison against the brown or Norway rat but is not recommended for use against any other species of rat or rodent. A disadvantage of the poison is the fact that a tolerance is quickly built up by rats which have eaten a less than lethal amount. In practice, therefore, it has been found that Antu cannot be effectively used at closer intervals than four to six months in the same locality. Antu may be utilized in preparing food baits containing 0.75 to 3.0 per cent Antu by weight. Also, considerable success has been achieved by placing 20 per cent Antu powder near rat burrows or in runways making it necessary for the rat to walk through the material, a portion of which adheres to the feet. The rats then lick the feet in the process of preening and consume toxic amounts of Antu in this manner.

9-74. Trapping. Another effective method of reducing rat populations is through the use of a well-planned trapping program. Among the many traps on the market, the simple inexpensive "snap" or "guillotine" trap is usually found to be best adapted for all-around usage. Cage traps and unbaited steel traps are sometimes utilized if it is desired to capture live rats for inspection of their ectoparasites. Traps should be set in runways, behind boxes, along walls, or in other sheltered places where concealment is easy and rodents are moving. For good results a great many traps must be used. A dozen or more traps are needed for a heavily infested dwelling, and 50 to 100 or more for a large building or farm. The trapping campaign must be short and decisive, or the rats become wary and avoid the traps no matter how well they have been placed. Trapping activities are usually most successful when utilized following a rat-poisoning campaign that did not achieve complete control.

9-75. Fumigation. Fumigation is another method of rat extermination which may be effectively employed in places fitted for such an undertaking. Fumigation is recommended and extensively used to free ships from rodents and other vermin. Hydrocyanic acid gas is perhaps the most effective fumigant, but since it is extremely dangerous to man, great care must be exercised where this method is employed. Its principal use is in the fumigation of ships under the supervision of the U.S. Public Health Service. A disadvantage to the use of fumigants in buildings is the possibility of unpleasant odors resulting from dead rats in walls, under floors, and in other obscure places.

Approximating fumigation is the use of calcium cyanide, which is sold under the name of Cyanogas A-Dust and other proprietary names. The poison can be obtained in granular or powdered form, and it can be introduced into rat burrows by means of a pump devised by the poison manufacutrer. When exposed to the atmosphere, calcium cyanide gives off hydrocyanic acid gas which will spread through any enclosed space. In using this material and other fumigants in buildings or other indoor areas it is necessary that the premises be tightly closed, with door and window cracks sealed with paper. The fumigant should be allowed to remain in the building for at least four hours, at the end of which time the treated

FIG. 9-30. Dusting with Cyanogas to kill domestic rats. (*Photograph courtesy of U.S. Public Health Service, Communicable Disease Center.*)

building should bė thoroughly ventilated. This method of using hydrocyanic gas is fairly safe, but during actual application inside buildings the workman should wear an appropriate gas mask.

Where convenient and safe in exterior places, a hose may be connected to the exhaust of a tractor or an automobile, and the burned gases will serve effectively in destroying rats, provided that all openings to burrows are tightly closed to prevent the entrance of fresh air and dilution of the toxic gases. In shallow burrows under buildings and in similar places, a wad of cotton the size of an orange saturated with carbon bisulfide ("high life") may be stuffed into the mouth of the burrows, the entrance further closed by filling with earth, and the rats suffocated in their holes. This method was used in California to destroy ground squirrels during antiplague activities.

9-76. Ectoparasite Control. Obviously, if the number of fleas can be reduced, there is a corresponding reduction in disease transmission both from rat to rat and from rat to man. This line of attack, called ectoparasite control, has achieved good results. Common methods of rat ectoparasite control include the application of 10 per cent DDT dust to rat runways and burrows in amounts of approximately 2.5 pounds of dust or 0.25 pound of technical DDT per premises, depending on the extent of rat infestation and the area to be treated. In normal activity, rats will pass through the DDT and eventually spread particles of the toxicant throughout the fur. Fleas and other external parasites are killed in this manner. The dust is sometimes blown into burrows by some type of dust gun, usually a rotary type or a simple garden duster. Dust is best distributed on interior runways by spooning small piles at intervals along rat runways. Sifters, made from jars, cans, or boxes are also conveniently used for dust distribution when metal lids can be provided and punctured with several ⅛-inch holes. Handles are sometimes attached to sifters for convenience in reaching high runways.

In those areas of the world where typhus in rat populations has become endemic, it is recommended that DDT dusting for control of rat fleas be routinely practiced. Also, where any threat of plague is imminent, ectoparasite control should precede or accompany rodent-poisoning activities. If one of the rapidly effective poisons, such as red squill or 1080, is utilized as the rodenticide, flea extermination with DDT dust should precede the placing of poison baits by three or four days. However, if one of the slow-acting rodenticides, such as Warfarin or Pival, is employed, dusting can be carried out simultaneously with the placing of baits. Rodent poisoning without adequate provision for flea control often results in fleas leaving their dead rat hosts where blood is no longer available and seeking blood meals from man.

The public health significance of DDT dusting in murine typhus control is probably best illustrated by a comparison of human typhus morbidity before and after the utilization of 10 per cent DDT dust for rat ectoparasite control. During 1944, 5,401 human cases of typhus fever were reported to the National Office of Vital Statistics. Dusting programs were initiated in 1945 during which 5,193 typhus cases were reported. A reduction to 3,365 cases was noted in 1946, and only 1,901 cases were reported in 1947. This downward trend has continued with 200 or fewer human cases being reported annually for the years 1952 to 1954. Investigations reveal that flea counts on over 17,000 live rats have been reduced 84 per cent following DDT dusting.

9-77. Ratproofing. Rats tend to breed and multiply proportionately to the food supply available for them. Unless carried on continuously, other control measures provide only temporary relief unless rats are starved out by being excluded from food. The ratproofing of buildings is, therefore, considered an effective means of rat control. It is a simple matter to erect buildings of ratproof construction, and an ordinance requiring such construction, properly enforced, will result in a practically rat-free city. It is necessary to exercise vigilance at all times, however, to maintain a building in ratproof condition.

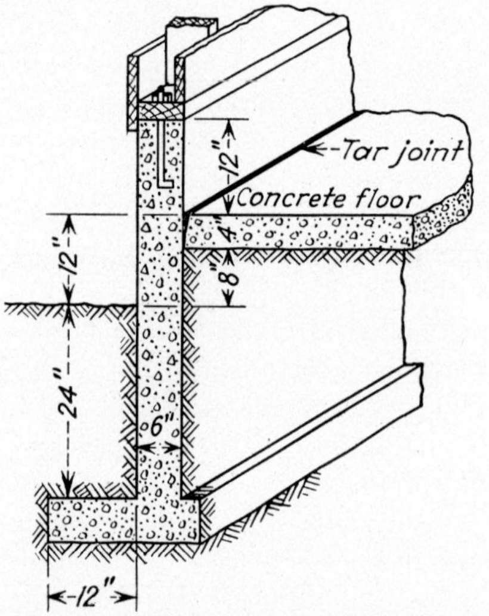

FIG. 9-31. Floor and foundation construction of a new building without a basement. This type of construction should be used for buildings where food will be handled or stored.

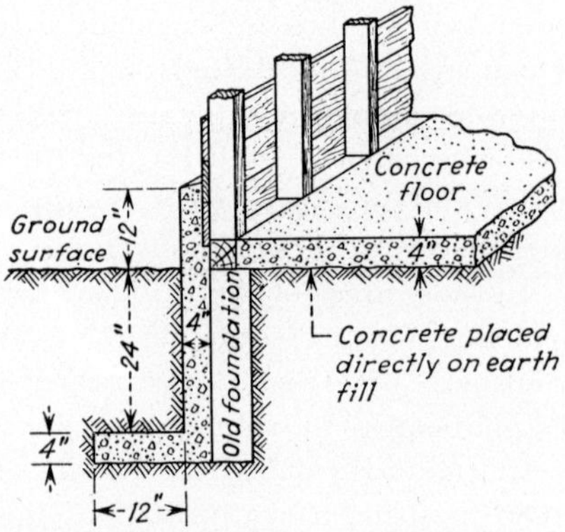

FIG. 9-32. Old building made ratproof by placing concrete curtain wall around old foundation.

The ratproofing of new buildings involves both interior and exterior ratproofing as well as the elimination of interior structural harborage. Ratproof construction of new buildings provides for the complete absence of nonessential openings through which rats may enter buildings. The liberal use of ratproof materials, such as 19-gauge or heavier ½-inch mesh hardware cloth, 24-gauge or heavier galvanized sheet metal, and Portland cement mortar will prohibit rat entry through essential openings of ½ inch or larger. Buildings should be constructed of materials impervious to rat attack, and approved methods of construction should be utilized. An approved design that fundamentally eliminates all unnecessary enclosed places, such as double floors and walls, should be employed.

Buildings in which food is handled or stored should have floors of ratproof material or of concrete not less than 4 inches thick poured directly upon the ground or earth fill. The floor should be sealed into the walls, and the walls must be of ratproof material, such as concrete, stone, brick, or tile, not less than 6 inches thick. To prevent burrowing beneath the building, the foundation walls should extend at least 2 feet into the ground to a horizontal offset of 12 inches, and must extend at least 1 foot above the floor.

Other buildings may be ratproofed by being elevated on pillars at least 18 inches above the ground and having the underlying ground kept free of rubbish and other rat-harboring material; or a curtain wall may be

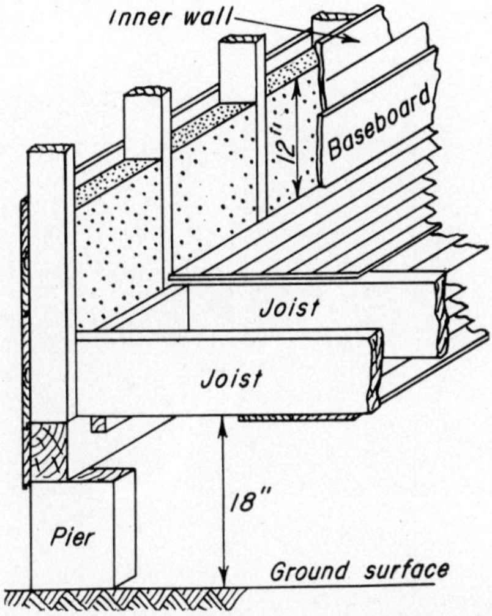

FIG. 9-33. When buildings are supported on posts or piers, they are made ratproof by raising them 18 inches or more above ground level and by placing concrete between inner and outer walls above sill. (*Courtesy of Portland Cement Association.*)

constructed at least 4 inches thick and extending at least 2 feet into the ground to a 12-inch horizontal offset at least 4 inches thick.

9-78. Rat Stoppage. Rat stoppage is a modified method of the orthodox ratproofing procedure which is applicable to existing buildings. It involves some inexpensive construction alterations designed to prevent rats from entering buildings by blocking off or stopping up all actual and potential passages by which rats might gain entry. Essentially, it is the closing of openings in exterior walls with materials through which rats cannot penetrate, together with such interior rat stoppage, harborage removal, and cleanup as may be necessary to reduce or eliminate rat breeding places.

Rat stoppage is accomplished, in part, by sealing all holes or cracks in foundations and walls and around pipes passing through walls with bricks or Portland cement mortar. Holes in wood floors or walls are stopped with fitted sheet metal. The lower edges of doors, the door casings, and the thresholds are covered with 24-gauge galvanized sheet iron. Preferably this should be "channeled" or bent around the edge of the door. The channels or plates at the vertical edges should extend at least 6 inches above the bottom of the door. Cellar and basement windows and other windows and ventilators allowing access by rats from the ground, roof, or trees are protected with galvanized 19-gauge metal screen or 3/8-inch or smaller hardware cloth that is securely fastened. Metal guards or

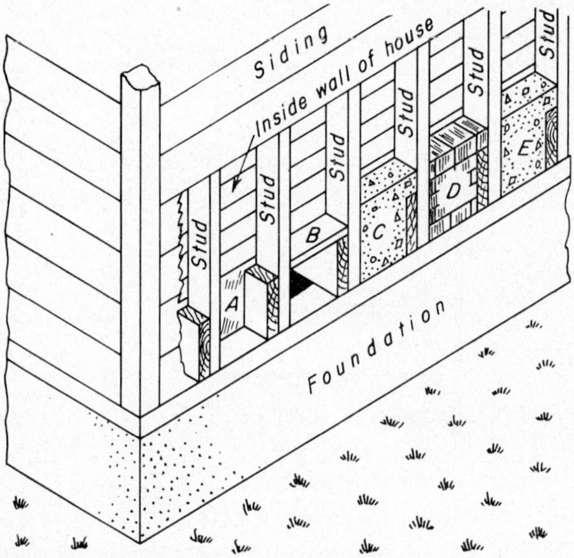

FIG. 9-34. Methods of excluding rats from double walls. *A*, metal plate; *B*, wood stop; *C*, cinder concrete; *D*, bricks; *E*, ordinary concrete.

other means are used to prevent rats from climbing pipes, rainspouts, or wires and using them as a means of entrance. Sheet aluminum is not satisfactory for stopping rats, as they are able to gnaw through it. If foundations are less than 24 inches deep, a curtain wall is installed outside in contact with the original wall to a depth of at least 24 inches with a 12-inch horizontal extension. The curtain wall may be of good concrete, 3 to 4 inches thick or of 24-gauge galvanized metal. Well-poured concrete floors will prevent the entrance of rats into buildings with foundations extending at least 24 inches into the ground, and they are superior to curtain walls in that they increase the value of the property.

After all avenues of rat entry have been stopped, poisoning or fumigation and trapping should be employed to kill the rats already within the

FIG. 9-35. Ratproofing details. Note screens over window and ventilators, door plates, guards at downspout and wires, and mortar around pipes. *(Courtesy of U.S. Public Health Service, Communicable Disease Center.)*

building. Continuous maintenance of the rat-stoppage alterations is required if they are to retain their efficiency.

9-79. Port Regulations. Since seaports are the usual points of entrance for plague, health authorities are especially careful to prevent rats from leaving ships. The Texas State Board of Health issued the following regulations governing this matter during a threatened plague epidemic:[1]

1. All ships docking at Texas ports, both foreign and coastwise, must fend off a minimum of 8 feet from wharf, using submerged fender or raft to hold ship away from wharf or dock.

2. All lines, hawsers, cables, etc., from ship to dock must be equipped with circular rat guards 36 inches in diameter equipped with a sleeve to hold same in

[1] These regulations are no longer enforced but served their purpose well at the time.

proper position a maximum of three feet from vessel. All rat guards must be approved by the Texas State Board of Health.

3. All hawse pipes must be plugged with tarred fabric. All hawse lines too small to hold rat guards or too close to side of vessel to use rat guards, must be covered with fabric and tarred a distance of 3 lineal feet—must be tarred daily before 6:00 P.M.

4. All gang planks and ship ladders must be removed at sunset and not be replaced until sunrise, except when during actual loading or unloading and then a guard must be placed at each gang plank or ladder to see that rats neither leave nor enter vessel.

5. Ropes, cables, swinging stages, ladders, hose, or any object upon which a rat may leave vessels must be taken aboard by sunset and may not be replaced before sunrise of each day.

In addition to such regulatory measures as the above enacted by the national and state health authorities, there is a movement toward the ratproofing of docks and wharves in many ports, and some ratproof structures have actually been constructed. Ratproofing of ships is also recommended.

9-80. Cooperative Efforts in Rat Control. The responsibility for preventing communicable disease within a state is vested in the state health department and, in turn, is usually delegated to local health agencies. All health groups must solicit the support of many other organizations, both public and private, and also the cooperation of the general public in combating rat-borne diseases. The reason for seeking this broad support lies in the fact that rats are so widely entrenched in the habitats of man that adequate control is impossible without widespread and coordinated effort.

It is easy to obtain public cooperation in rat control during a period when typhus fever or plague is threatened but usually difficult under ordinary circumstances. In general, educational measures should be continually utilized that will make the public aware of the hazards associated with rats. Householders and property owners should be encouraged to ratproof new buildings and apply rat-stoppage measures to old buildings, in addition to the routine placement of rodenticides and DDT dust where necessary. Adequate municipal ordinances are often helpful in promoting rodent-control techniques, especially with regard to those measures which help to eliminate the rats' food supplies and harborages.

BIBLIOGRAPHY

1. Moulton, F. R. (ed.): "Human Malaria," American Association for the Advancement of Science, Washington.
2. Tarzwell, C. M.: Effects of DDT Mosquito Larviciding on Wildlife, pt. I, *Public Health Repts.*, vol. 62, no. 15, 1947.

3. Tarzwell, C. M.: Effects of DDT Mosquito Larviciding on Wildlife, pt. II, *Public Health Repts.*, vol. 62, no. 35, 1947.
4. "Training Guide," U.S. Public Health Service, Communicable Disease Center, Rodent Control Series, Atlanta, Ga.
5. Hovell, C. S.: "Rats and How to Control Them," Bale and Sons, London.
6. Dyar, H. G.: Mosquitoes of the United States, *Proc. U.S. Natl. Museum*, vol. 62, no. 2447, art. 1, reprinted by the U.S. Public Health Service.
7. Le Prince, J. A. A. and A. J. Orenstein: "Mosquito Control in Panama," G. P. Putnam's Sons, New York.
8. Chandler, A. C.: "Introduction to Human Parasitology," John Wiley & Sons, Inc., New York.
9. Herms, W. B., and H. F. Gray: "Mosquito Control," The Commonwealth Fund, New York.
10. Matheson, R.: "Medical Entomology," Charles C Thomas, Publisher, Springfield, Ill.
11. Magoon, E. H.: "Drainage for Health," Rockefeller Foundation, International Health Division, New York.
12. "Malaria Control on Impounded Waters," U.S. Public Health Service and Tennessee Valley Authority, Health and Safety Department.
13. Watt, J., and D. R. Lindsay: Effect of Fly Control in a High Morbidity Area, Diarrheal Disease Control Studies I, *Public Health Repts.*, vol. 63, no. 41, 1948.
14. Howard, L. O.: "The House Fly, Disease Carrier," J. B. Lippincott Company, Philadelphia.
15. West, L. S.: "The House Fly," Comstock Publishing Associates, Inc., Ithaca, N.Y.
16. Rosenau, M. J.: "Preventive Medicine and Hygiene," 7th ed., by Kenneth F. Maxcy, Appleton-Century-Crofts, Inc., New York, 1951.
17. Coffey, J. H., and H. F. Schoof: "The Control of Domestic Flies," U.S. Public Health Service, 1949.
18. Von Zuben, F. J., Jr., L. J. Ogden, and R. E. Peel: House Fly Breeding at Sewage Treatment Plants in Texas, *Sewage and Ind. Wastes*, vol. 24, no. 10, 1952.
19. Herms, W. B.: "Medical Entomology," The Macmillan Company, New York.

CHAPTER 10

DISINFECTANTS AND INSECTICIDES

10-1. There is considerable popular confusion as to the meaning of the terms used in connection with disinfectants and allied agents. *Disinfection* is the killing or removal of those agents which cause infection. For instance, *pasteurization* is a certain means of killing typhoid and other disease bacteria; it is, therefore, a means of disinfection, but does not destroy all the spores of other bacteria. *Sterilization* is the destruction of absolutely all life. A *germicide* is an agent which kills bacteria. A *disinfectant* is therefore a germicide. *Antiseptics* are not germicides but merely agents that retard the growth or multiplication of bacteria. An antiseptic, therefore, will prevent or delay decay. Many disinfectants are deodorants also. But many deodorants have no effect upon germ life and merely mask one odor with another more powerful. The distinction between disinfectants and antiseptics is sometimes one of degree. A highly concentrated solution, for instance, will have disinfectant properties, while weaker concentrations are merely antiseptic. Insecticides are not, in general, good germicides.

10-2. Disinfection. The disinfection of water and foods has been discussed elsewhere. Here disinfection will be treated mainly as it is used in the control and prevention of communicable disease. A disinfectant should be used as a bar between the patient and the people about him. Disinfection should be applied, therefore, as closely as possible to the patient. It is frequently employed in treating the excretions and discharges of the patient and also fomites, the various objects with which the sick person comes in contact, such as clothing, bedding, handkerchiefs, and eating utensils. It is by means of the discharges and the fomites, particularly the former, that diseases are communicated, although direct contact may also be involved. Concurrent disinfection is the practice of treating all excreta as they are produced and fomites as they leave or sever contact with the patient during the course of the illness. Terminal disinfection is the final treatment given, after the patient is cured or removed, to bedding, fomites, and perhaps to the room which the patient has occupied. Terminal disinfection may also include fumigation.

10-3. Fumigation. Fumigation is the application of disinfectants in gaseous form, although the meaning of the term has been extended to include use of gas as an insecticide. While many cities as a routine measure formerly practiced fumigation at the termination of certain communicable diseases, such as measles, scarlet fever, and smallpox, this practice has been abandoned by health authorities. It would appear from observations made as to the number of new cases, in the same house, following a communicable disease that ordinary fumigation has but little effect. Also, the greatest danger of communication to others is generally during the early stages of the disease, long before fumigation is applied. Concurrent disinfection, terminal disinfection of fomites, and a thorough cleaning of the room appear to be more effective. In any event, fumigation affects surfaces only and will not exercise any germicidal effect within fabrics. Fumigation has a recognized field, however, in the killing of insects, rats, and mice in buildings, ships, and railroad cars. The agents used in fumigation for this purpose, however, are of little or no value as germicides.

PHYSICAL AGENTS OF DISINFECTION

10-4. Heat. *Fire* is the best of sterilizing agents. In the control of communicable disease, however, it can be applied only to those articles which may be destroyed. Bandages and dressings of various sorts and old bedding may be disposed of in this way. Sputum should be collected in paper cups and burned.

Steam is widely used as a disinfectant. For surface disinfection it can be applied as streaming steam, in which case the steam is not under pressure and a contact period of thirty to forty minutes is required. If the steam is generated in a closed tank or vessel and the articles placed therein are to be disinfected under pressure, a twenty-minute contact period will be required at 16 pounds per square inch and a fifteen-minute contact at 20 pounds per square inch. The latter method allows better penetration of the steam, particularly if a partial vacuum is obtained before the steam is generated. Large steam sterilizers are used in hospitals, bacteriological laboratories, and dairies.

Boiling kills disease germs in ten to fifteen minutes, although for safety it is better to continue the boiling for longer than the minimum mentioned. Boiling can be used to disinfect clothing and excreta in the absence of chemicals. Temperatures lower than boiling are also destructive to bacteria, particularly pathogenic, if continued long enough. This principle is illustrated by the pasteurization of milk.

Dry heat is also used to disinfect but does not penetrate so well as steam and may also injure fabrics. It is much less effective than wet heat.

For instance, dry heat at 300°F requires three to four times as long as boiling to destroy bacteria. Disinfection with dry heat may be carried out in an ordinary oven. As a rough test, the oven should be hot enough to brown ordinary absorbent cotton.

Cold is not a disinfectant, or at best acts too slowly to be considered. It does, however, prevent the multiplication of bacteria. On the other hand, some types of pathogenic bacteria, particularly typhoid, may be preserved for three months or more by freezing.

Dryness is injurious to bacteria. The desiccation of substances containing bacteria will in time cause their death. Clean, dry surfaces contain very few live bacteria. Dryness is even more effective in preventing the multiplication of bacteria.

10-5. Light. Sunlight is also an effective disinfectant. The rays toward the violet end of the spectrum have the greatest germicidal power, the ultraviolet rays being particularly destructive. For disinfecting purposes, floors, carpets, etc., may be exposed to sunlight. As the ultraviolet rays cannot pass through ordinary glass, it is preferable that objects to be disinfected be exposed to the direct sunlight. Ultraviolet rays are used directly only in the disinfection of water. Ordinary light, however, prevents the growth of bacteria and also appears to have some germicidal effect.

THE CHEMICAL AGENTS OF DISINFECTION

10-6. General Characteristics. Disinfectants must be used wisely. Rosenau[1] says:

> The ideal disinfectant must first and foremost possess a high germicidal power. It must not be rendered ineffective by the presence of organic matter; it must be reasonably stable, so as not to deteriorate under ordinary conditions; it must be soluble or readily miscible in water; if it forms an emulsion the emulsion should be permanent; it should be harmless to man and the higher animals; it should have the power of penetration; it should not corrode metals; bleach, rot or stain fabrics; and, finally, it should be reasonable in price.
>
> The stress of modern activities demands disinfecting processes that are instantaneous in their action, all-pervading in their effects, cheap, harmless, and free from unpleasant odors that might be offensive to the fastidious. Such perfect disinfectants are not known. It requires money and the expenditure of well-directed and intelligent energy to accomplish satisfactory disinfection. *No one substance is applicable to all diseases or to all substances, or even to the same disease or the same substance under different conditions.*

Various disinfectants have various qualities in different degrees which must be considered in choosing the proper agent for some particular purpose. The faculty of penetration is very important as bacteria, particularly in sputum and feces, are embedded in organic matter. The disinfectant, to do its work, must be able to penetrate this material. For this purpose chemical agents in the form of solutions are better than emulsions, although steam, dry heat, and boiling may also be used. Gases have a surface action only, although they will, of course, penetrate porous materials, such as fabrics. The presence of organic matter with the bacteria affects disinfection, particularly of sputum and feces, since those disinfectants which are oxidizing agents react chemically with the organic matter and speedily become ineffective as disinfectants. Formaldehyde is well suited for conditions of this type, although it does have objectionable properties from the standpoints of odor, irritability, and corrosiveness. Phenol, although widely used in the past, has largely been supplanted by more potent disinfectants, such as the chlorophenols and quaternary ammonium compounds, which are less corrosive and irritating. Time is also an element in disinfection. It is absolutely necessary that sufficient time be given for the disinfectant to make contact. In general, the weaker solutions or dilutions of disinfectants require longer periods to do their work. Raising the temperature of the dilutions materially speeds up the action.

10-7. Phenol Coefficient. As a means of standardizing the killing power of disinfectants, the phenol coefficient has been devised. This is the killing power of the disinfectant in question standardized against the killing power of phenol, typhoid bacilli being used as the organisms to be killed. Although the Rideal-Walker and the Hygienic Laboratory methods were formerly used, the method advocated by the Association of Official Agricultural Chemists is now generally accepted for determining the strength of disinfectant solutions. Disinfectants should be purchased only from reputable manufacturers under a guarantee as to the phenol coefficient. If large quantities are used, a test of the coefficient should be made by a qualified laboratory.

10-8. Lime. This is the cheapest of all disinfectants. It also has the advantages of being odorless and safe to use. Hydrated lime, which may be purchased in sacks, is the most convenient. When mixed with eight to ten times its weight or four times its volume of water, milk of lime is obtained. This is very useful in the disinfection of feces. At least the same bulk of milk of lime as feces should be used. Milk of lime is also used as whitewash in dairy barns, where it is said to kill spores and spore-formers lodged in cracks. Lime is also a deodorant. When air-slaked, it is of no value. The indiscriminate scattering about of dry lime in open toilets, barns, etc., is of little or no use.

10-9. Chlorine. Chlorine is one of the most important bactericides in the field of sanitation. Its principal uses in its various forms in the sanitary field are for disinfecting drinking water, swimming-pool water, sewage, hands of milkers, udders of cows, glasses, dishes, and other utensils used in handling, preparing, and serving milk and other foods. Its application and the forms in which it is used are given in Art. 5-18.

10-10. Quaternary Ammonium Compounds. These compounds are on sale as sanitizing agents for dishes, glassware, and other food utensils. Research and field studies have indicated that some of these compounds are effective bactericides for the treatment of various utensils and food-processing equipment. The bactericidal effectiveness of specific quaternary ammonium compounds varies and is influenced by the concentration of active agent, temperature, pH, and exposure time, as well as by interfering substances present in natural waters. The interference of natural waters with quaternary ammonium compounds is due principally to bicarbonates, sulfates, and chlorides of calcium and magnesium. Any treatment which tends to precipitate, remove, or inactivate calcium or magnesium reduces the interference, as do increased pH and temperature.

Not all quaternary ammonium compounds remain bactericidally effective through a wide range of water hardness. The value of sequestering agents in reducing the interference of hard waters has been demonstrated. Products containing alkyl (C_8–C_{18}) dimethylbenzyl ammonium chlorides, paradiisobutylphenoxyethoxyethyldimethylbenzyl ammonium chloride, alkyl (C_9–C_{15}) tolylmethyltrimethyl ammonium chlorides, or didodecenyldimethyl ammonium chloride have been found to be bactericidally effective in waters containing up to 500 parts per million of hardness when compounded with sufficient tetrasodium pyrophosphate to provide 0.2 per cent concentration in the solution used and when used (1) at concentrations of 200 parts per million or more, (2) at pH levels of 6.0 or higher, (3) at temperatures of 75°F or higher, and (4) for a two-minute exposure period.

The above-named compounds without sequestering agents are also effective within certain limits of water hardness under the conditions of use enumerated above; however, the level of hardness at which bactericidal activity is reduced below that necessary for effective treatment varies among the four named compounds and may be influenced by other ingredients in a proprietary formulation. Accordingly, the limiting hardness should be established for the use of each quaternary ammonium product. Unless it is stated on the label, the health officer should request such information from the manufacturer.

Until such time as a reliable chemical test is developed which will indicate the bactericidal efficiency of quaternary ammonium compounds, bacteriological data should be used to establish the usefulness of quaternary ammonium compounds and sequestering agents other than those named above, or the above-named compounds for use (1) at temperatures less than 75°F, or (2) at a pH below 6.0, or (3) when combined with a compatible sequestering agent in waters above 500 parts per million of hardness, or (4) without, or with less than, the specified amount of sequestering agent[2].

10-11. Carbolic Acid. This is a term applied to a crude mixture of phenols and cresols which is obtained from coal tar. It has a higher phenol coefficient than phenol alone—usually about 2.75. It is used in solutions of 2 to 5 per cent. It cannot be depended upon to destroy spores. With the exceptions of anthrax and tetanus, however, the germs of most communicable diseases are not sporeformers. Carbolic acid is more effective if the solution is warm or hot. One of its uses is in the disinfection of barns, pens, and stables. This disinfectant and the closely allied substances phenol and cresol are poisonous and cannot be used in relation to foods or eating utensils.

10-12. Phenol. This is a crystalline substance which is soluble in water and is the chief constituent of carbolic acid. It is affected very little by organic matter and is, therefore, useful in disinfecting sputum and feces. In common with the other coal-tar disinfectants, however, it is not particularly valuable in disinfecting against smallpox and the other diseases in which the active organisms have not yet been discovered. It has little effect upon spores.

10-13. Cresol. This term includes a large group of disinfectants which are sold under various trade names. They are mixtures of phenols and cresols with inert tar oils and an emulsifying agent such as soap, tar, or rosin. They have a characteristic carbolic-acid odor. They can be obtained with phenol coefficients up to 6 without organic matter and between 3 and 4 with organic matter. The emulsifying appears to lower their penetrating abilities, and this results in a loss of efficiency in the presence of the organic matter in which bacteria are frequently buried. The soapy emulsion, however, makes this type of disinfectant especially effective on greasy surfaces.

10-14. Formaldehyde. The most useful of the gaseous disinfectants is formaldehyde gas. It has very little insecticidal value but is very toxic to bacteria. It also acts as a deodorant. Although irritating to the eyes and nasal passages, it is not poisonous. As it is not very efficient in penetrating fabrics, it cannot be depended upon to accomplish more than a surface disinfection. Though fairly effective in the destruction of spores, it should not be relied upon to kill the spores of anthrax or tetanus.

Formalin is a watery solution of formaldehyde containing about 40 per cent of the gas. Formalin is very widely used as a disinfectant and is especially valuable for the treatment of body discharges. For fumigation with formaldehyde the gas is generated from formalin. The usual method of generation is by the aid of potassium permanganate. For every 1,000 cubic feet of air space in the room to be fumigated, 50 milliliters of formalin is required. To this is added 250 grams of permanganate. The permanganate is first placed in a deep pan or bucket, and then the formalin is poured over it. The chemical reaction which takes place results in the release of formaldehyde gas. Since there is a heating and bubbling in the container, it must be deep enough to prevent boiling over, and the floor should be protected by setting the container on a board or bricks. A six- to twelve-hour contact period is required. There are other methods of evolving the formaldehyde, but this is the most popular. Fumigating chemicals can be obtained commercially, conveniently arranged for use. Fumigation with formaldehyde is not very efficient at temperatures lower than 60°F.

Disinfection may also be carried out by spraying the formalin on such articles as books or into closets, drawers, etc. Fumigation of small rooms may be accomplished by spraying bed sheets and hanging them up to give off the gas. The ordinary bed sheet will hold 8 ounces of formalin without dripping, and this will be sufficient for 1,000 cubic feet of air space. The room should be kept closed for eight hours.

10-15. Bichloride of Mercury. This chemical, known as corrosive sublimate, is a powerful bacteriostat, but it has the disadvantage of corroding metals. Also, it is very poisonous. If solutions are made up for use, they should be colored so that there will be no danger of their identity being mistaken. The tinting may be done by a few crystals of potassium permanganate or ordinary household bluing. Bichloride of mercury loses some of its disinfecting power if in contact with albuminous matter and is not particularly suitable for feces. It is generally used in 1:500 and 1:1,000 solutions. In the former strength it will kill spores after an exposure of one hour. The effectiveness and speed of action of this disinfectant are greatly increased by the use of warm solutions.

10-16. Other Disinfectants. *Alcohol* is both an antiseptic and a germicide. It is effective as a germicide in solutions of 50 to 70 per cent. It has the peculiar faculty of being ineffective if the alcohol is absolute, that is, if no water is present. The reason for this is that the alcohol has no effect upon dry bacteria. The water in the solution, therefore, is needed to moisten the bacteria so that the alcohol can destroy them.

Pine oil is a clear, dark, reddish-brown liquid obtained as a by-product of the turpentine industry. Most pine-odor disinfectants are compositions containing 60 to 80 per cent pine oil and about 10 per cent soap, with the balance water. Pine-type disinfectants are also on the market. Unless they contain some other germicidal ingredient, pine-oil disinfectants are not effective against gram-positive organisms.

Many other acids in addition to carbolic may be used as disinfectants if in sufficient concentration. *Sulfuric acid* in a 1:1,000 solution kills typhoid bacilli in one hour. *Hydrochloric acid* is weaker, although a 4 per cent solution of normal acid is antiseptic and will kill many bacteria. *Acetic, citric, formic,* and *salicylic acids* are considerably weaker. *Boric acid* in a 2 per cent solution is a germicide to the less resistant bacteria and antiseptic to others. Salicylic and boric acids are frequently used illegally as food preservatives.

Iodine is generally used in a 2½ per cent solution in 70 per cent alcohol. It is used as a skin disinfectant and in surgery. It may also be used to disinfect water.

Potassium permanganate is an effective germicide but is an extremely active oxidizing agent and, therefore, quickly loses its value against bacteria when in the presence of organic matter. This chemical has also been used to disinfect water.

10-17. Detergents. Detergents, including soap, are not disinfectants except as they may act mechanically to remove bacteria along with dirt. A detergent is a *surface-active agent,* that is, a compound that affects the face layer of one surface in contact with another. The surfaces affected may be air and water, oil and water, glass or metal and water, or any surface between two substances. If a surface-active agent combines wetting, dispersing, and emulsifying, it is a cleanser and is called a detergent. A good detergent[3] should (1) be soluble to some extent; (2) permit penetration of the water solution into capillaries by lowering interfacial tension, *i.e.*, permit wetting; (3) disperse or break up particles which have gathered together; (4) link, by emulsifying, the dirt or grease particles with the water rather than with each other or with the substance to be cleaned.

Soap, which is a chemical combination of a fatty acid and an alkali, is a wetting, dispersing, and emulsifying agent and therefore a surface-active agent and a detergent. Soap acts well only in waters of over pH 10. This means that extra soap must be used to raise the wash water to this high alkalinity. Soap is also a softening agent; *i.e.*, it will combine with the hardness-producing compounds in the water—the carbonates, bicarbonates, and sulfates of calcium and magnesium—to form insoluble compounds. The softening is accomplished before the detergent action takes place. This means a wastage of soap and also the presence of undesirable insoluble compounds in the wash water. Therefore soap is limited in its desirability for household use and for some industrial purposes where wetting and emulsifying action are required.

Other surface-acting agents are synthetic, consisting of manufactured compounds not readily found in nature. A synthetic may accomplish any one of the three actions mentioned above or it may accomplish all, in which case it is a synthetic detergent.

Synthetic detergents were devised (1) to be effective in neutral or acid solutions, (2) to be effective in hard waters without softening, and (3) to be effective without forming insoluble magnesium or calcium compounds in hard water. Several groups of synthetic detergents are available, including the quaternary ammonium compounds when combined with an alkali. This, as indicated in Art. 10-10, is a combined detergent and disinfectant.

In general the detergent ability of the various groups of agents, including soap, varies not only between groups but also among the individuals of a group as to the dirt to be removed—soil, rust, oil, fat, or soot—and also with the surface to be cleaned—crockery, metal, paint, enamel, skin, cotton, wool, or nylon. The effect of the water characteristics has already been mentioned. Commercial brands of synthetic detergents are built up by the addition of such neutral salts as sodium or calcium chloride to increase detergency properties. Others are mixtures of compounds of the same general type to broaden the range of applicability. Still others contain sequestering agents that will prevent formation of sticky curd in hard water. These are pyrophosphates, tetraphosphates, and hexaphosphates. The buyer must either depend upon the statement of the manufacturer as to the applicability of a particular detergent or learn by trial whether it is the kind best suited for his purposes.

10-18. Methods of Disinfection. In addition to the disinfection of water, milk, and food utensils, which is discussed elsewhere, the usual fields for disinfection in public health work involve urine, feces, sputum, body and bed linen, and bedrooms. At least two hours' contact should be provided for all disinfectants. The disinfection of feces is of great importance, particularly in the case of diseases of the intestinal tract. The discharges should be caught in an impervious vessel and immediately treated with the disinfectant. If the feces are in masses a small stick should be used to break them up and to mix in and incorporate the disinfectant thoroughly. During the period of contact the vessel must be covered to prevent access of flies. Lime is an excellent agent for this purpose. A cupful of hydrated lime is sufficient for one bowel movement. Lime and excreta should then be covered with hot water. The small stick used for mixing may be left in the vessel. If milk of lime is used at least enough should be added to equal in volume the matter to be disinfected. A 10 per cent solution of formalin is frequently used and is also excellent as a deodorant. A 5 per cent solution of carbolic acid will be effective. Emulsified disinfectant should not be used for feces or sputum.

Sputum is a medium for spreading many of the common communicable diseases, including tuberculosis, the common cold, chickenpox, pneumonia, whooping cough, diphtheria, etc. This matter, therefore, must be carefully disinfected. So far as possible it should be caught in paper cups or gauze cloths and burned. Handkerchiefs so soiled should be soaked for one hour in 5 per cent bichloride of mercury before laundering.

If the sputum is caught in cups which cannot be destroyed, the cups may first be partially filled with a solution of carbolic acid or phenol. The practice of partially filling cuspidors in public places with disinfectants is a good one. A 5 per cent solution of carbolic acid is the usual disinfectant for this purpose, although pine oil of equal strength has a pleasanter odor.

Sickroom attendants should disinfect their hands after handling patients and soiled clothing. This can be accomplished by wetting the hands with a 70 per cent solution of alcohol.

Bed and body linen, including napkins, towels, sheets, pillow covers, and underwear, may be steamed, boiled, or soaked for one hour in a 5 per cent carbolic solution, 10 per cent formalin, or 1:1,000 bichloride of mercury before laundering.

Dead bodies are not likely to disseminate disease. The possibility of spreading of infection may be prevented, however, by wrapping the bodies in a sheet soaked in 1:500 bichloride of mercury solution, or 5 per cent carbolic acid until disposed of, or the skin surface may be washed with 10 per cent formalin. With modern methods of burial it is not likely that bodies will be sources of danger.

10-19. Disinfection of Rooms. At the beginning of the sickness all unnecessary objects should be removed from the sickroom. During the period of illness cleaning should be accomplished by scrubbing and other dustless methods so far as possible. Dusting should be done with a dampened cloth. The terminal cleaning may be done with water to which bichloride of mercury has been added. If the walls have been soiled, painting or repapering may be advisable. This procedure, together with complete airing and as much sunlight as possible, may be applied to replace the old-fashioned fumigation.

INSECTICIDES

10-20. The effectiveness of insecticides for public health usage depends upon a variety of factors which should be considered as they apply to local conditions. It has been well demonstrated that such related factors as the adequacy of application procedures, the formulations used, the types of surfaces treated, local atmospheric conditions, the extent of the insect infestation and breeding potential, and the level of resistance to chemicals in the insect population can affect the results obtained by an insecticide treatment.

Cost is often an important consideration in the choice of an insecticide for a particular usage. The high cost of the trial-and-error method of selecting an effective economic poison may be reduced by critical analysis of the history of insecticides previously used in the area and by simplified field tests for resistance in the insect population coupled with careful field observations.

10-21. Insecticide Formulations. New pesticides for the control of insects and rodents of public health importance continue to be introduced quite frequently. Insecticides are usually commercially available in one or more of the forms in which they are used in public health activities—technical-grade material, dusts, wettable powders, emulsifiable concentrates, solutions, and aerosol preparations.

Technical-grade insecticide is the raw product used in preparing such formulations as emulsions, dusts, solutions, etc., and is not ordinarily chemically pure. Technical-grade DDT, for example, contains approximately only 70 per cent of the isomer effective against insects of public health significance. The material, however, is considered as 100 per cent DDT when making up solutions, emulsions, or dusts.

Insecticidal dusts are prepared by grinding toxic ingredients, such as DDT or benzene hexachloride, in inert carriers like talc or pyrophyllite. Dusts are marketed in the concentrations required for field use since the inert and toxic materials must be blended together during the grinding process.

Wettable powders consist of a blend of inert dust and a toxic ingredient, such as DDT or chlordane, to which a suitable wetting agent, such as sodium lauryl sulfate, has been added. Wettable powders are added to water to form suspensions, which require continuous agitation to prevent settling of the considerable amount of inert material present. Suspensions are most often used in spraying such places as stables and other outbuildings when the residue is not objectionable.

Insecticidal solutions are marketed both as concentrates and finished sprays. Concentrated solutions usually contain the toxic ingredients and a solvent. Concentrated solutions must be diluted for field use with kerosene or similar mineral oils; for example, 40 per cent chlordane concentrate is diluted to 2.5 to 5 per cent, a finished spray, before use. Finished-spray solutions are concentrations suitable for immediate use. Solutions are not emulsifiable or soluble in water.

Emulsifiable concentrates are concentrated solutions to which an emulsifier has been added. When the concentrate is mixed with water, the emulsifying agent forms a very thin coating on each individual droplet of the solvent containing the insecticide, thus preventing separation from the water carrier. A finished *emulsion* is made by diluting a concentrate with sufficient water to form a concentration suitable for immediate use—for example, 5 per cent DDT emulsion.

Aerosol formulations are commercially available in convenient containers (the so-called "aerosol bomb") for producing a fine fog to control flying insects in an enclosed space, such as the home. Typical formulations contain 0.1 to 0.6 per cent pyrethrins, Allethrin or Lethane; a synergist such as piperonyl butoxide, 1.0 to 2.0 per cent DDT or Methoxychlor; 10 to 12 per cent petroleum distillates; and 85 per cent propellants such as Freon 11 and Freon 12. For control of insects in large buildings or outdoor areas such as picnic grounds or drive-in theaters, there have been developed several types of equipment which disperse insecticides in the particle-size range (1–50 microns) generally classified as aerosols.

10-22. Pyrethrum. The term "pyrethrum" is applied to powders or dusts made of the flowers of a plant belonging to the chrysanthemum family and to various formulations of the active ingredients of these flowers in suitable solvents or diluents. Pyrethrum is the least toxic to mammals of all the insecticides commonly in use. The most extensively used extract has been one containing 2.5 per cent pyrethrins which, when diluted with 19 parts of kerosene, produces a finished spray of approximately 0.1 per cent toxic principle. The use of a synergist such as piperonyl butoxide increases the toxicity of pyrethrum to many insects and makes possible the use of lower concentrations of pyrethrins, particularly in combination with other insecticides.

Pyrethrum is used extensively in dusts, sprays, and aerosols against a variety of insects. Emulsions containing 0.006 per cent pyrethrins applied at a rate of 55 gallons per acre give control of mosquito larvae. Household sprays and aerosols containing a combination of 0.025 to 0.05 per cent pyrethrins, 0.025 to 0.5 per cent synergist, and various other insecticides are effective against roaches, flies, and mosquitoes. Pyrethrum dusts, powders, and ointments are used in controlling animal parasites such as fleas, lice, and mites.

10-23. Allethrin. This is a synthetic material with insecticidal properties similar to pyrethrum. Technical Allethrin is a clear amber fluid that is readily miscible with kerosene, xylene, and other organic solvents but is not soluble in water. It differs from natural pyrethrins in that it has a pleasant odor.

Allethrin has been found less effective than natural pyrethrins against many species of mosquitoes but about equally effective against flies. The effectiveness of Allethrin is increased by the addition of synergists such as piperonyl butoxide and sesame oil; however, the increase is less than that resulting when synergists are added to natural pyrethrins. Its principal use has been in low-pressure aerosols at 0.4 per cent concentration for the control of household insects. At 0.46 per cent in a talc powder, Allethrin may be used in the control of DDT-resistant human body lice.

10-24. DDT (dichloro-diphenyl-trichloroethane). Technical DDT is an almost odorless white, crystalline powder having a tendency to form lumps. Though not soluble in water, it is moderately soluble in kerosene and vegetable oils and highly soluble in such organic solvents as benzene, trichlorethylene, xylene, and acetone. DDT may be purchased as the technical-grade product in the form of dusts, wettable powders, solutions, emulsifiable concentrates, and aerosol preparations.

Technical-grade DDT may be formulated as an emulsifiable concentrate as follows:

Technical DDT—104.5 pounds
Triton x-155, or equivalent—1 gallon
Xylene—40.5 gallons

When the concentrate is made, the DDT is first dissolved in the xylene until the solution is clear. Then the emulsifier is added, and the combination is mixed for several minutes.

This will yield approximately 50 gallons of 25 per cent DDT concentrate on a weight-volume basis. A 5 per cent finished emulsion is prepared by diluting 1 part of this concentrate with 4 parts of water by volume.

A formulation of technical-grade DDT that will yield approximately 40 gallons of 35 per cent DDT-water emulsifiable concentrate may be made as follows:

Technical DDT—125 pounds
Xylene—31.5 gallons
Triton x-155, or equivalent—1 gallon

A 5 per cent finished spray may be made by diluting 1 part of concentrate with 6 parts of water. A 5 per cent spray is suitable for both residual and outdoor space-spraying activities and for mosquito-larviciding operations, provided that sufficient care is used not to overdose waters in which fish life is present (see Chap. 9).

A suitable solution of approximately 5 per cent concentration for use as a residual spray, outdoor space spray, or larvicide can be made by dissolving 20 pounds of technical grade DDT in 50 gallons of No. 2 fuel oil or kerosene. A very satisfactory field strength (approximately 1 per cent) solution for mosquito-larviciding operations may be prepared by dissolving 4 pounds of technical-grade DDT in 50 gallons of oil.

Since DDT is slowly soluble in kerosene or fuel oil, all lumps should be broken up before the solution is made. After the DDT has been placed in the oil, several days should be allowed for solution to take place, with occasional agitation during that period. Solution may be facilitated by first making a slurry of the DDT in several gallons of oil, breaking all remaining lumps and pouring this into the drum; or the DDT may first be dissolved in one of the organic solvents, such as xylene or acetone, before it is placed in the oil.

Various other household insects can be controlled through the use of DDT formulations. A 5 per cent emulsion or solution will, in most instances, control bedbug infestations. A 10 per cent dust is usually effective in the control of infestations of the human body louse (*Pediculus humanus humanus*) and of the human head louse (*P. humanus capitus*). DDT dusts are effective in the area control of ticks. A 10 per cent DDT dust has been found effective in the control of fleas and other ectoparasites of rats when applied to rat runs and harborage areas. Where insects have not developed resistance to DDT, it is still the preferred insecticide for public health use.

The extensive usage that has been made of DDT without apparent harmful effects on humans indicates that it is a relatively safe insecticide. The presence of DDT in milk, however, is considered a contaminant; therefore, it should not be used in dairy barns or on dairy animals; nor should it be used on foods. In any use of DDT or other insecticides, precautions should be taken to avoid direct skin contact and to avoid inhalation of the dusts, mists, or powders. Clothing that has become excessively contaminated should not be worn, and skin areas that have come into contact with the chemical should be washed with soap and water immediately.

10-25. BHC (benzene hexachloride). This chemical is available commercially as technical-grade material in the form of dusts, wettable powders, solutions, and emulsifiable concentrates. The technical material is a crystalline solid, white to buff-colored, with a strong musty odor. It is composed of a mixture of the various isomers, only one of which, the gamma isomer, is known to be highly toxic to insects. The commercial technical grades contain from 12 per cent to 90 per cent gamma isomer. Each commercial preparation is labeled to indicate the per cent of gamma isomer which it contains; consequently, in preparing formulations, the field operator should make certain that the end formulation contains the desired amount of gamma isomer.

BHC is effective in the control of many pests of public health importance, but because of the objectionable odor its use is limited largely to outdoor applications. An emulsion applied at the rate of 1 pound of technical BHC (12 per cent gamma isomer) per acre has given good control of mosquito larvae in landlocked ponds for one month without injury to fish. When applied by airplane in a fuel-oil solution at the rate of 0.1 pound of gamma isomer per acre, it has been an effective mosquito larvicide.

This chemical can be employed as a residual spray, space spray, or larvicide for housefly control; however, when flies are resistant to other chlorinated hydrocarbons, they usually develop resistance to BHC rapidly. A 5 per cent emulsion of benzene hexachloride (12 per cent gamma isomer) has proved to be an effective space spray and residual spray. This formulation has also been effective as a larvicide when applied to garbage-can areas, animal excreta, and other wastes at the rate of 200 milligrams of BHC per square foot; however, for good penetration of wastes it should be diluted to 1.25 per cent. Benzene hexachloride should not be used as a residual spray in dairy barns or areas where contamination of food or animal feed may result, and the treatment of ground litter in chicken pens may result in the eggs and flesh of the chickens acquiring an offtaste or odor.

10-26. Chlordane. Technical chlordane, a dark, oily liquid, is available in two grades, refined and agricultural, which are equal in their insecticidal properties. Other commercially available formulations are dusts, wettable powders, emulsifiable concentrates, and solutions.

A satisfactory emulsifiable formulation yielding 50 gallons of concentrate containing approximately 25 per cent technical chlordane on a weight-volume basis can be prepared as follows:

Technical chlordane—8 gallons
Triton x-155, or equivalent—2 gallons
Xylene—40 gallons

A 2.5 per cent field-strength emulsion can be prepared from this concentrate by diluting 1 part concentrate to 9 parts water by volume or a 5 per cent emulsion by diluting 1 part concentrate to 4 parts water by volume. A 5 per cent emulsion or solution is suitable for residual spraying when applied at a rate of 200 milligrams per square foot (approximately 1 gallon to 1,000 square feet) to porches, fences, barns, and similar outbuildings. A 2.5 to 3 per cent chlordane emulsion or solution is satisfactory for "spot" treatment of selected surfaces inside dwellings, such as baseboards, doors, and window frames.

As a larvicide for the control of houseflies and as an exterior space spray for adult fly and mosquito control, chlordane may be employed in the form of a 2.5 per cent emulsion. With continued use of chlordane in an area, however, the housefly population usually develops resistance to this chemical.

Chlordane dusts and wettable powders can be successfully employed as soil treatments in the control of cat and dog fleas, some species of ticks, and ants.

10-27. DDD. This is a white crystalline solid very similar to DDT in appearance and physical properties. It is available as technical-grade material in the form of dusts and wettable powders and in paints. Although its widest usage is in the control of insects important in agriculture, DDD may be employed against most of the insects of public health significance. Under the same conditions, DDD is generally less effective than DDT but can be used successfully in an oil solution as a mosquito larvicide and is less toxic to fish than DDT.

10-28. Diazinon. Technical-grade Diazinon is a pale- to dark-brown liquid. It is commercially available also as a wettable powder, poison bait, emulsifiable concentrate, and dust. This organophosphorus compound has a human toxicity level permitting its safe usage as a residual spray at strengths of 1 to 2.5 per cent. Its residual effectiveness in fly control is greatly increased when sugar is added to the field-strength sprays at a rate of 2.5 parts of sugar to 1 part of the toxicant.

Diazinon has been accepted for use as a residual spray for fly control in dairy barns. The usual formulation, containing 2.5 per cent toxicant and 6.25 per cent sugar (1 part to 2.5 parts), is applied at the rate of 100 milligrams of Diazinon and 250 milligrams of sugar per square foot, or approximately 1 gallon of the formulation to 1,000 square feet of surface. Satisfactory fly control has been obtained for several months in experimental barns by the installation of cords $3/16$ inch in diameter, impregnated with a 25 per cent Diazinon-xylene solution, at the rate of 30 linear feet of cord per 100 square feet of floor area. A bait containing 0.1 per cent (liquid) or 1.0 per cent (dry) Diazinon with an attractant (sugar, syrup), when repeatedly applied to fly-concentration sites, has also given satisfactory fly control. At a dosage of 50 milligrams per square foot, Diazinon has proved a much more effective fly larvicide than other organophosphorus compounds.

Although Diazinon is less toxic to humans than some of the other organophosphorus compounds, extreme caution should be exercised in its use, particularly while preparing formulations or making routine applications.

10-29. Dieldrin. Dieldrin is a white crystalline solid; however, the technical grade may have a buff to light-brown color. It is available as wettable powders, dust concentrates, emulsifiable concentrates, solutions, impregnated pellets, and low-percentage dusts. Extreme caution should be exercised in handling this material, particularly the concentrated formulations, as the acute toxicity to mammals is approximately four or five times that of DDT.

Dieldrin has been employed successfully in housefly control when applied as an emulsion of 0.625 to 1.25 per cent to outdoor surfaces (barns, fences, vegetation) and to porches of dwellings at rates of 25 to 50 milligrams per square foot (1 gallon of emulsion to 1,000 square feet of surface). When dieldrin is widely used in an area or where houseflies are already resistant to DDT, BHC, or chlordane, resistance to dieldrin has often developed very rapidly.

Dieldrin fuel-oil solutions, applied at rates of 0.1 to 0.2 pound of dieldrin per acre for larvae and adult control, respectively, have been effective in the control of DDT-resistant salt-marsh mosquitoes. Residual applications of dieldrin have been substituted for DDT in malaria-control operations in various areas of the world where the anopheline vectors are showing resistance to DDT, or for combined control of malaria and other vectors. The use of dieldrin for residual treatment of homes in the United States, however, is not justified, since DDT continues to be effective against *A. quadrimaculatus*.

As a residual larvicide for the control of mosquito breeding in shallow, landlocked fresh-water ponds, a dieldrin emulsion applied at a rate of 1 pound of dieldrin per acre gives effective control for one or two years, but is totally destructive to fish life and most other aquatic organisms. Preflood treatment, at the same rate, of landlocked, shallow areas has also given successful mosquito breeding control.

Dieldrin as a 0.5 per cent spray or a 1 per cent dust can be used effectively as a spot treatment for control of cockroaches.

10-30. Dipterex (Bayer L 13/59). This chemical is a white to pale-yellow crystallinelike powder. It has been used as a public health pesticide principally in poison baits for fly control. Liquid baits containing Dipterex are generally formulated of a 0.1 per cent toxicant and a 10 per cent attractant and applied at a rate of 1 gallon per 1,000 square feet of floor area. Dry baits of this chemical generally contain 1 per cent toxicant and an attractant and are applied at a rate of 2 to 4 ounces per 1,000 square feet. Rapid reductions of housefly populations have been achieved at such places as dumps and animal shelters.

10-31. Heptachlor. As a public health pesticide this chemical is available as emulsifiable concentrate, dust, wettable powder, and granular formulations. Heptachlor appears to be a dependable larvicide for the control of DDT-resistant salt-marsh mosquitoes when applied by airplane at rates of 0.1 pound per acre in a fuel-oil solution or 0.05 pound per acre in an impregnated granular formulation. Effective abatement of adult mosquito populations has been secured with a ground-applied mist at 0.07 pound of heptachlor per acre.

Host flea populations have been effectively controlled for long periods by the application of 2.5 per cent dusts to ground squirrel burrows.

10-32. Lindane. This is the gamma isomer of BHC, with a purity of not less than 99 per cent. It is a white crystalline solid, has a slightly musty odor, and possesses fumigating properties. Formulations of lindane include wettable powders, dusts, solutions, and emulsifiable concentrates.

Although lindane has the highest acute toxicity of the various isomers of BHC, its low chronic toxicity and the relatively low dosage rates required make it acceptable for use in controlling flies in dairy barns. The application of lindane as a residual spray at a rate of 25 milligrams per square foot (1 gallon of a 0.625 per cent emulsion per 1,000 square feet) has been successfully employed in fly control. Lindane emulsions may also be used at the same rate as a larvicide on such fly sources as garbage areas, manure, and industrial wastes.

For the control of salt-marsh-mosquito larvae and adults the application of an aerial spray of lindane in fuel oil at a rate of 0.1 pound of lindane per acre has been very effective.

A 2 per cent emulsion of lindane has been successfully employed as a space spray for the control of flying insects of public health significance.

Lindane emulsions may also be employed for the control of DDT-resistant bedbugs, cat and dog fleas, ticks, and mites; and a 1 per cent lindane powder has given excellent control of infestations of DDT-resistant human body lice.

10-33. Malathion. This brown liquid organophosphorus compound is available as technical-grade material in the form of dusts, wettable powders, solutions, emulsifiable concentrates, and poison baits. It apparently has a much lower mammalian toxicity than other organophosphorus compounds, with the general toxic hazard approaching that of DDT.

The use of malathion as a public health pesticide has been primarily in the area of housefly control and roach control. It is approved for use in dairy barns, and the residual application of a 2.5 per cent malathion–12 per cent sugar emulsion has provided excellent fly control for a period of several weeks. Liquid baits composed of 0.1 per cent malathion and 10 per cent attractant (sugar, molasses), applied at a rate of 1 gallon per 1,000 square feet of floor space, and dry baits containing 1 to 2 per cent malathion and 10 per cent attractant, applied at a rate of 2 to 4 ounces per 1,000 square feet, can effectively control flies in dairy barns. The required frequency of treatments depends upon the extent of the fly infestation, and the results secured depend upon the thoroughness of the operator in making applications as needed. As a larvicide for controlling fly larvae, malathion has not proved nearly so effective as several other insecticides, particularly Diazinon.

Where cat and dog fleas have become resistant to the chlorinated hydrocarbons, the application to infested yards of a 2 per cent malathion emulsion at a rate of 1 gallon to 1,000 square feet has been very effective. Control of infestations of cockroaches resistant to chlorinated hydrocarbons has been attained by applying a 3 per cent malathion solution or emulsion to roach harborages and runways. Formulations containing 1 part malathion and 2 parts perthane applied at a 4 per cent concentration have also proved effective in control of resistant roaches.

10-34. Methoxychlor. This white crystalline solid, somewhat similar to DDT, is available as wettable powders and as oil concentrates.

The toxicity hazard of methoxychlor is less than that of DDT. Also, since methoxychlor is stored in animal fat to a very much smaller degree than DDT, it is acceptable for control of flies in dairy barns.

A 5 per cent emulsion is used for housefly control at a rate of 200 milligrams of methoxychlor per square foot (approximately 1 gallon per 1,000 square feet). In some areas wettable powders have given better results; however, both formulations have given erratic results against DDT-resistant flies. More effective toxicants, therefore, are usually employed for the treatment of exterior surfaces at dairies.

10-35. Parathion. This is an extremely dangerous material, and utmost caution should be exercised in handling it in any form. Because of its extreme toxicity, parathion has not found general application as a public health pesticide.

Parathion-impregnated cotton cords ($\frac{3}{32}$ inch in diameter) have given satisfactory housefly control for several months when installed in dairy barns at the rate of 30 linear feet of cord per 100 square feet of floor area. The cords are installed by affixing short pieces (approximately 18 inches in length) by one end to overhead portions of the structure, such as rafters, ceilings, etc. The individual making routine cord installations should wear cotton gloves and use only commercially prepared cords. Fly densities are usually reduced to control levels within two to three weeks after cord installation.

Cords are impregnated by immersing them in a 5 to 10 per cent parathion-xylene solution and allowing them to dry. Cotton cord of a $\frac{3}{32}$-inch diameter should be used, since houseflies have demonstrated a pronounced preference for this size and material. To reduce the possibility of the cords being used for purposes other than fly control, they should be colored or marked. Because of the extreme toxicity of parathion, the cords should be prepared only by experienced formulators.

BIBLIOGRAPHY

1. Rosenau, M. J.: "Preventive Medicine and Hygiene," 7th ed., by Kenneth F. Maxcy, Appleton-Century-Crofts, Inc., New York, 1951.
2. Milk Ordinance and Code: 1953 Recommendations of the Public Health Service, *U.S. Dep. Health, Education, Welfare Pub.* 229.
3. Larson, T. E.: Synthetic Detergents, *J. Am. Water Works Assoc.*, vol. 41, no. 4, 1949.
4. "Operational Memoranda on Economic Poisons," U.S. Public Health Service.
5. "Public Health Pesticides: 1956 Report from the Communicable Disease Center," U.S. Public Health Service.

CHAPTER 11

MILK SANITATION

THE DAIRY

11-1. Milk is not a mere beverage; it is a balanced food which supplies protein, fat, carbohydrates, mineral matter, and vitamins in the proper proportion to meet the needs of the human body. Its chief advantages as a food are that it is a well-balanced ration; is easily digested; contains no waste materials, such as bone, peelings, skin, or shell; requires no cooking; and is cheaper than many other products having the same food value. A quart of 4 per cent milk, according to Kelly and Clement[1], furnishes about 670 calories. The protein in milk is the flesh-, muscle-, tissue-, and bone-building constituent; the fat supplies energy and provides fatty tissue; and the carbohydrates, mainly as milk sugar, furnish energy or are converted into fat. Mineral matter, or ash, is necessary for bone and teeth formation. The vitamins A, B, and C are also present in milk, and these promote growth in the young and aid in the prevention of rickets, beri-beri, and scurvy. Even under the best conditions, however, normal milk lacks adequate amounts of vitamin C. Also, since this vitamin is not heat-stable, its concentration may be further reduced through pasteurization. For this reason physicians recommend that infants or young children fed on milk from cows be given a small quantity of orange or tomato juice in order to make up any vitamin C deficiency. Milk is also frequently fortified with vitamin D and is relatively rich in vitamins E and K.

Providing sanitary conditions for the handling of milk and milk products provides many serious problems for the sanitarian. The conditions under which it must necessarily be produced, the ease with which it may be contaminated, and the rapidity with which it spoils—all these factors contribute to the difficulties confronting the public health official who is responsible for the safety and quality of a city's milk supply.

11-2. Milk as a Vehicle of Infection. Table 11-1 gives the reported outbreaks of milk-borne disease from 1923 to 1950. It will be seen that typhoid and paratyphoid fevers, scarlet fever, and septic sore throat are far less conspicuous in more recent years than they were in the past. These downward trends are important indications of the advances in milk sanitation. The reported increase in the number of outbreaks of dysentery, food poisoning, enteritis, and undulant fever is explained by the fact that reporting of diseases and their probable causes is becoming more complete; this, in turn, may be attributed to more alert health departments and their increasingly careful scrutiny of milk supplies.

Tuberculosis of cows usually affects their salivary glands or some part of the alimentary tract; the feces of infected cows frequently contain tubercle bacilli. Hence, if milk should become contaminated by manure and should be drunk without being properly pasteurized, transmission of bovine tuberculosis to persons through this means is possible. In far-advanced cases of bovine tuberculosis, however, milk may be infected directly by a diseased udder or possibly by droplets given off by the cow in coughing. Transmission of tuberculosis from human origin through milk is usually the result of careless handling of the milk by infected persons or by exposure of milk to flies or dust. Some authorities estimate that in some areas one-fourth of all cases of tuberculosis in children under sixteen years of age are of bovine origin, while others consider that 7 per cent of all cases of tuberculosis are of the bovine type.

Typhoid, paratyphoid, and dysentery organisms may reach milk from the unclean hands of milkers or other dairy employees who may be carriers or in the early stages of illness. For that reason, dairy workers should wash their hands thoroughly and disinfect them before milking. The importance of clean habits, such as washing the hands after excretion of urine or feces, should be impressed upon all milk handlers. Disinfection of the hands before milking or handling the milk is also necessary. Exposure of the milk to flies, particularly if there are insanitary toilets in the neighborhood, is dangerous. Allowing cows to wade in sewage-polluted water may allow infectious material to lodge on teats and udders. This, of course, invites contamination of milk at milking time. The use of polluted water at the dairy may also result in dangerous milk.

Those diseases transmitted by throat and nose discharges, such as diphtheria, septic sore throat, and scarlet fever, almost invariably reach milk from the dairy workers who are carriers or who are in the early stages of the diseases. Spitting, sneezing, coughing, or even forcible speaking during the process of milking or while in the vicinity of uncovered milk may result in infection. Sneezing into the hands or handling of handkerchiefs during milking is dangerous unless the hands are washed and disinfected before milking is resumed. Streptococci and staphylococci of human origin may gain lodgment in the teats and udder of the cow and grow there. The former may cause scarlet fever or septic sore throat, and the toxins generated in the milk by the latter may cause severe gastroenteritis. They may be indicated by inflammation or hard lumps (indurations) in the teats or udder.

TABLE 11-1. SUMMARY OF MILK-BORNE DISEASE OUTBREAKS REPORTED BY STATE AND LOCAL HEALTH AUTHORITIES AS HAVING OCCURRED IN THE UNITED STATES DURING THE YEARS 1923 TO 1950

Year	Typhoid			Paratyphoid			Scarlet fever and septic sore throat			Diphtheria			Dysentery			Food poisoning and gastroenteritis			Undulant fever			Miscellaneous			Total, all diseases		
	Outbreaks	Cases	Deaths	Outbreaks	Cases	Deaths	Outbreaks	Cases	Deaths	Outbreaks	Cases	Deaths	Outbreaks	Cases	Deaths	Outbreaks	Cases	Deaths	Outbreaks	Cases	Deaths	Outbreaks	Cases	Daeths	Outbreaks	Cases	Deaths
1923	15	423	31	0	0	0	7	406	6	1	5	0	0	0	0	0	0	0	0	0	0	0	0	0	23	834	37
1924	25	693	48	10	372	16	6	354	0	1	23	0	2	110	1	0	0	0	0	0	0	0	0	0	44	1,552	65
1925	31	580	43	2	37	4	10	1,108	8	1	14	1	0	0	0	0	0	0	0	0	0	0	0	0	44	1,739	56
1926	49	1,189	83	2	19	1	11	1,789	10	2	24	0	0	0	0	1	150	0	0	0	0	3	192	1	68	3,363	95
1927	24	430	35	2	53	0	4	389	5	2	15	0	0	0	0	1	50	0	3	17	1	0	0	0	36	954	41
1928	25	421	48	0	0	0	11	1,449	55	2	48	0	1	126	17	2	104	0	5	21	0	0	0	0	46	2,169	120
1929	29	541	36	1	38	1	19	1,891	14	0	0	0	1	8	0	1	24	0	0	0	0	0	0	0	51	2,502	51
1930	30	575	41	0	0	0	11	1,158	7	0	0	0	1	64	2	6	171	6	0	0	0	0	0	0	48	1,968	56
1931	21	217	16	1	22	0	9	1,059	8	1	22	0	1	65	0	1	13	0	0	0	0	0	0	0	34	1,398	24
1932	23	254	22	0	0	0	9	356	6	0	0	0	0	0	0	1	32	0	0	0	0	0	0	0	33	642	28
1933	25	299	26	1	17	0	10	753	9	2	19	3	0	0	0	0	0	0	0	0	0	4	260	1	42	1,348	39
1934	26	345	27	1	400	0	9	478	8	1	9	0	0	0	0	5	292	0	0	0	0	0	0	0	42	1,524	35
1935	16	172	14	2	50	0	11	1,065	7	0	0	0	1	131	0	13	411	0	0	0	0	0	0	0	43	1,829	21
1936	15	114	5	1	21	0	18	1,553	23	0	0	0	0	0	0	4	188	0	4	15	0	0	0	0	42	1,891	28
1937	15	208	11	0	0	0	14	1,384	3	0	0	0	0	0	0	12	523	0	0	0	0	2	35	0	43	2,150	14
1938	18	187	17	0	0	0	12	674	7	1	31	3	2	166	0	9	627	0	0	0	0	0	0	0	42	1,685	27
1939	6	51	1	2	24	0	9	1,324	6	0	0	0	2	324	0	19	749	0	1	4	0	2	33	0	41	2,509	7
1940	14	120	10	0	0	0	5	482	0	0	0	0	2	197	0	17	855	0	4	19	0	1	5	0	43	1,678	10
1941	12	120	4	0	0	0	3	219	0	1	5	0	3	126	0	15	483	0	3	96	0	0	0	0	37	1,049	4
1942	5	42	0	1	4	0	6	620	0	1	36	0	1	40	0	23	1,341	2	5	42	0	2	68	0	44	2,193	2
1943	6	37	1	0	0	0	3	200	0	1	20	4	0	0	0	25	1,278	0	4	22	2	1	33	0	40	1,590	7
1944	7	359	18	1	6	0	2	171	0	0	0	0	2	34	0	23	816	0	3	20	0	2	43	2	40	1,449	20
1945	3	72	4	0	0	0	3	308	0	1	53	2	1	22	0	18	1,673	11	2	19	0	1	14	0	29	2,161	17
1946	1	7	0	0	0	0	0	0	0	0	0	0	1	15	0	11	696	0	5	66	0	1	11	0	19	795	0
1947	3	57	7	1	28	0	0	0	0	0	0	0	0	0	0	16	162	0	2	6	0	0	0	0	22	253	7
1948	1	11	0	0	0	0	1	67	0	0	0	0	2	126	1	11	350	1	0	0	0	2	59	0	17	613	2
1949	1	7	0	0	0	0	0	0	0	0	0	0	0	0	0	10	218	0	2	4	0	2	17	0	15	246	0
1950	0	0	0	0	0	0	0	0	0	0	0	0	0	0	0	7	54	0	3	8	0	0	0	0	10	62	0
Total, 1923–1950....	446	7,531	548	28	1,091	22	204	19,257	182	18	324	13	23	1,554	21	251	11,260	20	46	359	3	23	770	4	1,040	42,146	813

SOURCE: U.S. Public Health Service.

Undulant fever, or brucellosis, is caused by an organism known as *Brucella abortus*, which is responsible for contagious abortion among cattle. The bovine, porcine, and caprine strains of the organism are considered especially common to cattle, hogs, and goats, respectively. The porcine, which occasionally affects dairy cattle, appears to be particularly likely to cause consumers of the milk to contract undulant fever. Goat milk is also frequently infected. Pasteurization of the milk is the best safeguard, although efforts should be made to eliminate contagious abortion from dairy herds. The disease is assuming increasing importance in the field of public health because of the adoption of legislative measures to control brucellosis in cattle.

In California, milk was found to be involved in the transmission of Q fever.

11-3. Essentials of Milk Sanitation. The prevention of milk infection is the most important feature of milk sanitation, not only as a means of preventing disease but also as a measure that inspires public confidence, thereby leading to a higher milk consumption, a result that all health workers desire. But disease prevention is only one aspect of the subject. Clean milk is also a necessity, and clean milk is that which has a small number of bacteria in it. Unclean utensils, the entrance of dust and manure, and storage at high temperatures all directly affect the bacterial population. Large numbers of bacteria also cause quick-souring and bad-tasting milk. Odors may be absorbed by milk which is left standing in a cow stable or refrigerator, although odors also appear in milk soon after they are inhaled by the cow. Milk sanitation then has two objects: the production of *safe* milk and the production of *clean* milk. The essentials to attaining these objectives are given below:

1. *Healthy cows.* This implies freedom from tuberculosis, contagious abortion (Bang's disease, or brucellosis), and other specific diseases and also from infections of the udder.

2. *Clean and healthy workmen.* The freedom of dairymen from communicable disease is of vital importance. Their personal cleanliness is of little less moment.

3. *A clean, airy, dustless barn* with sanitary cow yard and surroundings.

4. *A separate milk room,* well constructed, properly screened, and supplied with pure water.

5. *Utensils and equipment of proper design.*

6. *Effective sterilization and scrupulous cleanliness* of pails, cans, coolers, bottles, and other equipment with which milk comes into contact.

7. *Prompt cooling and proper handling of milk,* including the milking, bottling, capping, and delivery.

8. *Pasteurization.* This is given as essential to *safe* milk, for experience has shown that with all other possible precautions infection may still

enter, and pasteurization is the most practicable method of overcoming such danger.

In the following articles further details of the above essentials will be set forth.

11-4. Milk and Bacteria. As it is removed from the cow's udder, milk contains some bacteria. Ordinarily these are harmless, but if the animal is diseased some may be pathogens. Inevitably, other bacteria enter the milk from the air, through contact with dust, the milker's hands, and the surfaces of milk pails, cans, coolers, and other utensils. How many enter thus depends upon the skill, cleanliness, and carefulness of the dairyman. Pathogens enter by the methods given in Art. 11-2. Under favorable conditions some of them may increase. However, the rapid increase of bacteria shown in Fig. 11-1 is caused by the growth of nonpathogens, including those which cause souring.

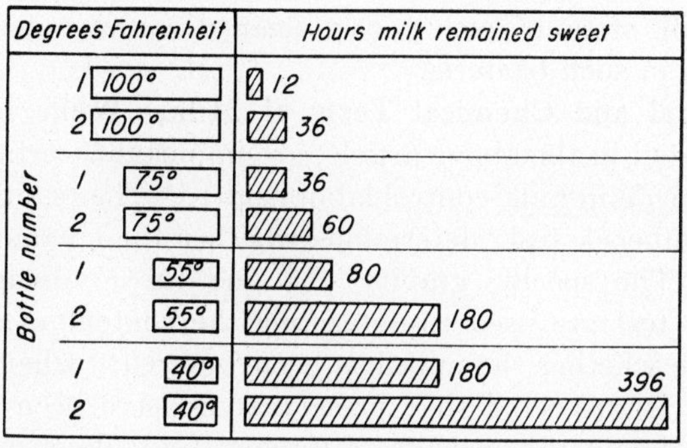

FIG. 11-1. Effect of high count and temperature of storage. Milk from bottle 1 contained 280,000 bacteria per milliliter; that from bottle 2 contained 16,400 per milliliter. (*Courtesy of U.S. Department of Agriculture.*)

The bacteriological tests of milk include obtaining the "total count," which means the determination of the number of organisms which will grow on agar plates under the standard laboratory conditions[2]. The total count is also obtained by counting with the microscope the clumps of bacteria seen in the field and by counting individual organisms. The clump count and the plate count are comparable, but the individual organism count is normally four times the others. They are all expressed as the count per milliliter.

Reduction tests with methylene blue and resazurin have been utilized as a quick method of estimating the grade of raw milk. Because of many limitations, however, decreasing emphasis is placed on them as controlled tests. In fact, the "Milk Ordinance and Code: 1953 Recommendations of the Public Health Service" omits mention of them in the definition of average bacterial plate count and direct microscopic count and cooling temperature; however, communities that find it necessary to permit use of the reduction tests may do so by making suitable modifications in the ordinance.

Pasteurized milk should be tested for coliform organisms. These bacteria are killed by pasteurization, and their presence in pasteurized milk is an indication of dangerous aftercontamination.

Thermophilic bacteria are nonpathogenic organisms which flourish and increase at high temperatures. They are considered as entering milk with dust and give trouble by causing high counts in pasteurized milk. Their presence is indicated on the agar plate by many very small "pinpoint" colonies. Thermoduric bacteria are also nonpathogenic and frequently found in the raw milk. They are able to withstand the pasteurizing temperature and thus are also responsible for high counts. They are especially likely to occur in milk from dairies where milking machines are used and where the methods of cleaning and storing the machines are poor. The milk stone of such poorly cleaned equipment is likely to be especially high in such bacteria.

11-5. Physical and Chemical Tests of Milk. While bacteriological tests, as indicated in the above article, are important, certain other tests are routinely made in milk-control laboratories. The test for the butterfat content (Babcock test) determines whether the cream content is up to standard. The specific gravity test and the cryoscope, or water-freezing-point, test are used to determine the content of solids not fat and to indicate whether the milk has been watered. Chemical tests are made when it is suspected that preservatives have been added to the milk. The sediment test consists of forcing a sample of milk through a disk of filtering material. It gives an indication of the amount of dirt in the milk.

The phosphatase test indicates whether milk has been properly pasteurized or not. If it is suspected that the temperature has not been high enough or the holding time has been too short, the test should be applied. The "Milk Ordinance and Code: 1953 Recommendations of the Public Health Service" states that this test should be routinely performed by every pasteurization plant. This test is also reliable in the detection of underpasteurization of cream, ice cream, sherbet, chocolate milk drinks, butter, sweet buttermilk, cultured buttermilk, most of the principal kinds of cheese, and cheese whey.

11-6. The 3A Sanitary Standards for Dairy Equipment. Three groups who are interested in the subject of milk sanitation on a national basis—the public health authorities, dairy-equipment manufacturers, and the users of dairy equipment—collaborate in developing a set of standards recommending the observance of certain sanitary principles in the design of various items of dairy equipment. These three groups are represented by the Committee on Sanitary Procedures of the International Association of Milk and Food Sanitarians, Inc., the Milk and Food Program of the U.S. Public Health Service, and the Sanitary Standards Subcommittee of the Dairy Industry Committee. The latter subcommittee is composed of members from the American Butter Institute, American Dry Milk Institute, Dairy Industries Supply Association, Evaporated Milk Association, International Association of Ice Cream Manufacturers, Milk Industry Foundation, National Cheese Institute, and National Creameries Association.

The development of standards is a continuing program, with revisions being made as deemed necessary. As the standards are established, they are published in the *Journal of Milk and Food Technology.* Among the items covered by the standards are fittings used on milk-products equipment, thermometer fittings and connections, storage tanks, milk pumps, weigh cans and receiving tanks, homogenizers, automotive transportation tanks, electric motors and motor attachments, can-type milk strainers, filters using disposable filter media, determination of holding time of high-temperature short-time pasteurizers, plate-type heat exchangers, milk pumps, internal tubular heat exchangers, installation and cleaning of cleaned-in-place pipelines, holding and/or cooling tanks, thermometer fittings and connections, and automotive milk-transportation tanks for bulk delivery and/or farm pickup service.

11-7. Healthy Cows. All cows from which milk is obtained and sold in towns under the Milk Ordinance are required to be tested at least once every six years if located in an area accredited by the Bureau of Animal Industry, United States Department of Agriculture, as having a bovine tuberculosis incidence of 0.2 per cent or less. Where this standard is not maintained, the herds should be subjected to annual tuberculin tests until that incidence is reduced to 0.2 per cent. All cows discovered to be reactors must be immediately removed from the herd, branded with the letters TB, and slaughtered under the direction of the livestock sanitary officials in the presence of an accredited veterinarian.

Milk yielded during a period of fifteen days before calving and usually for four or five days (occasionally several weeks) afterward is not normal and should not be sold. Slimy, ropy, or bloody milk may indicate udder infections. The cow should be separated from the herd, and the milk should not be sold.

The slightest suspicion that a cow is not in good health should result in the rejection of its milk, pending thorough examination of the animal by a veterinarian. The dairy inspector should look for abnormal conditions of teats and udders, particularly inflammation and lumps, and should recommend the services of a veterinarian. If the lumpiness or induration is extensive, affecting one or more quarters of the udder, the cow should be excluded from the milking herd, even though its milk seems normal.

The Milk Ordinance and Code requires that after a certain number of years after its adoption, usually three, all milk and milk products to be sold should be from herds following one of the brucellosis-eradication plans recommended by the Bureau of Animal Industry and administered by the state livestock sanitary authorities. These plans involve brucellosis-free testing routines aimed at making the dairy herds in the United States free of brucellosis.

11-8. Health and Habits of Dairy Workmen. Dairy workers should be given physical examinations and their histories taken. If the health officer considers it necessary, laboratory examinations are made to determine whether they are carriers of disease. Should any illness occur upon a dairy farm, the producer or distributor should immediately notify the health authorities.

Personal cleanliness of the milk handler is, of course, necessary, particularly during milking and other periods of contact with the milk. This applies to the clothing as well as to the hands. Hands should be washed, disinfected, and dried immediately before milking, and should there be any interruption whereby the hands may have become contaminated, as in handling a handkerchief or touching the floor or any unclean object, the disinfectant should again be used. The worker should never indulge in sneezing, coughing, spitting, or the use of tobacco while handling milk. Since colds and other respiratory irritations are sometimes the first symptoms of serious diseases, it is advisable to exclude persons so affected from milking or other close proximity to the milk.

The disinfectant used for hands can also be used for other purposes. Compounds of chlorine and chloramines are most suitable and can be purchased in solution with directions and instructions as to the making of dilutions. Bactericides other than those mentioned should not be used unless approved by the health authorities. An inexpensive disinfectant can be made up by the dairyman as follows: Take a 12-ounce can of chlorinated lime (chloride of lime) and mix with enough water to work it into a thin paste. Add 1 gallon of water and mix thoroughly. This is the standard stock solution and must be kept tightly corked in a jug or bottle. Use 1 tablespoonful of the solution to 1 gallon of water. This dilution will disinfect hands of milkers, teats and udders of cows, and utensils. Chlorinated lime can be obtained from most drugstores, but care must be taken to ensure that it is not old and weak. The stock solution will lose its strength in ten days, after which time a new one should be made up.

11-9. The Dairy Barn and Surroundings. The dairy barn must be kept clean lest dust and dirt from its atmosphere enter the milk during the milking and affect its quality. Barns should be well ventilated, and there should be no crowding. Efficient artificial illumination must be provided for milking during the hours of darkness. To allow easy cleaning, the floor and gutters must be constructed of concrete or some other impervious material and must be graded to drain properly. The walls and ceilings should be painted once every two years or whitewashed every year. This allows easy inspection and encourages the dairyman to keep walls and ceilings clear of cobwebs and other dirt and dust. Tight ceilings are necessary if cattle feed is stored above the barn.

Weather conditions in certain areas of the country are such that "loafing" pens, called pen-type stables, may be provided for cows waiting

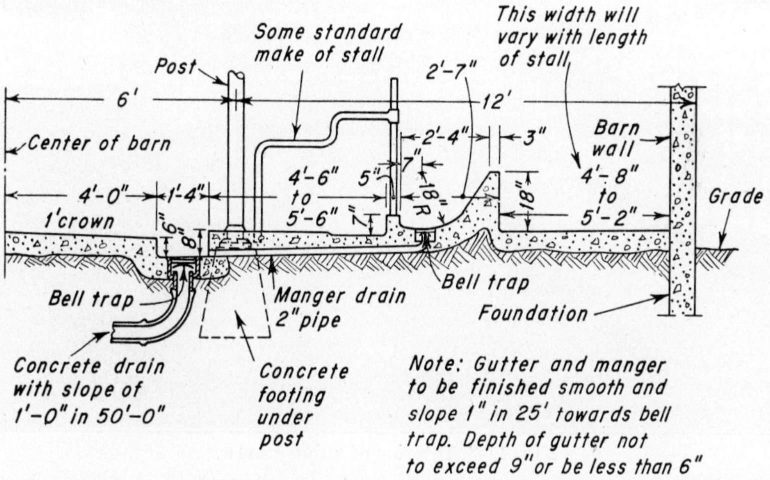

FIG. 11-2. Half cross section of a well-designed dairy barn, showing dimensions based on best practice. (*Courtesy of Portland Cement Association.*)

to be milked. They can be located adjacent to, but not actually in, the milking area. However, they are not permitted in the southern section of the United States, where indoor pens create a tremendous fly-control problem.

The water used at a dairy farm to cleanse surfaces that come in contact with milk should be obtained from a supply which meets all public health standards with regard to location, protection, and operation (see Arts. 5-31 to 5-35). Generally, well water should be used except when other sources, such as a cistern or surface-water supply, has been given sufficient treatment in the judgment of the public health authority to render it safe for this use. The well, of course, should be located so that it is not subject to contamination from privies, cesspools, and similar sources. Cross connections should be avoided; these include submerged inlets in cattle drinking cups, wash vats, etc. The water supply should preferably be piped into, or otherwise made easily accessible to, both the milkhouse and the dairy barn. The method of sewage disposal employed for the farmhouse as well as any other toilets in the establishment is important from several standpoints, including effective fly control, protection of the source of water supply, and maintaining a generally clean area.

FIG. 11-3. Interior of a dairy barn.

11-10. The Toilet. Too often the toilet on the dairy farm is far from sanitary. The open-back surface toilet is especially undesirable here because of the danger of infected flies reaching the milk. Most dairies have, or should have, an abundant water supply, so that there is no reason why flush toilets with a septic tank and disposal field should not be used. If there is not sufficient water, pit toilets of the improved type with self-closing seats, properly located with respect to the water supply, may be used. The method for disposal of dairy wastes should meet all state standards.

11-11. The Milkhouse. All handling of milk, with the exception of the actual milking, should take place in a separate structure designated as the milkhouse or milk room. In order that no odors will be absorbed by the milk, and as a protection against flies and dust, the milkhouse should always be separated from the barn; it should not open directly into the barn or into a room used for sleeping or domestic purposes, and it should be used for no purpose other than the handling or processing of milk.

The practice of handling milk previous to sale in the farm kitchen, where it is likely to be tampered with by children, perhaps suffering with one of the children's diseases, is not to be tolerated. A completely satisfactory milkhouse is well lighted and ventilated, having a window area equal to 10 per cent of the floor area, with walls and ceilings that can be easily cleaned and painted or otherwise finished in a satisfactory manner, and with a tight floor of concrete, or other impervious material, graded to drain. All openings are screened to exclude flies. The screen doors

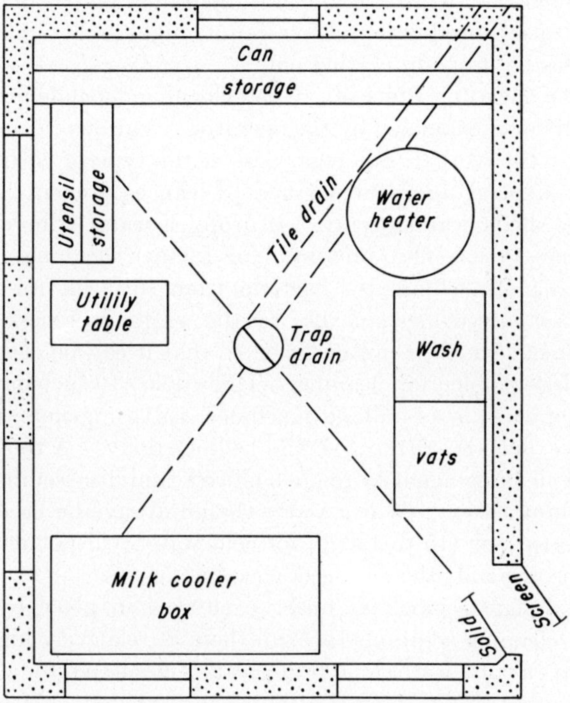

FIG. 11-4. Recommended design for a milk room.

must open outward and be provided with springs to ensure prompt and automatic closing. Water should be piped into the milkhouse.

11-12. Design of Utensils. Milk pails and cans should have as few seams as possible, and the necessary ones should be soldered flush so that there will be no cracks to prevent efficient cleaning; better still, the improved seamless pails and cans may be used. The same applies to coolers and other utensils. Badly rusted and dented tinware is unsatisfactory, as it cannot be kept clean. Milk cans should preferably have umbrella-type covers. Woven-wire milk strainers are not permitted. If straining is practiced, it should be done with single-service pads that are not to be re-used.

11-13. Cleaning and Sanitizing of Equipment. *Cleaning* means the removing of all fats, proteins, and salts of the milk, as well as other foreign matter, from the surface of milk utensils. Destruction of bacteria which remain on the surface of utensils after cleaning, when such action is accomplished by physical or chemical agents, is termed *sanitizing.* Efficient cleaning aids the sanitization because films of grease, salts, or other matters protect the bacteria from destruction and provide a medium in which they will grow. Therefore a poorly cleaned and poorly sanitized utensil will increase the bacterial count of all milk placed in it. Hence it is essential to the production of low-count, high-quality milk that these two processes be properly carried out.

11-14. The Cleaning Process. Good cleaning depends primarily upon the time and effort expended by the operator. Various cleaners are available to assist the worker, but regardless of the type of cleaner used, the final results depend upon the worker. Clean equipment is bright and shining and sheds water evenly. If drops of water adhere to surfaces, there is some grease film present, and further cleaning is necessary. Good cleaning also eliminates bacteria from surfaces, for most of the bacteria are removed mechanically by the washing process and rinsing.

All equipment which is not designed so that it can be cleaned in place should be disassembled for cleaning. This applies to such dairy farm and milk plant apparatus as milking machines, valves, coolers, pasteurizers, and pipelines, and the cleaning should be done daily. A thorough brushing aids the cleaning agent to remove all soil, and disassembling aids and makes brushing easier. Warm water should always be used, preferably at a temperature of 115 to 120°F, for cold water will not remove grease. Warm water also aids the action of cleaning agents.

Properly designed pipelines may be cleaned in place by circulating appropriate cleaning solutions through them at relatively high velocities. First, usually, a rinse water at 100 to 120°F is circulated for a short period of time, the rinse water being continuously discarded. After this initial rinse, an alkaline, nondepositing cleaning solution, heated to 120°F, is circulated for fifteen minutes before it is discharged. Sometimes an alternate acid cleaning solution heated to 120°F or above is circulated for fifteen minutes. The length of time such solutions are circulated is dependent upon the water supply at the dairy. After the acid or alkaline solutions are used, a thorough rinsing of the lines is required, and a bactericidal solution is run through the lines immediately prior to their next usage period.

A good cleaning agent will dissolve in the wash water to make a clear mixture free from floc, and it should remove the fats, proteins, and salts without forming combination curds (see Art. 10-17). Strongly alkaline cleaners act as saponifiers of the fats; if a wetting agent is also included in the cleaner, an emulsifying effect is obtained which speeds up the flowing of the film from the surfaces. Such alkaline cleaners as trisodium phosphate and sodium metasilicate, working at pH 10.5, are good protein-dissolving agents[3]. At other pH values they are less effective.

Hard waters affect the action of cleaners. A detergent such as trisodium phosphate will unite with calcium and magnesium salts, which are the causes of hardness in water, to form an insoluble precipitate. Until all the calcium and magnesium are so combined with the phosphate, *i.e.*, until the water approaches zero hardness, the detergent does little or no good. This explains why more cleaner must be used with some waters than with others. Unfortunately, too, the precipitated salts unite with the milk solids to form a film which sticks to the utensil surfaces. The film is known as "milk stone" or "water stone," and it will increase the bacterial count of milk that comes in contact with it.

There are three compounds in general use that operate in hard waters without forming stone: pyrophosphates, tetraphosphates, and hexaphosphates. The first is the least effective and the last the most. They will also remove milk stone, but only gradually. A number of compounds that dissolve calcium and magnesium salts are on the market as stone removers. Abrasives are also used, particularly to remove this film. Obviously these are unnecessary if the proper cleaning methods are used. As Mallmann points out, where milk-stone removers are used intermittently in conjunction with an inefficient cleaner, intermittently good and bad cleaning and intermittently good- and poor-quality milk result.

11-15. Sanitizing with Chemical Agents. Sanitizing or disinfecting by chemical agents is not a short cut to obtaining clean utensils. They must first be cleaned, and then the sanitizing agent will destroy any bacteria remaining on the surfaces. The best time for sanitizing is just before the utensil is used; however, if cleaning and sanitizing are properly done and the utensils are properly stored, there should be no great danger of high bacterial counts.

The principal sanitizing agents used in dairy practice are the oxidizing compounds, the sodium and calcium hypochlorites, the former being sold in liquid form and the latter as a powder. They are sold under various trade names, and the containers give the percentage of chlorine and the methods of use for various purposes (see Arts. 5-18 and 10-9). Use involves making solutions or dilutions of a required strength of available chlorine. Another group of chlorine oxidizers are the chloramines. They are more stable than the hypochlorites and give good results when used in hot-water rinses. The chlorine here is liberated more slowly than from the hypochlorites, and accordingly more contact time must be allowed.

Several precautions are necessary in the use of chemical disinfection: (1) The surfaces should be clean, for films will protect the bacteria.

(2) Sufficient time should be provided. Most bacteria are killed within ten seconds of contact, but those which are surrounded and protected by other organisms require a longer time. Hence the contact period should be at least two minutes, longer if possible. (3) The strength of the disinfecting solution should be so much in excess of the killing dose that, as its strength is dissipated by use, there is still sufficient residual strength to kill all the organisms on the surface. While a killing dose of chlorine is less than 1 part per million of available chlorine, at least 100 parts per million should be in the applied solution and must be discarded when the concentration drops below 50 parts per million available chlorine. (4) The water in which the chlorine disinfectants are diluted should not be too alkaline. It will take four to five times as much chlorine in solution to kill at a pH of 9 as it will at a pH of 7, and the time of exposure should be lengthened. This is another reason for using the high concentrations recommended under (3) if the pH of the water is variable or unknown. At a milk plant, however, this important information should be available. (5) Temperature is important. An increase of 10°C or 18°F doubles the activity of the chemical. It would be inadvisable, however, to use chlorine solutions in water having a temperature of more than 160°F, as the chlorine may be driven off.

The effectiveness of disinfection can be checked in several ways. The orthotolidine solution (Art. 5-19) or the starch-iodide method may be used to determine the available chlorine in solutions. Test sets with instructions are available. Starch-iodide papers are also used. These are strips of sensitized paper immersed in the solution, and a change of color is noted. The results given are only roughly quantitative. Bacterial tests can also be made. A sterile cotton swab is rubbed over the surface, or sterile water is flushed over it, and the swab or rinse water is examined for the number of bacteria (see Art. 12-14).

11-16. Heat as a Sanitizing Agent. Heating, as a method of sanitization, penetrates the film on the surface of utensils and provides disinfection even though the utensils have not been properly cleaned. The high temperatures required, however, generally discourage the use of this method, and it is therefore not recommended for dairy farms.

If dry heat is used, the temperature must be extremely high (320°F) for a long period of time. This necessitates a large oven or heating chamber for storage during the disinfection period.

Moist heat, however, is widely used at milk plants, either as flowing steam or as water at a temperature of 170°F. A quick rinse in hot water or a short exposure to a steam jet is of small value because the utensil must have time to reach the temperature of the steam or water. In order that bacteria may be destroyed, the temperature of the surface of the utensil must remain at least 170°F for two minutes.

11-17. Milking. Bacterial contamination of the milk during the milking process will provide the maximum opportunity for the bacteria to multiply, resulting in an increased count and a lowering of the quality of the milk by the time it reaches the consumer. It is necessary, therefore, for dairy workmen to be extremely careful in observing all standards of cleanliness during the milking process (see Art. 11-8). Dust in the air is likewise a source of contamination and should be kept to a minimum by maintaining cleanliness in the barn. One good practice to observe is to place the feed and allow the dust to settle before the cows are milked.

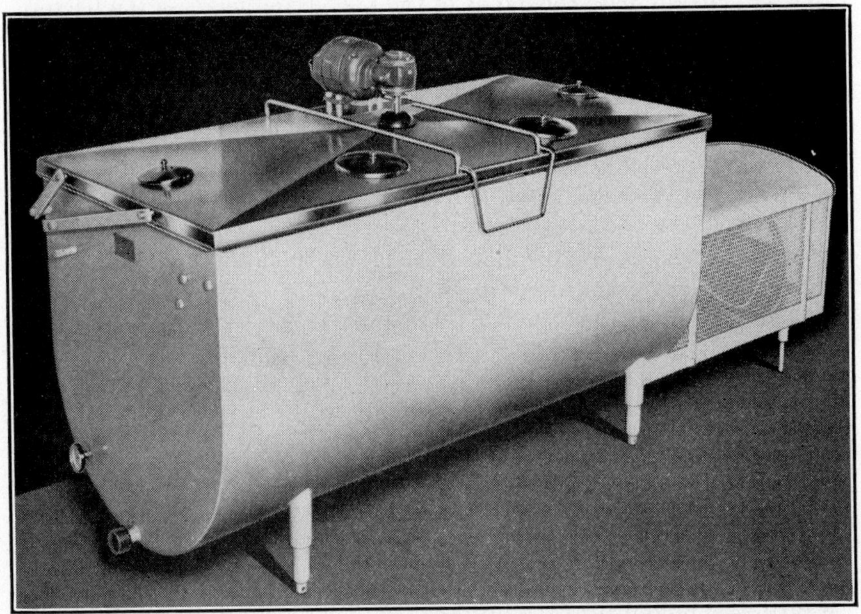

FIG. 11-5. A farm bulk milk tank. (*Photograph courtesy of Creamery Package Manufacturing Co., Chicago.*)

The cleanliness of the cow is equally important. The cow's flanks should be carefully brushed to remove all visible dirt; the teats and udders should be washed and sponged with water containing a disinfectant similar to that used by the milkers in disinfecting their hands, as mentioned in Art. 11-8. The excess disinfectant is removed with a cloth, which has also been subjected to the disinfecting treatment. It is recommended that the hair on the tail and under the flanks of the cow be clipped at periodic intervals.

Wet-hand milking is not permissible. As each cow is finished, the milk is carried directly to the milk room to be strained and cooled. In lieu of using the milkhouse for the straining operation, an effectively screened straining room may be provided in or near the barn or stable but not opening into it. This procedure, however, is not recommended, because it delays the cooling of the milk. An alternative is pouring and/or straining from the milk pails or milking-machine pails into a 5- or 10-gallon clean milk can provided with a well-fitting cover. In this case, the cans are placed at a distance from the cows or raised above the floor so that they are protected from manure or splash, with the cover closed when milk is not being poured. Self-closing covers are recommended.

The milking stool must be kept clean. A dirty, manure-encrusted stool will contaminate the hands of the milker and increase the bacterial count of the milk. Aluminum stools or other kinds which can be scrubbed and cleansed with hot or boiling water may be used. In any case, they should be handled as little as possible by the milker.

11-18. Milking Machines. The use of milking machines has some advantages and some drawbacks. Danger of infection from the hands of the milkers is lessened, and there is less opportunity for dust, manure, and other bacteria-containing material to fall into the milk. In many cases, however, the use of milking machines has resulted in high-count milk. Upon investigation, this was found to be due to the difficulty of sterilizing the materials used, particularly the rubber hose. Very high temperatures are injurious to the hose, and yet the minute cracks which appear in it after use make necessary the most careful and thorough treatment. Milking machines also tend to accumulate milk stone, which furthers the production of thermoduric bacteria and results in unduly high bacterial counts in pasteurized milk. It is important, therefore, that cleaning and sanitization of milking machines be very carefully done. In poorly designed machines, it has been found that milk sometimes gains entry into the air line. If such air lines are not properly cleaned, this milk drips back into the container and results in contamination. In any event, whether machines are well or poorly designed, air-line hoses should be maintained in a sanitary condition.

Mallmann and coworkers[4] conducted a series of experiments in the cleaning and sanitizing of milking machines. Groups of milk producers were chosen, each of whom followed a different but generally acceptable method of cleaning and sanitizing the milking machines. All groups disassembled and washed the apparatus daily. Group 1, the control group, followed its usual procedures. Group 2 used an alkaline cleaner (Solvay 600) and BK powder as a hypochlorite. After the cups and tubes had been cleaned, they were stored in the hypochlorite, and a hypochlorite rinse was given just before using. Group 3 also used Solvay 600 as a cleaner, BK powder, and an alkali (Rubberkleen). After being cleaned, the cups and tubes were stored in the alkali, and the hypochlorite was used as a rinse just before milking. Group 4 used Solvay 600 for cleaning. Storage was in 1:6,400 dilution of a quaternary ammonium compound (Art. 10-10) for sanitizing, and there was a rinse before use in the same compound at the same dilution. Group 5 used a combined cleaner-sanitizer compound. This was a mixture of alkaline cleaners, a wetting agent, and a quaternary ammonium compound. It was used as recommended, in such concentration that the quaternary compound would be 1:4,000. The producers of this group used the compound, followed by a clear-water rinse. All equipment was stored dry, and there was no rinse before using. The milk samples obtained from all the producers were pasteurized in the laboratory and then tested for total count.

The conclusions that can be drawn from the investigation are interesting. The quaternary compounds were most effective in sanitizing the equipment. This was the method used by Group 4. Group 3 also showed uniformly good results. No method was noticeably inadequate. The rinse with a sanitizing agent just before milking is apparently important. The effect of careful operation was well brought out. The good producers were able to obtain better results with any of the methods described than the poor producers attained by the best methods. This emphasizes what milk sanitarians have long known, that care and intelligence must be combined with proper agents and equipment in order to produce good milk and that the former requirements are the more important.

11-19. Straining. The milk-straining process is the first step to be taken immediately after the cow is milked. This is preferably done in the milkhouse; but if it should be done in the barn, the conditions explained in Art. 11-17 should be observed. There is a tendency for the uninformed dairyman to place too much reliance upon straining. It removes hair and the larger particles of dust and manure, but some of the manure goes into solution, and the bacteria, of course, tend to remain in the milk. Straining, no matter how efficiently done, is never a substitute for cleanliness and care in milking. The best strainer is composed of two pieces of perforated metal holding a thin layer of sterilized absorbent cotton between them. After use, the cotton is thrown away. The metal apparatus with supplies of cotton can be obtained from manufacturers of dairy equipment. Since wire strainers cannot be properly cleaned, they are not permissible.

11-20. Cooling. Milk is an ideal medium for the multiplication of most disease-producing organisms. Their activity ceases, however, at temperatures of 50°F and below. Therefore prompt cooling of the milk to that point—or, better still, to 45°F—is an important factor in the production of low-count milk. Milk that is to be delivered raw to the consumer should be cooled immediately after the milking process to 50°F or less. This is desirable under all conditions, but if the milk is to be delivered to a milk plant for pasteurization or separation within two hours after milking, it need not be cooled. If it is delivered after two hours to the milk plant for pasteurization or separation, it should be cooled to 60°F or less immediately and kept at that temperature. More than cooling is necessary; the low temperature must be maintained until the milk is delivered to the consumer. Milk should not be allowed to freeze.

Cooling is accomplished in various ways. The crudest method consists of submerging the cans of milk in troughs or tanks of ice water. This is

Fig. 11-6. A surface cooler, with covers partially removed. (*Courtesy of Cherry-Burrell Corp., Chicago.*)

frequently the only method of cooling at many farms which sell or ship milk in bulk. In this case the troughs should be of concrete, preferably insulated by layers of cork, with insulated covers. A removable wooden rack should be placed on the bottom of the tank. It should be borne in mind that a 30-gallon tank of water at 37°F will cool a 10-gallon can of milk from 85 to 50°F in half an hour and keep it at that temperature so long as the can remains in the tank. A mechanical stirrer should be used to keep the cold water circulating around the cans. Ice, of course, should never be placed in the cans themselves.

Another method of cooling consists of coils or pipes over which the milk trickles in a thin film and through which ice water or cold brine is circulated (see Fig. 11-6). This, of course, implies a refrigerating system and in general is used only at the larger dairies and at pasteurizing plants. Surface coolers in milk plants are covered to protect the milk from dust and flies. Coolers require careful cleaning and sanitizing. The latter should be done preferably just before using, or a rinse with a sanitizing agent should be used.

11-21. Bottling, Capping, and Delivery. Bottling in small dairies is usually done by small machines which fill only one bottle at a time. At large dairies or creameries more elaborate bottling machines, capable of filling many bottles at a time, are used.

Hand capping of milk bottles has the defect of permitting contamination of the milk or the cap by the hand of the worker. It is permissible to place milk in approved types of paper carton. Approved types of caps for milk bottles may be constructed of paperboard; metal foil, such as aluminum foil, is also approved and commonly used.

As the bacterial count of milk immediately starts to climb when the temperature rises above 50°F, it is necessary in warm weather that milk be kept iced during delivery. This is done by packing fist-sized lumps of ice around the necks of the bottles.

PASTEURIZATION

11-22. Pasteurization is the application of heat to milk for the purpose of destroying disease-producing organisms. It is the one practical method of ensuring safe milk. On the other hand, it is not to be considered as a palliative measure to apply to unclean milk or milk that is far advanced in decomposition. In fact, undesirable tastes or odors of milk, if already present, are likely to be intensified by the heating.

Opponents of pasteurized milk frequently harp on the fact that its vitamin C content is destroyed in the process and that children consuming it are therefore deprived. As mentioned in Art. 11-1, however, the vitamin C content of raw milk is an uncertain factor, and the diet of babies requires reinforcing with orange or tomato juice. In an investigation of the effects of raw and heated milk (which included boiled and pasteurized milk), a survey was made by the U.S. Public Health Service[5] covering 1,875 children, ranging in age from ten months to six years, who had consumed heated milk only and 1,762 children who were fed raw milk only. The survey covered 39 cities in 10 states. The results are given in Table 11-2. The greater amount of rickets among the children who drank raw milk was ascribed to the fact that only 27.6 per cent of them received cod-liver oil as compared with 41.6 per cent of the other children.

The destruction of bacteria by heat is dependent upon the temperature and also upon the length of exposure to the unfavorable temperature. While pathogenic organisms are more susceptible than most of the harmless bacteria, the susceptibility varies with the species. Diphtheria organisms are most easily killed, a temperature of 130°F with an exposure of thirty minutes being effective. With a like exposure, streptococci succumb at 133°F, typhoid bacilli at 136°F, and the tubercle bacilli, the most resistant to heat, at 139°F. Shorter exposures require higher temperatures. For instance, a twenty-minute period necessitates an increase of 1 to 2° over that of the thirty-minute period, and a ten-minute exposure

TABLE 11-2. COMPARISON OF RAW AND PASTEURIZED MILK CONSUMPTION AMONG CHILDREN

	Heated milk	Raw milk
Diphtheria	32 cases 17.1 cases per 1,000	40 cases 22.7 cases per 1,000
Scarlet fever	43 cases 23 cases per 1,000	73 cases 41.4 cases per 1,000
Intestinal disturbances (not including diarrhea)	208 cases 111 cases per 1,000	395 cases 196 cases per 1,000
Rickets	59 cases 31.5 cases per 1,000	90 cases 51.1 cases per 1,000
Average weight of children	33.6 pounds	33.2 pounds
Average height of children	37.5 inches	37.4 inches

requires about 3° still higher. Still higher temperatures kill the pathogens in very short times. At 160°F, for example, the desired result is obtained in fifteen seconds.

Too high temperatures are undesirable because of their destructive effects upon the normal cream line of the milk and the enzymes. They cause coagulation of the albumin, produce a "cooked" taste, and bring about chemical changes in the salts, fats, casein, and sugar. The cream-line effect is the earliest noted if the temperature is increased or the period prolonged over and above that necessary for destruction of the pathogens. The temperature of change of the cream line varies from 3° above the killing temperature of tuberculosis organisms at a forty-minute exposure to 7° above at a ten-minute exposure, being 5° above at thirty minutes. A thirty-minute period for milk pasteurization has been established as being convenient in the operation of many commercial pasteurizers. Since the tuberculosis organisms with this exposure are killed at 139°F, and since the cream line is affected at 5° higher, or 144°F, it will be seen that there is a range between the two values that permits pasteurization with safety and without damage to the other qualities of the milk. This had led to the usual requirement by state and city health authorities that milk pasteurization be accomplished by heating to at least 142°F and holding that temperature for thirty minutes. However, to allow for fluctuations, it is recommended that in the low-temperature pasteurizers the minimum temperature be placed at 143°F, which is the temperature required by the "Milk Ordinance and Code–1953 Recommendations of the Public Health Service."

Pasteurization is fatal to pathogens and to nearly all other disease-producing organisms; the total reduction is usually 90 per cent or more, varying with the number of thermophilic and thermoduric bacteria present. It will be seen, therefore, that pasteurization is not sterilization. High-count raw milk, which is likely to contain high concentrations of thermoduric bacteria, after pasteurization will show considerable numbers of bacteria. Souring of milk is delayed by the process, but is not prevented. It should also be recognized that pasteurized milk may become contaminated with pathogenic organisms through careless handling after pasteurization.

11-23. Pasteurization Methods. Those types of pasteurization equipment that are most commonly used, and the sanitary problems connected with them, are briefly described in this article.

Vat Type. The most common type consists of a vat into which the cold or partially heated raw milk is run until it is filled, after which heat is applied to bring the milk to the pasteurization temperature, and that temperature is maintained until the required thirty minutes has elapsed. The milk may be heated by steam or hot water which circulates through a pipe coil in the vat or through a hollow vat wall. In order to ensure uniform temperature throughout the milk, some method of agitation is used. After the pasteurization period is over, an outlet valve is opened and the milk runs through piping to the cooler and bottler. This pasteurizer is manually operated.

Automatic-holder Type. This type provides continuous operation of the pasteurizer. The milk is heated to the required temperature or slightly above and then flows through a timed valve into a holding tank or pocket. As the pocket is filled, the valve diverts the milk flow into the next empty one. At the end of the holding period, a timed outlet valve empties the pocket and the pasteurized milk flows usually first to a regenerator and then to the cooler and bottler. The emptied pocket is then ready to receive another batch of milk. Provided that the design of the milk heater, the size and number of the pockets, and the pumping capacity are all proper, operation is continuous. A further economy is possible by passing the pasteurized milk through a regenerator, where it gives up a part of its heat to the cold milk just before the latter goes to the heating unit. The heating unit is of the tubular type and consists of milk pipe surrounded by a larger tube through which hot water circulates. A thermostatically controlled steam valve regulates the temperature of the heating water. Heat must also be applied to the holding vats or

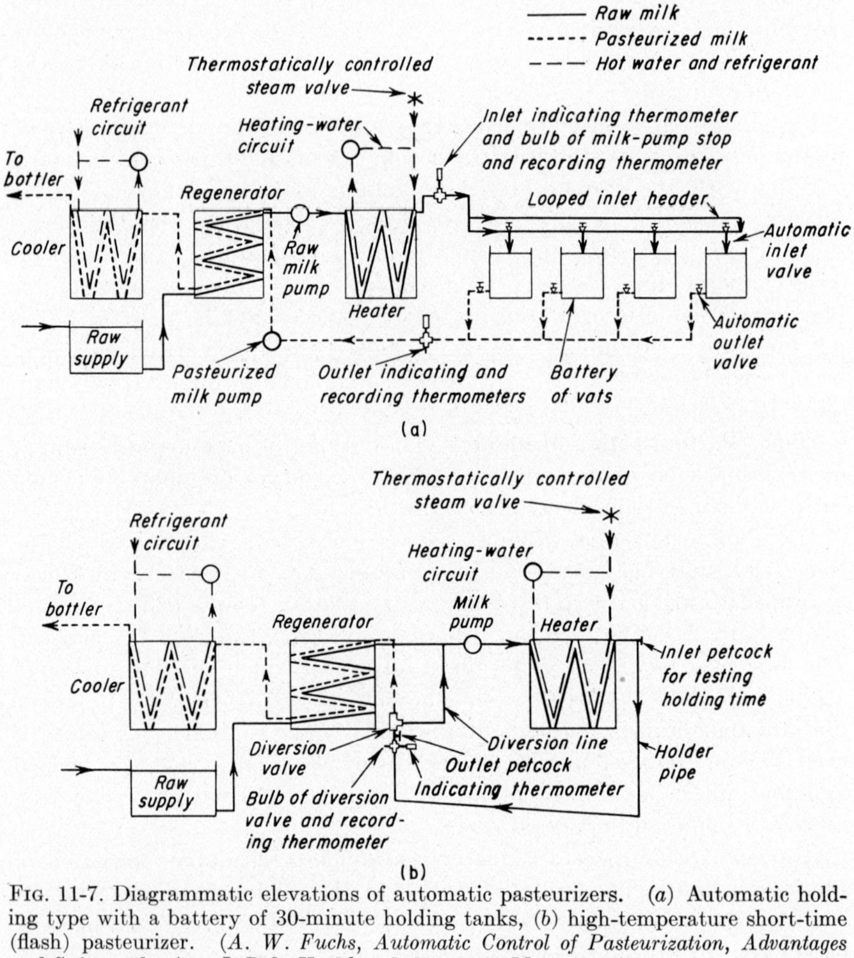

FIG. 11-7. Diagrammatic elevations of automatic pasteurizers. (*a*) Automatic holding type with a battery of 30-minute holding tanks, (*b*) high-temperature short-time (flash) pasteurizer. (*A. W. Fuchs, Automatic Control of Pasteurization, Advantages and Safeguards, Am. J. Pub. Health, vol.* 30, *no.* 5, *May*, 1940.)

pockets. Figure 11-7*a* is a diagram of an automatic-tank, or pocket-type, pasteurizing plant.

High-temperature Short-time Type. This is also a continuous-flow pasteurizer. After the milk has been preheated in the regenerator, its temperature is rapidly brought up to that of pasteurization, at least to 160°F, and is held there by passage of the milk through a holding tube for a period of fifteen seconds, after which the milk is returned to the regenerator, cooled, and bottled. Figure 11-7*b* is a diagram of a high-temperature, short-holding-time pasteurizer. The "flash" method was used to some extent in this country about 1890, but inadequate control methods caused it to be ineffective, and it was abandoned in favor of the holding types. The modern types, which are accurately designed and controlled for proper temperature and time, have been found to be as safe as the holder types. Since they require far less space than the holder types,

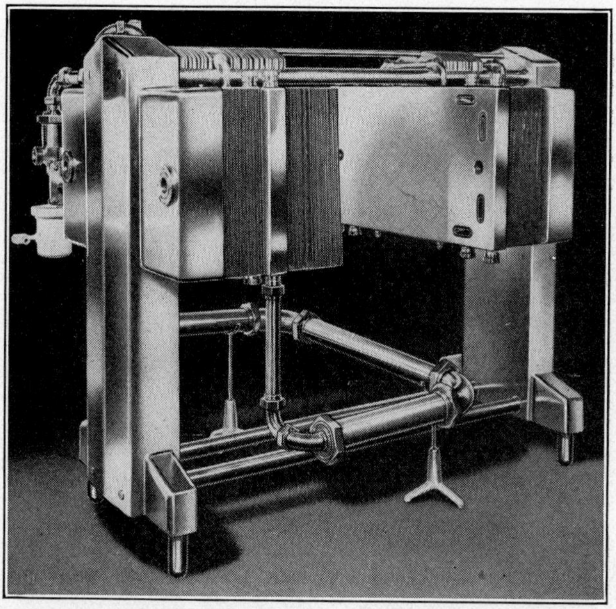

FIG. 11-8. High-temperature short-time pasteurizer. Hot water and milk or coolant pass between alternate metal plates. Large pipe below is the holder. The three sections (shown separated) permit regeneration, heating to pasteurizing temperature, and cooling. (*Courtesy of Creamery Package Manufacturing Company, Chicago.*)

they are being installed in increasing numbers by the larger milk-processing companies.

Vacreator Vacuum Pasteurizer. The Vacreator is a piece of equipment designed to provide continuous pasteurization of milk under vacuum and at a high temperature. It is claimed that this system is effective in removing seasonal weed flavors and other off-flavors which appear from time to time in the milk. In operation, milk is introduced into the pasteurizer and heated almost instantly to a temperature greater than 190°F by the introduction of live, filtered steam. The product of this heating is then drawn through to vacuum chambers where it is cooled and water is removed by a condenser system. The removal of water at this point in the processing is presumed to carry away the off-flavors of the milk. After flowing through these chambers, the milk is passed out of the Vacreator equipment. Vacreator pasteurizers are designed for operation where large volumes of milk are processed.

11-24. Sanitary Control of Pasteurization. If pasteurization is to render milk safe and free from cooked taste, all practical precautions should be taken to ensure the attainment of the proper temperature throughout all of the milk and the maintenance of that temperature for the required length of time. This is accomplished through properly

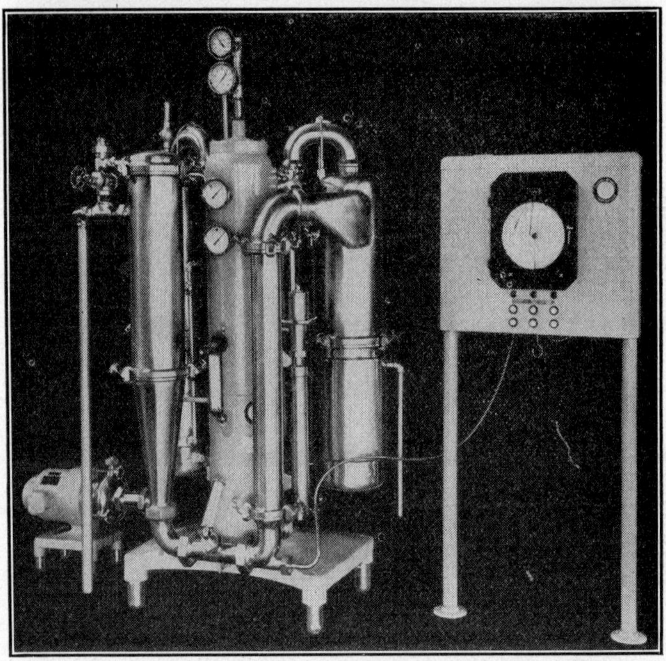

FIG. 11-9. Vacreator with control panel. (*Photograph courtesy of Cherry-Burrell Corp., Chicago.*)

designed apparatus, the use of thermometers, and the use of safeguards to prevent raw or partially pasteurized milk from leaking into completely pasteurized milk.

Vat Type. The vat pasteurizer is controlled as to temperature by means of a recording thermometer which records on a chart the temperature obtained and the elapsed time. The charts become a permanent record. Recording thermometers, however, may not be sufficiently accurate for the purpose, and accordingly an accurate indicating thermometer is also placed on each vat as a check upon the recording thermometer.

Foam will not be properly heated, and the same applies to milk splashed on the vat surfaces above the milk. Accordingly, a small amount of live steam or hot air is allowed to enter the vat above the milk. An indicating thermometer to show air temperature above the milk is used, and a temperature at least 5°F higher than the milk temperature is maintained. The steam line is provided with a trap to prevent discharge of water into the milk.

A defect noted in the earlier vat pasteurizers was a pocket of cool milk between the outlet valve and the wall of the vat. A close-coupled

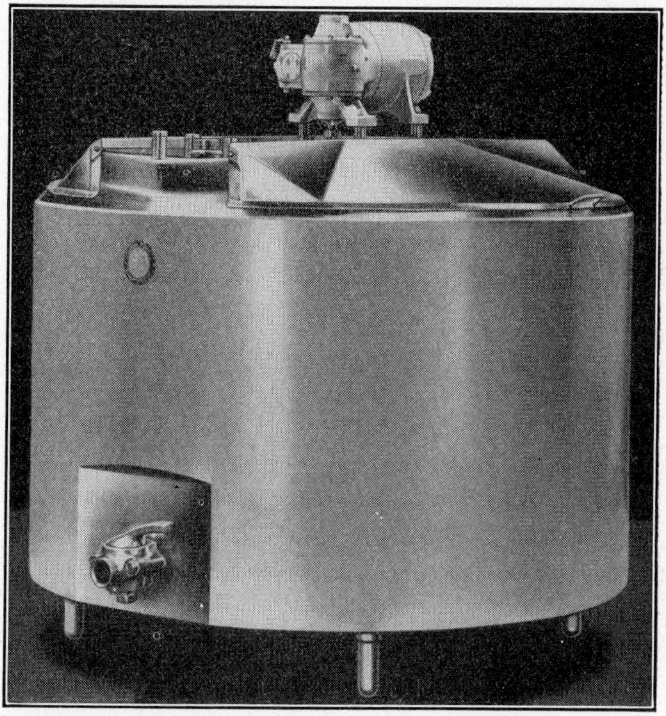

FIG. 11-10. Round processor, 300-gallon capacity. *(Photograph courtesy of Cherry-Burrell Corp., Chicago.)*

outlet valve should be used with a flaring passage from the inner wall of the vat to the valve. The diameter of the flare at the inner wall must be equal to the distance from the inner wall to the inlet side of the valve. The valve should be of the "leak-protector" type; *i.e.*, if any leakage occurs, the leaking milk is wasted and does not pass down the discharge pipe, or the discharge pipe may be disconnected during the holding period. The inlet valve should also be of the leak-protector type and so arranged that wasted milk does not enter the vat.

Automatic Continuous-flow Types. It was formerly supposed that the manual control of the batch-type vat pasteurizer would be more likely to produce safe milk than the automatically controlled continuous-flow types. Checks made by the phosphatase test have indicated, however, that the human equation involved in manual control is less reliable than automatic control, although the latter is by no means perfect.

Temperature control is important. Thermostats are installed to maintain proper temperature, but since they occasionally get out of order or the heat source fails, an automatic milk-flow stop is necessary to stop the forward flow of subtemperature milk. There are two types of automatic milk-flow stops. One automatically shuts off the milk-pump motor whenever the milk temperature falls below the pasteurization temperature and automatically starts the pump when the milk again

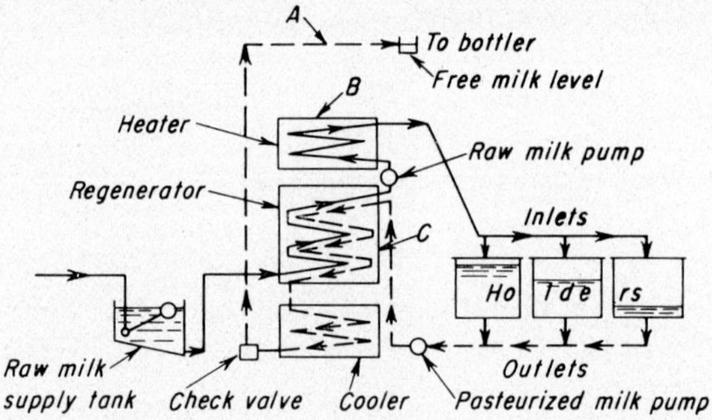

FIG. 11-11. Diagrammatic elevation of an automatic pasteurizer illustrating how proper pressure is maintained in the regenerator. →→, raw milk. ←--←, pasteurized milk. Raw-milk supply-tank overflow is lower than lowest raw-milk point in regenerator and hence ensures negative raw-milk pressures. Raw-milk pump sucks raw milk through regenerator to heater and holders. Pasteurized-milk pump forces pasteurized milk through regenerator, cooler, and check valve to point *A* in pasteurized-milk line, which is above highest raw-milk point *B* by at least 3 per cent of difference in elevation between *B* and lowest raw-milk regenerator point *C*, thus maintaining proper relative pressures during shutdowns. Check valve prevents reduction of pasteurized-milk pressures during shutdowns.

reaches the proper temperature. The other type is a flow-diversion valve which automatically diverts the milk back to the heater whenever the temperature is too low and reestablishes forward flow when the temperature has risen.

Milk-flow stops should be sealed so that they cannot be changed without the knowledge of the responsible persons. There should be no chance of bypassing milk around them, and they should be set to operate at a temperature sufficiently below the routine temperature to avoid unnecessarily frequent operation. This is undesirable as, with each cutout, there is a surge forward of subtemperature milk for a few seconds. The bulbs of indicating and recording thermometers should be located as near as practicable to the bulb of the milk-flow stop so that all may react to the same temperature. These requirements apply to both types of milk-flow stops.

In the case of milk-pump stops some special precautions are advisable. These are (1) the stop should be located within the influence of a heating unit, or the pump will not restart; (2) manual electric switches on the pump motor should be prohibited, or an operator may reestablish forward flow without regard to temperature; (3) all forward gravity flow of milk during the pump shutdown should be prevented. In the case of flow-diversion valves the following must be guarded against: (1) failure of the electric power that operates the valve, (2) omission or jarring loose of the clip that connects the valve seat and the actuating mechanism, (3) tightening of the valve stem packing so that the valve cannot move properly, (4) absence of a leak escape that will prevent leakage forward during diversion, (5) incomplete closing of the forward-flow seat so that leakage past it exceeds the capacity of the leak-escape device.

The proper holding time must also be safeguarded. No milk should be added to a tank or pocket after the beginning of a holding period, and overflow from one pocket to another should be impossible. Unless tubular heaters have an air vent, they should be sloped so that air or other gases cannot accumulate and thereby reduce the cross section, increase the velocity, and reduce the holding time. Tests of holding times should be made when pasteurizers are installed or after alterations.

A 3A standard method has been developed[6] for determining the holding time of high-temperature short-time pasteurizers by injecting a salt solution and measuring conductivity. An electrode equipment with a syringe connection is installed in a sanitary tee at the upstream end of the holder, and another electrode is installed on the indicating thermometer fitting at the downstream end of the holder. Fifty milliliters of saturated salt solution are injected by means of the syringe in the upstream electrode. The time interval occurring between the first change in conductivity noted in the upstream and downstream electrodes is measured by a stop watch. The procedure is repeated until the variation between minimum and maximum readings is not more than 0.5 of a second in six successive tests. Since this test has to be conducted with water in the pasteurizer, correction should be made to compute the actual holding time for milk. On a volume basis, this correction is applied by means of a simple proportion relating holding times in volumes. If the correction is on the basis of weights, the specific gravity of milk must be taken into consideration. (For definition of 3A standards, see Art. 11-6.)

In tubular holders the holding time is sometimes checked by injecting a dye solution through a petcock at the inlet to the holder and observing the time required for the color to appear at the outlet. Air and foam heaters are required in the holding tanks or pockets. Where regenerators are employed, the raw milk must be automatically kept at a lower pressure than that of the pasteurized milk, and this condition must be maintained both during operation and during shutdowns. This is required so that any leakage which may occur will be from the pasteurized milk into the raw milk. Accomplishing this requires a knowledge of hydraulics, and solution of the problem depends upon the layout of the pasteurizing system and the necessary piping. In general the raw-milk pump is placed on the upstream side of the regenerator so that the pipe to the pump is, during normal operation, a suction pipe and under very low or negative pressure. The outlet of the pasteurized milk is placed so that the free level of the milk is above the highest point to which the raw milk rises in the system. This difference in levels should be at least 3 per cent of the difference in elevation between the highest point of the raw milk and the lowest point the raw milk reaches in the regenerator. In Fig. 11-11, which also includes an enclosed cooler, point *A* must be higher than point *B* by at least 3 per cent of the difference between *B* and *C*.

11-25. The Pasteurization Plant. The plant should be so constructed that the pasteurizing, processing, cooling, and bottling operations shall be carried on in a room separate from that where containers are washed and given bactericidal treatment. Cans of raw milk should not be unloaded directly into the pasteurizing room, and a separate receiving room is desirable. Rooms in which milk, milk products, or cleaned containers are handled or stored should not open directly into stables or living quarters, nor should pasteurization plants be used for any purposes other than the processing of milk and operations pertaining thereto. Pasteurized milk and milk products should not be permitted to come in contact with equipment that has been in contact with raw milk, unless such equipment has been cleaned and given bactericidal treatment.

The floors of pasteurizing plants should be constructed of concrete or some equally impervious material, be graded to drain, be provided with trapped drains, and be kept clean. Walls and ceilings should have a smooth, washable, light-colored surface and be kept clean. Flies must be excluded by screens or fans at entrances. Openings through which cans or crates are loaded may be protected by flaps or fans. Good ventilation and lighting are necessary. The latter will usually be satisfied by providing window space equal to 10 per cent of the floor space. For artificial lighting, the intensity should be a minimum of 10 foot-candles on all working surfaces. Toilets and hand-washing facilities must be provided, but the toilet rooms should not open directly into a room in which milk, milk products, containers, or equipment are handled or stored. The toilet room should have self-closing doors, be kept clean, and have a sign directing employees to wash their hands before returning to work.

Warm running water, soap, and individual towels should be provided. The water supply should be safe, easily accessible, and adequate in quantity.

The piping and fittings used to convey milk or milk products are of the so-called sanitary type. These are standardized equipment made of noncorrosive metal so constructed that all interior surfaces, including valves and connections, are of such size and shape that they are easily accessible to sight and touch and are so designed as to permit easy cleaning. This requires dismantling of the piping system for cleaning and bactericidal treatment. All necessary joints and seams are soldered

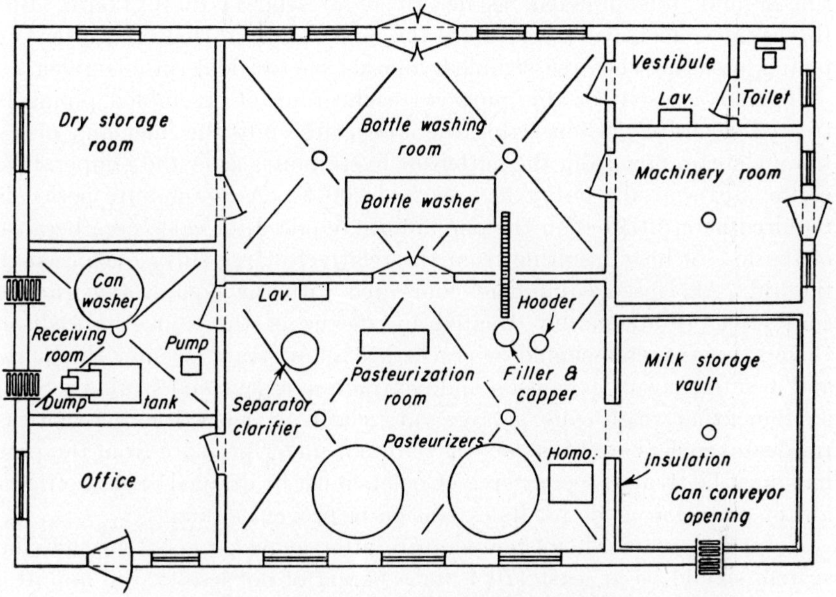

FIG. 11-12. Plan of a pasteurization plant.

flush, and the same requirements hold for cans and other utensils. With special types of piping and fittings, it is feasible to clean the piping system without dismantling (see Art. 11-14).

The milk and milk products should be bottled and capped mechanically. Hand bottling and capping, with its accompanying danger of contaminating the pasteurized milk, obviously should be discouraged.

11-26. Operation of the Plant. The operating personnel of the plant should be free from disease, wear clean clothing, and keep their hands clean at all times while handling milk, containers, or equipment. They should also be conversant with the principles of sanitation as they apply to the milk plant. It is especially important that they be instructed as to the importance of preventing contamination of the milk after pasteurization. Outbreaks of typhoid fever, for example, have been caused by an unsuspected typhoid carrier adjusting by hand the caps of bottles which had been capped in a faulty manner by the mechanical capper. Such an occurrence would indicate violation of the requirements that a worker thoroughly wash his hands before resuming work after a visit to the toilet and that milk in bottles improperly capped be returned to the raw milk.

The plant and all its equipment should be kept scrupulously clean. The equipment requires washing with a solution of alkaline washing powder followed by a bactericidal treatment, immediately after the day's run of milk is completed, as described in Arts. 11-13 to 11-15. But this is not sufficient. Just before the next run is started, and after the piping, etc., has been reassembled, another bactericidal rinse is given.

If *steam* is used for this purpose, each group of assembled piping is treated separately by inserting the steam hose into the inlet and maintaining steam flow from the outlet for five minutes after the temperature of the steam at the outlet has reached 200°F. A five-minute period is required here rather than the one minute required for cans, etc., because of the loss of heat resulting from the relatively large surface exposed to the air. All closed equipment connected with the pipe system can be considered as adequately treated by means of the above procedure. Covers, unions, etc., should be cracked to allow steam to enter the joints and also to prevent expansion and contraction cracks and strains. Such equipment as weigh cans, storage vats, clarifiers, separators, pasteurization vats, coolers, and bottlers that are not under pressure from the pipe line must be treated separately. Coolers must be drained of the refrigerant or provision made for its expansion to prevent damage.

If *hot water* is used, its temperature after being pumped through the system should be at least 170°F for a period of not less than 5 minutes. Other precautions are as prescribed under the steam treatment.

If *chlorine* is used, the solution appearing at the outlet end should show a concentration of at least 50 parts per million as shown by the orthotolidine test. Surfaces that cannot be reached by the flowing solution may be treated with steam or by spraying with a chlorine solution. In the latter case the solution sprayed should have the concentration indicated above as it runs off the area being treated.

If the plant becomes infected with thermophilic bacteria, more intensive bactericidal treatment will be required or a change in methods is advisable. If the steam or hot-water method has been used, higher temperatures for longer periods should be applied.

Bottles and cans may be washed as indicated for dairies. In large plants, however, it is recommended that automatic bottle washers be used. These machines soak the bottle in an alkaline solution having a strength of at least 2.4 per cent, including at least 1.6 per cent of caustic soda.

After bactericidal treatment, all multiuse milk containers and equipment must be so stored that they are protected from dust, flies, and splash. They should be handled so that the hands and clothing of workers do not touch the cleaned surfaces that come in contact with the milk. Bottle caps, cap paper stock, parchment paper, and single-service containers must be stored where they will remain clean and dry. At the beginning of each run, the first cap from each tube, the first few caps from each roll of cap stock, or the first parchment paper should be discarded as they have been exposed to contamination.

MUNICIPAL REGULATION OF MILK SUPPLIES

11-27. Most cities which are making any pretence of carrying on public health work exercise more or less supervision over the milk supplies. In some cases it consists only of ordinances, with little or no attempt at enforcement. In other cases good control is obtained through wise ordinances and an efficient inspecting force and laboratory. Many of the larger cities require that all milk be pasteurized. By 1952 more than 90 per cent of the market milk consumed in the United States was being pasteurized. The tendency is to extend the requirement, and in general the use of pasteurized milk is growing.

While inspection alone can do much toward controlling the quality and production of milk, it is handicapped without frequent laboratory tests of the milk. The condition of the dairy and the methods of handling invariably are reflected in the bacterial count of the milk. The counts, therefore, are a check on the reports of the inspector, while persistently high counts of milk from an apparently good dairy may lead to the inspector's finding an unsuspected trouble, such as infected udders, inefficient sterilization of utensils, or poor cooling.

11-28. The Milk Ordinance and Code. There are three general types of milk ordinance now in use in the United States: one requires all milk to be pasteurized; another classifies milk as raw or pasteurized but does not grade either; and a third classifies milk as raw or pasteurized and provides for a number of grades in each class. All these ordinances set up minimum standards as to milk handling and bacterial counts. The Public Health Service[7] of the U.S. Department of Health, Education, and Welfare has promulgated a milk ordinance and code which is a modification of the third type. The states are being encouraged to assume leadership in the obtaining of better milk by approving the Milk Ordinance and Code and stimulating the cities to pass it. After passage, in many instances, state personnel aid in the building of the city's enforcement organization. Alabama adopted the program in 1924, and its example has been followed by many other states with satisfactory results. The Ordinance has not only improved the quality of the milk in those cities which passed it, but has also increased the consumption of milk. According to Leslie C. Frank the consumption of market milk was increased 90 per cent on the average in 14 Alabama towns after the ordinance had been in effect one to three years.

A further advantage of the Milk Ordinance and Code is that it allows rating or scoring of a city's milk supply by the state health department upon the basis of the percentage of the total milk which is of high grade or pasteurized. Competition between cities in this respect effects a gradual improvement in the quality of the city's milk supply and increases the interest of public and city councils, thereby assisting the health officer in his work.

The Ordinance requires that the grade of milk be placed on the bottle cap, thereby tending to place the buying of milk upon the same basis as most commodities, its quality. Grading also has a tendency to drive poor milk out of the retail market, particularly as people become educated to the meanings of the different grades. It also tends to reward the dairyman who is careful and clean and protects him from the unfair competition of the unclean, careless, and unscrupulous dairyman.

The Ordinance may require that all the milk be pasteurized if the state of public health education is such that this requirement does not cause too much opposition. In any event it states the grades to which sale is restricted, as decided by the city itself. In most cities applying the Ordinance, only Grade A raw and Grade A pasteurized milk or milk products may be sold to the final consumer or to restaurants, soda fountains, grocery stores, or similar establishments. This requirement does not, however, exclude milk that cannot qualify as to the above grades, for it may, after pasteurization, be used in the manufacture of such products as butter and cheese.

Enforcement of the Ordinance is usually effected through a permit, which is granted if the dairyman conforms to the requirements of the Ordinance and revoked if he violates the Ordinance. If he persists in selling milk in the city without a permit, he is subject to a fine, although he may also be fined for selling milk with false or misleading labels. The health officer may also degrade the milk if he finds violations of the provisions of the Ordinance. If violations of any of the items of sanitation are found upon any inspection of a dairy or milk plant, a notice is given and a reasonable time is allowed, never less than three days, to make the required improvement. If improvement has not been made by the second inspection, the grade of the milk is determined by conditions then existing.

The outstanding features of the Ordinance are as follows:

1. *Requirement of Stated Conditions for Production and Handling.* The Ordinance requires testing of cows; healthy cows; proper construction and cleanliness of the dairy barn, milkhouse, and equipment; health and cleanliness of the workmen; cleanliness and sanitization of equipment; a safe water supply; and adequate sewage or excreta disposal. These requirements have been discussed in detail earlier in this chapter. As an aid to the inspector, an inspection blank is used that lists all the requirements. Should he find the dairy or milk handling deficient in one or more items, he so designates upon the blank by a check against the item. Standard inspection blanks for dairies and milk plants are illustrated in the public health bulletin previously referred to[7]. Violation of dairy requirements on two successive inspections calls for the revocation of the dairy's Grade A permit.

Grade A pasteurized milk must be processed in a plant which has all the safeguards previously discussed. All bottles in which Grade A milk is sold are required to have a lip-protecting cap which extends to cover the largest diameter of the pouring lip. Milk which is not processed in accordance with Grade A requirements is not permitted to be sold under Grade A labels but may be used for manufacturing purposes.

2. *Bacteriological Standards.* In addition to satisfying the standards governing handling and production, the milk must conform to bacteriological requirements. Since poor production and handling methods are usually indicated by high bacterial counts, the two requirements constitute a useful correlation.

The bacterial plate count of Grade A raw milk for retail sale or the direct microscopic clump count cannot exceed 50,000 per milliliter. That for Grade A raw milk for pasteurization should not exceed 200,000 per milliliter, as delivered from the farm; however, the raw milk should at no time between dumping and pasteurization have a plate count or clump count exceeding 400,000 per milliliter. Grade A pasteurized milk is Grade A raw milk which has been subjected to pasteurization, the effectiveness of which is determined by a phosphatase test. The bacterial plate count of pasteurized Grade A milk prior to delivery must not exceed 30,000 per milliliter, or the coliform count of the milk should not be greater than 10 per milliliter. Grade B raw retail milk does not meet the bacterial standard for Grade A raw milk but conforms with all other requirements, and the bacterial count or the direct microscopic clump count is not more than 200,000 per milliliter. Grade B raw milk for pasteurization should have a plate count or direct microscopic clump count not exceeding 1,000,000. Grade B pasteurized milk, made from raw milk for pasteurization of a quality of not less than Grade B, must not have a bacterial count exceeding 50,000 per milliliter. Grade C pasteurized milk is milk that does not conform to the requirements for Grade B pasteurized milk.

The bacterial standards used in grading milk are doubled for cream and omitted in the case of sour cream and buttermilk.

3. *The Grading Feature.* It should be recognized that the grade of the milk depends upon all the requirements mentioned above. Once it is determined, the grade of the milk is emphasized. The caps of all milk bottles must be plainly marked with the grade determined at the previous grading period. Milk must be served in restaurants in the original containers only or from an approved bulk dispenser. The grading period is not more than six months, and at least once in that period the dairies and milk plants must be inspected.

In addition to the more important features given above, there are the usual definitions and the prohibition of adulteration and use of preservatives. There is also the requirement that milk contain not less than 3¼ per cent milk fat and not less than 8¼ per cent solids-not-fat.

In many states it is legal for the cities to adopt a short form of the Ordinance[7]. It makes the Code, and further revisions of it, a part of the Ordinance without the necessity of passing it in detail or printing it in the local newspapers. A state law recognizing the Ordinance is useful, as it may forbid dairymen to use Grade A bottle caps unless their milk has actually been subjected to regulation under the Ordinance.

11-29. Inspection and Sampling. An efficient dairy inspector requires a great deal of specialized knowledge, in addition to keen powers of observation, tact, and firmness. The best inspectors are not necessarily former dairymen. Veterinarians and agricultural school graduates who have specialized in dairy science have been successful, while sanitarians and sanitary engineers are entering the field to a large degree, the last-named particularly in connection with pasteurization plants.

Inspections should be made at least monthly, with follow-up visits if necessary. Under the Milk Ordinance and Code, the grading visits are usually made every three months, although inspections should also be made at shorter intervals. Inspections should, so far as possible, be made at milking time.

The collection of samples is also a part of the inspector's duties. Since knowledge of the condition of the milk when it reaches the consumer is desired, the samples are collected from the delivery wagons in the case of retail dealers and from the cans at the milk plants if the milk is delivered to a creamery or pasteurization plant. Samples of the pasteurized milk are also collected before it is delivered to the consumer.

If bottles are collected, they should be selected at random and the tops should be covered with paraffin paper or parchment to avoid contamination en route to the laboratory. They should be kept at temperatures below 45°F; however, when the sample is plated for the plate count within four hours from the time of collection, the temperature may be as high as 50°F. When samples are collected at milk plants or receiving stations, they may be taken from well-stirred cans, storage tanks, or from the weigh vat. The importance of stirring is emphasized because the cream usually has a higher bacterial count than the balance of the milk. After each usage, stirrers, thermometers, sampling tubes, and dippers should be rinsed in clean water of not more than 80°F and placed in a hot-water solution maintained at 180°F or in a hypochlorite solution with a concentration of at least 100 parts per million available chlorine. The utensils are allowed to remain in the sterilizing solution for a minimum of 1 minute. The samples should consist of at least 10 milliliters of milk.

The samples have tags attached to them, showing date and time of collection and an identifying number. The name of the dairyman or milk plant is not shown, so that the laboratory personnel do not know the source of the milk.

When insufficient funds are available for complete inspection service, the Milk Ordinance permits the local health officer to accept the inspection reports covering producer dairies which are made by inspectors of the receiving milk plants. This is permissible, however, only if such reports are officially checked periodically and found satisfactory.

11-30. The Laboratory and Testing. The laboratory is important in the control of the quality of milk. It should be ample in size for the amount of work that it has to do and should be staffed with persons who are acquainted with the technique of milk testing. In cities which have a public health laboratory as a part of the city health department the milk work is taken care of there. In small cities it is possible to use a well-trained inspector who can do his own testing, and in this case the testing may be confined to butter fat and solids-not-fat. In either case, testing methods should follow the methods given in the book "Standard Methods for the Examination of Dairy Products"[2]. The Milk Ordinance permits recognition of the reports of commercial laboratories covering raw milk to be pasteurized if they are officially checked periodically and found satisfactory.

The laboratory makes routine tests of the butter-fat content of milk and cream and milk solids-not-fat to determine whether the requirements of the Ordinance are satisfied. Other tests sometimes made are the determination of the presence of preservatives and the sediment test, which shows the presence of dirt as caught on a filtering disk.

Most important of the tests is the bacterial plate count, which gives the count per milliliter as determined by incubation on a nutritive medium, and the counting of colonies, or the microscopic clump count. The plate count and the clump count are comparable and are generally used unless otherwise indicated. In enforcement of the Ordinance and determination of the milk grade, logarithmic averages are used. The use and value of the logarithmic average can be shown by an example. Common logarithms are used. For grading purposes it is usual to take the last four counts as determined by the laboratory. It is assumed that the figures are as follows:

Counts	*Logarithms*
33,000	4.52
21,000	4.32
12,000	4.08
220,000	5.34
	4)18.26
	4.56 = average logarithm

The count corresponding to the average logarithm is 36,000, whereas the arithmetical average of the counts is 71,000, which is too high for A grade. The logarithmic average is used because it does not penalize the dairyman so heavily for high counts that are in the nature of accidents. It is obvious, in the example given, that the milk produced is, in general, satisfactory as to count, and it would be unfair to degrade the milk because of the effect of the one unsatisfactory count. Tables of logarithms can be furnished to the record clerk, who can use them without having a knowledge of mathematics. The Ordinance permits the use of the lowest three of the last four tests to obtain an average count.

In the grading of milk supplies, coliform counts are also required to be taken on Grade A products. These counts are allowed a maximum of 10 per milliliter. The "three-out-of-four method" is used to determine compliance with this standard. In using the three-out-of-four method, whenever more than one of the last four consecutive coliform counts of samples taken on separate days is beyond the prescribed limit, the health officer notifies the plant of its excessive count and then takes an additional sample. If this additional sample exceeds a prescribed limit, an immediate degrading is called for.

11-31. Collection and Delivery of Milk. Vehicles used for collecting milk from dairies or milk stations and for retail delivery should be constructed with permanent tops and with permanent or roll-down sides and backs. They must be kept clean, and no materials capable of contaminating the milk should be transported at the same time as the milk. Vehicles should display the name of the milk dealer.

Delivery of milk from farms to plants has been expedited in certain areas by the development of the farm-tank pickup system. This system utilizes a refrigerated bulk-holding tank on the dairy farm for the collection and storage of milk until the time of delivery to the plant. There are a number of designs of bulk farm tanks, but they usually have the common features of being constructed of stainless steel throughout and being provided with a removable measuring-stick device which positively measures the milk level in the tank. Farm tanks are provided with mechanical agitators and with an indicating thermometer to show the temperature of the contained milk. Several different types of emptying valves are provided, but all such valves are required to be designed so that they are easily inspected and cleaned. The farm-tank pickup trucks are similar in design to other milk transports. They are usually provided

Fig. 11-13. Farm tank pickup truck. (*Photograph courtesy of Heil Co., Milwaukee, Wis.*)

with a pump and a refrigerated compartment for carrying the milk hose and butter-fat samples.

In the operation of the tank-truck pickup system, the tanker driver arrives at the dairy farm and connects the hose from the pickup tank to the dairy farmer's bulk-holding tank. Before the connection is made, however, both the valve on the holding tank and the fittings on the end of the tanker hose are uncapped and given bactericidal treatment. A measure of the gallonage contained in the holding tank is also taken by the tanker driver. The holding-tank agitator is started, and after several minutes of agitation a butter-fat sample is taken. After the tank is completely loaded, the truck returns to the milk plant, where the milk is then drawn off into the plant holding tank.

Raw milk which is delivered must be placed in its container at the farm where it is produced, and pasteurized milk must be placed in the delivery container at the plant. No transfer of milk from one container to another is permissible in the vehicle or in a store or anywhere except at a bottling or milk room especially equipped for the purpose. This requirement prevents the dangerous practice of filling returned milk bottles with milk or milk products while on the milk route.

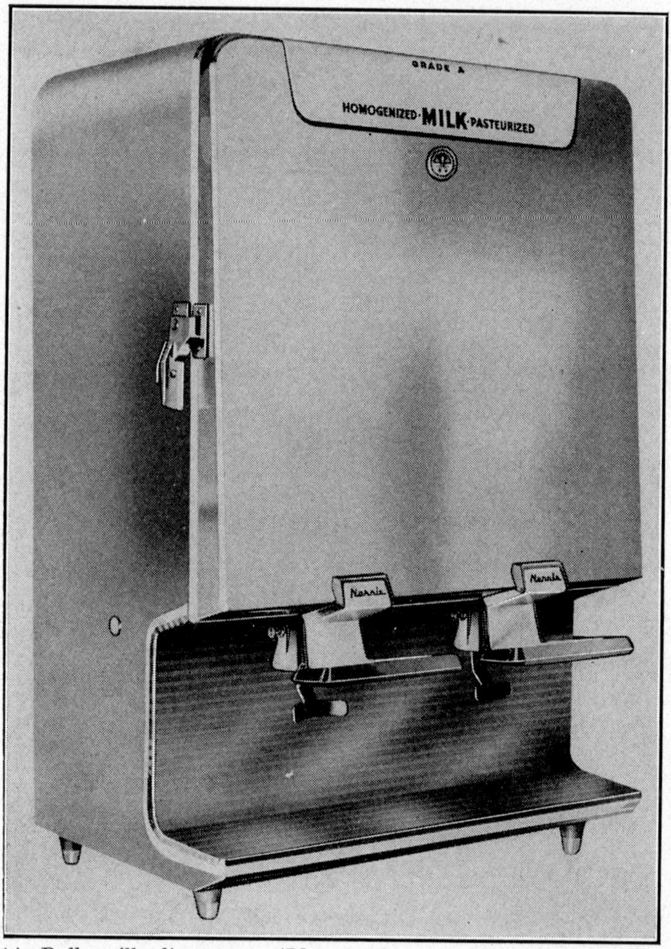

FIG. 11-14. Bulk milk dispenser. *(Photograph courtesy of Dispenser, Inc., Meim, Minn.)*

Hotels, soda fountains, etc., should serve milk only in the original containers or approved milk dispensers. Until served, the milk must be kept below 50°F.

Outstanding among a number of modern developments in the retail handling of milk is the use of bulk milk dispensers in eating establishments.

Bulk milk dispensers are designed so that the milk container cans may be filled in the milk plant and can then be delivered to the eating establishments, where they are placed in a bulk milk dispenser cabinet. This cabinet is designed to meet sanitary standards and has doors of sufficient size to receive the dispenser cans. In the bottom of these cans are fittings where a plastic or rubber tube is attached. After the can is placed in the dispenser cabinet, this tube is threaded through the dispenser valve, which controls the flow of milk through a pinchcock arrangement. When a can is emptied, it may be removed from the dispenser cabinet to be replaced by another full can. There are also other arrangements for controlling the flow of the milk from the dispenser can.

Since bulk milk dispensers are not generally designed to agitate the milk after cans are placed in the cabinet, they may be used only for homogenized milk. Advantages claimed for bulk milk dispensers are the abilities to maintain lower temperatures in the milk and to provide certain economies in handling the product. They also eliminate accumulations of dirty bottles around eating establishments.

Dispenser cans are usually required by enforcement agencies to be sealed at the plant. These seals are not broken until the cans are again returned to the plant for cleaning, bactericidal treatment, and refilling.

The delivery of milk or milk products to and the collection of milk or milk-product containers from residences in which there are cases of communicable disease transmissible through milk are subject to special requirements to be prescribed by the health officer.

11-32. Rating of Cities. In states where the Milk Ordinance and Code is in use, the U.S. Public Health Service has listed semiannually those cities which have a market milk rating of at least 90 per cent. This practice was suspended from 1943 to 1946 owing to wartime deterioration of milk quality, but reporting was resumed in 1948. Listings are made in two classes: cities in which all milk is pasteurized and those in which both raw and pasteurized milk are sold. A market milk rating in cities of either class means that the weighted average of the percentages of compliance with the various items of sanitation required by the Ordinance for Grade A raw milk or Grade A pasteurized milk is 90 per cent or more. The weighting is done according to the amount of milk produced by each dairy. It is possible, of course, to compare scores between cities as a means of encouraging competition.

The ratings must be determined by the state milk-sanitation authority in accordance with the method prescribed by the Public Health Service[8]. A listing is good for not more than two years. When a city falls below the 90 per cent mark, it will not be resurveyed for at least six months, so that it will be penalized by being dropped from one listing. The Public Health Service makes occasional check surveys of the cities listed by the states. If a check rating shows less than 90 per cent but not less than 85 per cent, the city is removed from the list after six months, unless a resurvey in the probationary interim shows a rating of 90 per cent or more. If the check rating is less than 85 per cent, the city is removed from the list immediately.

11-33. Interstate Milk Shipments. Formerly the problem of interstate milk shipments was not serious for any metropolitan area other than the extremely large ones such as New York. By 1950, however, 32 states, the District of Columbia, and Alaska were importing milk and cream for public consumption and 34 states were exporting these products[9]. Among the factors influencing this trend were the development of refrigerated transport, industrialization, accelerated urbanization, and increase of population. The practice regarding sanitary control of milksheds consisted of each community's being responsible for inspections and the institution of control measures wherever the milk was produced, regardless of the distance from the community. The economic problem this practice produced soon became evident with increased interstate shipment. In fact, trade barriers were consciously or unconsciously established to the extent that interstate and intrastate commerce was being seriously interfered with.

In October, 1950, the Supreme Court ruled that a city could not adopt discriminatory health regulations which act as trade barriers against interstate commerce and pointed out two alternatives for remedial action, namely, having the city rely upon its own officials for inspection of distant milk sources or upon the inspections made by health authorities at the source, as provided in the Milk Ordinance and Code of the Public Health Service. The Ordinance establishes reciprocity as a basis of acceptance of outside milk, defining the criteria to be met. In the following year the Senate Committee on Agriculture and Forestry held public hearings concerning the cause and effect of restrictive regulations and endorsed a plan for the Public Health Service to increase its efforts to develop a cooperative program with the states for the certification of interstate milk shippers.

At national conferences on interstate milk shipments, representatives of various state health departments have met periodically to study this problem. They have recommended that states receiving interstate milk shipments recognize the inspection and supervision by full-time health and agricultural department personnel, either local or state. They selected the 1953 recommendations of the Public Health Service embodied in the Milk Ordinance and Code as the basic standard. Also, they recognized a certified rating plan whereby receiving states would accept ratings made by certified rating officials of either the Public Health Service or health departments having sole jurisdiction of milk sanitation in a particular area. Certification includes survey ratings on producing farms, receiving stations, or plants and enforcement ratings of the supervisory agency. It was agreed that the Public Health Service would standardize the rating procedure of its own personnel and state rating officials, spot-check laboratories of the state agency participating in the shipment of milk, and publish lists of interstate shippers for semiannual distribution.

11-34. Certified Milk. In 1912, the American Association of Medical Milk Commissions formulated certain rules for the production of certified milk. These are complete and somewhat stringent regulations governing the conditions of the dairy, its surroundings, utensils, methods of milk handling, and health of workmen, with prescribed chemical and bacteriological standards. The total count must never exceed 10,000 bacteria per milliliter. The milk is certified by a local or county commission of doctors who give their services gratis to enforce the rules of the parent organization.

Only a very small proportion of the total amount of milk used in cities is certified. Unless it is pasteurized, it is still possible that an unrecognized carrier or case of communicable disease may infect the milk. Furthermore, compliance with the rules of the association tends to increase the price of certified milk to such a point that most families are unwilling to buy it.

11-35. Milk Products. Under the Public Health Service Milk Ordinance, milk products include cream, sour cream, half and half, reconstituted half and half, whipped cream, concentrated milk, concentrated milk products, nonfat milk, flavored milk, flavored reconstituted milk, cultured buttermilk, cultured milk, cottage cheese, creamed cottage cheese, homogenized milk, goat milk, vitamin D milk, buttermilk, skim milk, reconstituted or recombined milk, skim milk, and cream, milk beverages, and any other product designated as a milk product by the health officer. Some of the above terms may require definition. Homogenized milk is milk that has had its fat globules broken up to such an extent that no visible cream separation occurs on the milk within forty-eight hours storage and the top 100 milliliters of a quart bottle (or proportionate amount in another container) differs no more than 10 per cent of itself in fat percentage from that of the remaining milk, as determined after thorough mixing of each portion. The Milk Ordinance and Code prohibits the mixing of homogenized milk or cream with unhomogenized milk or cream. This "partial homogenization" has been practiced by some milk plants to increase the apparent butter-fat content when the milk is viewed in a bottle, for the homogenized material would come to the top. Vitamin D milk is that which has had its natural vitamin D content increased by an approved method to at least 400 U.S.P. units per quart. Reconstituted or recombined milk results from recombining milk constituents with water so as to comply with the requirements as to butter fat and solids-not-fat. Reconstituted or recombined cream results from the combination of dried cream, butter, or butter fat with cream, skim milk, or water.

Milk products, as defined above, should be controlled and graded in the same manner as milk. As mentioned previously, however, bacterial standards differ in the case of cream, where designated counts are doubled, and in the case of sour cream and buttermilk, where they are omitted entirely.

11-36. Dried Milk. Dried whole milk is the product resulting from the removal of water from whole milk and contains not less than 26 per cent butter fat and not more than 5 per cent moisture. It is made either by spraying the milk into a warm chamber, where the small drops are dried, or by passing it in a thin sheet over hot rollers. The American Dry Milk Institute has set up standards for the manufacturers of dried milk in order to bring about uniformity in their products. The more important of these requirements are as follows: The milk must have been pasteurized in the liquid state, either before or during the process of manufacture, at a temperature of 143°F for thirty minutes or its equivalent in bacterial destruction. The whole milk must be free from preservatives and be normal in color, odor, and flavor. The drying plant must be in a sanitary condition, and all equipment which comes into contact with the milk should be of sanitary stainless steel or equally corrosion-resistant and non-copper-bearing material, or the respective copper and iron requirements shown by chemical analysis of the milk must be complied with. The bacterial content per gram must not exceed 50,000 for the premium and extra grades of spray-process milk and 125,000 for the standard grade. For the roller process the requirements are 50,000 and 125,000 for extra and standard grades, respectively. Sanitary standards are set up for dairies and milk plants which produce or handle milk for the drying plant.

Dried skim milk or nonfat dry milk solids are produced in the same manner as dried whole milk. The water content of dried skim milk is not over 5 per cent and the fat content not over 1.5 per cent. It is used in commercial bakeries and in making ice cream, and it is added to many meat products, such as sausage. The sanitary requirements are the same as for dried whole milk except that the bacterial content per gram is required to be not over 100,000 for the extra grade and 300,000 for the standard grade.

11-37. Butter. Butter, while not herein defined as a milk product, should be controlled as to sanitary quality. The butter-making process cannot be depended upon to kill disease bacteria. Therefore, the milk and cream used should be produced under sanitary conditions and should always be pasteurized before using. A problem arising in connection with butter is that sour cream is sometimes purchased by milk or cream depots from farms where there is no control over sanitary conditions.

Much of this cream is filthy and should not be considered suitable for human consumption, even though it is pasteurized by the milk plant. Responsibility should be placed upon the milk plants for the cleanliness of the milk and cream that they process. State laws or city ordinances may prescribe the minimum allowable butter-fat content of butter and may also prohibit the sale of reworked or "renovated" butter.

11-38. Cheese. Cheese should be subjected to sanitary control. According to Fabian[10], from 1883 to 1946 there were 59 epidemics, 2,904 cases of disease, and 117 deaths caused by cheese. Probably there were many more unrecognized outbreaks. The rule should always be that cheese must be made from pasteurized milk and cream. Aging of cheese at not too low a temperature will destroy disease bacteria even if the cheese is made from raw milk. Many states are not requiring the pasteurization of all milk or cream for cheese and allow, as an alternative, aging for at least 60 days before sale. This appears to be too short for cheddar-type cheese, for which 90 or even 120 days is preferable. Soft cheese cannot be aged, and pasteurization is necessary.

11-39. Frozen Desserts. The situation with regard to sanitary control of frozen desserts has been very unsatisfactory. The Public Health Service has studied the problem and proposes standards that have been embodied in an ordinance and code which is recommended for adoption by cities and promulgation by the state health departments. It is offered in two forms: one allowing enforcement by grading, degrading, and permit revocation; the other enforceable by permit revocation only and not having the grading feature. The grading type is probably more desirable, and its provisions are discussed here. Copies of the Ordinance and Code are obtainable from the Public Health Service.

The Ordinance governs primarily handling and quality of the frozen desserts, but, wherever possible, sanitary control should also be applied to the milk and milk products from which they are made. A frozen dessert is defined as any frozen or partially frozen combination of two or more of the following: milk or milk products, eggs or egg products, sugars, water, fruit or fruit juices, candy, nut meats, or other wholesome food products, flavors, color, or harmless stabilizer, and is considered as including ice cream, ice milk, milk sherbet, frozen custard, ices, and similar products. Standard compositions for the various frozen desserts are determined by the Food and Drug Administration of the U.S. Department of Agriculture. The "mix" in preparation of frozen desserts is the unfrozen combination of all the ingredients with or without fruits, fruit juices, candy, nut meats, flavor, or harmless color.

The grading ordinance defines three grades—A, B, and C—and it is suggested that in those cities which already enjoy good sanitary control of frozen desserts, only Grade A should be sold. In other cities it may be advisable to permit sale of both A and B grades. For qualification as Grade A, the dessert must be prepared in a plant that conforms in construction, cleanliness, use of sanitary piping, washing and bactericidal treatment of equipment, and cleanliness of personnel to the standards required in a pasteurization plant by the Public Health Service Milk Ordinance. Milk and fluid milk products as they arrive at the plant must be immediately cooled to 50°F or below, unless they are to be pasteurized within two hours; and the pasteurized mix must be immediately cooled to 50°F or less. The mix must be pasteurized at a temperature of at least 155°F with a holding time of at least thirty minutes, although the state health authority may approve some other method which has been demonstrated as equally efficient. One acceptable alternative is the use of a pasteurization time of twenty-five seconds and a temperature of 175°F. The average bacterial count of the pasteurized mix or the frozen dessert at no time before delivery shall exceed 50,000 per gram for Grade A. Average counts are obtained from the last four consecutive samples, and they may be obtained from the plate count or direct microscopic count of clumps, in which cases the logarithmic average is determined, or the reductase test may be used. The raw milk and milk products used as ingredients must have bacterial counts not exceeding 200,000 per milliliter or gram, if the count or direct microscopic clump count is used, or 800,000 if individual organisms are counted, or having an average reduction time of not less than six hours. Milk and milk products that are used in the pasteurized, condensed, evaporated, or dried state must have an average bacterial plate count not exceeding 50,000 per milliliter or gram. These limits on the ingredients should be doubled in the case of cream.

Grade B frozen desserts comply with Grade A standards with the following exceptions: Floors of the manufacturing plants may be of tight wood or linoleum instead of concrete, tile, etc., and flood drains are not required. Walls and ceilings need not have light-colored surfaces, provided that they are kept clean. The lighting requirement is not so stringent as to even distribution. The average bacterial count of the pasteurized mix or frozen dessert must at no time prior to delivery exceed 100,000 per gram. Milk and milk products used as ingredients must have average counts not exceeding 1,000,000 per milliliter or gram by the plate count or direct microscopic clump count; 4,000,000 by the count of individual organisms; or an average reduction time not exceeding 3½ hours. Milk and milk products used as ingredients in the pasteurized, condensed, evaporated, or dried state must have a bacterial plate count not exceeding 250,000 per milliliter or gram. This limit on the ingredients are doubled in the case of cream. Grade C frozen desserts are those which violate any of the requirements for Grade B.

The grading period is six months; that is, the health officer announces the grades of all frozen-dessert plants at least once every six months, and the plants are inspected at least once during that period. All containers enclosing mix or frozen desserts except those filled from bulk containers in retail dispensing must be plainly labeled with the name and grade of the contents, whether raw or pasteurized, and the name and street address, or permit number, of the manufacturing plant. A descriptive word or phrase indicating composition or flavor may be added.

BIBLIOGRAPHY

1. Kelly, E., and C. E. Clement: "Market Milk," John Wiley & Sons, Inc., New York, 1931.
2. "Standard Methods for the Examination of Dairy Products," American Public Health Association, New York.
3. Mallmann, W. L.: Notes on Dairy Cleaners and Cleaning Dairy Equipment and Notes on Sanitization of Dairy Equipment, *Mich. Agr. Exp. Sta. Quar. Bull.*, vol. 27, no. 1, August, 1944.
4. Mallmann, W. L., E. Kivela, A. L. Bortree, E. Churchill, and L. H. Begeman: "The Influence of the Method of Sanitizing Milking Machines on the Bacterial Count of Milk," Twentieth Annual Report of the New York State Association of Milk Sanitarians, reprint 1946.
5. McCollum, E. V.: Nutritional Aspects of Milk Pasteurization, *Am. J. Public Health*, vol. 24, no. 9, September, 1934.
6. "3A Standard Method for Determining the Holding Time of High-temperature Short-time Pasteurizers by Means of the Salt Conductivity Test," formulated by International Association of Milk and Food Sanitarians, U.S. Public Health Service, Dairy Industry Committee, reprinted from *J. Milk and Food Technol.*, vol., 13, no. 5, September–October, 1950.
7. "Milk Ordinance and Code: 1953 Recommendations of the Public Health Service," *U.S. Dep. Health, Education, Welfare Pub.* 229,
8. *Public Health Repts.*, vol. 53, p. 1386, reprint 1970, 1938.
9. Scheele, Leonard A., and Harry G. Hanson: "The Views of the United States Public Health Service on a National Program for Interstate Milk Shipments," paper delivered at the Fifth Annual Meeting of the Dairy Products Improvement Institute, Inc., New York, Jan. 17, 1952.
10. Fabian, F. W.: Cheese and Its Relation to Disease, *Am. J. Public Health*, p. 987, August, 1957.
11. Parker, H. N.: "City Milk Supply," McGraw-Hill Book Company, Inc., New York.
12. Fuchs, A. W.: Contamination of Pasteurized Milk by Improper Relative Pressures in Regenerators, *Public Health Repts.*, vol. 53, no. 13, reprint 1921.
13. Fuchs, A. W.: Recent Amendments of the U.S. Public Health Service Milk Code, *J. Milk and Food Technol.*, vol. 11, no. 3, May–June, 1948.
14. "Frozen Desserts Ordinance and Code," U.S. Public Health Service.
15. Noles, Samuel O., and H. H. Wilkowske: Practical Sanitary Aspects of Bulk Milk Dispensers, *J. Milk and Food Technol.*, vol. 17, no. 7, July, 1954.
16. Symposium on Bulk Pick-up of Milk, *Milk Plant Monthly*, vol. 44, no. 5, May, 1955.
17. March, R. P.: Farm Bulk Milk Handling, *J. Milk and Food Technol.*, vol. 17, no. 7, July, 1954.

CHAPTER 12

FOOD SANITATION

12-1. Food affects health in many ways, and scientific knowledge of the subject is increasing continually. The vitamins, unbalanced diets, the effects of diet deficiencies, allergies to certain foods, and overeating are all matters of importance to the physician, dietitian, and nurse. The person interested in sanitation, however, is primarily concerned with six agencies through which food may cause suffering or death. These are:

1. Animal parasites, such as tapeworms and trichina worms. These gain entrance to the human body through the eating of infected meat or fish which has not been cooked sufficiently to kill the immature worm.
2. Bacteria, such as tuberculosis or typhoid bacilli in milk, and typhoid in oysters or on lettuce or celery. Organisms of the Salmonella group, which cause food infection or poisoning, are also in this category.
3. Toxins given off by certain bacteria growing in the food. Botulinus organisms and some of the staphylococci are important in this respect.
4. Poisons placed in foods for preserving purposes, coloring, or adulteration; or entering by accident, such as insect poison mistakenly used for flour or sugar, poisonous spray residues left on fruits or vegetables, or poisons from containers, although this is rare.
5. Use of poisonous plants or other materials as foods. Instances are eating of poisonous toadstools mistaken for edible mushrooms and out-of-season consumption of the mussel of the Pacific Coast, which is poisonous during the months of June to September.

It will be noted that ptomaine poisoning has not been included in the list. What is popularly called ptomaine poisoning may be one or both of the second or third classifications given above.

12-2. Food and Drug Laws. The Federal Food and Drug Act of 1906, as amended in 1938 (the Federal Food, Drug, and Cosmetic Act), prohibits the adulteration of foods for interstate shipment. To protect their citizens from injurious and fraudulent foods prepared and consumed within the same state, many states have also passed food and drug acts. They usually follow closely the Federal law. The provisions concerning foods, which include drinks, flavorings, and condiments, are considered as being violated in the following cases:

1. If the food bears or contains any poisonous or deleterious substance which may render it injurious to health.

2. If it bears or contains any added poisonous or added deleterious substance which is unsafe. This section has resulted in much controversy and investigation. It is aimed at the practice of adding chemical preservatives to foods. These include formaldehyde, boric acid, borax, salicylic acid, and others. There is difference of opinion as to whether, in the small amounts generally used, such preservatives are injurious or not.

3. If it consists in whole or in part of any filthy, putrid, or decomposed substance, or if it is otherwise unfit for food. Examples are dried fruits which are wormy or spoiled, chocolate or candy which has been nibbled by mice, or rats, and oysters polluted with sewage.

4. If it has been prepared, packed, or held under insanitary conditions whereby it may have been contaminated with filth or otherwise rendered injurious to health.

5. If it is, in whole or in part, the product of a diseased animal or of an animal which has died otherwise than by slaughter.

6. If its container is composed, in whole or in part, of any poisonous or deleterious substance which may render the contents injurious to health.

7. If any valuable constituent has been in whole or in part omitted or abstracted therefrom, or if damaged, or if inferiority has been concealed in any manner. An example of this is skimming of milk and selling it as regular milk. There is no objection, however, if the milk is afterward sold as skim milk.

8. If it bears or contains a coal-tar color other than one from a batch that has been certified in accordance with regulations.

9. If it is a confectionery and it bears or contains any alcohol or nonnutritive article or substance except harmless coloring; harmless flavoring; harmless resinous glaze, not in excess of 4 per cent; natural gum; and pectin. This paragraph does not apply, however, to any confectionery by reason of its containing less than 0.5 per cent by volume of alcohol derived solely from the use of flavoring extracts or to any chewing gum by reason of its containing harmless nonnutritive masticatory substances.

It will be seen that the food section of the Federal Food, Drug, and Cosmetic Law mentioned above is concerned not only with the safety of food products that move in interstate commerce but also with fraudulent practices. The law and the fair enforcement by the Food and Drug Administration has had a stabilizing effect on industry, has promoted fair practice, and has made a great contribution to public health.

Misbranding is also made unlawful. This calls for honest labeling of the product as to its character, origin, constituents, and the amount in the container.

12-3. Parasites. This subject is also discussed in Art. 1-12. The beef tapeworm is common in the United States, cohabiting with man without injurious effect except as a possible cause of anemia and nervous symptoms. The adult worm lives in the intestines of man and perpetuates the transmission cycle by depositing eggs which leave with the feces. Cattle which eat infected food or drink water ingest the eggs. Larval worms issue from the eggs into the intestines of the animal. From the intestines they enter the muscles, and there encyst themselves to wait until the animal is slaughtered and the beef eaten. The cysts, also known as measles, are visible to the naked eye. Effective cooking of beef will kill tapeworm larvae.

The pork tapeworm is less common in this country than the beef tapeworm. It is somewhat similar to the latter except that hogs instead of cattle are involved. There is one important difference. The person harboring an adult worm may infect himself with eggs from his own excreta, larval worms hatched in his own intestines encysting themselves in his muscles. Should they choose the eye or the brain for this purpose, there may be serious results. This parasite is, therefore, considered more dangerous than the beef tapeworm. The practice of allowing hogs access to human excreta in open toilets or elsewhere is responsible for much infection, although the hogs also infect each other. Effective cooking of pork will kill the larvae in the measle form.

The fish tapeworm causes very severe anemia. It is very likely to occur among people who eat much fresh fish, particularly if it is eaten raw. The life cycle of this parasite is somewhat more complicated than that of the other tapeworms mentioned. The adult lives in the human intestines; the eggs are in the feces and infect the water of rivers or bays. In the water the eggs hatch into small motile embryos, which at the first opportunity enter the body of a small crustacean (Cyclops). If the crustacean is eaten by a fish, the larva makes its way somewhere into the muscular tissue of the fish, there to wait until it is eaten by man. Preventive measures are thorough cooking of fish and proper disposal of sewage.

Trichinosis, which is due to trichina worms, is quite common abroad and occurs in the United States, more often, no doubt, than is reported or recognized. In 1946, 5 outbreaks of trichinosis were reported, with 25 cases and 1 death. Probably there were many more unreported cases and outbreaks. This is indicated by the fact that investigations made by the New York State Trichinosis Commission, based on numerous autopsies, indicated that 17 per cent of the people of the United States had had trichinosis at some time during their lives.

Its greater prevalence in Europe, especially in Germany, is due to the custom of eating raw pork in sausage. The larvae are embedded in the muscles in an oval cyst about 1/25 inch long. When the flesh containing them is eaten, they are set free in the stomach, move into the intestines, and there reach maturity. The adults are not long-lived, but the larvae will survive for many years in their cysts before dying or being absorbed. The females are 1/12 to 1/6 inch long and the males about 1/17 inch long. The females are viviparous and in about a week produce young totaling 1,000 to 2,000 over a period of six weeks, although most will be born in the first two weeks. The young migrate over a period of three days to encyst in muscular tissue. Trichinosis, the disease, only occurs if the infection is severe, and then signs of the disease occur in one to two weeks after the trichinous meat has been eaten. The movement of the worms into the muscles is accompanied by intense pain, fever, and other symptoms. Autopsies indicate that in fatal cases millions of larvae have become encysted. Infection is not obtained through feces but only through infected meat. Therefore, hogs which have been fed on garbage containing pork scraps and slaughterhouse offal are very likely to be infected. Rats living around slaughterhouses are usually heavily infested, and it is possible that the hogs may eat dead rats. It is estimated that, in general, 1 to 2 per cent of all hogs in the country are infested. Meat inspection is of little avail against this disease. Here again thorough cooking is necessary, although the trichina worm is easily killed, only 137°F being required. The pork should be cooked until it is white all through. Refrigeration at 5°F for a period of twenty days will also kill larvae. Pickling, salting, and smoking also kill when done thoroughly. Some hams and other pork products are commercially processed in such a manner that all trichina are destroyed and no further cooking by the housewife is necessary. These products are generally labeled accordingly.

12-4. Vesicular Exanthema. Vesicular exanthema is a virus disease of swine. The economic importance of feeding cooked garbage to hogs has resulted in control of this disease, which was threatening the swine industry. The United States Department of Agriculture has recognized that the cooking of garbage not only results in better weight gains in swine but also prevents other diseases common to swine from spreading in epidemic proportions over the country.

12-5. Food Poisoning. This term is loosely used to cover infections and intoxications caused by eating infected food and often characterized by vomiting, abdominal pain, diarrhea, chills, prostration, and gastroenteritis. These signs usually occur four to twelve hours after ingesting the food, although the extreme limits may be two to seventy-two hours even in the same outbreak. It is quite common, but the fatality rate is low. The U.S. Public Health Service received reports of 194 outbreaks of food poisoning of this type in 1953 causing 9,914 cases. Reporting is far from complete. According to Karl F. Meyer[2], several hundred thousand cases of food poisoning occur annually in the United States.

In the official report of the American Public Health Association entitled "Control of Communicable Diseases in Man" (8th edition, 1955), food poisoning is distinguished from food-borne infection:

The effects of food poisoning are promptly evident, and the amount of particular food ingested has a relation to severity, suggesting the importance of preformed elements [see page 69 of the report]. Food-borne infection with a number of intestinal pathogens, with streptococci, and with agents of diphtheria, tuberculosis, and undulant fever follows a usual incubation for the particular disease, and clinical course and manifestation are not as a rule materially altered by the circumstance of the food serving as a vehicle of infection.

1. *Staphylococcus intoxication* is a poisoning (not an infection) of abrupt and sometimes violent onset with severe nausea, vomiting, prostration, and sometimes severe diarrhea. Deaths are exceedingly rare. Isolation of large numbers of staphylococci from suspected food permits presumptive diagnosis. The toxin is stable at boiling temperature, but staphylococci multiply in food, producing toxin which causes poisoning. The source of contamination is not known in most cases, but it is believed to be of human origin. The most common vehicles of transmission are custard-filled pastry; processed meats, especially ham; and milk from cows with specifically infected udders. The interval between taking food and the onset is a half-hour to four hours, usually two to four. Preventive measures include:

a. Prompt refrigeration of sliced and chopped meats and of custards and cream fillings to avoid multiplication of staphylococci accidentally introduced; filling of pastries with custard immediately before sale, and adequate heat treatment of finished product. Avoid improper care of leftover foods.

b. Education of food handlers in strict attention to sanitation and cleanliness of kitchens, including refrigeration, hand washing, and the danger of working while having skin infections. There have been many outbreaks of food poisoning from foods infected by staphylococcus organisms from boils, pimples, or other infections on the hands of food handlers.

2. *Botulinus intoxication* is a highly afebrile poisoning (not an infection) characterized by headache, weakness, constipation, oculomotor or other paralysis, and absence of diarrhea. Death by heart or respiratory paralysis occurs in about two-thirds of the cases and usually within three to seven days. Biological and toxicological tests may confirm presence of the bacterium or its toxin in suspected food or stomach contents. The toxin is produced in improperly processed food only under anaerobic conditions and particularly in nonacid foods. The toxin is easily

destroyed by boiling, but spores require higher temperatures. The reservoir of botulinus bacillus is the soil and the intestinal tract of animals. The toxin is formed by anaerobic growth of spores in food. The mode of transmission is by ingestion of food containing botulinus toxin—usually uncooked food from jars and cans inadequately processed during canning. Most poisonings in the United States are due to home-canned vegetables. In Europe, most cases are due to sausages or other smoked or preserved meat. Symptoms usually occur within eighteen hours after food containing the toxin has been eaten. Since most cases of botulinus poisoning in this country have been traced to home-canned fruits and vegetables, it is highly important that housewives and others concerned with home canning of foods be educated in the essentials of safe processing in regard to the time, pressure, and temperature factors.

According to the "1953 Summary of Disease Outbreaks"[3] ten cases of botulism, four of them fatal, were reported from five different states. Home-canned foods found to be vehicles of infection included headcheese, canned corn, beets, asparagus, string beans, huckleberry juice, and lobster tails.

3. *Clostridium welchii poisonings* are occasionally reported, particularly in Great Britain. Outbreaks reported have been caused by meat which has been cooked, allowed to cool slowly, insufficiently refrigerated, and served the next day or later, either reheated or cold. Incubation periods are 8 to 22 hours. Signs and symptoms are acute abdominal pain and diarrhea, rarely nausea and vomiting. Prevention consists in excluding food handlers known or suspected of being infected, cooking of meat immediately before consumption, or rapid cooking followed by rapid cooling and refrigeration.

4. *Salmonellosis* may be indicated by a variety of signs and symptoms. The most common is an acute gastroenteritis with diarrhea and abdominal cramps. Fever, nausea, and vomiting are frequently present. Deaths are uncommon, but somewhat more frequent than for staphylococcal food poisoning. *Salmonella* organisms may be recovered from feces or from the site of a localized infection during the acute illness. There are numerous species of *Salmonella*. Of the group pathogenic for animals and occasionally for man, the source and reservoir of infection are feces of patients; convalescent carriers; feces of domestic fowl, household pets, rodents, and domestic animals; eggs of ducks, and less commonly of chickens. Epidemics are usually traced to:

a. Improperly prepared food, especially meat pies and roast fowl. This means insufficient cooking, either at too low a temperature or for an insufficient period.

b. Insufficiently cooked foods containing dried hen eggs or duck eggs.

c. Unpasteurized milk or dairy products.

d. Pastries or other foods contaminated by rodent feces, possibly through the medium of cockroaches, and served with no further cooking.

e. Food prepared by an infected food handler.

Sporadic cases probably originate through direct contact with an infected person or animal. The incubation period in an epidemic is from six to forty-eight hours, usually about twelve hours. The principal preventive measures are:

a. Thorough cooking of all foodstuffs derived from animal sources, with particular attention to preparation of fowl, egg products, and meat dishes

b. Protection of prepared food against rodent and insect contamination

c. Refrigeration of all food during storage

12-6. Spray Residues. The observation by health authorities of dangerous amounts of arsenic on fruits offered for sale has led to investigation of spraying practices and application of measures by the Food and Drug Administration, U.S. Department of Health, Education, and Welfare. Cases of poisoning have been attributed to this cause, and in all probability some unrecognized poisoning occurs. The poisons used to control insects on fruits are arsenate of lead and a supposedly safer substitute, fluorine compounds. Tolerances have been established for the amounts of the dangerous substances in fruit and vegetables and have been placed at 0.01 grain per pound for arsenic, 0.018 grain per pound for lead, and 0.01 grain per pound for fluorine. Aldrin is a recently developed insecticide that is quite toxic. A tolerance for aldrin of 0.1 part per million on fruits and vegetables on which it is required will be without hazard to man. Benzene hexachloride (BHC) and the gamma isomer known as lindane have come into general use as insecticides. A tolerance for lindane of 10 parts per million and a tolerance of commercial benzene hexachloride of 5 parts per million on fruits and vegetables on which it is required are without hazard to man. Tolerances for other spray insecticides and fungicides are listed in the *Federal Register*, vol. 19, no. 204, Oct. 20, 1954. Fruits that are shipped interstate are analyzed and seized if the tolerances are exceeded. Apple shipments form the principal seizures. As preventive measures the administration has worked out spraying programs that involve the minimum danger of excessive residues and washing methods that remove the poison. Washing requires an acid solution, since the poison is frequently mixed with a binder of casein or oil. Authorities in a few states are cooperating with growers to safeguard intrastate shipments, and the health departments of some cities are also checking incoming fruits and vegetables.

12-7. Canned Foods. While, from the epidemiological standpoint, canned foods are the safest foods we have, some control is exercised over them by health authorities. Many states inspect canneries and do not allow the product to be sold unless it conforms to their sanitary requirements. Sanitarians are required to eliminate from the shelves of wholesale and retail groceries and restaurants any canned goods showing signs of spoilage.

Grading of canned goods is attempted by canners on the basis of texture, firmness, and flavor. But it is difficult to keep packs of uniform quality, and in general the labeling by the canners as to whether the product is a fancy grade or otherwise has meant very little. Grading is purely voluntary on the part of the processor; he engages the services of the U.S. Department of Agriculture if he wishes to grade his food and label it accordingly. Some progress has been made in this direction, and some canned foods are graded by Federal inspectors as A, B, or C, corresponding to fancy, extra-standard, or standard. Substandard goods may be sold, if suitable for food, but must be labeled as substandard.

The cans used are made of steel coated with tin. The tin coating is not perfect and may contain some small holes. Protective enamels, which are usually synthetic resins baked on the metal sheets at high temperatures, are used on the interiors of many cans. They prevent a harmless but discoloring reaction between certain foods and the metal of the can. The can seams are made by crimping the edges of the metal and sealing with a thin gasket. The cans should be clean before filling.

Fruits or vegetables that are to be canned are processed as follows: (1) Sorting, which eliminates rotten or undesirable material. (2) Washing by soaking and spraying. (3) Peeling and trimming. (4) Blanching, which is the application of hot water or steam. It wilts some bulky vegetables, prevents discoloring of others, cleans peas of mucilaginous material, and removes some of the air from the tissues. (5) Placing in the cans. (6) Exhausting, which consists of heating to such a temperature that air and other gases are driven out. Air removal prevents oxidation of the can contents later, while the partial vacuum resulting after the cans are sealed prevents excessive pressures during the processing. It results in concave ends for the cans after the process is complete. A mechanical vacuum may also be applied and cans sealed in it. (7) The cans are covered and sealed while the contents are at the exhausting temperature. (8) Processing, the heating or cooking of the contents to prevent spoilage, does not necessarily ensure complete sterilization, because a few resistant thermophilic spores would necessitate such high temperatures that the food would be unsalable. These spores are of no consequence. The processing time and temperature depend upon the nature of the food and have been established by research, much of which has been done in the Research Laboratory of the National Canners' Association. (9) Cans are immersed in cool water to relieve pressure and prevent overcooking and germination of thermophiles, which would occur during slow cooling.

Inspection of cans for spoilage presents no difficulties. The normal can has no leaks around the rims or seams, and the ends are slightly concave. A "swell" has bulging ends. A "flipper" has one end that bulges when the can is tapped sharply against a hard surface and does not return unless pressed in. A "springer" has a bulging end, which, when pressed in, causes the other end to bulge. Swells must pass through the flipper and springer stages.

Swells, flippers, and springers may be caused by overfilling the can, insufficient exhaustion of air, or transportation of cans to high altitudes. The vast majority, however, are caused by fruit attacking the metal of the can and evolving hydrogen gas. Practically all such swelling occurs a year or more after canning. It does not make the food dangerous. It is true that small amounts of tin compounds are formed by reaction with certain foods, but research has shown that these compounds are harmless. There is no basis for the popular belief that some poison is formed if food is left in the can after it is opened, but opened cans that still contain food should, of course, be placed in the refrigerator to prevent contamination of the food by flies or other agents of disease transmission.

Decomposition caused by the action of microorganisms occurs practically only in nonacid vegetables. It is generally not dangerous, but the possibility of botulism must be borne in mind. Since the public cannot be expected to distinguish between the decomposition of fruits and vegetables, the rule should be that all swells, flippers, and springers be condemned. The sanitarian should also make certain that the contents are destroyed, for swells may be punctured, to release the gas, the holes soldered up, and the contents reprocessed and sold.

Inspections of canning plants should be made while the plants are in operation. The following requirements should be enforced. Washers, blanchers, etc., should be emptied and cleaned at least once a day. Overflow brine, syrup, or juice should not be re-used. Protection of cans and covers from dirt and insects should be required; no cans or other containers should be filled by dipping, and no pails or vessels used for food packing should be used in cleaning operations. There should be daily removal of refuse; a tight roof; watertight and smooth table tops and floors, graded to drain, and kept clean. Toilet rooms should be screened, have self-closing doors, and there should be one toilet for each 15 employees. Adequate washing facilities with soap and towels should be available. Personnel should be free from disease and have clean hands and clothing; female employees should wear clean, washable caps. Spitting should not be permitted in rooms where food is processed. There should be a safe water supply, and liquid wastes should be disposed of without danger or nuisance.

12-8. Dried Foods. Dried fruit, vegetables, and meats have not been reported as causing outbreaks of food poisoning. *Salmonella* organisms have been isolated frequently from dried whole egg, and some *Salmonella* outbreaks in man in Great Britain have been suspected on good evidence of having been caused by spray-dried eggs. Reconstituted eggs should be cooked immediately, for if they are incubated for some hours so that bacterial multiplication results, only thorough cooking (in terms of time and temperature) will destroy all the *Salmonella* organisms present.

Insanitary handling of food prior to or during dehydration results in high bacterial content, possibly including organisms of the coliform group, and the presence of yeasts and molds. This condition may lead to poor flavor of the product and early spoilage while the food is being stored. Bacterial standards for dried foods have been advocated as a means of controlling the sanitation of handling, processing, and storing. In the absence of such standards, plant sanitation should be emphasized, since the consumer of dehydrated foods is entitled to an assurance that they have not been prepared under filthy conditions.

12-9. Paper Containers. Paper containers for milk and other foods apparently present no sanitary problems[4]. Coliform bacteria cannot be found in the pulp stream in paper mills or in the finished paper. Bacteria are destroyed by pulping under pressure with chemicals, bleaching with chlorine, and passage over drying rolls at high temperature. Lack of moisture causes bacteria to die out in the paper; only harmless aerobic spore-bearing organisms survive. Standard bacterial counts have been suggested for determining the sanitary quality of paper, but they appear to have no value.

12-10. Sanitation of Refrigerated Locker Plants. Refrigerated locker plants are designed and constructed to store food at low temperatures in lockers of about 25 cubic feet capacity. The processing requires (1) a chill room, where the food is reduced in temperature; (2) a quick- or sharp-freeze room, in which the food is quickly frozen; (3) the locker room. In some plants an aging room is also included for a period of storage at moderate temperature after chilling. The plant may also include facilities for butchering cattle, hogs, and poultry for storage in the lockers. Such service may also include curing, smoking, or barbecuing the meat.

In addition to the usual sanitary requirements for food-handling establishments discussed in this chapter, the locker plant presents a few special problems. The temperatures of the various rooms should be as follows: In the chilling room 34 to 36°F, with a tolerance of 10° for a reasonable time after food has been placed in the room. In the aging room 38°F, with a tolerance of 4°. In the quick-freeze room −10°F or lower in rooms when still-air cooling is employed and 0°F or lower where forced-air circulation is used, with a tolerance of 10° for either type of installation for a reasonable time after food has been placed in the room. Accurate thermometers must be kept in each room, and the one in the locker room must be of recording type with a weekly chart.

At least one gas mask of a type approved by the U.S. Bureau of Mines must be on hand in case of leaks of the refrigerant.

Foods not for human consumption must be so marked. All foods must be quick-frozen before being stored in lockers, and they must be wrapped in nonabsorbent paper so as to exclude air. Each package shall be marked with its contents, the locker number, and the date of quick freezing.

12-11. Vending Machines. Vending machines of all kinds have made their appearance. Those dispensing coffee, milk, fruit juices, soup, and sandwiches require supervision to assure a good product.

12-12. Frozen Foods. The U.S. Department of Agriculture, under the authority contained in the Agricultural Marketing Act of 1946, may develop standards for grades for frozen foods and fruit beverages. The product is graded for its appearance, color, flavor, and defects. The product must comply with the food and drug laws. As more research work and studies are made on frozen foods, additional quality specifications undoubtedly will emerge.

12-13. Health Certificates. Laws of some states require that all food handlers employed to serve the public have certificates indicating that they have been examined by competent physicians and have been found free from communicable disease. The certificates have to be renewed at intervals of six months or a year, and the employer is required to keep them on file for checking by the inspectors of the food-handling establishments.

Experience with health certificates has been far from satisfactory. Before a physician can be sure that a food handler is free from tuberculosis or venereal disease, or is not a carrier of typhoid fever or diphtheria, special examinations and tests are required that would cost too much for either the employer or the employee to pay. Consequently only a superficial examination is given by the physician in return for a small fee. This procedure also ignores the fact that a food handler may develop disease shortly after he has been examined. Both the employer and the employee realize the small value of the examinations, and they may lose respect for the health department which enforces the requirement, while the public may have a false sense of security. The present tendency is to disregard the health certificate and concentrate on listing known carriers of disease and having sick workers report to the health officer.

Some of the city health departments have attempted to test all food handlers in their own laboratories to determine typhoid carriers. This has involved a tremendous amount of work, for food handlers are numerous, probably 2 to 5 per cent of the total population, and there is a considerable turnover of workers in the industry. Also a single test in many cases does not detect the carrier. It has been found, therefore, that the money required for this work can be used to better advantage elsewhere. It is useful, for example, for the city or county health department to keep a file of known typhoid fever carriers. These names would be obtainable in part from cases of typhoid fever which, as a result of tests of the convalescents, had been shown to develop into carriers. Such a file, together with registration of all food handlers, would allow elimination of carriers from food-handling occupations. Of assistance, too, would be the education of food handlers as to the recognition of the early signs of disease and the importance of immediately reporting to a physician for diagnosis and treatment.

SANITATION OF EATING AND DRINKING ESTABLISHMENTS

12-14. Cleaning and Bactericidal Treatment of Utensils and Equipment. The diagram in Fig. 12-1 shows the importance of the multiuse utensils of a public food-handling establishment in transmitting diseases. Respiratory and intestinal infections may be transmitted through unclean eating utensils.

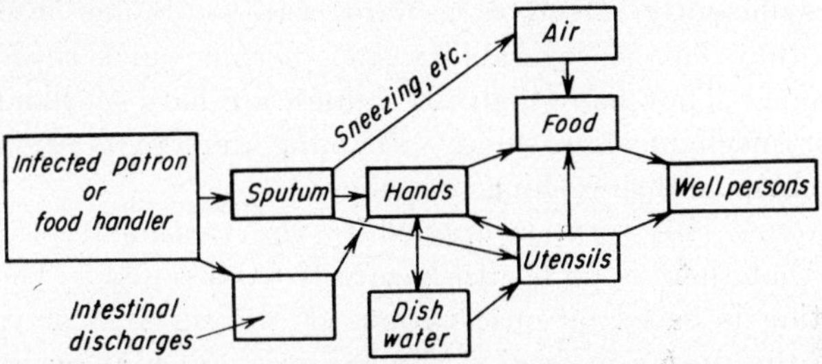

FIG. 12-1. Principal methods of transmission of respiratory and intestinal diseases at food-handling establishments. The double arrows indicate possible travel of infectious material in each direction. Flies and contaminated water are also possibilities but have not been indicated.

Reference to the diagram will indicate the importance of the dishwater. Unless the water is hot enough or a bactericidal treatment is used, it may serve to transmit disease and also endanger the workers whose hands are frequently immersed in it, and, of course, if the washing and disinfecting process is not properly done the danger of the utensils to the patrons is apparent. All washing operations by hand should be carried on in a three-compartment vat. The complete washing process should include the following: (1) rinsing or thorough scraping to eliminate large food particles—this will keep the wash water in better condition; (2) washing in water at a temperature of 110 to 120°F with a soap or other detergent; (3) a rinse, combined with an effective germicidal process.

The Detergent. The detergent is the cleaning agent (see Art. 10-17). It works by dissolving and emulsifying the grease or other soil on the utensils so that it flows off into the water. Bacteria are also carried off in the process, although some remain on the surfaces. The ideal detergent would not be injurious to the hands of the dishwasher and would be efficient in both hard and soft water. In hard waters the calcium and magnesium salts present unite with the detergent to form a sticky curd which causes a film on the surfaces after washing. The film protects bacteria in the sanitizing process. Some detergents include sequestering agents to prevent the formation of the curd or to reduce its stickiness. Choice of the detergent, and particularly the amount used, depends upon whether hand washing or machine washing is used and upon the hardness of the water.

Soap and the foaming commercial detergents as well are good detergents in waters having a hardness of not over 300 parts per million. Sodium carbonate is an alkaline detergent which has been much used although its efficiency is low in all ranges of soft to hard waters. Other alkaline detergents containing the polyphosphates, particularly the hexaphosphates, have the sequestering action mentioned above, and are, therefore, sufficiently effective in hard waters. Some observers also claim that they increase rinsability, *i.e.*, permit quick rinsing without leaving a film. They have high pH values, are hard on hands, and are suitable for mechanical washing. Foaming detergents should not be used in mechanical dishwashing processes.

Sanitization. This term is applied to the treatment of dishes and utensils so that there is no health hazard to their re-use. The efficiency of sanitization is based on observations of the survival of various test bacteria on the presumption that the less resistant pathogens have been killed by the process. Actually sanitization is another word for disinfection. Sanitizing agents, however, are not usually called disinfectants since Federal law requires that disinfectants have a phenol coefficient (Art. 10-7) on the container, and the efficiency of some sanitizers cannot be tested by obtaining a phenol coefficient.

Heat is an effective sanitizer if it is properly used. Immersion of the utensils for at least two minutes in clean, hot water at a temperature of at least 170°F or for half a minute in boiling water is effective. Unless the water is actually boiling, control should be obtained by a thermometer and preferably by a thermostat placed on the water heater or immersion vat. Pouring hot water over the dishes is not effective, nor is the use of water in which the worker can place his hands. If hand washing is used, metal baskets, lined with wood strips to prevent marking the china, are required to immerse and remove the dishes from the hot water. After removal from the hot water the dishes should remain in the baskets until dry and then be stored in such a manner that they will not be contaminated before they are used again. Where heat is used, a three-compartment washing vat will be needed, one for washing, the second for heat treatment, and the third for rinsing. Care should be taken that the wash water does not become excessively dirty before it is changed.

A chlorine solution may also be used for bactericidal purposes. Immersion should be for at least two minutes in a lukewarm solution containing at least 50 parts per million of available chlorine if hypochlorites are used, or a concentration of 100 parts per million if chloramines are used. The rinse should be made up at a strength of 100 parts per million or more of hypochlorites, and it should not be used after an orthotolidine test shows that the chlorine residual has been reduced to less than 50 parts per million. Some organic chlorine compounds are sold for this purpose. They produce less chlorine odor but must be used with caution, for they are apparently less efficient than hypochlorite. Their efficiency should be checked by the tests given below. If chlorine is used, a three-compartment washing vat is needed, one for washing, the second for a plain rinse, and the third for the chlorine rinse. If desired, the dishes or glasses may be rinsed again in clean running water, to remove the chlorine odor, and then permitted to dry either in the basket or on a drain shelf or tray. The odor, however, soon leaves in any case. In this or the heat method of disinfection care should be taken that no air is entrapped in the dishes or glasses to prevent actual contact with the hot water or solution. Chlorine should not be used to disinfect silver or silver-plated articles, for it will turn them black.

Quaternary ammonium compounds are being used as sanitizers to a considerable extent. Compounds containing iodine and bromine have also been found effective for bactericidal treatment.

Combination detergent-sanitizers have been available and may be used to an increasing extent in the future. Since the quaternary ammonium compounds are less affected by organic matter than is chlorine, they are showing promise when combined with alkaline detergents. Mallmann believes that they should be used in the hand washing of utensils and all washing of bottles and glasses. They have proved successful in washing dairy utensils, although it is advocated that just before use the utensils receive an additional rinse with a bactericide.

Mechanical Dishwashing. Mechanical methods of dishwashing are more satisfactory than hand washing, if the dishwasher is properly designed and operated. The efficiency of mechanical machines depends upon temperature, spray pattern, time of spraying, nozzle size, and pressure. Mechanical dishwashers used in large kitchens are of the single- or multiple-tank types. The single-tank washer has one tank which contains heated wash water with a detergent. The wash water is pumped from the tank through sprays which direct the water against the utensils to be washed, and the water drains back to the tank and is recirculated. Before returning to the tank it passes through a strainer tray which has openings smaller than those of the sprays. After the wash the utensils are exposed to a hot rinsing spray which comes directly from the hot-water heater and after use is generally discharged into the wash water after passing through a strainer. The multiple-tank

FIG. 12-2. Cutaway view of a multiple-tank dishwasher. (*Courtesy of Univeral Washing Machine Co., Nutley, N.J.*)

washer has a rinse-water tank and pump in addition to the wash-water tank. Since the rinse water is also recirculated, a curtain rinse of hot water directly from the hot-water source is applied to the utensils as they leave the machine. Thus no recirculated water remains on the washed dish or utensil.

The dishes and silver, after rinsing or scraping, are placed in baskets or trays. The baskets then are placed on an endless belt which automatically moves them through the machine. Push-through types are also made, but these are undesirable since the attendant may reduce the required washing period. Controlled timing for wash and rinse is desirable. The temperature of the wash water should be from 140 to 160°F. Higher temperatures bake some foods, such as eggs, on the utensils. The water pressure and amount should be high enough to get good mechanical action from the jets. The optimum amounts of these have been determined by the National Sanitation Foundation and vary with the size of machine[5]:

> The minimum number of gallons of wash water at 140° to 160°F required to be sprayed uniformly over each rack of dishes in not less than 40 seconds shall be determined by multiplying the total area of the rack by 0.23. The pump delivery capacity shall be determined by multiplying such rack area by 0.35. For racks of all sizes, the pressure at the jet during the washing operations shall be sufficient to deliver the wash water to all portions of the racked dishes with a cutting velocity. Such velocity shall be just under that which will dislodge standard restaurant coffee cups from racks.

After the washing, the dishes are rinsed in water not less than 180°F at the dish for at least ten seconds. It is recommended that the water pressure be 15 to 25 pounds per square inch, with a flow rate of 9 gallons per minute per 20- by 20-inch dish rack in single-tank, stationary-rack, hood-curtain, and door types. If the racks are of a different size, the flow rate should be varied proportionately[6]. A recirculating pump applies the wash water. In many machines the rinse water is discharged after use into the wash water, thus keeping it relatively clean.

The detergent, which must be kept at proper strength, is added mechanically or by hand, although the latter has not been found to be very satisfactory. Detergents in blocks have been used. They are placed in the wash water and dissolved as the water is used. No rule can be given as to the amount of detergent to be used since it depends upon the character of the water, particularly its hardness. Results should be checked by tests.

The sanitarian, when checking dishwashing machines, should especially note a number of possible deficiencies. The machine may be of the push-through type, which means that the baskets or trays remain in the sprays only as long as the operator permits. The total time should never be under one minute, preferably more, and as much as possible of this period should be in the rinse, provided proper washing is obtained. Temperatures of the wash and rinse waters should be checked and also the amount of detergent in the wash water, which may be highly variable because of the entrance of rinse water. Stacking of the dishes, particularly the cups and the spoons in the trays, should be noted, for they may not be properly exposed to the water. Dishes should be inspected and testing swabs used. The machine should be checked to make certain there are no cross connections to the public water supply.

Glasses are frequently washed in warm water containing an alkaline detergent having a formula similar to that given above, the cleaning being done by rotating brushes which vigorously scrub the interior and exterior. The glasses are then rinsed in a chlorine solution. This procedure results in fewer broken glasses and a better appearance.

Dishes should preferably dry by drainage, but if towels are used they should be clean. High-temperature rinses promote rapid drying.

The National Sanitation Foundation, in its laboratory, has conducted a series of studies and has developed standards for soda-fountain, luncheonette, and food-service equipment, including standards for spray-type dishwashing machines. Manufacturers meeting these standards may use the National Sanitation Foundation seal of approval. These standards have been most helpful to food regulatory officials.

Tests. The efficiency of dishwashing and bactericidal treatments can be determined bacteriologically. The Subcommittee on Food Utensil Sanitation, 1943, of the American Public Health Association recommends the following tests on cleansed and disinfected utensils.

The laboratory first prepares a dilute phosphate buffer solution[7] that is nontoxic to bacteria. If the utensils to be swabbed are likely to have chlorine and/or quaternary ammonium compound on them, the solution must contain a neutralizing agent. Utensils to be examined should include at least glasses, cups, and spoons, if used. Select at least four of each at random, using one swab and swab container for each group of four or more utensils. When collecting samples, take a swab from the container and press it against the inside of the container to remove excess water, leaving the swab moist, but not wet. Then swab slowly and firmly three times over significant surfaces of four or more similar utensils, reversing the direction each time. Significant surfaces of glasses and cups consist of the upper half inch of inner and outer rim, and the entire inner and outer surfaces of the bowls of spoons and tines of forks. Swab completely across plates, each of two diameters at right angles, and around inner surface of bowls halfway between bottom and rim. After swabbing each utensil, return the swab to the container of dilution water, rotate the swab in the dilution water, and press out excess water before swabbing the next utensil. Replace swab in container of dilution water after completing the swabbing of all utensils in a group. Keep the dilution water samples iced while in transit to the laboratory and until samples are plated. Plate the samples preferably within four hours of swabbing; but where this cannot be done, samples must be properly refrigerated and analyzed within twenty-four hours. From the bacterial count of the solutions the average plate count per cup, glass, or spoon surface can be obtained. The average should be not over 100. Higher counts are presumed to be caused by inadequate cleaning and bactericidal treatment.

Rough tests are available that will demonstrate the presence of grease or film on utensil surfaces. If water will not run completely off a china or glass surface, the presence of some soiling material is indicated. If sugar is dusted over a dry surface and there is adherence, there is evidence of grease.

12-15. Storage and Protection of Food in Restaurants. From a preceding article it will be seen that infection of foods, followed by storage at room temperatures, results in food poisoning. Therefore, protection of foods against infection and proper storage after handling are important. Common practice in the past has been to require the storage of foods at temperatures less than 50°F. This may have been a reasonable requirement when ice was depended upon for refrigeration, but mechanical refrigeration permits storage at lower temperatures with the accompanying additional protection. The National Sanitation Clinic[8] recommends that the maximum air temperature be 40°F for storage of raw meat, raw poultry, eggs, milk, cheese, and butter, when the storage period is to be less than seven days. Foods which have been cooked should be cooled as quickly as possible through the danger zone of quick bacterial multiplication (98 to 60°F) and stored at 40°F or lower until served. The cooling can be done in the refrigerator, preferably in open shallow pans. This procedure applies to meats, poultry, sliced meats, sea foods, minced foods, sandwich fillings, egg salad mixtures, and similar foods that are not kept hot while being served.

Custards and custard-filled pastries are frequently involved in disease outbreaks and should be cooled to 40°F within an hour after preparation. They should not be taken from the refrigerator for display or sale for periods of longer than one hour. All such products exceeding twenty-four hours in age should be destroyed. An exception is made with hot custards which must be maintained and served at temperatures exceeding 150°F.

The Sanitation Clinic discussed the temperature for hot-food service units and, in the absence of research in the matter, recommended that the minimum holding temperature should be 150°F. If the hot foods cannot be kept at this temperature for any reason, they should be cooled rapidly to 40°F or less and then brought up to 150°F before re-serving. This applies particularly to foods of animal origin and those containing protein. Leafy vegetables and foods of very low protein content may be held for periods not exceeding two hours at room temperatures (60 to 90°F).

Unwrapped or unenclosed food and drink on display should be protected by glass or otherwise from public handling, sneezing, and other contamination. Hand holes of approved type may be placed for self-service in counter fronts.

Other requirements include elimination of food handlers who have colds or lung infections or who have pimples or other pus-containing lesions on their hands or arms and keeping to a minimum the handling of all foods that have been cooked or that are served raw. Butter and ice should not be touched by the bare hands. Safeguard the tasting of samples of food in the kitchen by requiring that it be done from special dishes, one for each person, with spoons or other articles that are cleaned and sanitized after use.

12-16. Inspection of Food-handling Establishments. Satisfactory sanitary conditions in establishments where food is processed, prepared, and served are obtained only if there is an efficient inspecting force operating under an adequate city ordinance, or other legal authority, which can, when necessary, be successfully enforced through the courts. Court action is uncertain as to outcome and should be avoided by using more constructive measures, such as the assistance and advice of inspectors who are thoroughly acquainted with the principles of sanitation and their applications to food handling.

The success of the Milk Ordinance and Code, which grades dairies and milk plants, has led the U.S. Public Health Service to prepare an ordinance that grades restaurants, the term being defined to include cafeterias, taverns, sandwich stands, soda fountains, etc., and also kitchens in which food and drink are prepared for sale elsewhere to the public[9]. While the ordinance is so worded that grading is optional, it is probable that under usual circumstances the grading feature should be included in the ordinance as it is adopted by the city. A code also accompanies the ordinance and, unless there are legal difficulties, the code may be mentioned in the ordinance as providing an interpretation of its features. A permit is required before a restaurant can open for business, and it may be suspended or revoked for violation of the ordinance.

The grades defined are A, B, and C. If the restaurants in the city are already in good condition, only A grade establishments may be permitted to operate; otherwise A and B may be permitted. A restaurant that is degraded to a lower grade than the ordinance allows may be permitted to operate during a period not exceeding 30 days. For example, a restaurant may be degraded to C and, if it does not make improvements during this period to regain Grade A or B, the health officer may revoke the permit, and the restaurant will be required to go out of business. Grades must always be displayed in a conspicuous place. This also applies to temporary grades resulting from degrading.

A Grade A restaurant, in addition to maintaining general cleanliness, complies with the following requirements. Floors of rooms in which food or drink is stored, prepared, or served must be of concrete, terrazzo, tile, etc.; of wood covered with linoleum; or of tight wood. Walls and ceilings must be light-colored, washable, and, if near sinks or dishwashing vats or machines, must be impervious. Doors and windows must be flyproof, with the doors self-closing. Fans may be used at doors which are otherwise unprotected to prevent entrance of flies. Lighting must be such that there is an illumination of at least 10 foot-candles 30 inches from the floor in all working rooms, but not in the dining room. Storage rooms require only 4 foot-candles. Ventilation must be effective enough to prevent disagreeable odors and condensation. This may require installation of stove hoods and exhaust fans. Adequate toilet facilities must be furnished. The toilet room must have self-closing doors and must not open directly into a room where food, drink, or utensils are handled or stored. A booth open at the top will not qualify as a toilet room. The toilet room must be properly lighted, ventilated, and have signs directing employees to wash their hands before returning to work. The water supply must be safe, adequate in quantity, and accessible where needed. Adequate hand-washing facilities, including warm water, soap, and sanitary towels, must be provided for employees.

Utensils must be free from cracks, noncorrosive, and easy to clean. Utensils containing or plated with cadmium or lead must not be used, though solder containing lead may be used for jointing.[1] Display cases, windows, counters, and shelves must be easy to clean and kept in good repair. Utensils and dishes must be washed and given bactericidal treatment by one of the methods described in the preceding article. Utensils must be stored where they are protected from flies, splash, dust, and other contamination. They should not be handled by the surfaces that come in contact with food. Paper cups, straws, and other single-service containers must be purchased in sanitary cartons and stored therein in a clean dry place until used. Laundered towels and other cloths must be stored in a clean place until used. Spoons, dippers, etc., used to dispense frozen desserts, when not in use, must be kept in water maintained at 170°F, or in clean running water. Garbage must be stored in impervious containers which have tight-fitting lids and which are emptied as frequently as necessary. They must be washed when emptied. Sewage must discharge through a plumbing system complying with the local plumbing code and emptying into a public sewer. If there is no sewer, the method of disposal must be approved by the state health officials. Perishable food and drink must be kept at temperatures below 50°F until consumed. This also applies to cream-filled pastries.[2] The ice used should be from a source approved by the health officer. Only safe

[1] There have been outbreaks of sickness caused by ingestion of acid foods or drinks which have been in contact with lead or cadmium.

[2] Some authorities consider that storage should be at 40°F or less (see Art. 12-15).

water may be used to wash ice. Refrigerator drains must discharge into an open sink or drain that is properly trapped so that no backflow of sewage into the refrigerators is possible.

The food sold must be wholesome, free from spoilage, and protected from dust, flies, vermin, droplet infection, and overhead leakage at all times. This means that unwrapped foods on display must be protected by glass or otherwise, although approved hand holes for self-service are permitted. Serving of ice and sliced butter must not be done by direct contact with fingers or hands. Bottled milk and other beverages must not be submerged in water for cooling. Food and drink must not be stored in basements or cellars subject to flooding by sewage or water. Milk, fluid-milk products, and frozen desserts must come only from sources approved by the health officer. Milk and fluid-milk products must be served in the original containers or from a bulk container with an approved dispensing device which conforms to the previously mentioned requirements for utensils and which has no surfaces that may come into contact with the milk or that may be accessible to droplet infection, manual contact, dust, or flies, except at the orifice. All parts of the dispensing device that come into contact with milk must be cleaned and given a bactericidal treatment at the milk plant. It must be filled and sealed at the plant so that none of its contents can be withdrawn, except through the dispenser, and no substance can be introduced. The dispenser must also mix milk and cream thoroughly, if this is necessary. The last two requirements may not be practical for small establishments, nor will the requirement of service in the original containers apply to cream for coffee or cereals. For this service it is permitted to dispense from the original bottle, a dispenser, or urn, provided that other requirements covering dispensing devices are satisfied. All oysters, clams, and mussels must come from sources approved by the state health department, provided that if the source is outside the state the shipper's name appears on the current approved list of the U.S. Public Health Service. Shucked shellfish are to be kept in the original containers until used. Employees must wear clean outer garments and keep their hands clean while handling food, drink, utensils, or equipment. Employees may not spit or use tobacco in a room where food is prepared. None of the operations connected with a restaurant may be conducted in a room used for living or sleeping quarters. Adequate lockers must be provided for employees' clothing, while soiled linens, coats, and aprons must be kept in containers provided for this purpose. No silver-cleaning or -polishing agent used may contain cyanide.

The requirements for Grade B restaurants, while not compromising on cleanliness, do not require high-quality floors, walls, or ceilings; screened windows, doors, or fly-repelling fans; elaborate lighting, including the 10 foot-candles of illumination standard; elaborate ventilation; lockers for employees, separate receptacles for soiled linen, or use of separate rooms for living quarters. All the other requirements for Grade A restaurants must be satisfied. Grade C restaurants are those which cannot conform to the requirements of Grade B.

Itinerant restaurants, mobile restaurants, and industrial catering operations are sometimes overlooked by the health department. The health officer may, if he sees fit, exempt this type of restaurant from the requirement of securing a permit, and the restaurant is not graded. It should not be allowed to operate, however, unless it complies with the following requirements: The surroundings must be clean. Food, drink, and utensils must be protected from contamination. The food and drink sold must be clean, wholesome, and free from adulteration. An adequate supply of safe water must be available for drinking and cleaning of utensils. All multiuse utensils must, after each use, be thoroughly washed in hot water and a satisfactory detergent, rinsed with clean water, and stored so as to be protected from contamination. Toilet and hand-washing facilities must be readily accessible to employees. Dishwater must be disposed of without nuisance. Requirements as to ice, refrigeration, garbage and refuse, and communicable disease among the employees are practically the same as for permanent restaurants.

Restaurant owners, or managers, or the employee concerned must notify the health officer immediately if he or any employee contracts any communicable disease, or has a fever, a skin eruption, or a cough lasting more than three weeks. The employee must notify the owner or manager of any such condition, and both are held jointly and severally responsible if they violate this requirement. A placard containing this section of the ordinance must be posted in all toilet rooms. When suspicion arises as to the possibility of transmission of disease from any restaurant employee, the health officer is authorized to apply any or all of the following measures: immediate exclusion of the employee from working at all restaurants; closing of the restaurant until no further danger of a disease outbreak exists; adequate medical examinations of all the restaurant employees, including such laboratory examination as may be indicated.

The inspector who checks the restaurants is supplied with grading sheets which list the requirements as separate items. He uses a sheet for each establishment and checks those items that he finds being violated. The grade of the restaurant is so determined. The use of inspection sheets for this type of work is recommended whether the standard ordinance is used or not, since it is less likely that the inspector will overlook items.

The Standard Ordinance requires that inspections be made at least once every six months. It is highly desirable, however, that inspections be made every two months, although this may be unnecessary for such establishments as stores, bakeries, markets, and candy factories, for which twice a year may suffice.

While the Standard Ordinance is recommended as practical and enforceable, many cities operate under ordinances of other types. A popular one is that which lists items and gives a numerical weight to each, presumably based upon its public health significance. This gives a score, usually with 100 as perfect, and the score is posted in the establishment, together with the inspection sheet. While this procedure has the advantage of requiring consideration on the part of the inspector of all significant sanitary items, there is a tendency in practice for inspectors to give a somewhat uniform score to the great majority of restaurants. On the other hand, an attempt at evaluation of all items results in small differences in the scores. From a practical standpoint, it cannot be said that a restaurant which has a score of 92 is a safer place for its customers than is one with a score of 91. The public, however, cannot be expected to realize this. The grading system of the Standard Ordinance eliminates these small and insignificant differences.

The above discussion has been applicable to city health departments operating under city ordinances. In rural areas and unincorporated villages the problem is a smaller one, since there are fewer public food-handling establishments. Some control should be applied, however, and a county health department may have this as its responsibility. It may operate to enforce state food laws, although these are rather general in nature. Or it may adopt a voluntary grading system patterned upon the items of the Standard Ordinance. All restaurants that comply with the requirements are permitted to display a Grade A placard which is granted by the health department. Publicity may be used to make the public cognizant of the significance of the placard.

12-17. Field Tests at Food-handling Plants. It may be considered advisable to provide the inspector with a foot-candle meter to check illumination in kitchens. He should be equipped with a thermometer and an orthotolidine testing set to determine temperature and available chlorine in wash and rinse waters. An alternative is to use starch-iodide papers for chlorine determinations. They can be purchased and are convenient but are not very accurate. Some cities have made considerable progress in field testing. For example, the City Health Department of Baltimore has devised and provided its inspectors with a small kit[10] for making field tests. Simple procedures have been developed for the following tests: detection of spoilage of shucked oysters and crab meat, cyanide in metal polish, cadmium from utensils plated by this metal, available chlorine in disinfectant solutions, fluoride-containing insect powders that have not been colored blue as required by Maryland regulations, sulfites in meat products, and arsenic spray residues by food utensil swabbing. If needed, equipment may be added for making the phosphatase test, alkalinity test of bottling plant wash waters, and foam test for renovated butter and oleomargarine. The field tests are not used as a basis for prosecution but to assist the inspectors in obtaining conformity to regulations and information that will lead to submitting of samples to the bureau of laboratories for confirmatory analyses.

12-18. Instruction of Food Handlers. Food-service personnel are necessarily recruited from a group that has little or no knowledge of sanitation and methods of disease transmission. In the past this has seemed an insuperable obstacle to the development of health knowledge among these workers. Of late some cities have conducted lectures and classes for food handlers using motion pictures, slides, and exhibits, with considerable success. Restaurant owners are requested to allow their employees the necessary time off for attendance, but their cooperation is entirely voluntary.

The National Sanitation Clinic[8] recommends a course of five lessons, each of two hours, to be held two or three times a week. The course should cover the following main topics: (1) objectives of the course; responsibility of food handler; how the food handler may help himself; (2) how to stay well; (3) flies, roaches, and rats and how they spread disease; garbage and refuse control; (4) foods, their sources, handling, and protection; food poisoning; (5) cleaning and sanitization; handling and storage of equipment; paper service; general housekeeping; (6) employee cleanliness; good working habits.

It has been suggested that additional specialized courses be given to waitresses, dishwashing-machine operators, pasteurization plant operators, and to bakers and other specialized food-handling workers. The Instructor's Guide: Sanitary Food Service, *U.S. Public Health Service Publication 90*, presents a comprehensive outline for instructors in conducting training classes for food-service personnel. The Baking Industry Standards Committee has also developed some helpful guides.

Where food-handler training programs have been given, the benefits have been striking in improved sanitation, better health of workers, decreased labor turnover, improved morale among workers, increased efficiency in operation and maintenance of establishments, reduced wastage and spoilage of foods, and reduced likelihood of damage claims.

Of course, the organization and administration of such training is a large undertaking, not only because of the large number of food handlers but also because of the turnover among the workers. It should, however, bring about improvements in a field which has lagged behind in the general progress of public health.

MEAT INSPECTION

12-19. Meat requires inspection more than any other food except milk. This is due to several causes: the rapidity with which meat decomposes; the possibility of the animal's being diseased, particularly with some disorder transmissible to man; and the ease with which the meat may become infected. Meat inspection is performed by the Bureau of Animal Industry of the U.S. Department of Agriculture and also by inspectors of many of the cities. That this inspection is necessary is indicated by figures given by the Bureau of Animal Industry [11]. In nearly 2 per cent of the carcasses inspected some disease or condition was found which necessitated condemnation of all or a part of the meat. The Bureau has jurisdiction only over meat that is shipped from state to state or for export. Animals slaughtered under other conditions receive either no inspection or only that of local health officials.

When it is considered that most of the inspections mentioned above were made at stock centers where range cattle, comparatively free from disease, were handled, it is apparent that the greatest need for meat inspection is in the smaller cities where killing of local stock is carried on. It has been found that in some sections 10 per cent of the dairy cattle are infected with tuberculosis, and most of these finally reach the small slaughter pen. The poorer grade of animals or those which may be suspected of disease are not taken to slaughterhouses where there is inspection, if unregulated killing is done. Furthermore, the uninspected slaughter pen of the country or small town is usually in a most deplorable sanitary condition. It is a place of foul odors and millions of flies, a happy hunting ground for rats and buzzards. The offal is rarely handled properly but left to decompose in heaps or sometimes thrown into neighboring streams.

12-20. Inspections. Meat inspection requires the services of a competent veterinarian capable of recognizing pathological conditions. The ante-mortem examination is made whenever possible and is for the purpose of detecting symptoms of disease. Suspicious animals are slaughtered separately. The post-mortem examination is the most important and is applied first to certain glands, heart, and tongue, and if these are found suspicious the abdominal viscera, lymph glands, and sex glands are examined. There are many diseases and conditions for which meat is rejected, of which the following are most common: tuberculosis, anthrax, hog cholera, tapeworm cysts, septic conditions, pneumonia, bruises, and injuries. In many cases only parts of the carcasses are condemned. Tuberculosis of cattle and hogs in the earlier stages is usually confined to certain glands. If there is no evidence that the tubercle bacilli have invaded the bloodstream, only the infected portions are rejected. Only the tissues containing the tapeworm cysts are condemned unless they are very widely distributed and numerous. Knives which have been used to cut animals found to be infected must be disinfected in hot water at 170 to 200°F before being used again. Meat which is passed is stamped at all primal wholesale cuts, at 13 places on each half of beef.

It is frequently necessary for one inspector to cover several abattoirs, and it is impossible for him to make ante-mortem inspections. Under these circumstances the viscera are removed from the carcasses, tagged, and held until his arrival. This is not recommended because of the possibility of switching organs and carcasses.

12-21. Abattoirs. The problem of getting good meat other than that which is Federal-inspected is greatly simplified by having a municipal abattoir at which all killing must be done. This may be required through

FIG. 12-3. Municipal abattoir, Austin, Tex.

the passage of an ordinance which provides that all animals be slaughtered and dressed at the abattoir or under equally good conditions. The city meat inspector may be placed in charge of the abattoir. This allows ante-mortem and post-mortem examination of all animals and, with proper supervision of the abattoir, ensures sanitary handling of the meat, by-products, and offal.

It is advisable that the abattoir be municipally owned and operated. If this arrangement cannot be made, it is sometimes possible to organize a stock company of the local butchers for the purpose of building and operating the plant. In either case all animals to be slaughtered are brought to the abattoir, and a fee is charged per animal handled. Cold-storage space should be required. In addition to the possibility of effective meat inspection and better sanitation, the municipal abattoir allows the use of various products which are commonly wasted at the small slaughterhouse. These include the intestines, which are cleaned and

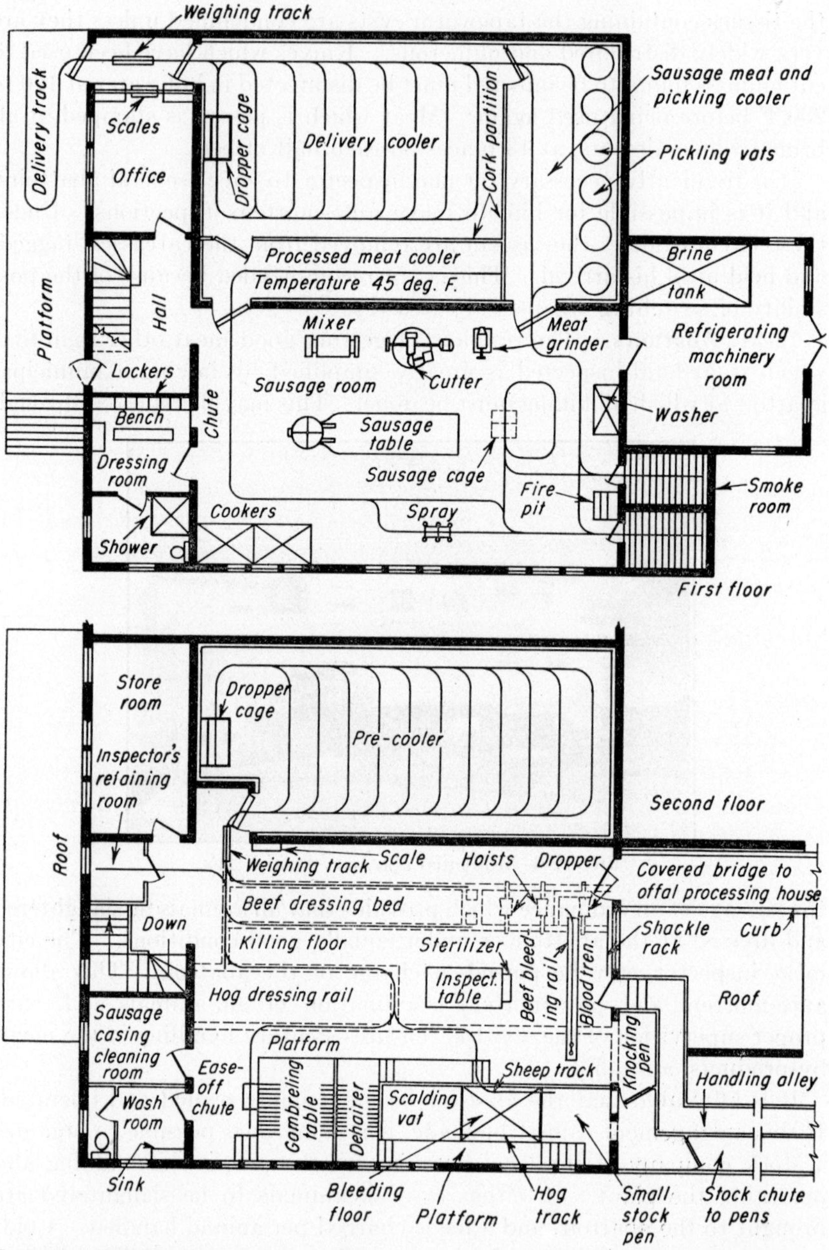

FIG. 12-4. First- and second-floor plans of a municipal abattoir as recommended by the Texas State Department of Health. Offal-processing facilities are not shown. A more detailed plan will be found in the U.S. Department of Agriculture publication "Information for Applicants for Federal Meat Inspection and Owners and Operators of Official Establishments," rev., May, 1955.

used as sausage casings, and the blood and scraps, which are treated to extract grease and tallow and the remainder dried and pulverized for fertilizer or animal feed. A city of 8,000 population or more can support a municipal abattoir.

In 1909 the city of Paris, Tex., erected a municipal abattoir to remedy existing unsatisfactory slaughtering conditions. Several other cities, including Austin, Tex. (1955 population, 150,000), have erected abattoirs. The scraps and offal from the plant are rendered, and the sale of the by-products helps to take care of the operating expenses.

12-22. Markets. The inspection of meat markets has much in common with the inspection of other food establishments as discussed in Art. 12-16. The meats should not be kept on open counters exposed to flies, dust, and handling by customers. Special attention must be given to the cleanliness of the counters, refrigerators, meat blocks, iron hooks, meat- and sausage-grinding machines, the knives and their handles. If an ordinance requires that all meat be inspected, search should be made for the official marks of approval on all the meat cuts in stock and also on the meat products.

POULTRY INSPECTION AND SANITATION

12-23. At the turn of the half-century, approximately one-fourth of the poultry processed in the United States was produced in plants voluntarily operating under Federal inspection and sanitary regulations, while quite a number of states and municipalities provided little or no supervision.

With the introduction of new methods in processing and merchandising, the consumption of poultry and poultry products has greatly increased in recent years. Poultry and poultry products are responsible for a number of food-borne illnesses. Several outbreaks of psittacosis in Texas, for example, were investigated by J. V. Irons and attributed to this cause. The increasing interest in poultry sanitation recently exhibited by states and municipalities, and their requests, prompted the Public Health Service, in cooperation with the Public Health Poultry Liaison Committee, to develop a poultry ordinance. It follows the pattern set by the Milk Ordinance and Code, and if it is adopted as readily by cities, it will bring about uniformity of programs and create greater confidence in the safety of the product by the consuming public.

In addition to requiring that all operations, from the live-bird pens to the retail establishments, including processing, packaging, storage, and transportation, be in accordance with good sanitation practice, the Ordinance provides for ante-mortem and post-mortem inspection. Some items covered by the Ordinance are:

1. A post-mortem inspection of each carcass shall be performed by an inspector at the time of evisceration. . . .

2. No viscera or any part [of it] shall be removed from any dressed poultry except at the time of evisceration and post-mortem inspection.

3. Each carcass shall be opened so as to expose the organs and the body cavity for proper examination by the inspector and, if passed, shall be prepared immediately after inspection as eviscerated poultry.

4. Poultry and poultry products in which there is no evidence of disease or other condition rendering such poultry or poultry products unfit for use as human food, and which comply with all applicable provisions of this Ordinance, shall be passed [and labeled] . . . .

12-24. Operating Procedures. Dead birds must be removed from coops and batteries. Feed must be withheld from live poultry for the time necessary to prevent material from the crops from contaminating poultry carcasses during evisceration. If dressed carcasses are vented (*i.e.*, fecal contents are expelled from the cloaca by pressure on the posterior portion of the abdomen), the venting must be performed under flow or spray of water in such a manner that the fecal material is washed away without contaminating the carcass. Cropping, if conducted, must be accomplished by forcing the crop contents out through the esophagus and mouth.

Poultry and poultry products must be chilled or frozen immediately after processing and must be maintained in a completely frozen state. The defrosting and refreezing of poultry and poultry products are prohibited.

This ordinance has much to commend it, and ample time should be allowed for processors to comply with the requirements before enforcement is started.

SHELLFISH SANITATION

12-25. Raw oysters produced or handled under insanitary conditions may cause typhoid fever and other intestinal diseases. Oysters, clams, and mussels become infected from the water in which they are grown or during the process of handling, shucking, packing, or shipping. The menace of contaminated oysters is increasing with increased pollution of coastal waters, particularly of the bays and estuaries in which the oyster beds are located. As the oyster requires only a moderately saline water, the oyster-producing areas are necessarily near the mouths of rivers. Since many cities are located near river mouths and discharge their sewage untreated, the danger is apparent.

The discussion given here also applies to clams and mussels, which are potentially as dangerous as oysters. Mussels and clams of the entire

West Coast and of eastern Canada are dangerous in another way, as indicated in Arts. 12-1 and 12-35.

12-26. Oysters and Water Pollution. A healthy oyster, under optimum conditions, pumps as much as 4 liters of water an hour. From the water it extracts its food, and from the water coliforms and possibly typhoid, dysentery, and other pathogenic organisms may also be accumulated, either in its alimentary canal or in the shell liquor. If polluted oysters are placed in clean water, the passage of the water through them cleans them.

Perhaps the most important factor in the production of safe oysters is the control of sanitary conditions in the growing and bedding areas. This, aside from reducing the actual pollution by remedial measures, requires location of beds where the pollution hazard is least. To establish safe areas requires exhaustive studies of the sources and amounts of pollution entering rivers above tide water and the approximate dilution. The amount of pollution entering within the tidal area should also be studied and the dilution obtained so far as possible. Tidal flow and currents must also be traced in relation to the beds. Effect of bottom topography and winds must also be learned. By cross-sectioning the areas which are being investigated and making determinations of the coliform bacterial contents of surface and bottom water under various conditions, the effects of dilution can be studied. These data should make it possible to determine the remedial measures needed and also the possible safety of the bed as located. This information is in the nature of a sanitary survey and requires competent sanitary engineering knowledge and judgment for proper interpretation.

12-27. Certification. The certification of oysters, mussels, and all varieties of clams is a cooperative arrangement. Responsibility for formulating and enforcing control measures and the issuing of certificates to the shellfish shippers rests upon the health, agricultural, or conservation departments of the states in which the oysters are produced and from which they are shipped to other states. The U.S. Public Health Service specifies the minimum requirements for its approval of state certification. It also inspects and rates a representative number of shucking and packing plants annually in the state, cooperates with the states in making sanitary and bacteriological surveys, or makes such surveys independently but in agreement with the states. The entire state procedure and machinery for sanitary control of shellfish are examined and rated annually by the U.S. Public Health Service. It also publishes and keeps current a list of interstate shippers of shellfish certified by the producing states for the information of health officers and other interested persons in the consuming states.

Shipments of shucked shellfish and shell stock must be properly tagged, with the tags showing the name and address of the consignee, name and address of the shipper, name of the state of origin, the certificate number of the shipper, and the date of shucking or date of dredging, in the case of shell stock.

The health authorities of the states, cities, and countries where the shellfish are consumed should check the sources of all shellfish consumed in areas under their jurisdiction. Sanitarians should be furnished with the lists of approved shippers and, on their visits to restaurants, should make certain that shellfish served have been received from certified shippers. Dealers should be required to keep complete records of shipments so that information will be available in case of epidemics.

Certificates are granted after satisfaction of the sanitary requirements discussed in the following articles.

12-28. Classification of Waters. Waters in which shellfish are grown are classified in three categories. *Approved waters* are those from which shellfish may be taken without serious question as to their safety because of distance from sources of pollution, dilution, and the time factor. The median bacteriological content of these waters, as indicated by samples taken at points most likely to be exposed to fecal contamination, should not show presence of the coliform group in excess of 70 per 100 milliliters of water expressed in terms of the most probable number. Bacterial reexaminations of the area must be made whenever sanitary surveys (made not less than every two years) indicate a change in conditions. *Moderately polluted or restricted waters* are those which are questionable, and a decision as to whether an area in this class may be used for the taking of shellfish should be based, in each instance, upon the findings of a sanitary survey and bacteriological examinations of the water. The bacteriological tests must indicate that the median bacteriological content of the water, expressed in terms of the coliform organisms, must be between 70 and 700 per 100 milliliters, expressed in terms of the most probable number. Partial sanitary resurveys of such areas are required yearly, and complete surveys are made whenever deemed necessary. The taking of oysters from such areas is permitted only when the coliform content of the oysters does not exceed 20 per 100 milliliters, expressed as the most probable number. *Grossly polluted waters* are those from which shellfish for market purposes must not be taken. They include areas subject to gross pollution by direct discharge of sewage; areas exposed more or less continuously to even slight direct contamination with human fecal discharges from near-by sources; areas which, though usually of good quality, are exposed to occasional direct and immediate contamination with human discharges; or areas where bacteriological examinations indicate greater pollution than permissible for the other two areas.

12-29. Gathering and Relaying. No shellfish may be removed from beds for immediate shipment to market unless they have been taken from approved waters. Permission may be granted by the state health department having jurisdiction for the removal of shellfish from moderately polluted waters to approved waters under the following conditions: written permits for such removals, which are granted only to responsible persons or firms and which may be revoked for violations of regulations; shellfish removed from grossly polluted areas during the shellfish-marketing season must not be marketed from the approved areas without written permission from the state agency; removal and re-laying must be under the supervision of the state; shellfish removed from moderately polluted waters for re-laying must remain in a designated area of approved waters for at least fourteen days when the water in this area has a temperature above 50°F, and when the water is below 50°F shellfish must not be re-laid. The above regulations, it should be noted, permit removal from polluted to approved areas when the shellfish can be expected to cleanse themselves in a reasonable time.

Boats used in the taking of shellfish must be kept in such a state of cleanliness and repair that shellfish are not subject to contamination from bilge water, leakage, or other sources. Decks, holds, bins, etc., used for the storage of shellfish must not be washed with polluted water. Reasonable precautions must be taken while the boats are over the shellfish grounds to prevent pollution through the discharge of human wastes. Tight containers for human wastes are required for all boats that are away from shore more than three hours, and the wastes must be disposed of in such a manner that they do not endanger the shellfish. While in storage, the shellfish must be protected against contamination at all times.

12-30. Bacteriological Standards. Methods of sampling and testing shellfish are to be found in a report of the American Public Health Association[13]. When a series of tests indicates a most probable number of coliforms of 230 or more per 100 milliliters in oyster shell stock sampled at the growing areas or in shucked oysters at the point of shucking, it should be interpreted as an indication of unfavorable conditions or practices in the handling or production, and investigations leading to improvement are necessary. It is permitted, however, that occasional samples with a most probable number of 2,400 coliforms per 100 milliliters may be tolerated. If this occurs in more than two consecutive samples, corrective measures should be taken.

No fixed standards are available for shellfish other than oysters, and the chief reliance for their good quality must rest upon the quality of the water in which they are grown. If, however, a most probable number of 2,400 coliforms per 100 milliliters or more occurs in a series of samples taken at the producing area or shucking point, investigations of the producing or handling conditions are necessary.

12-31. Processing Shellfish. *Conditioning* is the process which permits shellfish to free themselves from retained sand, grit, or silt by storing them in tanks of water. It is applied only to shellfish from approved beds. The water used, after treatment, should be equal to drinking water bacteriologically. It must be of a salinity at least equal[1] to that in which the shellfish were grown. The dissolved oxygen content of the water should be not less than 30 per cent of saturation. Fill-and-draw tanks must be emptied every twenty-four hours and refilled, while continuous-flow tanks must receive water at a rate that replaces the water every twenty-four hours. The tank must be water-tight, have its edges at least 1 foot above the high-water level of any adjacent body of water, and not receive any surface drainage. Employees must be experienced and skilled at their work, and reports of operations must be sent monthly to the state control agency.

Cleansing is practiced to improve the bacteriological condition of oysters taken from clean or moderately polluted areas. The requirements and processing are the same as for conditioning except as follows: only clean-washed live shellfish, having a coliform content of less than 24,000 per 100 milliliters as most probable number are submitted to the process; the water temperature must be over 50°F; the shellfish are retained at least twenty-four hours; the results of tests for each batch of oysters cleansed give most probable numbers for coliforms of not more than 230 per 100 milliliters, and for each batch of soft clams the corresponding requirement is less than 2,400 per 100 milliliters; no treated shellfish should be released for consumption without the authority of a plant operator who is approved or licensed by the state agency; the plant operator must be experienced in his work, possess knowledge of water treatment, and be approved by the state authorities.

Floating consists of keeping market-size shellfish on structures of wood or other materials supported by pontoons or piling in shallow water near shore until they are sold. *Wet storage* is storage in water of shellfish intended to be marketed within three months, whether the storage is in natural bodies of water or in tanks. These processes must be surrounded with precautions because waters "near shore" are especially liable to contamination by sewage. Written approval is required from the state authority, and this approval is accompanied by a sketch showing the locations of floats or tanks, potential pollutional hazards, and the measures taken for protection.

12-32. Shucking and Packing Plants. The plants in which oysters are shucked and packed for shipping must conform to the general require-

[1] Storing oysters in water of a salinity lower than that to which they are accustomed sets up osmotic action which causes them to swell or "bloat."

ments for food-handling plants, including cleaning and sanitizing of utensils, as already discussed. Some regulations meriting special attention are that storage bins or rooms used for shell stock must have adequate drainage; utensils must be free from seams or have them soldered flush; "nesting" of empty pails during the shucking season is not permitted; shellfish must be cooled to 50°F or below within two hours after shucking; shucking and packing should be done in separate rooms; ice must not be allowed to come in contact with the shucked stock. In the plants handling only shell stock, unoccupied bins, or portions of bins must be washed at the end of the day's operations with water of approved quality. It is recommended that flushing with chlorine solution be done after the washing. Refrigeration rooms or iceboxes must be washed out weekly, or oftener if necessary.

12-33. Shipping. Oysters, clams, or mussels in the shell must be packed in clean barrels or sacks and shipped under such temperature conditions as will keep them alive. Shucked stock must be stored and shipped under such temperature conditions as will prevent spoilage. Outside containers for ice are required. It is desirable that the shucked stock be kept at 50°F or below until it reaches the consumer but that it not be allowed to freeze except where approved freezing processes are applied. Only approved containers that can be sealed to prevent tampering and that are marked with the shipper's certificate number may be used. Shipments of both shell and shucked stock must be tagged with the standard tags (see Art. 12-27).

12-34. Effect of Cooking. While consumption of raw shellfish is far more dangerous from the standpoint of disease incidence, cooking does not always make contaminated shellfish safe. Oyster stews, for example, are sometimes made by bringing the milk to a boil, pouring in the cold oysters, and serving immediately. This is not effective in killing disease organisms. The most satisfactory method is to boil the oysters in their own juice separately, heat the milk separately, and then combine. Frying for two minutes kills most pathogenic organisms, but some may survive for eight minutes. Subjecting shucked oysters to live steam for five to ten minutes and shell oysters for ten to fifteen minutes destroys typhoid organisms. The principal safeguard against contracting disease from shellfish, it will be noted, is control at the source by competent sanitary authorities.

12-35. Poisoning Caused by Shellfish. On the West Coast mussels and Alaska clams may be toxic at certain times. Also clams and mussels in some areas of the Canadian east coast may be toxic during the colder months. In both the Pacific and the Atlantic, the trouble is caused by a dinoflagellate, a plankton organism on which the shellfish feed. They are likely to be abundant in dangerous numbers at times in certain areas, and they are more likely to be abundant in areas near the open sea. Canadian control measures include the restriction of collection in certain areas at certain times. No commercial fishing is permitted at all in some areas. All commercial fishing is under control, and the output of shucking and canning plants is sampled before it may be sold.

BIBLIOGRAPHY

1. "Federal Food, Drug, and Cosmetic Act and General Regulations for Its Enforcement," U.S. Food, Drug, and Cosmetic Series, no. 1, rev. 4, June, 1953.
2. Meyer, Karl F.: Food Poisoning, *New Engl. J. Med.*, vol. 249, nos. 5, 9, 12, pp. 765–773, 804–812, 843–852, 1953.
3. Daver, C. C., and Granville Sylvester: 1953 Summary of Disease Outbreaks, *Public Health Repts.*, vol. 69, no. 6, p. 542, 1954.
4. Tanner, F. W.: Paper and Paper Board in the Food Industry, *Am. J. Public Health*, vol. 38, no. 12, December, 1948.
5. "Spray-type Dishwashing Machines," University of Michigan, School of Public Health, National Sanitation Foundation, Ann Arbor, Mich.
6. Mallmann, W. L., L. Zaikowski, D. Kahler, and P. DeKoning: "A Study of Mechanical Dishwashing," University of Michigan, School of Public Health, National Sanitation Foundation, Ann Arbor, Mich.
7. "Standard Methods for the Examination of Dairy Products," 10th ed., American Public Health Association, New York.
8. "The First National Sanitation Clinic," University of Michigan, School of Public Health, National Sanitation Foundation, Ann Arbor, Mich.
9. *Am. Public Health Assoc. Year Book* 1936–1937.
10. Korff, F. A., and E. Kaplan: Field Equipment for Food Inspectors, *Am. J. Public Health*, vol. 32, no. 10, October, 1942.
11. Melvin, A. D.: State and Municipal Meat Inspection and Municipal Slaughter Houses, *U.S. Bur. Animal Ind. Circ.* 185.
12. "Poultry Ordinance," U.S. Public Health Service, 1956.
13. "Recommended Method of Procedure for Bacteriological Examination of Shellfish and Shellfish Waters," American Public Health Association, New York.
14. "Thirteenth Year Book of the American Public Health Association, 1947–48," pt. II, *Am. J. Public Health*, vol. 38, May, 1948.
15. Bach, G. M.: "Food Poisoning," University of Chicago Press, Chicago.
16. Tolerances for Pesticide Chemicals, *Federal Register*, vol. 19, no. 204.
17. "Instructor's Guide: Sanitary Food Service," *Public Health Service Publ.* 90, U.S. Dept. of Health, Education, and Welfare.
18. Chandler, A. C.: "Introduction to Human Parasitology," John Wiley & Sons, Inc., New York.
19. Thom, C., and A. C. Hunter: "Hygienic Fundamentals of Food Handling," The Williams & Wilkins Company, Baltimore.
20. Tanner, F. W.: "Food-borne Infections and Intoxications," Garrard Press, Champaign, Ill.
21. Shrader, J. H.: "Food Control," John Wiley & Sons, Inc., New York.
22. "Canned Food Reference Manual," American Can Company, New York.
23. Manual of Recommended Practice for Sanitary Control of the Shellfish Industry, *U.S. Public Health Bull.* 295, 1946.
24. Rosenau, M. J.: "Preventive Medicine and Hygiene," 7th ed., by Kenneth F. Maxcy, Appleton-Century-Crofts, Inc., New York, 1951.

CHAPTER 13

VENTILATION AND AIR CONDITIONING

13-1. Ventilation is defined as the process of supplying or removing air to or from any space by natural or mechanical means. Such air may or may not be conditioned. Complete air conditioning is the control of all those factors affecting both physical and chemical conditions of the atmosphere within any structure. These factors include temperature, humidity, motion (air movement), distribution, dust, odors, toxic gases, and bacteria, most of which affect in greater or less degree human health or comfort.

Successful ventilation and air conditioning require the services of an engineer who is a specialist in the subject, or money may be wasted. The basic principles that should be understood by the sanitary engineer and sanitarian are discussed here.

13-2. Composition of the Earth's Atmosphere. The air envelope overlying the earth's surface is a composition of various elements, present in the following proportions by volume: nitrogen, 78.1 per cent; oxygen, 20.9 per cent; carbon dioxide, 0.03 per cent; argon, 0.9 per cent. The balance is made up of other inert gases and a varying proportion of water vapor. The nitrogen, argon, and other inert gases occur in practically the same proportions. The others vary somewhat, although not to any great extent. Other contaminants frequently or occasionally encountered are organic matter from human or animal bodies; smokes, fumes, mists, and gases produced by various industrial processes; and pollens from various plants, some of which cause hay fever or asthma.

13-3. Effects of Occupancy. There are five effects resulting from human occupancy of unventilated or poorly ventilated rooms: (1) the oxygen content is reduced; (2) the amount of carbon dioxide present is increased; (3) organic matter and odors are given off from the skin, clothing, and mouths of the occupants; (4) the temperature is raised by heat generated in the body processes; (5) the humidity is increased by the moisture in the breath and evaporation from the skin. All these effects are greatly increased if the vital processes are speeded up through physical exertion.

The consumption of oxygen in breathing, of course, results in a reduction of the amount in the atmosphere of a closed room and a proportional increase in the amount of carbon dioxide. In breathing, an adult contributes about 0.7 cubic foot of carbon dioxide per hour to the atmosphere. Children contribute somewhat less; the average in mixed groups can be taken at about 0.6 cubic foot per hour. The reduction of oxygen and the increase of carbon dioxide, except in tightly closed rooms and for long periods, are of no importance, probably requiring only a slightly increased rate of respiration. According to the *U.S. Bureau of Mines Circular* 33, 0.5 per cent of carbon dioxide, at the expense of oxygen, would require a slight increase of lung ventilation, while 10 per cent cannot be endured for more than a few minutes.

The early belief that carbon dioxide was poisonous led to ventilation codes calling for new fresh air per person per minute that would keep the carbon dioxide content to a low level. These requirements were as high as 30 cubic feet per person per minute. At present, however, the carbon dioxide content is not considered as a reliable index for new fresh air or for prevention of odors. The abandonment of this requirement has led to requirements nearer to 10 cubic feet of new fresh air per minute. Local codes, however, specify this factor of ventilation and air conditioning.

In nature the carbon dioxide produced by animals or otherwise in combustion is used by green plants which take up the carbon and release the oxygen.

13-4. Air Contaminants. These include carbon monoxide, a poison which results from incomplete combustion of fuel (Art. 13-23); smoke, also resulting from combustion of fuel (Art. 19-32); various mists, fumes, gases, and vapors which are produced in certain industrial processes and which are discussed in Chap. 17; dusts, which are produced in city streets and in nature but which also accompany industrial processes; pollens, which are released into the air by certain plants and which may cause hay fever or asthma (Art. 19-30); and bacteria, which may cause disease. Air conditioning may have to eliminate or prevent any or all of these impurities.

13-5. Bacteria in Air. It is supposed that bacteria are not suspended in the air alone but are carried by particles of dust, organic matter, or moisture. According to Winslow[6], street dust may contain 50 million bacteria per gram and indoor dust up to 5 million per gram. Of these, 1 in 1,000 of the street bacteria and 1 in 4,000 of the indoor bacteria are of the intestinal type. Except during high winds outdoors and dry sweeping indoors, little of the dust gets into the air, and consequently it is of little consequence. The number of bacteria in indoor air may vary from 1 to 1,000 per cubic foot. Infection of open wounds from air is possible, and infections of other sorts, particularly of respiratory diseases, may occur by means of bacteria attached to droplets discharged into the air during coughing, sneezing, and talking. They may be carried to other persons or to food by air currents, or they may settle and be incorporated in dust.

13-6. Organic Matter and Odors. The odors which can sometimes be detected in crowded or poorly ventilated rooms are due to perspiration mingled with organic compounds from skin and clothing, and also from decomposition taking place in mouths. They must be prevented by a sufficient addition of fresh air to keep down the concentration of organic matter, as indicated in a preceding article. These noticeable body odors were formerly supposed to be the cause of disease and were supposed to be generated in direful amounts wherever crowds were assembled. Years ago the term "crowd poison" was in common use, and delicate ladies were frequently known to faint from its effects. The idea that vitiation of the atmosphere by decomposing organic matter in general is responsible for disease has been definitely discredited. While no specific disease results even on long exposure to vitiated air and unpleasant odors, bad effects may result through causing nausea, loss of appetite, and perhaps aggravation of certain illnesses. In this connection, Prof. C.-E. A. Winslow, of the Yale School of Medicine, reports that the exposure of young guinea pigs to the odors from decomposing organic matter quite definitely retards their growth[6]. An exception must be made in the case of poisoning of air by carbon monoxide, the fumes of lead, and other poisonous substances which may have very serious results.

13-7. Heat Loss. Air conditioning is primarily a matter of removing excess heat generated by human bodies or otherwise and secondarily of removing dust, fumes, and odors. Heat is lost by conduction, convection, and radiation. By conduction, air in contact with the heat source becomes warmed. The greater the difference in temperature, the more rapidly does loss by conduction proceed. By convection, currents are set up, removing the warmed air and replacing it with cool air, and conduction continues. By radiation, heat is lost from the warm body to the cool body without warming the intervening air. With the human body there is also a loss of heat through evaporation of perspiration.

Loss of heat from the body will be rapid (1) when there are cold objects in the room—walls, for example—so that radiation is high; (2) when the air temperature is low and conduction loss is high; (3) when there is enough air movement to prevent a blanket of warm air from enveloping the body; (4) when the skin surface is moist and cooling by evaporation is in process; and (5) when the relative humidity of the air is low and evaporation is speeded up. In still air, radiation accounts for about 45 per cent of the total heat loss, convection for 30 per cent, and evaporation for 25 per cent. Evaporation losses consist of about 11 per cent from the lungs and 14 per cent from the skin. Evaporation from the lungs varies with relative humidity, while evaporation from the skin is apparently confined to periods of sweat production. All these considerations enter into air conditioning, which essentially is control of the temperature, air movement, and humidity of rooms so that occupants are comfortable.

13-8. Effective Temperature. Effective temperature is defined by the American Society of Heating and Air-conditioning Engineers as an arbitrary index of the degree of warmth or cold felt by the human body in response to the combined effects of temperature, humidity, and air movement. The numerical value of the effective temperature for any given air condition is fixed by the temperature of moisture-saturated air which, at a velocity of 15 to 25 feet per minute, or practically still air, induces a sensation of warmth or cold like that of the given condition. Thus any air condition has an effective temperature of 65° when it induces a sensation of warmth like that experienced in practically still air at 65°F and saturated with moisture. But the same degree of comfort is not always experienced all along the line of a constant effective temperature, for discomfort may be felt at excessively high and low relative humidities. It is also dependent upon the clothing worn and the method of heating the space. The most comfortable effective temperature in summer seems to be 71°F and in winter 66°F. Effective temperatures can be calculated from charts prepared by manufacturers of air-conditioning equipment.

13-9. The Katathermometer and Air Motion. The cooling power of air is highly important and mainly dependent upon its temperature and motion. The katathermometer is used to determine the cooling characteristics of the air of a room. There should, however, be no difference between the temperature of the air and of objects in the room. The apparatus consists of an alcohol thermometer with a bulb ⅝ inch in diameter and ½ inch long with a stem 8 inches long, reading from 100 to 95°F and graduated in tenths of a degree. To take readings the bulb is heated in water until the alcohol has risen into a reservoir above the 100°F mark. The bulb is carefully dried, and the time in seconds required for the liquid to fall from 100 to 95°F is recorded, preferably with a stop watch. The dry katathermometer loses its heat by radiation and convection. Hence with still air or with constant air velocities, the time of cooling is a function of the air temperature. Also if the dry-bulb temperature is known, the velocity of air movement can be deduced from the speed of cooling. Each katathermometer must be individually calibrated and have its own formula for use in determining the cooling effect of air or air velocities. Anemometers with rotating or deflecting vanes are used for rough measurements of air motion. New thermoanemometers have been developed which are quite accurate in these low ranges.

Possible limits of variation in air motion may range from 5 to 50 feet per minute, but satisfactory results in air conditioning are more likely at 15 to 30 feet per minute. It is suggested that the limit of 5 feet per minute may be taken as the minimum during the heating season and 50 feet per minute as the maximum during the cooling season.

13-10. Humidity. The amounts of moisture occurring in the air are small but important in effect. The amount of moisture which the air can carry varies with its temperature. At 0°F it will hold only 0.5 grain of water vapor per cubic foot. At 32°F it will hold 2.1 grains, and at 98°F it will hold 18.7 grains. At the above values the air is saturated and can hold no more. If the temperature is lowered, the excess moisture condenses to the saturation point for the lower temperature. This is known as the dew point. For any humidity, therefore, the temperature may be lowered so that the air becomes saturated. Conversely, cold air after being heated and with its moisture-carrying power increased has a much lower humidity at the higher temperature and hence becomes drying in its effect. The percentage of moisture which air at any temperature contains when compared with the amount which it could contain if saturated is the relative humidity. Relative humidity is measured by a comparison of wet-bulb and dry-bulb thermometers. The bulb of one thermometer is covered with damp wicking or cloth. The evaporation from the cloth lowers the temperature of the mercury in the thermometer. The drier the air, the quicker the evaporation and the lower the wet-bulb temperature. The difference between this temperature and that of the ordinary dry-bulb thermometer is a measure of the relative humidity. For instance, at a dry-bulb temperature of 80°F the wet-bulb temperature may show 73°F; the difference at this particular dry-bulb temperature indicates a relative humidity of 60 per cent. Tables or charts are used to obtain the relative humidities when the dry-bulb temperatures are known and the difference between wet-bulb and dry-bulb readings. The sling psychrometer, or hygrometer, is a convenient means of measuring relative humidity. It consists of two thermometers—a wet-bulb and a dry-bulb—mounted on a handle so that they may be twirled through the air. The cover of the wet-bulb thermometer is moistened, and the thermometers are twirled until the difference in temperatures is uniform. This allows quicker determination of the relative humidity than is possible by fixed thermometers.

13-11. Comfort Standard of Ventilation. Our present knowledge of air conditioning allows drawing no definite conclusions as to relationships between air condition and health. So far as known, air conditions that give a feeling of well-being or comfort are those which are most conducive to health. The feeling of comfort must be induced by proper control of temperature, humidity, and air movement together with precautions against accumulations of body odors, fumes, and dusts.

Exertion increases the metabolism rate of the body and raises body temperature. Therefore conditions must be different where exercise or strenuous work is in progress from those in rooms where occupations are sedentary. Character of clothing is also important. The American Society of Heating and Air-conditioning Engineers has conducted many experiments to determine the comfort zones at various combinations of relative humidity, temperature, and air movement. A graph known as a

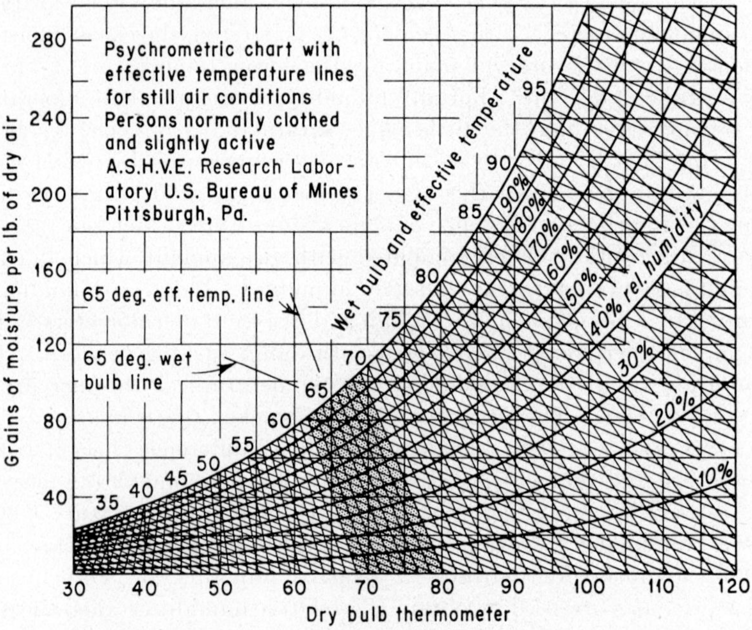

FIG. 13-1. Psychrometric chart. *(Copyright, American Society of Heating and Air-conditioning Engineers. From A.S.H.V.E. Trans., vol. 38, 1932.)*

psychrometric chart can be constructed based upon wet-bulb and dry-bulb temperatures and, if air movement is negligible, the effective temperature can be included. Figure 13-1 illustrates such a chart with a comfort zone indicated for persons normally clothed and slightly active.

13-12. Physiological Effects of Heat. In order to maintain itself at the proper temperature, the body is continually adjusting itself to the effective temperature of the air. Although in cold weather somewhat more heat is generated, most of the changes involve the skin and the blood vessels that are directly beneath. If the air is cold, the blood is withdrawn from the skin to the inner parts, thereby tending to prevent too great a loss of body heat. If the air is warm, but still cooler than the blood, the capillaries or small blood vessels beneath the skin expand, thereby bringing blood near the surface and allowing the excess heat of the body to flow to the air. The greater the difference between the temperatures of body and air, the more rapid the heat flow. If the air is at body temperature or higher, perspiration is secreted by the skin, and its evaporation lowers the body temperature. It is apparent, therefore, that with high air temperature and high humidity occurring together, evaporation is retarded and the heat is oppressive. Considerable air movement, however, aids evaporation and results in cooling of the body. Low air temperature combined with high humidity is likely to cause discomfort because the accumulation of moisture in small amounts in the clothing lessens its efficiency as a nonconductor of heat. Moistening of air in connection with heating is advantageous, however, as it prevents too rapid evaporation from the skin and thereby allows somewhat lower temperatures with comfort.

In a hot room the mucous membranes of the nose normally show swelling, redness, and moisture, while cold results in opposite effects. Drafts or currents of cold air on the face or sudden temperature changes cause contraction of the blood vessels with resulting local anemia, without, however, diminishing the swelling or loss of moisture. This loss of the protecting blood supply allows an increase of bacteria and may result in the development of colds or other respiratory infections. Continual exposure to overheated air increases the liability to the abnormal condition mentioned above. Those people who are habitually in still, overheated air are most susceptible to the bad effects of chilling drafts. High temperatures combined with high humidity, as in the case of laundry workers, may result in chronic respiratory diseases.

METHODS

13-13. Ventilation is a problem for dwellings, schools, industrial plants, office and business buildings, and such places of public assembly as theaters. Originally, ventilation consisted simply of furnishing sufficient "fresh" air, at as comfortable a level of temperature as was obtainable, and of keeping out noticeable odors and drafts. In the winter this consisted of heating with stoves, and in summer it depended upon windows, natural air currents, and fans. In industrial plants, dusts and fumes were removed by exhaust systems, and where required by certain processes the air was humidified. Of late years a more positive attitude has been taken toward ventilation, with the result that it is now required not merely to furnish warm air but also to cool it, dry or moisten it, or otherwise condition it so that it will be comfortable at all times of the year. Air conditioning has been found to be profitable. It makes theaters and stores more attractive in warm weather and, more important, increases the output of industrial and office workers by increasing efficiency and by reducing lost time and labor turnover.

Ventilation, with heating as the only air treatment, is still all that is applied in most homes and in the smaller schools. As the cost of air conditioning is being reduced, however, it is being applied more and more not only to commercial buildings but also to moderately priced residences.

13-14. Methods of Heating. The methods of heating buildings may be classified under three headings: (1) places direct heating the source of heat within the room and may be a radiator or stove; (2) indirect heating employs a central heating unit, which may be an ordinary furnace or steam coils over which the air passes, and the heated air is furnished to the rooms through ducts by fans or gravity; (3) the direct-indirect system employs heat sources in the rooms and also introduces warm air from a central furnace.

In so-called "radiant heating," which is an indirect method, rooms are heated by circulating hot water through coils of pipe within the floors, ceilings, or walls. The advantages claimed for this method are the following: (1) no radiators or ducts interfere with floor area or decoration; (2) air currents are absent, so that curtains remain clean; (3) greater comfort is obtained, particularly near the floor, as heat is supplied where it is most needed; (4) savings of 10 to 25 per cent are claimed in fuel bills, and first cost is the same or less than for the conventional steam or hot-water system. Electric coils and new glass-covered electrically heated radiant panels are also available for installation near baseboard level or in ceilings.

As indicated, coils are usually placed in the floor, although ceiling locations are occasionally used. Placing coils in the floor allows use of low-cost concrete floors, but efficient systems have been installed beneath wood floors. Ordinarily floor temperatures up to 90°F or slightly higher have been found acceptable. Pipes are either placed on fill beneath the concrete or embedded in it. Concrete covering is usually equal to the outside diameter of the pipe or 2 inches, whichever is the greater. Pipe material must be highly resistant to corrosion, easily worked, and with a coefficient of expansion close to that of the concrete. Drainage and venting should be provided for.

All the above systems may be operated automatically by means of thermostats which operate the valves of radiators or dampers placed in ducts for the purpose of keeping rooms at a desired temperature. Since thermostats have been known to get out of order, they should be checked occasionally by accurate thermometers. As a matter of fact, rooms occupied for any purpose should have thermometers, although it should be recognized that temperature is only one factor in air quality.

13-15. Air Interchange. As previously mentioned, the earlier notion as to the requirement for good ventilation was based upon an erroneous belief about the effect of carbon dioxide, particularly if the concentration of that gas exceeded 0.06 per cent. In spite of proof to the contrary this requirement, which necessitates the furnishing of 30 cubic feet of fresh air per person per minute, is still specified by some state and city laws, ordinances, and regulations governing schools and factories. An objection to such a high air change is the production of uncomfortable drafts. An air velocity of 15 to 25 feet per minute is preferred in occupied areas of rooms, but as long as anemometer readings are below 50 feet per minute drafts are not felt by occupants.

Sufficient air change is not a problem for the residence. For the school the system of window ventilation with gravity exhaust as described in Art. 13-17 is satisfactory if complete mechanical air conditioning is unobtainable. In theaters and possibly in factories where heat loss is small in proportion to the large number of people present large volumes of air or cooled air must be provided. It should be recognized that a man loses 400 British thermal units per hour when seated at rest at effective temperatures from 70 to 88°F, and that this increases greatly when movement occurs. Some of the heat loss is sensible loss, *i.e.*, due to radiation, and the rest is lost by evaporation (latent heat). It varies as follows:

	70°F	88°F
Sensible loss per hour..................	300 Btu	90 Btu
Evaporation loss per hour.............	100	310
	400 Btu	400 Btu

13-16. Natural Ventilation. This depends upon windows, doors, skylights, and roof ventilators. Natural ventilation cannot be used successfully in theaters, auditoriums, large schools, or large churches, but must be depended upon in homes, small offices, and small schools. Normally it supplies an ample amount of air for a dwelling. It should be kept in mind that air movement into rooms through windows and walls depends upon winds and temperature differences between inside and outside air. Roof ventilators are actuated by wind forces, and their efficiency depends upon their resistance to air flow, height of draft, efficiency of utilizing wind energy, and location on the roof. Ventilation by windows and transoms requires judgment. For instance, merely opening a window at the bottom may produce no air movement and no entrance of fresh air. Windows open at top and bottom or a window open at the bottom together with an open transom may give good results. The disadvantages of this type of ventilation are the dependence upon wind direction and the difficulty of control, including the possibility of entrance of smoky, dusty, and generally undesirable air.

13-17. Window Ventilation with Gravity Exhaust. Based on investigations of school ventilation extending over five years, the New York State Commission of Ventilation recommends this system for school use. Air enters the windows and is drawn out through an exhaust duct in the opposite wall at the ceiling. Radiators must be located beneath the windows and must extend the full width of those windows through which the air is obtained. The radiators should be automatically controlled by thermostats or have fractional hand-controlled valves placed at the top of the supply end of the radiator. Metal radiator shields should be placed to protect the nearest pupils from excessive radiated heat. Deflectors are needed at the bottom of the windows. These may be of glass 1 foot high or, better still, may be made with curved vanes. The windows should open from the bottom and not from the top.

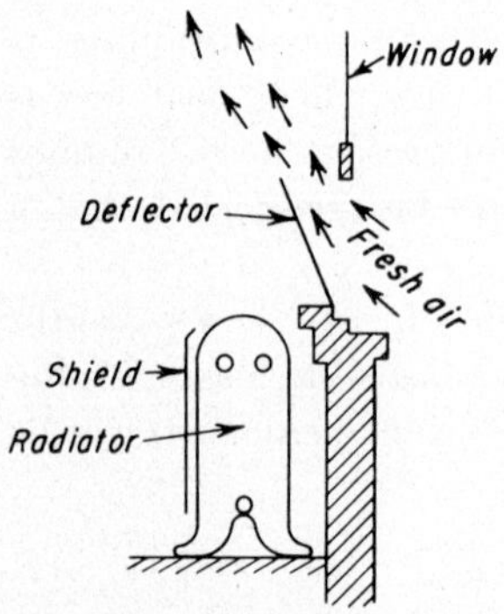

FIG. 13-2. Arrangement of radiator and deflector for window ventilation.

The exhaust duct goes through the roof and acts like a chimney. It is carried up in the interior of the building in order that there may be a difference of temperature to cause upward movement. Warming coils are sometimes placed in the duct to add to its efficiency, and a cowl should always be placed over the top opening as a preventive against downdrafts. The exhaust opening in the wall should provide 8 square feet. A damper should be provided to allow adjustment of the exhaust duct area to weather conditions.

This arrangement of windows, radiators, and exhaust allows the following process. The incoming cold fresh air mingles with the warm air from the radiator, is deflected upward, and moves toward the exhaust. As it moves, it cools and falls toward the floor, where it is warmed by the body heat of the room occupants. It then rises again and escapes through the exhaust duct.

The room should not, of course, be overcrowded. Successful results with this method were obtained in New York with a space allowance of 250 cubic feet per second-grade child and 310 cubic feet per sixth-grade child. The air flow obtained amounted to 20 cubic feet per person per minute or less. Comparisons were made and illness records kept of fan-ventilated schoolrooms (with 30 cubic feet of air per minute per person) and those ventilated by the window-inlet method. The former, owing to the high air flow, necessitated higher temperatures. 68.5°F, to prevent uncomfortable drafts; the latter were kept at more favorable temperatures. Since temperatures higher than 68°F are inseparable from the fan-ventilation system, it would appear that for school use the window inlet with gravity exhaust should be used. More cases of respiratory disease occurred among the pupils of fan-ventilated rooms, but this difference was later found to be due to characteristics of the school population and variations in distances of travel to the schools.

There are some disadvantages, however, to the window-inlet system. More responsibility is placed upon the teacher, as she must watch the thermometer and manipulate the windows, radiators, and damper accordingly. Also the use of windows as inlets may necessitate the use of air that is undesirable because of smoke and dust.

For combined heating and ventilating of schools, unit heaters or space heaters are also used. One is placed in each room, and air is supplied by a duct through the wall or a window. The air, which is drawn in by a fan, is heated by steam, electric grids, or gas, coal, or oil burners, with dampers or louvers to control the amounts of fresh and recirculated air. Exhaust is by means of windows or a duct. An air filter can be attached for dusty localities. If combustion occurs within the unit, it must be well vented. (See Art. 16-8.)

13-18. Artificial Ventilation. In the vacuum system of ventilation the air is exhausted to the outside by a fan or blower, thereby causing a lower pressure inside and a leakage inward through windows, doors, and walls. This method is largely used in kitchens to remove odors; in industrial plants to remove dusts and fumes, the inlets to the ducts being placed near the point of their production; and in other circumstances where local ventilation is required.

The plenum system forces air into the room and causes a leakage outward, although exhaust ducts may also be provided. The forcing is accomplished by centrifugal fans which operate in a manner similar to that of the centrifugal pump or by impeller fans which are larger editions of the ordinary small electric fan. The former are more generally used in ventilation by ducts. The plenum system has the advantage of allowing control of the amount of air furnished, its source, and the treatment it may require. It is the method used for supplying air to air-conditioned buildings.

The ducts of a plenum system require careful design. Each room should be governed by separate dampers; and a small branch duct rather than merely an opening in the main duct should supply the air. To prevent the entering air from causing drafts, its velocity at the outlet grille should not exceed 500 feet per minute. In the duct it may be up to 3,000 feet per minute if the noise is not objectionable. The air usually enters at ceiling height, except where the problem is to remove heat generated by large numbers of people, as in a theater, in which case the air is applied through many outlets located under the seats.

Since the temperature of the room air is lower than that of outside air during the cooling season and higher in the heating season, it is economical to recirculate air, and accordingly most air-conditioning systems are arranged to recirculate a large part of the air from the occupied space and to take from the outside the quantity necessary to prevent concentration of odors. The total amount of air handled depends upon the amount of heat to be added or removed and the permissible difference between the temperature of the air as it enters the occupied rooms and the air already present. Great differences are undesirable because of the discomfort they may cause, although good mixing as the air leaves the duct is beneficial. For comfort ventilation during the cooling season the entering air is introduced into occupied rooms at a temperature 2° cooler than is to be maintained in the room for every foot the center of the grille is above the floor.

Health officers of some cities have expressed concern as to the possible effect during very hot weather upon persons of entering and leaving buildings which have been cooled. It is feared that too great a difference in temperature may be injurious. Accordingly the ordinances of some cities allow a maximum temperature difference based upon the outdoors temperature, but others specify that the indoors air shall not be more than 10°F lower than the outside air.

13-19. Attic Fans. The attic fan provides a method of artificial ventilation which has been installed in many residences. It is not, of course, a method of air conditioning. In summer, heat accumulates in the attic and after sundown heat is radiated downward from the ceiling and also from interior walls, furniture, etc., to keep the air of the house warm, even though the outside air has become cool. The attic fan draws cool air through the open windows of the lower story. On its way to the fan it sweeps over walls and objects, cooling them, and then is discharged into the attic by the fan. It escapes from the attic through a louvered opening. The attic fan, therefore, cools by setting cool air in motion in the occupied portions of the house and reducing the radiation of heat from the interior surfaces. For the fan to be effective, it must have sufficient capacity to remove per minute an amount of air equal to the volume of those rooms which are to be cooled, excluding closets, pantries, etc. For example, if the total volume of the rooms to be cooled is 7,000 cubic feet, the fan capacity should be 7,000 cubic feet per minute. In the North, however, a rate of 20 to 30 changes per hour is standard. Kitchens may not be ventilated by this means, lest it result in the spread of cooking odors and possibly of fire. If the weather is very hot, the windows of only a few rooms, say the bedrooms, may be opened and the doors of other rooms closed. Two-story houses require a fan capacity that changes the air of the entire house once every minute and a half, unless the two stories are not connected, in which case a separate fan is needed for each story and each requires a capacity of the total volume per minute.

The air leaves the occupied rooms through an opening or grille in the ceiling, usually of a hall, since this is likely to be centrally located. The grille must have clear openings of sufficiently large total area so that the air velocity does not exceed 750 feet per minute. The duct leading from the grille to the fan should be airtight, and the louver area, which allows the air to leave the attic, should be ample in area also. Wood louvers have the effect of reducing net area by 50 per cent [1], while metal louvers reduce the area by 30 per cent. If ½-inch-mesh metal screen is placed over the louver to prevent entrance of birds or rodents, the area should be increased by 50 per cent; if 16-mesh screen cloth is placed over the opening, the area should be increased by 100 per cent.

Attic fans are usually operated for only three to four hours after sunset, or for the same time during the coolest period of the night. Some users then close all windows until about noon. In especially hot weather the fans may be operated all night. In this case it may be advisable to have a two-speed motor and to use the slower speed after the initial cooling has been accomplished, thereby saving power. The slower speed may also be used during cooler weather. If the fan is used in the daytime, all windows should be closed while it is operating, except those on the shady side of the house. Moving air through the attic during the day keeps the rooms below cooler, since the air currents reduce radiation through the attic into the house. Attic fans are not expensive, and their operating costs are low. They should be purchased only from reputable manufacturers who have thoroughly tested their fans and can guarantee performance. They are made in capacities of from 3,000 to 30,000 cubic feet per minute. Window fans, which are excellent for kitchens and can be used instead of attic fans, usually do not exceed 8,000 cubic feet per minute.

13-20. Air Conditioning. Figure 13-4 shows the various devices that are used in air-conditioning systems. This article briefly describes these devices and explains what they accomplish. Figure 13-3 shows one type of air-conditioning unit.

Filters. Filtration removes soot and dust from the air. Dry filters are most commonly used. They are discarded when they are dirty, while others are cleaned by vacuum-cleaning methods. Viscous filters use mats of crimped metal ribbon or glass wool that are coated with a viscous nondrying oil. When the mats are dirty, they are washed and reoiled, although some inexpensive types are discarded. Automatic filters are self-cleaning and may be of higher capacity. They have filtering mats or panels moving over endless chains, and at the low point of their path they pass through a bath of oil for cleaning and reoiling. The water spray also has cleaning ability. Many of the dust particles are carried down by the drops of water, while others are caught on the plates which eliminate droplets from the air (Fig 13-3). Electrolytic methods have also been used. Electric precipitators are used where exceptionally dust-free air is required, as in hospitals, or in collection systems where valuable chemical or mineral dusts are recovered. They consist of a high-intensity ionizing field and a secondary field where the dust is precipitated. They are very expensive but low in operation cost.

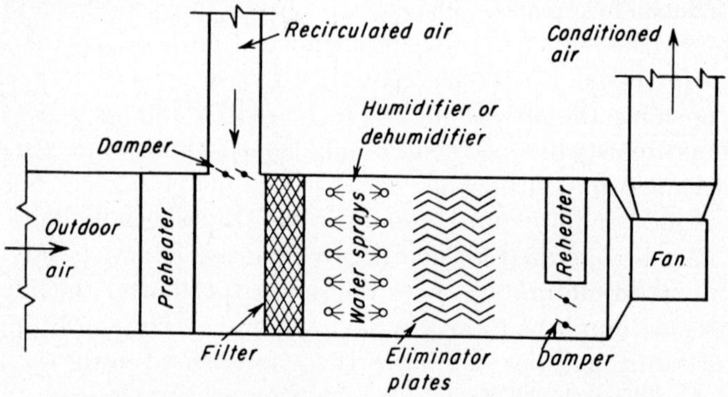

FIG. 13-3. Diagram showing spray-type air conditioner.

Heating. In air-conditioned buildings some of the heat loss from the building during cold weather may be provided by radiators in the rooms. The outside air introduced by the forced-draft, or plenum, system must then be heated, either by a warm-air furnace or by coils through which steam or hot water circulates.

Humidifying and Dehumidifying. Humidifying may be done by passing air over pans of water having a very large surface or over cloth strips which are kept wetted by capillary action. If large amounts of air are to be moistened, spray humidifiers are generally used. The simplest spray system passes water directly from the city water system through spray nozzles which break the water up into very small drops. Another method is to impinge water jets against flat surfaces to form the spray. In either case the water may be wasted or, in large installations, it may be more economical to re-use the spray water by means of a tank and pump. In this case the principal water loss is caused by evaporation. The spray humidifiers are followed by elimination plates so arranged that the air must follow a tortuous path between them. This removes droplets from the air.

Humidification of the air in the winter is important and at times very necessary. The hotter the air, the more water it evaporates and carries. Although the cold outside air may have a high relative humidity, when it is heated the relative humidity is very low. Although the drying shows no definite harmful effects on people, it can make them very uncomfortable and may cause a dermatitis in the form of flaking or scaling of the skin. If the air is humidified too much, condensation takes place on the windows, although this can be prevented or reduced by

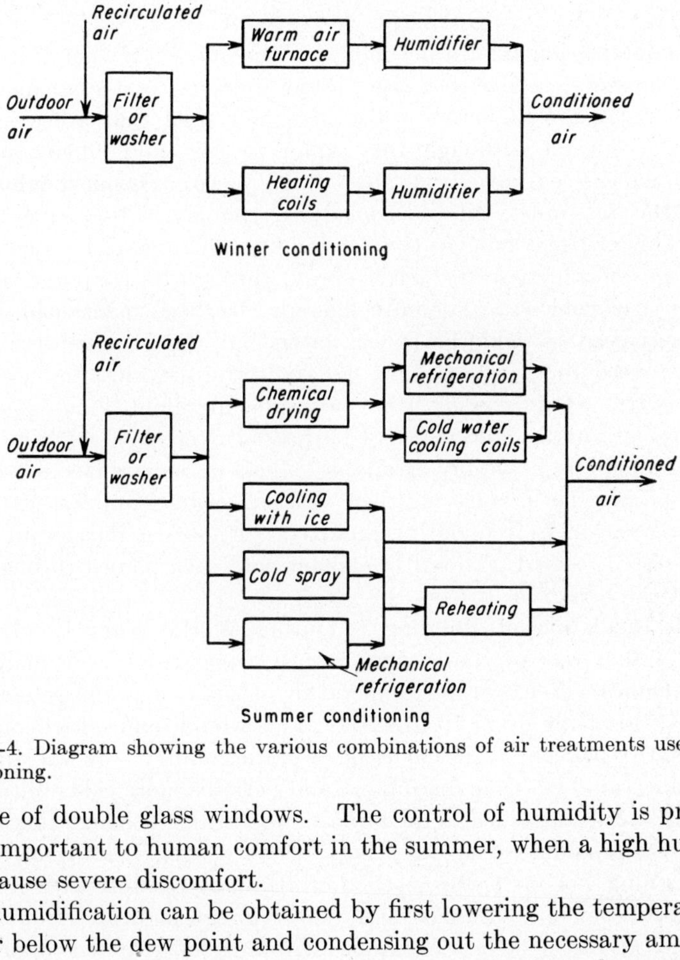

FIG. 13-4. Diagram showing the various combinations of air treatments used in air conditioning.

the use of double glass windows. The control of humidity is probably most important to human comfort in the summer, when a high humidity may cause severe discomfort.

Dehumidification can be obtained by first lowering the temperature of the air below the dew point and condensing out the necessary amount of moisture and then reheating with a dry heat to the desired temperature. The cooling of the air may be done in several ways, but the most dependable is mechanical refrigeration of a type similar to that used in a household refrigerator. The "frost" on a household box shows the moisture that has been removed by cooling. When warm air is passed through a water spray, evaporation takes place and cools the air. In a very dry climate this is satisfactory, particularly if a source of very cold water is available. Frequently mechanical refrigeration, and at times ice, is used to cool the spray water. In wet or humid climates there is little or no evaporation, but some cooling of the air is still obtained. Usually a water spray humidifies rather than dehumidifies. Whenever the air is dehumidified by refrigeration, it is usually necessary to reheat the air. If this is not done, there is a sensation of clamminess caused by the high humidity.

Dehumidification is also accomplished by means of chemicals which adsorb moisture, used either as a liquid spray or as a solid made into filters. There are numerous substances now used that are considered equally acceptable although they differ in cost and efficiency, some being much easier to reactivate than others. After chemical dehumidification the air must still be cooled; so the air is frequently cooled first. This at times relieves the dehumidifier of some of its load.

Cooling. Cooling by the water spray, through its evaporative effect or the use of cold water, or both, has already been mentioned. Ice is sometimes used to cool the spray water, but this is expensive and is generally used for such buildings as auditoriums which are used only occasionally. Spray cooling is not advisable in humid climates since the humidity is raised. The air may be passed over coils containing cool water if there is a supply available. This is sometimes possible in residential installations having their own well-water supplies. Mechanical refrigeration is frequently employed. It uses a refrigerant which is compressed, cooled, allowed to expand, and then passed through coils where it can absorb heat from the air.

13-21. Insulation of Buildings. During World War II, when the saving of fuel was of special importance, suggestions were made that during the heating season the temperature of homes and offices be kept at 65°F instead of the usual 70 to 72°F. This would reduce fuel consumption about 20 per cent in the colder parts of the country. It was supposed that there would be some discomfort and perhaps more colds until occupants became accustomed to the lower temperature, although these undesirable results could presumably be lessened by the wearing of heavier underclothing. A far better method of attaining comfort with economy is the insulation of buildings, and the stoppage of drafts from doors, windows, and fireplaces. Weather stripping of exposed doors and windows may result in a 20 per cent saving of fuel, while complete house insulation, which includes wall and roof insulation in addition to weather stripping, may save as much as 60 per cent of fuel. This improvement greatly increases comfort by preventing unduly cold walls and ceilings, to which the warmer bodies of occupants radiate heat, while in the summer the cooler ceilings and walls do not radiate so much heat to the occupants.

13-22. Disinfection of Air in Occupied Rooms. While there has been a tendency to minimize the importance of air as a transmitter of disease, it is recognized that it does play a significant role in the spread of many diseases, including influenza and pneumonia, and such childhood diseases as mumps, measles, chicken pox, scarlet fever, and whooping cough.

Such diseases, as previously explained, are spread by direct and indirect contact, and it is difficult to say how important air-borne infection is in relation to the other methods. It is known, however, that bacteria and viruses of human origin occur in the air in droplets, in droplet nuclei, and in dusts. Droplets originate from secretions of the nose, throat, and mouth. When they are expelled during talking, coughing, sneezing, or spitting, some may be inhaled by near-by persons or they may fall upon food or objects which are handled in such a manner that the infection is quickly spread to other persons. Transmission of this type is considered direct or indirect contact. The larger droplets quickly settle and dry on near-by surfaces, such as floors, tables, clothing, and bedding. The smaller droplets evaporate in the air, and their dried residues, called "droplet nuclei," float about in the air and drift with currents. Dust in the air, therefore, may be contaminated by droplets and droplet nuclei or by contact with infected handkerchiefs, bandages and dressings of infected wounds, bedding, and clothing.

Investigations and experiments in air disinfection have not produced consistent results. In some cases disinfection appeared to be beneficial, and in others there was no appreciable effect. According to present knowledge, it is justifiable only in hospitals under certain conditions. Further research may indicate its value in schools and barracks but probably not in any other buildings.

Four measures are used to control or prevent infection of air in rooms: (1) ventilation; (2) ultraviolet irradiation; (3) disinfectant vapors; and (4) dust suppression. The value of these various methods has been tested by noting the reduction they effect in the total bacterial count of the air or in the number of test organisms added, such as certain microorganisms usually found in the nasopharyngeal tract and certain specific pathogens, such as beta hemolytic streptococci or influenza virus A. To obtain even more knowledge, records have been kept of disease incidence among persons living and/or sleeping in buildings where air has been treated. These records have been so contradictory as to throw doubt upon the value of air disinfection for general use.

Ventilation. This consists of opening windows or using fans with or without washing of air, so that there is a considerable interchange of air. Within practical limits of air interchange, there is no apparent effect upon disease incidence.

Ultraviolet Irradiation. Ultraviolet light is well known for its bactericidal effect, and under test conditions it greatly reduces the number of bacteria in air although under field conditions equal results are not always obtained. Fixtures are now available which, with the use of photometers, allow economical and safe use of ultraviolet light. Its use, however, requires installation and supervision by competent engineers. It must be recognized also that the ultraviolet ray, if not properly controlled, is uncomfortable for the eyes and may cause "sunburn" to the skin. It has no effect upon bacteria in dust.

Best results have been obtained in surgical operating rooms. The residual contamination of the air which remains after all the aseptic precautions are taken by doctors and nurses can be greatly reduced by irradiation, so that postoperative infections are substantially reduced. Ultraviolet irradiation of the upper air of hospital wards and the use of light screens at entrances to contagious wards and pediatric wards have been tried with good reduction of disease transmission in some cases and no effect in others.

Irradiation of upper air in military barracks and in schoolrooms has been tried. The schoolroom application apparently was valuable in preventing two measles epidemics and in reducing chickenpox but was less successful in controlling an epidemic of mumps. There was no appreciable effect in preventing infections of the upper respiratory tract in New Haven schools[15]. Studies of irradiation in schools are still under way. In barracks there was no effect.

Use of Disinfectant Vapors. Various disinfectants have been investigated for this purpose, but triethylene glycol appears to be the most useful because of its high bactericidal effect, its reasonable cost, and its freedom from odors, toxicity, and corrosiveness to metal surfaces. If air temperatures are high, complaints of stuffiness may result and, since its volatility is low, the concentration required for killing bacteria may be exceeded and fogging may result. The glycol, on the other hand, effectively permeates all parts of a room. Its bactericidal effect depends upon its relative saturation rather than the total concentration. It has been found to be most efficient when combined with dust-suppressive measures. Methods of vaporizing triethylene glycol and maintaining its relative saturation in the air have been developed on an experimental basis and may in the future be standardized for practical use. Perhaps when these technical problems have been worked out, this method will prove of greater usefulness.

Dust-suppressive Measures. A simple and effective measure for laying dust in hospitals and military barracks which have wood floors is to apply light paraffin oil or spindle oil. A saturation application to soft unvarnished wood is effective for three months or longer. If the floor is of hardwood, more frequent treatments are needed. The method is not applicable to concrete, linoleum, or waxed surfaces, but daily use of oiled mops or oiled sawdust during sweeping is equally effective.

Not all dust comes from floors. Much is discharged into the air from bedclothing, especially during bed changing, and accordingly various methods have been developed to impregnate blankets, bedding, and certain types of clothing with oil. A simple method which can be used in any well-equipped laundry is as follows. A stable oil-water emulsion, made with a neutral detergent, triton NE, is added at the time of the final rinse[2] in the laundry process. This treatment causes the clothing to retain its dust and bacteria. The effect remains after many months and after subsequent washings.

Dust-suppressive procedures are to be recommended as a hygienic measure. They result in a great reduction in the bacterial content of the air, and they are practical of application. There is insufficient evidence as yet, however, to establish their value in the control of respiratory disease[3].

13-23. Heating Appliances and Carbon Monoxide. The increased use of natural and artificial gas for heating purposes has developed a hazard which has frequently resulted in deaths. While many state and city health departments have launched educational campaigns on the subject, the public still requires further instruction.

Carbon monoxide (CO) poisoning from gas heating appliances is generally due to unvented appliances (space heaters and hot-water heaters), to "plugged-up" or faulty flues, and to lack of sufficient make-up air to support combustion and life. While faulty appliances previously caused great carbon monoxide production, a record of all injuries and deaths from carbon monoxide in Cincinnati for the past three years indicates that practically all were due to improper vents and lack of fresh air. The danger is increased by the fact that carbon monoxide is odorless and nonirritating. When breathed, it first causes headache, weariness, and dizziness, then nausea, vomiting, and finally death. The symptoms are caused by the fact that the carbon monoxide has a chemical affinity for the hemoglobin, thereby interfering with the normal oxygen-carrying power of the blood. Serious results may be caused by long exposures to low concentrations or short exposure to high concentrations. According to Webster[4] a blood saturation of 20 to 30 per cent of carbon monoxide produces headache and throbbing of the temples, and this result is noticed after exposure for 3½ to 5 hours in a concentration of 200 parts per million of carbon monoxide (0.02 per cent by volume) in room air. At 400 parts per million the same result is noted in 1½ to 3¼ hours. At 2,000 parts per million death occurs in one to two hours, while 5,000 parts per million causes death in 20 minutes. Table 13-1 gives the number and causes of asphyxiations occurring in Texas between 1950 and 1955.

Carbon monoxide is a common constituent of manufactured gas which, when burned under proper conditions, is transformed into harmless products. Burning of any fuel with an insufficient air supply, however, results in more or less carbon monoxide being produced. The so-called coal-gas poisoning, due to coal fires having their drafts cut off by dampers or soot accumulations, is essentially carbon monoxide poisoning. In connection with the use of gas, carbon monoxide may be given off by hot-water heaters, cooking stoves, some makes of solid-top gas ranges, radiant heaters, and gas lights with mantles. Poorly adjusted and

TABLE 13-1. DEATHS BY ACCIDENTAL POISONING BY CARBON MONOXIDE GAS AND UTILITY (ILLUMINATING) GAS IN TEXAS, 1950–1955

	1950	1951	1952	1953	1954	1955
Accidental poisoning by utility (illuminating) gas	15	22	15	13	10	10
Accidental poisoning by motor-vehicle exhaust gas	7	6	12	2	2	5
Accidental poisoning by other carbon monoxide gas	9	5	7	5	6	9
Total	31	33	34	20	18	24

SOURCE: Courtesy of Texas State Department of Health.

dirty burners are dangerous, as are homemade contrivances and amateur adjustments of appliances. According to the standards of the American Gas Association gas-burning appliances should not produce over 0.02 per cent carbon monoxide in the air-free products of gas combustion. In actual use this is frequently exceeded, and probably carbon monoxide poisoning in its less severe forms is more prevalent than is generally recognized.

Prevention of poisoning may be accomplished by simple precautions. Proper venting to flues carries off the products of combustion and is effective for ovens, water heaters, and room heaters. For ranges, a hood is necessary. Restrictions or dampers in the vents are dangerous. Under no circumstances should an unvented heater be used in a bedroom during sleeping hours. Radiant heaters[5], the most frequent cause of fatalities, should be given special attention. If they are of the nonluminous-, or blue-, flame type and are turned on only enough to cause glowing of three-fourths of the radiant material from bottom to top, and if the air supply into the gas feed pipe is sufficient, the heater may be used without a vent in a well-ventilated room. If the radiant material is glowing over its entire height or if insufficient air is being mingled with the gas, then carbon monoxide may be generated. Broken radiants resting upon the burner openings are also dangerous. Enlarging the perforations in the pipe so that more gas escapes is an exceedingly dangerous practice, as the proper relation between air supply and gas is destroyed. Luminous or yellow flames are produced by gas jets which derive their air supply from the surrounding air and not from an air hole in the pipe. Luminous flames should not be permitted to come into contact with metal surfaces, or carbon monoxide will be given off. Should a gas-burning apparatus produce a luminous flame when it normally should have a blue flame, the opening which supplies air to the gas feed pipe should be examined. Not infrequently dust or dirt clogs these openings. Adjustments of all appliances should be frequently checked by skilled employees of the gas company.

13-24. Automobile Exhausts. Many deaths have resulted from automobile exhaust gases in garages. These gases include carbon monoxide, and the concentration in small individual garages may be expected to become dangerous after a motor has been running for five to ten minutes. Motors should be kept tuned up and the exhaust system tight. Sleeping in a closed running automobile is dangerous. Because of the danger of exhaust gases entering closed cars, some cities are requiring by ordinance special safeguarding of closed buses. Many state health departments require adequate ventilation and tailpipe exhaust systems for repair garages. Adequate ventilation is the most effective method for control of the carbon monoxide hazard in garages. The amount of carbon monoxide exhausted is directly proportional to the richness of the mixture, and the so-called "wet" or "dry" mixtures have no bearing on the matter.

Ethyl gasoline contains tetraethyl lead, a highly poisonous compound which has been responsible for fatalities in laboratories and factories in connection with the manufacturing of the gasoline. There appears to be no danger in the proper use and dispensation of ethyl gasoline, but it should be used only as a fuel and for no other purpose.

BIBLIOGRAPHY

1. Badgett, W. H.: The Installation and Use of Attic Fans, *Texas Eng. Exp. Sta. Bull.* 52.
2. Loosli, C. G., *et al.*: The Oil Treatment of Bedclothes for the Control of Dust-borne Infection, *Am. J. Hyg.*, vol. 43, 1946.
3. Present Status of the Control of Air-borne Infections, Report of the Subcommittee

for the Evaluation of Methods to Control Air-borne Infections, *Am. J. Public Health,* vol. 37, no. 1, 1937.
4. Webster, R. W.: "Legal Medicine and Toxicology," W. B. Saunders Company, Philadelphia.
5. Jones, Yant, and Berger: Incomplete Combustion in Natural Gas Heaters, *U.S. Bur. Mines Tech. Paper* 362.
6. Winslow, C.-E. A., "Fresh Air and Ventilation," E. P. Dutton & Co., Inc., New York.
7. Phelps, E. B., "Public Health Engineering," The Macmillan Company, New York.
8. Allen, J. R., J. H. Walker, and J. W. James, "Heating and Air Conditioning," McGraw-Hill Book Company, Inc., New York, 1946.
9. "Heating, Ventilating and Air Conditioning Guide," American Society of Heating and Air-conditioning Engineers, New York.
10. Greene, A. M.: "Principles of Heating, Ventilating and Air Conditioning," John Wiley & Sons, Inc., New York.
11. Jennings, B. H., and S. R. Lewis: "Air Conditioning and Refrigeration," International Textbook Company, Scranton, Pa.
12. McCord, Carey P., and W. N. Witheridge: "Odors: Physiology and Control," McGraw-Hill Book Company, Inc., New York.
13. Berry, C. Harold: "Flow and Fan: Principles of Moving Air through Ducts," The Industrial Press, New York.
14. Hemeon, W. C. L.: "Plant and Process Ventilation," The Industrial Press, New York.
15. Gelperin, A., *et al.*: The Effect of Ultraviolet Light upon Absenteeism from Upper Respiratory Infections in New Haven Schools, *Am. J. Public Health,* vol. 41, no. 7, 1951.

CHAPTER 14

LIGHT

14-1. Light and health are related in several ways. The bactericidal effect of light has been mentioned elsewhere. Light has of late been proved to be of great value in the combating of certain diseases. It appears to have a stimulating effect upon the blood, particularly that portion of the blood supply which is in the outer parts of the body. This stimulation apparently helps the body to overcome tuberculosis infection. Sunlight has been found to be a specific in the treatment of rickets. The ultraviolet rays here appear to be the active agents. The stimulating effects of sunlight are negatived by glass and clothing, as these are opaque to the ultraviolet rays, and also by smoky and foggy atmospheres. The sanitarian has now a specific evil effect of excess smoke to point out in connection with the need for smoke prevention.

Inside illumination is receiving ever-increasing attention from physicians, engineers, educators, and employers. This interest in illumination has resulted in a recognition of the effect of insufficient lighting upon the eyes, the comfort, and the production of workers and upon the efficiency of school children. The importance of good lighting in reducing accidents and the need for street lighting that can cope with modern high-speed traffic have also been emphasized.

MEASUREMENT OF LIGHT

14-2. The *intensity of light* source is measured by the *standard candle.* This is the light as given by a candle which has been internationally agreed upon so that it is approximately uniform.

The *intensity of illumination* is measured by the *foot-candle.* This is the illumination given by a source of one candle to an area 1 foot away from the source (see Fig. 14-1).

The *luminous flux* is the amount or quantity of light, and its unit is the *lumen.* In Fig. 14-1, the area A is 1 square foot and since it is 1 foot away from the candle, it is illuminated to an intensity of 1 foot-candle. Strictly speaking, the surface should be curved so that each point is equidistant from the candle. The total amount of light passing through the area *A*, if it is considered as being transparent, is 1 lumen. Therefore, the lumen is the quantity of light required to illuminate 1 square foot to the intensity of 1 foot-candle. The lumen is useful in specifying the amount of light which a light source, or luminaire, must supply. For example, if 100 square feet must be illuminated to an intensity of 10 foot-candles, 1,000 lumens will be required.

The *brightness* of a surface which is emitting or reflecting light is expressed in *candles per square inch* or in *lumens per unit of area.* A surface that is emitting or reflecting light in a given direction at the rate of 1 candle per square inch of projected area has a brightness in that direction of 1 candle per square inch. Or, a surface which has a brightness equal to the uniform brightness of a perfectly diffusing surface emitting or reflecting 1 lumen per square foot has a brightness of 1 *foot-lambert.* The foot-lambert is also the average brightness of any surface emitting or reflecting light at the rate of 1 lumen per square foot. The

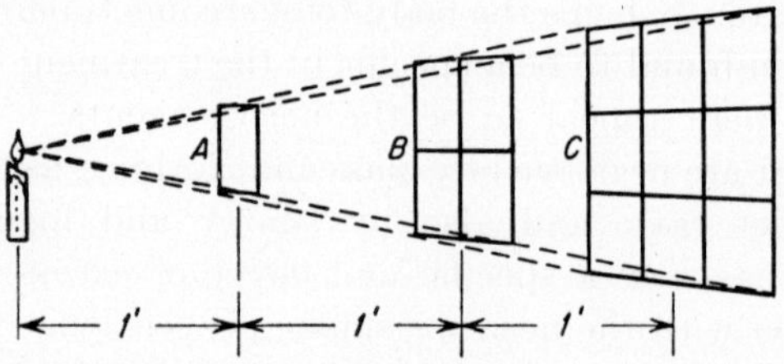

FIG. 14-1. The illumination at *A* is 1 foot-candle. The illumination on surfaces varies inversely as the square of the distance from the source to the surface.

lambert is the brightness of a surface emitting or reflecting 1 lumen per square centimeter. Since it is brightness which affects the seeing process, the foot-lambert rather than the foot-candle is the primary factor in the consideration of eye comfort and efficiency of seeing.

14-3. The Inverse Square Law. In Fig. 14-1 it will be seen that, if the surface is removed, the light which has illuminated it also illuminates *B*, but *B* is larger in area than *A* and therefore is less intensely illuminated. Since the two areas are bases of pyramids, their areas are proportional to the squares of their distances from the candle which is at the vertex, and if their respective distances are 1 foot and 2 feet, the area *B* is four times the area of *A* and its intensity of illumination is only one-fourth as much. Similarly, the area of *C* is nine times that of *A*, and its illumination is $\frac{1}{9}$ foot-candle. Hence the rule may be stated that the intensity of the illumination of a surface varies inversely as the square of its distance from the light source.

14-4. Cosine Law. In Fig. 14-2 the surface *OA* is perpendicular to the path of the light ray from the source of light, the source being considered so far away that light rays are practically parallel. The surface *OB* is at an angle α to the ray. The illumination on the two surfaces is inversely proportional to their areas, hence

$$\frac{\text{Illumination of } OB}{\text{Illumination of } OA} = \frac{OA}{OB}$$

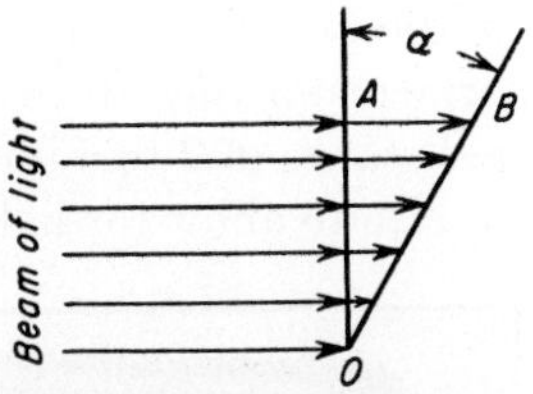

FIG. 14-2. Diagram illustrating the cosine law.

But OA/OB is the cosine of the angle α.

The rule then may be stated that illumination on a surface not perpendicular to the path of the rays is proportional to the cosine of the angle between the surface and the perpendicular surface.

14-5. Photometry. This is the measuring of the intensity of luminous source or the brightness of an illuminated surface. Photometers are devised for determining the luminous intensity of an unknown source. They involve the principle of comparison of a known source with one of unknown intensity and make use of the inverse square law.

A simple photometer, which illustrates the principle of photometry, is the bar type (Fig. 14-3). It consists of a paper or cloth screen with a waxed or greased spot. Two mirrors are arranged so that both sides of the screen can be viewed simultaneously. The screen is arranged so that it can be moved between two sources of light, one of known intensity, such as one or more candles. The greased spot transmits more light through it than does the plain section of the screen. It reflects less

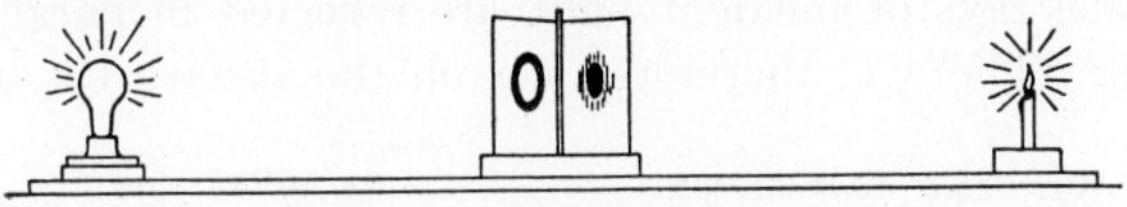

FIG. 14-3. Bar photometer showing use of oblique mirrors (photometer not balanced).

light, however, than does the surrounding paper. Hence, if the paper is illuminated to the same intensity on both sides, the spot becomes indistinguishable from the surrounding paper. The distances are measured and the inverse square rule then applied.

For checking illumination the foot-candle meter is very useful. It has the further advantage of being small, portable, and inexpensive. It can be used by inspectors in determining and measuring illumination at the factory worker's bench or at the schoolroom desk (see Fig. 14-4).

Measurement of intensity of illumination is important, but it must be recognized that it is only one factor in the matter of obtaining eye comfort and efficient seeing. The brightness of objects, which is related to the reflection of the light cast upon them, and the contrast between the brightness of various surfaces in the field of view are equally important. Measurement of brightness is done by brightness meters. Rough approximations of brightness can be obtained with some types of foot-candle meters. For reflecting material, the cell is placed against the test surface and then drawn away slowly until a constant reading is obtained (a distance of 2 to 6 inches). The meter reading at that point multiplied by 1.25 to allow for light striking the cell at oblique angles is the approximate brightness in foot-lamberts. The foot-lambert brightness of an emitting surface is measured by placing the cell against the surface and multiplying the reading by 1.25.

FIG. 14-4. Foot-candle light meter. (*Photograph courtesy of General Electric Company, Cleveland, Ohio.*)

14-6. Reflection. Whenever light strikes a surface, the light is absorbed or reflected. If the surface is rough and black, practically all is absorbed. If the surface is light-colored, a large proportion will be reflected. The law of reflection is that the angle of incidence equals the angle of reflection. This means that the angle which a ray of light makes with a surface it strikes is the same as the angle which the reflected ray makes with the same surface. As shown in Fig. 14-5, if the reflecting surface is very smooth, or polished, the parallel or approximately parallel rays of incident light are reflected in parallel or nearly parallel lines. The eye, therefore, sees on the surface the image of the

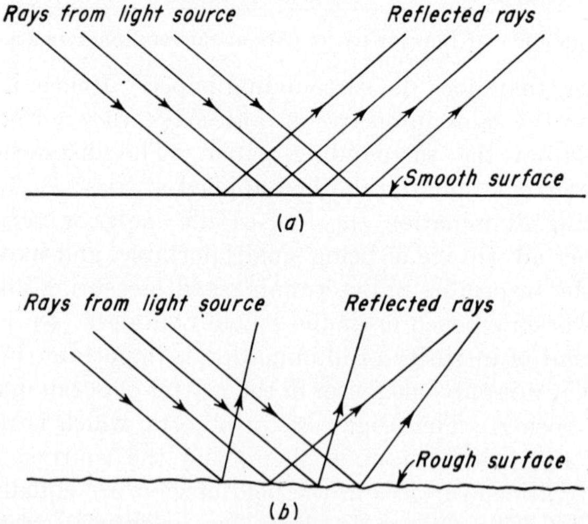

FIG. 14-5. Types of reflection. (*a*) Regular or specular reflection; (*b*) diffused reflection.

source of light. This type of reflection is known as regular or specular reflection. If the reflecting surface is rough, it is, in effect, made up of many small planes arranged at various angles, with the result that the incident light is reflected in lines that are not parallel. This is known as diffused reflection, and the eye which intercepts the rays can perceive no image of the source.

Reflection resulting from wall and ceiling surfaces is very important in the illumination of rooms, particularly in daylight lighting and the indirect and semi-indirect systems of artificial lighting. Of the light which strikes walls or ceiling, part is absorbed and the balance is reflected to strike other surfaces where more is absorbed and the balance reflected

TABLE 14-1. REFLECTION FACTORS OF PAINTS OF VARIOUS TINTS

Classification	Reflection coefficient, per cent
White plaster	90–92
Flat mill white (mat)	75–90
Light cream	74
Light pink	67
Light yellow	65
Light blue	61
Light buff	58
Light green	47
Light gray	49
Medium blue	36
Medium gray	30
Red	13

and so on until it is all absorbed. Each reflection contributes to illumination over that of the lamp alone. Therefore ceilings, walls, and floors of low absorbing and high reflecting powers aid materially in illumination. The lighter colors reflect more light than the darker ones, black being completely absorbent unless the surface is highly glazed or polished, in which case there is some specular reflection. Table 14-1 gives reflection factors for paints of various colors.

14-7. Contrast. Visibility is obtained by bringing lumens from the lamp or lamps to produce foot-candles of illumination on the work or any object in which the observer is interested. Merely bringing lumens is not sufficient; for visibility some of the light must be reflected and the surface, must thus have a brightness. For example, if the object or work receives 30 foot-candles and 60 per cent is reflected, the brightness of the work is 18 foot-lamberts while 40 per cent of the light is absorbed.

If this surface is close to another one that reflects little or no light, the contrast makes for visibility. As an example, the black ink of printing reflects little or no light while the paper on which the letters are printed reflects nearly all the light. Hence there is a high contrast, visibility on the task is good, and reading is easy. Conversely, printing with a medium blue ink on pale blue paper would be much lower in visibility because of lack of contrast. At the extreme, sewing with black thread on black cloth is exceedingly difficult because of the almost complete lack of contrast. It can be said that good visibility depends upon a high *brightness contrast* of the critical detail to its background.[1]

The term *brightness ratio* is used to apply to the brightness of any two surfaces. It may be the ratio of the average brightness of the visual task to that of some surface in the surroundings. It is necessary to recognize three fields of vision in connection with brightness ratios and their effects upon vision (see Fig. 14-6). The visual task, whether it is reading a book or filing a casting, is called the *central field.* In the center of the central field is an area of 1 degree where very accurate seeing is required. The surrounding field extends approximately 30 degrees on each side of the line of sight. Thus its total area is 60 degrees in the center of the total visual field. The peripheral field is outside the surrounding field and includes an area of about 120 degrees vertically and 160 degrees horizontally centering on the line of sight.

As already indicated, high brightness ratios are desirable in the visual task to avoid excessive eyestrain. In the recommended standard practice for the lighting of schools, it is required that the brightness ratio between the visual task and near-by surfaces in the surroundings, a desk top for example, be 1 to $\frac{1}{3}$. In other words the desk top or other immediate surroundings of the task should not be less than one-third as bright as the visual task and no brighter than the task. We may say in general that in the surroundings the brightness ratio between the task and those surroundings should be small. In the entire field of vision of the eye, control is also necessary. Brightness ratios in this region should be less than 100 per cent and greater than 10 per cent of the brightness of the task; in other words, the ratio should be between 1 and $\frac{1}{10}$.

Glare occurs when there are high brightness ratios anywhere in the field of vision. It may be *direct glare,* which is due to bright light sources or

[1] This is also called "per cent contrast," which is the ratio of the brightness difference between an object and its background to the brightness of its background. In the case of the blue printing on light blue paper (see Table 14-1) it would be $\frac{61 - 36}{61} \times 100 = 41$ per cent. In the case of black printing on white paper, assuming that the printing absorbs all light and that the white paper reflects all the light, the contrast would be $\frac{100 - 0}{100} \times 100 = 100$ per cent.

areas inside or outside the room. The sources or areas may be quite small and very bright, or relatively large and with lower brightness. *Reflected glare* may be due to the image of some bright light source reflected in glass table tops, polished furniture, glazed paper, etc.

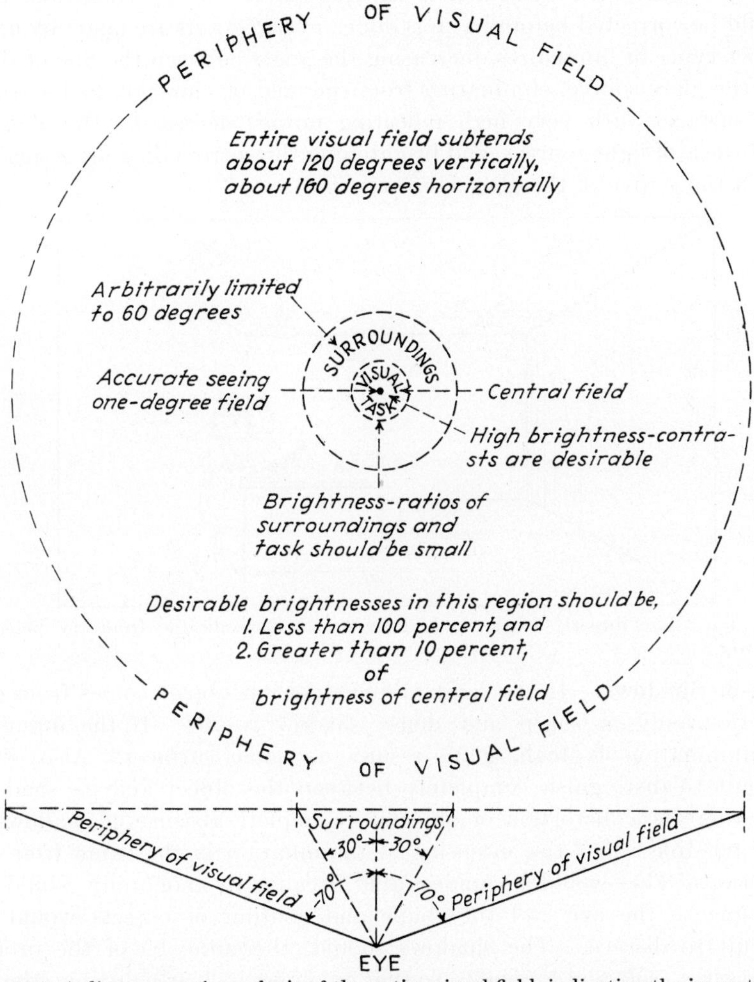

FIG. 14-6. A diagrammatic analysis of the entire visual field, indicating the importance of brightness, brightness-contrast ratios in its various parts, and suggested limitations. (*Reproduced by permission from M. Luckiesh, "Light, Vision and Seeing," D. Van Nostrand Company, Inc., Princeton, N.J.*)

Glare causes discomfort and directly influences the ability and the continued urge to see. It tends to be cumulative in its effects. A minor glare, which might be negligible when exposure is short, may become of serious importance after long exposure. Conditions which do not appear glaring while persons are performing tasks requiring only casual seeing may become uncomfortable when a critical task is to be performed, such as recognition of small but important details. A reduction of visual acuity and strain and nervousness may soon develop. Careful brightness surveys, made with instruments, will frequently indicate conditions that should be corrected before harm is done. Corrections are made by using proper types of luminaires, increasing the angle between the line of sight and the glare source, eliminating from the field of view polished surfaces and surfaces with very high reflecting power, decreasing the average brightness of light sources, and brightening the surrounding areas against which the source of the glare is seen.

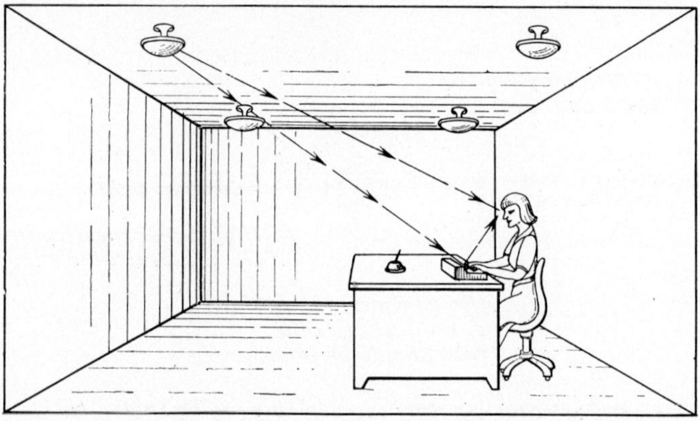

FIG. 14-7. Glare directly from the luminaire and also reflected from the polished desk top.

14-8. Shadows. If the light falling upon an object comes from one direction only, a sharp and dense shadow results. If the intensity of illumination is high, glare results on some surfaces. Also, it is difficult to distinguish completely between the object and its shadow, thus there is a distortion of objects. Complete absence of shadows is only possible when the intensity of illumination is the same from all directions. This would be undesirable because its monotony would be tiresome to the eye and the shape and contour of objects would be difficult to discern. The shadows should, therefore, be of the proper quality, *i.e.*, soft and luminous, so that an object is clearly distinguishable from its shadow and without harsh contrast in intensity of illumination. A rough test is to hold a pencil horizontally several inches above a white surface. If the shadow is blurred and not sharply outlined, light diffusion has been attained. The required uniformity of illumination is obtained by a proper ratio of the spacing distance of light sources to their height of mounting. A rough rule is that the spacing distance should be equal to the height.

14-9. Standards of Illumination Practice. The Illuminating Engineering Society has prepared standards or codes of practice for application to schools, industrial plants, and offices. Lighting of schools and industrial plants is discussed in Chap. 16. Recommended intensities of illumination for office lighting are given in Table 14-2. The intensities given are commensurate with the difficulty of the various seeing tasks and the current cost of lighting. These values should be obtained by proper design and then maintained by proper cleaning and replacement of deteriorated or failed lamps. Initial values should be increased by some percentage to offset depreciation of lamps and dirt accumulation, which may reach 30 to 50 per cent depending upon character of maintenance, dust conditions, and design of luminaires with respect to the gathering of dust.

TABLE 14-2. RECOMMENDED INTENSITIES OF ILLUMINATION FOR OFFICE WORK

	Foot-candles current, recommended practice
Difficult seeing tasks	50
Involving	
a. Discrimination of fine details such as 6- to 8-point type	
b. Poor contrast	
c. Long periods of time	
Such as auditing and accounting, business-machine operation, transcribing and tabulating, bookkeeping, drafting, designing	
Ordinary seeing tasks	30
Involving	
a. Discrimination of moderately fine detail such as 8- to 12-point type	
b. Better than average contrast	
c. Intermittent periods of time	
Such as general office work (except for work coming under Difficult Seeing Tasks above), private office work, general correspondence, conference rooms, active file rooms, mail rooms	
Casual seeing tasks	10
Such as inactive file rooms, reception rooms, stairways, washrooms, and other service areas	
Simple seeing tasks	5
Such as hallways and corridors, passageways	

Recommended brightness ratios are as follows: between tasks and surroundings, 3:1; between tasks and remote surfaces, 10:1; between luminaires (or windows) and adjacent surfaces, 20:1; anywhere within normal field of view, 40:1. These are the recommended maximums; reductions are desirable.

Room finishes, especially of ceilings, are important in determining brightness ratios between lighting equipment and its surroundings. Color and reflectance of surfaces have much effect upon utilization of light, as indicated in Art. 14-6. The following reflection factors are recommended: ceilings, 75 to 85 per cent; walls, 50 to 60 per cent; desk tops, 35 per cent; furniture, 30 to 35 per cent; floors, 30 per cent. Dull finishes (mat) are recommended for all painted and other surfaces.

TABLE 14-3. REPRESENTATIVE LEVELS OF ILLUMINATION

	Foot-candles
Starlight	0.0002
Moonlight	0.02
Street lighting	0.6–1.2
Daylight:	
At north window	50–200
In shade (outdoors)	100–1,000
Direct sunlight	5,000–10,000
Office lighting	30–50

14-10. Natural Lighting. In spite of the great strides which artificial lighting has made in late years and the difficulties sometimes encountered in obtaining effective natural light, the latter is the stand-by for homes, schools, offices, and even for industrial establishments where possible.

The recommended window-glass area of a workroom is usually 15 to 20 per cent of the floor area. Windows on only one side of the room usually give satisfactory illumination if the width of the room is less than twice the height from the floor to the top of the window. Large rooms, such as auditoriums, may require windows on both sides. For best working conditions in rooms lighted by windows, the distance of any working space from the windows should be no more than twice the height of the top of the window.

The amount of light furnished by windows to a point is largely dependent upon the sky area visible at that point. Windows facing blank walls get and transmit only reflected light. The lighting values of such windows, therefore, in addition to the amount of any sky visible depends upon their brightness and the reflection factors of the outside surfaces. Satisfactory lighting can usually be obtained when the visible sky subtends an angle of 5 degrees at any working point in the room. It is recommended that the sky exposure be at least 50 square degrees, preferably 5 degrees vertically and 10 degrees horizontally. Without special precautions window lighting results in larger proportions of light and perhaps glare from sunlight at points near the window. The closer windows are to the ceiling, the greater is the angle of the entering light to the line of vision, and thus danger of glare is reduced. Shades are used to give protection from glare, but the ordinary shade may cut off too much light. Shades of light-yellow, light-buff, or tan cause diffusion of light and prevent glare without absorption of too much light. For schools double shades are advisable, both operating from the middle of the window. Venetian blinds are valuable in deflecting light toward the ceiling. Where the sky is obstructed by buildings, prismatic glass in the windows greatly improves the natural lighting by distributing the light rays to the inner parts of the room. Basement lighting can also be effectively done with prismatic glass.

Skylights are used to supplement windows and should be used to a greater extent than at present. The saw-tooth roof for industrial plants lends itself to effective lighting. The glass side of the saw tooth should be toward the north rather than the south in order that the glass may transmit diffused daylight rather than direct sunlight.

14-11. Artificial Light. There are five systems of artificial lighting: direct, direct-indirect, semidirect, semi-indirect, and indirect.

In *direct lighting* 90 to 100 per cent of the light of the luminaires is directed in angles below the horizontal directly toward the usual working area. Direct lighting may be local or general. Since local lighting involves droplights close to the work, considerable glare may result unless shades are provided. When direct lighting is used, the luminaires should be placed high, preferably not less than 20 feet, unless enclosed in diffusing glassware to prevent glare. Glare is reduced if the ceiling is illuminated by good reflection from surfaces. Direct lighting has the advantage of being highly efficient, as little or no light is absorbed before striking the work. It causes harsh shadows, and glare results from reflection on smooth or glazed surfaces. Deep reflectors may be used, however, to hide the filaments and prevent direct glare, but they have no effect upon reflected glare.

In *semidirect lighting* 60 to 90 per cent of the light output is directed downward to the work. The small upward component illuminates the ceiling and thus reduces the brightness ratio between the luminaire and the ceiling. The luminaires have reflecting surfaces above the light sources to deflect most of the light downward. Glass or plastic enclosures or louvered bottoms provide diffusion and shielding.

In *direct-indirect* or *general diffuse lighting* the light is distributed equally in all directions, although strictly direct-indirect luminaires produce very little light in angles near the horizontal, and accordingly they are more desirable. In general the predominant lighting is from the downward component since it is not reflected. With these systems direct and reflected glare may be noticeable.

In *semi-indirect lighting* 60 to 90 per cent of the light is directed to the ceiling and upper walls, while dense diffusing glass allows some of the light to pass through directly downward. If the diffusing glass of the reflector is good, all glare and high brightness are avoided. The ceiling surface and upper walls must be highly reflecting. As the downward component increases toward 40 per cent, direct and reflected glare may require attention.

In *indirect lighting* 90 to 100 per cent of the light is directed toward the ceiling and upper side walls from which it is reflected to all parts of the room. As the ceiling thus becomes the light source, care must be taken that it is not a source of glare. Careful attention must be paid to room finishes. They must be as light in color as possible and kept in good condition. Luminaires have opaque inverted reflectors and are frequently set in recesses at the ceiling or in architectural coves.

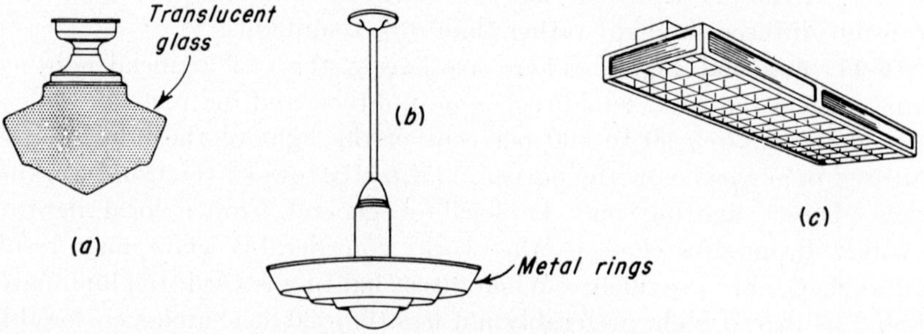

FIG. 14-8. Luminaires. (*a*) Direct-indirect, or diffused; (*b*) indirect; (*c*) fluorescent, direct-indirect with egg-crate louvers to shield eyes from glare.

No one system can be recommended to the exclusion of the others. Direct lighting gives high utilization and therefore lower cost, but good lighting on the task is attained only by close spacing of luminaires or the use of large-area–low-brightness equipment. Indirectl ighting provides good light on the work but utilization is low. The intermediate systems combine the characteristics of both these in varying degrees.

Much of the advantage of lighting systems, particularly in industrial plants, is lost through the accumulations of dust and dirt on bulbs and reflectors. This is particularly important in the indirect and semi-indirect systems. In some plants regular inspections of the lights are made by a responsible employee for the purpose of replacing burned-out bulbs and cleaning bulbs and reflectors.

14-12. Fluorescent Lighting. Although the gas-filled tungsten filament incandescent lamp is still the most widely used illuminant, the fluorescent lamp is increasingly popular. It consists of a glass tube filled with mercury vapor and having an electrode sealed in each end.

When the electric current is turned on, an arc is formed by current flowing through the mercury vapor. The arc generates some light but much more invisible ultraviolet energy, which excites fluorescent chemicals which coat the inside of the tube. Various fluorescent substances are used to obtain different colors. So-called daylight tubes are obtainable, but in practice they have been found to be objectionable, except where very accurate color discrimination is required. They tend to blur the visibility of objects and are unflattering to the human complexion. A slight yellowish tint to the light, which is obtainable in the "standard" daylight tubes and which occurs naturally in incandescent bulbs, is satisfactory.

An advantage is that the equipment which uses fluorescent lamps is much lower in brightness in the direct and reflected glare zones and provides a larger and more uniformly illuminated area. Shadows are also much softer. It is possible, however, to have brightnesses in such lamps so high that high brightness ratios occur, with detriment to eye comfort and efficiency. Complaints that there is too much light or that the light from the fluorescent lamps is hurting the eyes are usually caused by direct glare. Although shielding the light source so that the worker cannot see the lamp usually eliminates the complaint, care should be taken that no other unfavorable circumstances are also present.

Fluorescent lighting is economical in use of electrical current. For example, a 60-watt coil tungsten filament lamp emits 13.9 lumens per watt, while a 40-watt white fluorescent lamp emits 58 lumens per watt. These figures are for lamps which have been in use for 100 hours. New lamps give off more light. In general, fluorescent lamps produce 40 to 65 lumens per watt. The smaller use of current also reduces the heat generated by the lamp.

14-13. Good Lighting and Production. Good lighting safeguards eyesight and reduces accident hazards. It also saves the worker's time and cuts down the amount of spoiled work and is, therefore, economically profitable to the employer. This is an argument which should never be neglected by the sanitarian.

A report by the Illuminating Engineering Society (1921 *Transactions*) indicates that the whole cost of good lighting is usually equal to the cost of about 3 minutes of the worker's time each day. Hence, if it saves 3 minutes daily it pays for itself regardless of the cost of poor lighting. Tests made in shops as to the effect of light upon production indicated that increase of the average illumination from 0.2 to 4.8 foot-candles increased production in varying amounts from 6 to 100 per cent with an average of 35 per cent. Increased illumination from 4.6 to 12.7 foot-candles gave increases varying from 8 to 27 per cent and averaging 15 per cent[1].

It should be pointed out that a good lighting system is not an accident but the product of careful planning that considers the type of work to be done, size of the room, and the reflecting factors of the walls and ceiling. Manufacturers of luminaires can give the characteristics of the various types, and these combined with the room dimensions, candle power of the bulbs installed, reflection factors of the walls and ceilings, and spacing and mounting of the luminaires allow accurate design of illumination.

BIBLIOGRAPHY

1. *National Lamp Works of the General Electric Company Bull.* 36, Cleveland, Ohio.
2. Clark, Janet H.: "Lighting and Public Health," The Williams & Wilkins Company, Baltimore.
3. Phelps, E. B.: "Public Health Engineering," The Macmillan Company, New York.
4. Luckiesh, M., and A. J. Pacini: "Light and Health," The Williams & Wilkins Company, Baltimore.
5. Boast, W. B.: "Illumination Engineering," 2d ed., McGraw-Hill Book Company, Inc., New York, 1953.
6. Cady, F. E., and H. B. Dates: "Illuminating Engineering for Students and Engineers," John Wiley & Sons, Inc., New York.
7. Croft, T.: "American Electrician's Handbook," 7th ed., rev. by Clifford C. Carr, McGraw-Hill Book Company, Inc., New York, 1953.
8. Luckiesh, M.: "Light, Vision and Seeing," D. Van Nostrand Company., Inc., Princeton, N.J.

CHAPTER 15

HOUSING AND PREVENTION OF ACCIDENTS

15-1. Poor housing is a contributor to low physical and mental efficiency, and its relation to prevalence of disease is easy to recognize. Certainly if we consider public-health work as aimed at obtaining optimum conditions for physical and mental well-being, in addition to preventing disease, we must include improvement of housing in the program. Since poor housing is related to poverty, public opinion has tended to consider it an unavoidable evil, and up to two decades ago what little had been done was confined to a few laws or city ordinances directed at landlords and tenants to prevent some of the worst abuses. The growing strength of the public-health movement and the development of a more active community conscience have led to comprehensive studies as to what constitutes good housing and how the economic and legal hurdles which have intervened can be traversed or removed.

The American Public Health Association through well-qualified committees has formulated housing requirements and has grouped them under four headings: the satisfaction of fundamental physiological needs; the satisfaction of fundamental psychological needs; protection against communicable disease; and protection against accidents[1]. The discussion of housing needs in this chapter follows these principles.

Housing which does not comply with the more important requirements as to sanitation or which is in urgent need of repairs is known as "substandard" housing. An area in which substandard housing predominates, frequently accompanied by overcrowding, is known as a "slum." The Committee on the Hygiene of Housing of the American Public Health Association in its appraisal method of measuring the quality of housing considers that each of the following conditions represents a basic deficiency and that any dwelling having four or more such deficiencies is an extreme slum: (1) contaminated water supply; (2) water supply outside living unit or structure; (3) toilet shared or outside the structure; (4) bath shared or outside the structure; (5) more than 1.5 persons per habitable room; (6) overcrowding of sleeping rooms; (7) less than 40 square feet of sleeping area per person; (8) lack of dual egress; (9) installed heating lacking in three-quarters of rooms; (10) lack of installed electricity; (11) rooms lacking a window; (12) serious deterioration[2].

The term "blighted area" is applied by city planners to those sections of a city which are undesirable for residential purposes and are not in demand for commercial or industrial purposes. They frequently are adjacent to high-value business districts, and many property owners will not maintain properly the buildings in them in the hope that business will soon move in. Similar districts also tend to develop in or near industrial areas. Because of the traffic and noise the more prosperous people do not care to live in them, and the consequence is that buildings are converted to cheap rooming houses and tenements with high probability of their developing into slums. City planning which eliminates or prevents blighted areas is a means of slum prevention, but slum clearance, while also related to good city planning, is more closely connected with housing improvement.

SATISFACTION OF FUNDAMENTAL PHYSIOLOGICAL NEEDS

15-2. Heating and Ventilation. As already discussed, the factors controlling heat loss from the human body are air temperature, relative humidity of the air, air movement, and the temperature of such surrounding surfaces as walls, floors, ceilings, windows, and radiators, since the body radiates to them or receives radiant heat from them, according to which has the higher temperature. In the usual home in winter, air movement and humidity are not likely to be of importance. Air temperature and mean radiant or wall temperature when combined are called "operative temperature," and ordinarily it is the mean between the air temperature and the wall temperature. For normal persons who are wearing the usual type of clothing and at rest, this should be 65°F at knee height, 18 inches, in order to prevent chilling of the legs and feet. Air temperatures may be increased or decreased to compensate for deviations in the mean radiant temperature. In rooms occupied by old people or young children, the operative temperature may have to be 70°F at knee height. With ideal heating, temperatures at ankle height and at 5 feet would be almost identical. Unfortunately it is not uncommon for ankle-height temperature to be 65°F, the 5-foot temperature 70°F, the ceiling temperature 80°F—a total differential of 15°F. In poorly constructed dwellings, where proper temperatures may be difficult to achieve and heating facilities may be inadequate, the total differential may conceivably be as much as 30°F or more.

Climate is a factor in design of heating facilities as well as housing, but it should be possible to attain the above requirements under ordinary winter conditions. Heating engineers have adopted as a basis for design, an outside temperature 15°F above the lowest recorded temperature for a 10-year period.

Insulation, which is also useful in reducing heating costs, is an important item in reducing temperature differentials from floor to ceiling. Flooring materials of high heat-conducting potential, such as concrete or tile, should be avoided, particularly where children may play on the floor. Windows can be insulated by curtains.

For low-rent housing in one- or two-story dwellings the free-standing circulator type of stove is lowest in cost but is inferior for comfort to the circulating heater enclosed in a central distribution chamber and discharging warm air to adjacent rooms through grilles. Central heating is preferable for apartments and perhaps for large groups of one- and two-family houses, using either steam or hot water. Indirect heating with hot air may also be used. The ideal heating method for obtaining identical ankle-height and 5-foot temperatures is the radiant method (see Art. 13-14) with units installed in the floor or low in the walls.

Ventilation of homes is also concerned with adequate heat loss from the body. The factors involved are air temperature, mean radiant temperature, relative humidity, and air movement. In cold weather, operative temperature will be the determining factor and should not exceed 75°F in the zone of occupancy, or discomfort will result. Overheating in the winter season is common, and prevention should be possible by control of heating sources without resort to opening windows. Here steam heating and hot forced air provides flexibility in control.

In summer, air cooling and dehumidification are desirable but uneconomical for the low-rent house. The attic fan (see Art. 13-19) is practical as a means of drawing cool night air into a house to encourage sleep. Cross ventilation should be provided in each house by the proper placing of windows. They should also extend to within 6 inches of the ceiling so that hot upper air can escape. Windows of the casement type which swing either horizontally or vertically may be preferable to the ordinary double-sash type. They may also be used to deflect air currents in desired directions. Another factor of importance in summer is exposure to prevailing winds so that maximum air movement is obtained. Summer sunshine, particularly in the late afternoon, is undesirable in rooms principally occupied in the daytime. This must be considered, however, in relation to the amount of direct sunshine desired in winter.

A third requirement in ventilation is a sufficient air interchange, particularly in the heating period, to prevent accumulation of odors from human bodies, cooking, or various heat sources. The rate of air interchange required to prevent the accumulation of odors is variable, depending upon the total space involved, the number of persons present, and the degree of activity (see Art. 16-8).

Such an air change is obtained automatically in cold weather by normal leakage of air through ceilings and walls of usual porosity and around normally constructed doors and windows. The modern trend is to use a minimum floor area and ceiling height requirement in preference to the cubic-foot determination. Section 8 of the A.P.H.A. "Suggested Housing Ordinance" states, in part: "Every dwelling unit shall contain at least 150 square feet of floor space for the first occupant thereof, and at least 100 additional square feet of floor space for every additional occupant thereof, the floor space to be calculated on the basis of total habitable room area."

Fumes, odors, soot, and grime may enter by windows from industrial and other neighborhood sources, and they are not always subject to effective control under antinuisance regulations. Such possibilities, together with the direction of prevailing winds, are factors which should be considered in the choice of housing sites.

15-3. Lighting. Lighting of houses must be planned for both natural and artificial light. Definitions of the lighting terms used here are found in Chap. 14.

Natural Lighting. The minimum intensity of illumination in any occupied space should be 6 foot-candles on a horizontal plane 30 inches above the floor. With unobstructed exposure to the sky, this illumination will be attained in clear weather in the latitude of Washington, D.C., 39°, with a window-glass area of 15 per cent of the floor area, provided also that walls and ceilings are light in color. Since the average brightness of the sky varies both with latitude and with different regions of the country, corrections must be made. The average daylight illumination is 25 per cent higher in the states between the Mississippi and the Rocky Mountains and about 46 per cent higher in the states between the Rockies and the Sierra Nevada and Cascade Mountains than in the Eastern states. It is possible, therefore, that in the Plains and Plateau states, window percentages may be lower and thus housing costs can be reduced. Correction for latitude can be made at the rate of 2 per cent increase of the percentage for each degree of latitude north of 39°, and the same rate of decrease for each degree south. Thus at 45° latitude the window area would be increased by 12 per cent of 15 per cent, or to 17 per cent of the floor area.

The percentages given are for practically unobstructed sky. If there are trees or buildings which obstruct the sky, increased window area is required. The 15 per cent figure applies to sky angles[1] from 90 to 86 degrees; from 86 to 82 degrees to 16 per cent; 82 to 78 degrees to 17 per cent; etc. Since windows should extend almost to the ceiling for

[1] The sky angle is the angle between the vertical and a line from the lowest window sill to the lower edge of the visible sky.

both ventilation and lighting, an increase in area required by local conditions should be obtained by increasing their width.

Placing windows as high as possible gives the greatest sky angle in all parts of the room and thus secures the greatest lighting effectiveness. Windows extending to less than 30 inches from the floor tend to cause glare and obstruct furniture placement without increasing illumination to any extent. Inside walls should have reflection factors of at least 50 per cent and ceilings, 70 per cent. A mat (dull) finish paint should be used because glossy paints produce glare. Venetian blinds and window shades are useful to prevent glare, the former being especially valuable in allowing reflection to inner parts of the room.

Direct sunlight is desirable, for at least part of the day, for all dwellings, especially in winter. Sunlight, particularly its ultraviolet rays, is recognized as being of value to the body. The amount which enters a dwelling depends upon the sky angles of the windows and the orientation of the buildings. For dwellings in rows a desirable orientation is to face 20 to 30° east or west of south. This allows sunshine to penetrate the yard on both sides of the structure. Casements which open substantially throughout their area are more desirable than double-hung windows for admitting ultraviolet rays of sunlight. Ordinary window glass eliminates most of the ultraviolet rays.

Artificial Illumination. Where electricity is available, and this is desirable for lighting in order to avoid fires, sufficient illumination should be arranged so that all areas in the room may be covered by adequate light without glare, with at least three convenient outlets in the living room and two in other rooms. For accurate illumination with regard to foot-candle requirements, it is suggested that the I.E.S. standards be followed. For the control of glare, all bulbs should be shielded from view by suitable reflectors, globes, and shades to prevent excessive brightness against the background of the luminaire. Ceiling fixtures of the semi-indirect type, and floor lamps of the direct-indirect type go well together for local and general illumination. Shades of table and floor lamps should be of such thickness and color that their surfaces are not a source of glare.

15-4. Protection against Excessive Noise. Effects of excessive noise are given in Art. 19-18. Noises should be excluded from dwellings to the extent that the noise level does not exceed 50 decibels (Art. 19-19); 30 decibels should be the upper limit in sleeping rooms.[1] Housing sites should be chosen away from such sources of noise as factories, highways, railways, and athletic fields. Motor horns and radios should be con-

[1] These figures are based upon European practice and call for further examination under American conditions, where the greater numbers of radios and automobiles produce higher noise levels.

trolled. Small enclosed courts should be avoided in housing developments since noise may be reflected from the building walls.

Noises which are transmitted by the air in a multifamily dwelling can be reduced about 50 decibels by party walls equivalent to an 8-inch brick wall. Apartment doors opening into public passageways should be fitted to exclude noise.

Noises which are transmitted by the structure, such as footsteps or furniture moving, can be reduced about 15 decibels by proper construction. Airborne noise can also be reduced. Two thicknesses of wood flooring on standard joists with a lath and plaster ceiling effect a reduction of 10 to 15 decibels. If the laths or ceiling boards are fastened to the joists with spring clips and the floor is laid so as to allow some "play" between the subfloor and the joists, a reduction of well above 15 decibels may be obtained. Concrete floors are effective against air-borne but not against structure-borne noise. All plumbing, steam pipes, and valves should be correctly designed so that steam "hammer" and "singing" in valves do not occur. Refrigerating and heating equipment, pumps, and blowers should be so installed that vibrations are not transmitted to the structure. Plumbing stacks and water riser pipes should preferably not be located in living-room or bedroom walls.

15-5. Provision of Adequate Exercise and Play Space for Children. Playground and recreation space is considered to be essential to the physical and mental well-being of children and adults. It should be considered by all who are concerned with the construction of homes. This is primarily a problem of neighborhood and city planning and must be considered from the standpoints of the types of recreation to be provided, including indoor recreation, the amount and location of existing recreation facilities, the availability of trained recreation leaders, etc. In any case play spaces for very young children should be provided within each large group or block of buildings. Athletic fields within half a mile are desirable for adolescents.

15-6. Water Supply. The source of water for a single dwelling or a housing project should, wherever possible, be a city supply which is controlled as to quality by health authorities. If a well or some other individual supply must be used, methods of construction and protection should be as described in Chap. 5. Within the building the water supply should be protected from contamination by cross connections, or fixtures which have inlets at insufficient distances above the highest possible water level in the fixture. Where defects are found to exist, corrections should be made. Routine inspections of large projects should include checking on alterations which may be made from time to time.

15-7. Excreta Disposal. Water-carried sewerage should be available for all dwellings as the best means of preventing the spread of disease by flies or in other ways. A separate toilet should be available for each family, and it should be located high enough above the sewer to avoid danger of flooding. Compartments in which toilets are located should have floors and walls of material as nearly impervious as possible. The room should be well lighted, preferably by a window in daytime. The house drainage system should be tight. Possible backing up of sewage or storm water into basements should be considered when the site of the dwelling is chosen. If back-flooding of basements is feared, the hazard may be minimized by installing a check valve and gate valve in the branch serving the basement fixtures, or the outlets of the basement fixtures may be discharged into a sump from which an electrically operated pump can raise the sewage to discharge it into the sewer. Such pumps should be of the centrifugal type with float-controlled automatic start when the sump is full and a stop when it is empty.

Isolated dwellings may have water-carried sewerage with a disposal system as described in Chap. 4 or some type of privy as described in Chap. 3.

15-8. Prevention of Vermin. Accumulations of organic refuse breed flies, and piles of lumber and similar refuse provide harborage for rats and should not be permitted. Ratproofing as described in Art. 9-77 should be applied. Pools of standing water should be eliminated. If they are ornamental, frequent inspections should be made to determine the presence of mosquito larvae. If found, fish or larvicides may be used (Chap 9). Screening of windows and doors is a necessity to exclude flies and mosquitoes (see Arts. 9-45 to 9-47).

Where the population to be housed is likely to be infested with lice or bedbugs, treatment of clothing, bedding, and furniture may be desirable. Methods are given in Art. 19-13. Bedbugs and roaches which have invaded dwellings can be eliminated by the methods described in Arts. 19-11 and 19-12.

15-9. Food Storage. The observance of low temperatures for food storage is economical, but it is also a sanitary measure. As discussed in Chap. 12, certain pathogenic bacteria propagate in some foods, so that food poisoning or infection may result through ingestion of improperly preserved food. Every home should have facilities for storing food at 50°F or less. This can be done in a properly constructed icebox or in a mechanical refrigerator. The amount of refrigerated space required for an urban home depends upon the marketing habits of the housewife and the size of the family.

15-10. Provision of Sufficient Space in Sleeping Rooms. Experience in institutions and Army barracks has shown that, if the center-to-center distance between cots is less than 6 feet or the floor area per cot is less than 50 square feet, the spread of communicable disease by mouth spray is likely to occur. Satisfactory spacing of cots would provide 3 feet of clear space between them. That is the essential point.

PROTECTION AGAINST ACCIDENTS

15-11. Materials and Construction. Building codes specify materials and methods of construction, and if they are followed no danger should exist. Termite infestation sometimes causes accidents by weakening joists or stairways. Hence, in zones of serious infestation, wood members should be avoided in foundations and the clearance between the ground and woodwork should be at least 6 inches outside and 18 inches inside the foundation. The underspace should be cleared of wood scraps and ventilated with screened openings. Termite shields of metal of proper design are necessary between the foundation wall or columns and the woodwork.

15-12. Fire Protection. This calls for construction methods and materials that do not result in fire hazards and that provide adequate facilities for escape in case of fire. Elimination of fire hazards calls for more details than can be given here, but some important requirements should be pointed out. Electrical wiring should follow local codes. Stoves and heaters should be mounted clear of combustible floors and walls, but if they are near walls, there should be adequate air space and fireproof mats or screens. Smoke pipes also should be insulated from walls by thimbles and be properly supported. Chimneys should be supported by foundations on the ground, and all wood joints or partition members should be at least 2 inches away from them with the intervening space properly insulated with mortar or other material. Chimneys should be lined with fire-clay tile, and the joints should not coincide with the masonry joints.

In multiple buildings, stairways should be enclosed in fire-resistant materials. In buildings over two stories high, fire-resistant materials should be used in exterior walls, roofs, and first-tier beams, particularly between apartments and between stair halls and apartments and all shafts. Multiple dwellings over four stories in height should have noncombustible floors and floor joists, and buildings over six stories should be noncombustible throughout.

When framing with combustible members leaves hollow walls, fire stops, preferably of noncombustible materials, should be placed. On roofs, wooden shingles are undesirable because of possible ignition by sparks blowing from burning buildings. Most noncombustible types of roofs have sufficient insulating value to prevent ignition of the supporting boards. Protection offered by metal roofing can be increased by placing asbestos felt between the roofing and the boards.

Exits in case of fire should be carefully considered. Multiple dwellings should have at least two exits from each living unit, and the doors of these exits should open outward. An exception to two exits in multiple dwellings may be made if the stairways are in separate fire-resisting enclosures having self-closing doors at each floor.

15-13. Accident Prevention. Accidents occurring in the house include electric shocks and burns, gas poisoning, and falls. Danger of electric shock can be reduced by placing live conductors so that they are not exposed to contact, and by grounding metal enclosures of electrical appliances so that failure of insulation cannot cause shocks. All portable appliances and pendent fixtures should be so placed that no person can come simultaneously in contact with the fixture and plumbing or gas pipe or fixtures or other grounded metal. In no case should a wall switch be placed so that the occupant of a bathtub can reach it. If by reason of lack of room the switches or convenience outlets must be placed within reach of plumbing fixtures, the cover plate must be nonmetallic. In laundries and kitchens, or wherever hands may be wet, electric lights should be controlled by wall switches or pull chains which have an insulating link in them

Protection against gas poisoning should be obtained by the precautions described in Art. 13-23.

Falls may be caused by a wide variety of conditions which are difficult to foresee. But it is clearly essential to use safeguards on bathtubs, stairs, windows, balconies, and roofs. Bathtubs, particularly those of the built-in type surrounded by tile, should have handholds available. Steep stairs should be avoided; the angle of slope should be between 30 and 36 degrees, and the sum of the width of the tread and twice the riser height should be 24 to 25 inches. Satisfactory values are 10 inches for the tread width and 7 to 7½ inches for the riser. Steps, of course, should be uniform in dimensions. Stairs should have handrails, particularly outdoor stairs. Winding stairways too narrow for a foothold at the rail side are especially dangerous.

Window sills that are less than 30 inches from the floor should be avoided, especially at stairway landings. If such sills are unavoidable, one or more crossbars should be installed to prevent children from falling out; built-in screens are desirable from this standpoint. Casement windows, if designed with enough clearance at the hinges to permit washing from the inside, minimize the dangers in window cleaning. Rails or parapets are essential around porches, balconies, and accessible roofs, even if the fall is only 2 or 3 feet. In the North all sloping roofs which may have a pitch of perhaps 15 to 55 degrees and which terminate over steps or walks should be equipped with snow guards to protect passers-by. Good lighting is a necessity for all walks and stairs.

Protection against traffic accidents is not a detail of housing proper, but location of housing projects should be considered with traffic conditions in mind. Traffic hazards are greatly reduced if residential streets are planned so as to discourage through traffic. In some new housing communities this is done by using dead-end streets. Usual pedestrian routes should be planned so that it is unnecessary to cross a major traffic way except by overpasses or underpasses. Blind corners should be avoided by the proper placing of buildings and shrubbery. In planning the location and other aspects of playgrounds, special precautions are required in order to isolate them from traffic.

To illustrate the belief that home accidents are closely related to environmental factors, which include basic design and location of dwelling structures, an analysis has been made of a study conducted in 1952 and 1953 by the Richmond, Ga., County Health Department in a particular area of Augusta, Ga. This analysis by Henry C. Steed, Jr.[3] is summarized as follows:

The housing in tracts V and VI of Augusta, Ga., was classified according to the appraisal method developed by the Committee on the Hygiene of Housing of the American Public Health Association. Blocks were rated as Grade A, B, C, D, or E, with A the best, and E the worst. The most significant fact in comparing population estimates with class of housing is the extremely high percentage of nonwhite population living in the lower-class housing. Eighty per cent of the total population living in Grade E housing was nonwhite, while only 3 per cent of the total lived in Grade A housing.

The comparison of accidents by type with accident rate by grade of housing revealed the general trend in the entire city. The treatment rate for all types of injuries increases steadily as the standard of housing becomes poorer, except that in Grade E housing the rate shows a sudden drop. This general picture is true in all types of accidents; although home accidents drop slightly from Grade B to C and turn sharply upward in Grade D, the general trend is a rise in the rate of injuries as the class of housing becomes poorer. There are two factors which could possibly be responsible for the differences in injury rates, such as are indicated by the drop in the rate for Grade E housing. These are (1) the large proportion of the population which is nonwhite and (2) the variation of the socioeconomic status in the various classes of housing. One type of injury generally associated with poor housing is falls, for which this study shows a definite rise from 8.4 per 1,000 for Grade A housing to 17.2 per 1,000 for Grade E housing.

The grading system referred to above and developed by the A.P.H.A. committee is based on a "dwelling score," which is the sum of the penalty scores of the 30 items which are involved in the inspection of a dwelling unit. These items are grouped as to facilities, maintenance, and occupancy. Subtotal scores for these three groups are combined to give the total dwelling score.

Grade A (0–39 points) indicates good housing with minor problems of facilities, maintenance, or occupancy.

Grade B (40–79 points) indicates housing that has become blighted to a slight degree but which can be rehabilitated or repaired economically.

Grade C (80–119 points) indicates housing that has become so bad that rehabilitation is very difficult and may not be economically feasible because of the many major repairs necessary. Demolition and redevelopment should be considered.

Grade D (120–159 points) indicates very bad housing that should have second priority for demolition and redevelopment.

Grade E (160 or more points) indicates housing of extreme slum quality that should have first priority for demolition and redevelopment.

SATISFACTION OF FUNDAMENTAL PSYCHOLOGICAL NEEDS

15-14. Privacy. Privacy, to some degree and during some periods, is a necessity to most people. The ideal would be a room of one's own for everybody. This is not always possible, but at least a bedroom should have to be shared with only one other person and one of the same sex, except in the case of married couples and young children. Separate bedrooms for the sexes is required at the age of 10 years by English law (and by the city of Toronto, Canada) although some American authorities consider that this should be two years younger. Sleeping rooms of children over two years of age, according to psychiatric opinion, should be separate from those of parents. Bathrooms, toilets, and bedrooms should be accessible from halls or living rooms, not through other bedrooms.

Regulations against overcrowding also promote privacy. English legislation requires that not more than two persons occupy a bedroom. Two rooms are required for three persons, three rooms for five persons, four rooms for seven and one-half persons, and so on. Bathrooms are not counted as rooms. Infants under one year of age are not counted as persons, and children between one and ten are counted as half-persons. In dwellings, the practices of taking in boarders and subrenting rooms must be controlled. As families increase in size, some provision must be made for obtaining appropriate living units.

One of the most vexatious problems facing cities is the control of the conversion of old houses into "hot-plate" apartments and rooming and boarding houses. From the public health standpoint, conversion of single-family residences into multifamily or rooming houses is not necessarily undesirable as long as such conversion is done according to minimum standards of occupancy and facilities. This problem, of course, ties in with Art. 15-20, "Zoning and Housing." Most zoning ordinances assume that a land-use pattern, once established, remains relatively unchanged. This, of course, is not the case, for neighborhoods mature and certain changes are unavoidable. Zoning laws should, therefore, be written with these changes in mind in order to encourage honorable maturity within minimum standards for conversion.

15-15. Provision for Normal Family and Community Life. This could be called provision for sociability. Opportunities must be given for adolescent boys and girls to meet under wholesome conditions. This requires a living room of adequate size which can be used by all members of the family, plus reasonable space for withdrawal elsewhere during periods of entertainment. In housing projects where space has been kept

FIG. 15-1. Redlands Homes, 75-unit low-rent housing project in Redlands, Calif. (*Photograph courtesy of Public Housing Administration, Washington, D.C.*)

to a minimum in order to attain low rents, community meeting rooms for special entertaining are available. In some cases, accommodations for overnight guests have been included.

A normal community life for dwellers in a housing project is something of a compromise. They should not be cut off from the rest of the city, and there should be easy communication with the city's centers of culture and business. Other community facilities which should be easily accessible are schools, churches, entertainment, shopping, libraries, and medical service. If they are not available, at least some should be supplied as a neighborhood facility, if not for the project alone. This is a phase of city planning as applied to the particular area.

Another factor allied to the above, which may be mentioned as a reason for good housing rather than as a factor in planning, is the better morale of persons who live in decent home surroundings. Persons who live in substandard houses, particularly children, may develop a feeling of inferiority which may lead to serious social consequences.

15-16. Provisions for Cleanliness and Convenience. Obviously an ample supply of safe water is a necessity for personal and home cleanliness. Clean hands have a part in preventing the spread of disease, but cleanliness is also a factor in promoting good morale. Where water must be carried into a house, it is obvious that insufficient amounts are used. Hence every dwelling, for the protection of health and maintenance convenience, should have facilities within the building to assure adequate quantities of safe-quality water. About 20 gallons per person per day is the minimum for household use. The minimum facilities should include a washbasin, kitchen sink, and bathtub or shower. Hot water should also be provided.

To facilitate household cleaning, interior surfaces should be nearly impervious, with all joints as tight as practicable. Surfaces should be readily washable, and design should avoid, as far as possible, dust-catching angles and pockets.

Since the home is a workplace as well as a dwelling, consideration must be given to physiological and psychological factors which contribute to fatigue. This covers a wide variety of requirements concerning cooking, storage, laundering, and refuse disposal. Fatigue and strain on the back and abdominal muscles can be reduced by providing proper heights for different kitchen tasks. The best height for dishwashing appears to be 23½ inches above the floor, while for rolling dough, 33½ inches appears desirable, and for beating and mixing, 31½ inches. Compromises are likely to be necessary in some kitchens. Stools can be used also as a means of adjustment to existing surfaces during work.

In large housing projects, suitable chutes which discharge garbage and rubbish to incinerators have been used. Outdoor receptacles placed below ground to prevent access of animals are considered desirable, but in any case each living unit must have suitable garbage and rubbish containers so handled that animals and wind cannot cause the scattering of contents.

HOUSING AND GOVERNMENT

15-17. Benefits of Improved Housing. Impressive figures are available to show that good housing, particularly when combined with slum clearance, pays good dividends to the community in decreased incidence of disease and crime. These benefits also result in decreased cost of municipal services in those areas. A few instances will be given.

Western Reserve University sponsored a study of the long-time results of razing a five-block slum in Cleveland and replacing it with a new housing development called Carver Park. The population of the area is about 5,000.

Redevelopment brought the following results. Crime in Carver Park decreased 17.5 per cent from 1942 to 1947. During the same period in an adjacent slum area, among a carefully matched group of families, crime increased about 9 per cent. The tuberculosis rate in Carver Park declined 54 per cent. Per population unit, the tuberculosis rate in the near-by slum was more than twice as great. If the slum had not been removed, the city would have had to spend an estimated $25,000 a year more in relief rentals, $11,000 more for fire protection, and $25,250 more in tuberculosis care.

In San Francisco, the planning and housing association compared a slum area with the Marina district, an average well-kept neighborhood, with similar results. Both areas had populations of about 12,000. The slum had 36 times as many cases of tuberculosis as the Marina district. Three babies died in the slum for each one in the Marina area. While there were 4,771 adults arrested in the slum area, only 39 Marina adults were arrested. The slum had twice as many fires. In 1946 the cost to San Franciscans of maintaining city services in the slums as compared to the Marina district was twice as much for fire protection, four times as great for the juvenile courts, 89 times as great for police protection, and 100 times as great for health costs.

In Cincinnati, a study by the Public Health Federation revealed that the city's over-all death rate would be about 15 per cent lower were it not for the high mortality in the slums. The death rates for pneumonia and tuberculosis average three times as high in the slums as in the whole city. Accidental deaths occurred twice as often and the homicide rate was four times that of the city as a whole.

15-18. Housing Regulation. The above article indicates that housing improvement, with its accompaniment of lessening slums, reduces crime, fire, and disease. Recognition of these facts has opened the way to invoking the police power of government to prevent dangerous housing, to require remedies, and to punish violaters. Since police power in intrastate matters is vested in the states, the control may be applied by state laws or in cities by means of city ordinances. City ordinances cannot contravene in any particular the laws of the state in which they are located, but they may be more detailed. Four methods of legal control of housing have developed, and these are briefly described below[4]:

1. General housing laws, as passed by Michigan and Iowa, are based upon the excellent model housing law written by Lawrence Veiller in 1920. These laws deal with construction and upkeep of single- and multifamily dwellings and also with sanitary facilities, required space, lighting, etc.

In some states they provide for a housing enforcement official. Other states have enacted housing statutes of the old-line tenement-control type, which, of course, apply only to multifamily dwellings. Usually state housing laws apply only in cities over a certain size.

2. Some cities have adopted comprehensive local housing codes as ordinances. These incorporate the essential features indicated under 1.

3. Special laws or ordinances are passed defining unsafe or substandard dwellings and providing for remedial action by demolition, repair, abatement, or closure. These were usually passed to control flagrant conditions, but they are not sufficiently comprehensive.

FIG. 15-2. Avalon Gardens, 164-unit pre-World War II low-rent housing project built by the Housing Authority of Los Angeles, Calif. *(Photograph courtesy of Public Housing Administration, Washington, D.C.)*

4. Enabling acts may be passed by a state legislature or city council. These define the problems and the ends to be gained but leave to the proper department or official the authority to set the standard which will remedy matters. These standards are written in a code of administrative regulations, have the force of law, and can be enforced by the officer designated by the enabling law. For example, the enabling act includes a clause which, in the interest of health and morals, gives to a particular official the power to prescribe minimum standards of space per family or per person. In order to apply this provision, the responsible official formulates such requirements as may be needed and attends to their enforcement.

The establishment of administrative regulations has some advantages over the codes established in detail by law or ordinance. The latter can be amended only by a new law or ordinance, and obtaining this may be slow and difficult. The administrative code, on the other hand, can be made as detailed as necessary and, what is more important, details can be easily changed if found to be impractical or in order to meet new conditions or advances in knowledge. Housing officials prefer this type. An example of such a housing code is that of Baltimore.

15-19. Enforcement of Housing Regulations. Housing regulations, in addition to health matters, involve fire protection, structural condition, plumbing, and electrical wiring. This presents complications for enforcement which would involve at least three departments—fire, health, and building—considering that electrical, plumbing, and building inspection are all in the building department. To meet this situation in Hartford, Conn., it was proposed that nine inspecting items would be assigned to a combined inspectorate of the building and fire departments, that eight would be the responsiblity of the health department, and that two (ventilation and heating) would be handled jointly. In Cincinnati, which operates under a modern building code with comprehensive housing regulations for new and old dwellings, the building department has a force of special housing inspectors under a special supervisor, which inspects annually every dwelling in the major substandard areas, issues orders, and makes follow-up inspections to see that orders have been complied with. Fire hazards are inspected by the fire department.

It is apparent that the Cincinnati system is far better coordinated than is the Hartford plan. Duplication of inspections is kept to a minimum, record keeping is simplified, and enforcement is easier. In general, therefore, it may be said that a single housing authority in a city is to be preferred, although compromises as to a division of the inspector's duties are possible if the local situation makes them necessary. However, a central housing office and official are necessary for keeping housing records, including the inspection reports, the issuing of orders for vacating unfit housing, the demolition of unsafe buildings, and the remedying of other violations, together with the follow-up of such orders.

15-20. Zoning and Housing. City planning is becoming more and more important in urban affairs. Two of its important features are control of zoning and the subdivision of land. Control of land subdivision requires landowners to conform to certain regulations when they develop the land for residential or business purposes. The regulation covers minimum lot sizes and dimensions and width of streets, and in the case of large developments, the subdividers are encouraged to dedicate a portion of the land for parks and playgrounds. This type of regulation controls the density of population per acre and also assures a street width that suits neighborhood requirements. Minimum lot sizes can be varied in different districts to suit different income groups. Also, by proper attention to street widths and their relation to traffic movement, it is possible to discourage through traffic and thereby reduce accidents, particularly to children. Such planning also permits a reduction in the total street area, which, in turn, lowers first cost and maintenance cost of streets and thus reduces housing costs by lowering selling values of lots and taxes.

Zoning regulates the bulk of buildings, *i.e.*, the proportion of the lot that may be occupied by the building, and the uses to which the buildings may be put. The city is divided into districts: industrial, of which there may be several subdivisions, such as heavy and light; commercial, with several subdivisions; and residential, subdivided into apartment, high-value, and low-value, the latter having smaller lots for the smaller houses built for low-income families. Forming districts according to uses prevents industries and commercial firms from building high structures or establishing offensive or dangerous industries in residential areas. The zoning ordinances are very explicit as to space around residences to ensure sufficient light and air, and the heights of the buldings are also restricted. This is done by specifying the minimum allowable width of side yard, length of rear yard, and setback from the front line of the building lot. If row houses are permitted, minimum allowable widths of courts between the houses are specified. Required open space differs somewhat in the different residential districts, being somewhat smaller in the low-value districts. Similar restrictions are also placed upon apartment-house districts and commercial districts, although these are much more liberal. In a commercial district, for example, the allowable building height at the front lot line may be one and a half times the street width from lot line to lot line. If the owner wishes to build higher, he must set the next stories back a required distance. By another setback he may go still higher. This procedure allows the construction of skyscrapers without excessive interference with sunlight to other buildings.

It will be apparent that zoning and housing are allied. A city that is logically zoned has aided housing in several ways. It has ensured better living conditions in newly constructed dwellings. The encroachments of industry and business into residential districts has been curbed, and this prevents the formation of blighted districts, undesirable for residential purposes, which soon develop into slum areas.

15-21. Municipal Housing Programs. The difficulty of obtaining suitable houses in sufficient number for the poorer classes has led to many housing schemes. Some industrial plants have built their own towns, including not only the streets, sewers, waterworks, and other utilities but also the homes. These developments have not all been satisfactory from the standpoint of housing or other considerations. In some projects the homes are sold to employees on easy payments, while in others they are rented at a rate sufficient to allow a moderate or only a nominal return on the capital invested. The advantage to the worker is the avoidance of paying for large construction profit and the costs of the involved financing which accompanies present-day building.

Strictly municipal housing involves construction, maintenance, and rental at moderate rates of modern homes by the cities. It has been tried by European cities with success. Municipal tenements in London have apparently been profitable, although there is a question whether profits would have been shown if the usual accounting methods of business

FIG. 15-3. New Helvetia, 310-unit low-rent public housing project in Sacramento, Calif. (*Photograph courtesy of Sacramento, Calif., Housing Authority.*)

had been used. As a rule such municipal schemes have resulted in financial loss. There are other important considerations. To result in any appreciable betterment to the large populations concerned, municipal housing requires enormous sums of money. Furthermore, to avoid disaster, these sums must be expended with much more business acumen than is usually displayed by a city council or commission. Finally, experience abroad has shown that the demolition of a slum preliminary to the erection of model tenements or dwellings usually results in the original dwellers' scattering into and actually increasing the congestion of other slums, while the new model tenements, when completed, are occupied by an entirely different class of persons. The plan suggested in Art. 15-22 would overcome some of the difficulties mentioned.

15-22. Federal Government and Housing. The Federal government, by the Housing Act of 1937 and its frequent amendments, is showing increasing interest in the improvement of housing. The first prerequisite for federally aided low-rent public housing is a state enabling law permitting localities to establish housing authorities and to accept Federal aid to build and operate low-rent housing. A majority of the states and territories have such legislation. Generally the enabling law authorizes municipalities and/or counties having acute housing problems to establish a local housing authority. This enabling legislation permits local housing authorities to negotiate with and receive aid from the Federal housing agency. After an ordinance or resolution is adopted by the local governing body, the housing authority commission (usually composed of five members) is appointed by the head of the local government. The commission generally serves as an independent body. The actual administrative duties are performed by a salaried staff headed by an executive director. In Arizona, Michigan, and New Mexico, housing authorities are branches of the local government.

The Housing Act of 1954 placed much emphasis on the prevention of slums and urban blight. Under this act, local communities are required, as a condition to receiving Federal assistance for slum clearance and urban renewal, low-rent public housing, and certain new F.H.A. insurance programs, to develop and put into operation a *workable program*, using all means available to eliminate and prevent slums and urban blight.

Assistance is made available in order to stimulate conservation and rehabilitation of housing and neighborhood programs and to assure efficient and proper development and redevelopment of communities. Grants are provided to encourage cities in developing methods and techniques for the prevention and the elimination of slums and urban blight. The administration of related programs is coordinated to assure that Federal assistance will be provided with a minimum of waste and with maximum utilization of local initiative in providing financing and enterprise. The insurance of mortgages for F.H.A. sales housing, F.H.A. rental housing, F.H.A. cooperative housing, and F.H.A. assistance on the rehabilitation of slums has been liberalized. The act also provides loans to states and local public agencies for public facilities. Loans can also be made for college student housing and farm housing. The Federal National Mortgage Association is rechartered under the act so that private investments are gradually being substituted for Federal investments and private rather than Federal funds are being used for the purchase of mortgages. The *workable program* as interpreted by the Housing and Home Finance Agency should include the following basic elements to be successful:

1. Sound local housing and health codes
2. A general "master" plan for the community's development
3. An appraisal of the neighborhoods and kind of treatment needed

4. An effective administrative organization to supervise the program
5. Financial capacity to carry out the program
6. Arrangements for the rehousing of displaced families
7. Community-wide citizens' participation and support

Such a program is a good approach for a community to undertake if it is ready to help itself with or without Federal aid. Under the *workable program*, the Federal government can provide:

1. Loans and grants—up to two-thirds of the net cost—for clearing areas or replanting blighted areas for rehabilitation
2. Special F.H.A. mortgage insurance to share the risk of private investment in the rebuilding and rehabilitation of these replanned urban renewal areas
3. Special F.H.A. mortgage insurance for low-cost private housing, new or rehabilitated, for displaced families

Other aids that can be used for urban renewal purposes are:

1. Preliminary loans and annual subsidies for low-rent public housing for low-income families where wanted and needed
2. Special assistance for general planning and experimental approaches for urban renewal and technical and professional help on the community's particular urban-renewal problems

A majority of the states have passed laws to promote slum clearance. Under these laws, cities may condemn and purchase land for slum clearance and re-use for such public purposes as parks; or the city may sell part or all of the land to private interests for redevelopment for housing purposes, or it may use the land itself for housing projects.

Another promising development has been the interest of large business concerns in housing as an investment, rather than as a speculation. The Metropolitan Life Insurance Company has constructed large-scale housing projects which not only return a reasonable profit but also allow reasonable rentals. This is an indication of the possible results of a combination which has hitherto been conspicuously absent from the housing industry in the United States: careful planning, economical methods of financing, large-scale production with its economies, absence of the motive of speculation or sale at a profit, and careful management.

BIBLIOGRAPHY

1. "Basic Principles of Healthful Housing," American Public Health Association, New York, 1946.
2. Pond, M. A.: Housing and Health: Sanitary Aspect of the Dwelling, *Am. J. Public Health*, vol. 39, no. 4, April, 1949.
3. Steed, Henry C., Jr.: "Relations between Standards of Housing and Incidence of Accidents," Georgia State Department of Health, Home Safety Unit, Atlanta, Ga.

4. Ascher, C. S.: Regulations of Housing: Hints for Health Officers, *Am. J. Public Health,* vol. 37, no. 5, May, 1947; Improvement of Local Housing Regulation under the Law, *Am. J. Public Health,* November, 1942.
5. "An Appraisal Method for Measuring the Quality of Housing," pt. I, "Nature and Uses of the Method," 1945; pt. II, "Appraisal of Dwelling Conditions: Director's Manual," 1946, American Public Health Association, New York.
6. "A Report of the President's Advisory Committee on Government Housing Policies and Programs," U.S. Government Printing Office, December, 1953.
7. Public Law 560, chap. 649, 83d Cong., 2d Sess., H.S. 7839.
8. "A Primer on Rehabilitation under Local Law Enforcement," National Association of Real Estate Boards, Committee on Rehabilitation, Washington.
9. Publications of the Housing and Home Finance Agency.

CHAPTER 16

INSTITUTIONAL SANITATION

16-1. The provision and maintenance of an environment conducive to health at institutions of all types—including general hospitals, chronic-disease hospitals, convalescent homes, maternity hospitals, geriatric facilities, schools, jails, and prisons—encompass all the features of a well-rounded community public health program. To some extent the needs of the various institutions vary, depending on their uses. Although the fundamentals of water supply, plumbing, sewage disposal, heating, ventilation, and vermin control are much the same at all types of institutions, standards for lighting, recreational space, and special service facilities entail a close study of the type of institution, its uses, and the individuals involved.

Institutional sanitation is a recognized activity of health departments at both the local and state level. It is a function of the state to establish standards and to promulgate rules and regulations which permit the local representatives to supervise effectively the construction, maintenance, and operation of the institutions. The state should offer consultation services which may be utilized by the institution operators and designers as well as by local health departments. Another very important function of the state health department is the review of plans and specifications for new institutions. Close liaison between the state health department and such other state agencies as prison boards, hospital boards, and education departments is most helpful in carrying out this program.

SCHOOLS

16-2. The school health and sanitation program depends upon the size of the school, whether it is a rural or city school, the age group to be served, and the availability of health services from official and volunteer agencies other than those provided directly by the school administration. The rural school is required to provide many services that are furnished by the community in urban areas, and the absence of local health departments and volunteer health agencies increases the school's responsibilities. Standards for school health and sanitation are the responsibility of the state health department, and the local health agencies cooperate with the educational authorities in applying these standards. The state health department is also responsible for consultative services which are essential in implementing the more complicated phases of the program.

The complexity of school sanitation problems, along with the high degree of susceptibility of school children to communicable diseases, makes the role of the sanitarian one of great importance.

16-3. School Health Program. A school health program should include service in the following seven areas:

1. *Control of communicable disease.* This includes daily observation by the teacher, who should be instructed to note the signs and symptoms of illness. Although no attempt should be made to diagnose the specific disease or to treat the illness, the teacher should be alert to such evident signs as flushed face, rash, difficult breathing, abnormal cough, and pallor and should also ascertain the presence of such symptoms as chills, fever, and headache. The child who exhibits these abnormalities should be excluded from the classroom and sent to the office of the school nurse or principal, where the teacher's findings can be verified. The child is then sent home with a note of suggestion that the family doctor be called on for specific diagnosis and treatment. The note should also inform the parents that if the illness is a communicable disease, the child should not be returned to school until he has a readmission certificate from the local health officer.

2. *Minimizing noncommunicable defects.* This includes observations by the teacher as well as by specially trained individuals to detect any evidence of defective vision, hearing, speech, posture, and teeth in the children. When defects are noted, they should be referred to the parents with a recommendation that remedial care be given. It is advisable that follow-up visits by staff members be made. If financial difficulties prevent the parents from taking prompt, effective action, the community services and facilities should be utilized.

3. *Provision of health essentials in the school environment.* This is school sanitation, which is discussed in detail later in this chapter.

4. *Provision of health essentials through nutrition.* Many children are poorly fed because of poverty and ignorance. The provision of lunches in the school helps the poorly nourished child and inculcates good eating habits. The policy governing the school lunch program is a local matter and thus differs materially from place to place; however, most schools offer the lunch at cost or less to ensure that it is well received. The Federal government through the Department of Agriculture makes many food items available to the school lunch programs and provides a small cash subsidy for each child served. This permits the school to

offer free lunches to underprivileged children without creating a serious drain on the local funds. The lunches should be prepared under the direction of a nutritionist, or at least with the consultation and periodic supervision of one.

The furnishing of lunches requires a kitchen, serving room, and dining room and involves all the usual sanitary problems connected with food handling. The methods used should comply with the standards set forth in Chap. 12 with due consideration given the laws of the state in which

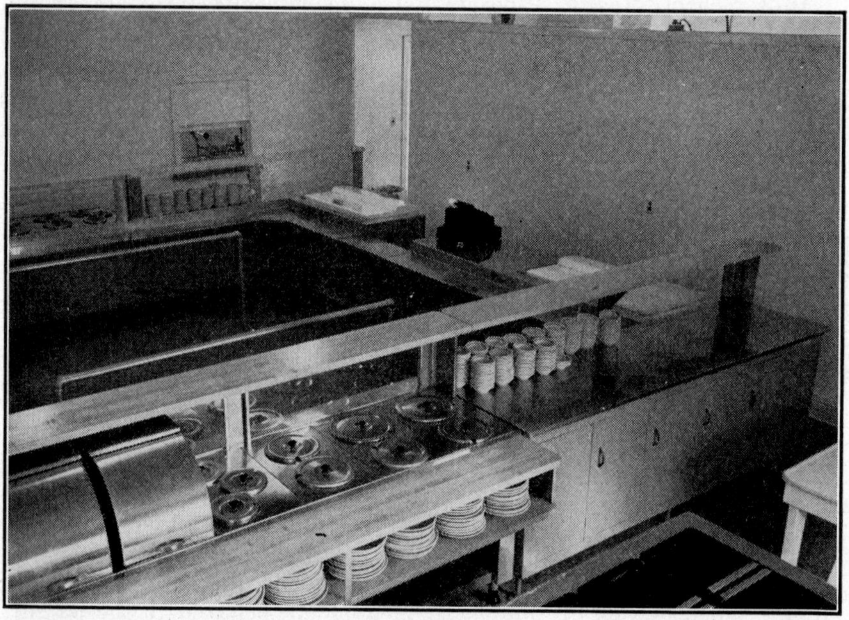

FIG. 16-1. Serving tables of a school lunchroom. Note protective glass screen. (*Pharr–San Juan, Tex., Independent School District.*)

the school is located. Some special considerations for school installations include the rounding of all table corners and the provision of at least 16 inches and preferably 18 inches of level space per child at tables where food is consumed.

5. *Provision of adequate physical activity for the children to promote their development of basic physical skills.* This includes provision for play and sports—both supervised and unsupervised, indoor and outdoor. The related facilities of playground space, equipment, gymnasium, and dressing rooms all require consideration in this connection.

6. *Health education.* The school curriculum should include sufficient material on health education to enable the child to form proper habits in regard to diet; care of teeth; sleep; protection of eyes, ears, and other sensory organs; posture; safety; and cleanliness. Teaching should

include the relationship of the individual, the school, and the community to the various aspects of the spread of communicable diseases and the role of sanitation in their control.

7. *Integration of school and community health programs.* It is essential that the school health program provide continuity with the preschool phase of the community program. It should also be correlated with the work of the local health department. This is especially true in the control of communicable disease and the solution of sanitary problems.

16-4. Location. The health and safety program of the school starts with the selection of the site and its development. The size of the school campus and the external social, industrial, and commercial environmental factors play important roles in the success or failure of a school health program. In rural areas the selection of a site is usually easier than in the case of urban schools; however, the considerations are similar. Minimum site areas should consist of 5 acres plus 1 acre for each 100 pupils to be served at elementary schools, and 10 acres plus 1 acre for each 100 pupils at secondary schools. The site should be well-drained and free from certain hazards such as ravines, bluffs, etc. Health and safety features of the adjoining properties should be thoroughly studied in the selection of a site, since disease, insects, rodents, and vermin are no respecters of property lines.

Noise, bad odors, and traffic congestion connected with industrial and commercial centers are to be avoided, and such traffic arteries as main streets and highways, as well as railroad lines, are both noisy and hazardous. If possible, however, access to the school should be such that pupils are permitted the opportunity to utilize the community facilities. The distance of travel required of both the walking and the bus-carried pupils should also be a factor in location. For elementary-school children, $\frac{3}{4}$ mile is considered the maximum for walking and a thirty-minute bus ride one-way the maximum for motor transport. For secondary schools the maximum walking distance should not exceed 2 miles and the one-way bus ride should not exceed one hour. In some sparsely settled areas, these factors must be balanced with other considerations and a compromise reached which is advantageous to the pupils served.

Another matter which should not be neglected in school locations is the opportunity to establish surroundings which are pleasing to the eye, thus helping to instill a feeling of pride, contentment, and happiness in the pupils. Accessibility of utilities such as water, electricity, gas, and sewer, if possible, as well as of fire protection, should be considered in the selection. In addition, the educational administrator must give thought to other factors, such as population growth, consolidation, annexation, and type of education plan projected.

16-5. Building. The program of education and the age level served are reflected in the building and particularly in the grouping of the various services, as well as educational departments. Provision should be made for expansion both as to total pupil load and program coverage. Some consideration is usually given to the flexibility of the building to permit revision of the educational program conveniently.

The service facilities, along with the administrative units, form the core or hub of the school plant and should be located in such a manner as to permit good operation and supervision as well as easy access for the delivery of supplies and equipment. Noisy activities such as shops, music departments, and indoor physical education facilities should be separated from the academic departments. In elementary schools, the primary grades are usually grouped together at such a location that the children may have access to the nearer playground areas, and the older students can then utilize larger playground areas at a greater distance from the building.

The entrances are located to permit sheltered dismounting from buses and cars. It is also advisable to plan the school layout to permit community use of the auditorium, cafeteria, and general-purpose rooms with a minimum of interference with the classroom areas. Many local community and climatic conditions must be considered in the planning of a school building, and none is of greater importance than the natural lighting, heating, and ventilation arrangements upon which the use and comfort of the school are dependent. In the South, where heat loss is relatively unimportant but cross ventilation is essential, the practice of using a sprawling finger design with orientation of the rooms to expose window walls to the prevailing breeze is frequently adopted. Open, single-loaded covered corridors are popular in dry, warm areas, whereas in damp or cold climates closed halls are necessary to afford protection from the elements to students when moving from one area to another. Under certain industrial or climatic conditions where fog, cloud cover, or smoke interferes with the reliability of natural light, it is an economical practice to disregard sky light in the building design since artificial light must be provided in such quantity as to meet the total need.

16-6. Interior Finish. Experience gained from using existing buildings provides valuable insight for the school administrator as to the materials and finishes which are readily adaptable to the local school and community needs. Serious thought should be given to the serviceability of various materials, since an initial capital investment saving may result in such a serious sacrifice in service that maintenance burdens are excessive.

For floors, the softwoods are undesirable because they have a comparatively short life, whereas hardwoods give good service if properly installed. Even after prolonged neglect, hardwood floors can be sanded and refinished to recover the qualities of a new floor. Asphalt-tile floors have been widely used in schools. They are cheap, easy to replace, light-colored, and easy on the feet. The disadvantages of asphalt tile are that it is subject to indentation, scarring, and deterioration from petroleum waste, waxes, and other solvents. Rubber flooring is similar to asphalt tile except that it is more expensive; the colors are brighter; and the synthetic rubber is more resistant to petroleum solvents. Cork flooring has a limited use, particularly where acoustical qualities are indicated. It requires rather extensive maintenance, such as lacquer or varnish seal and protection against alcohol. Concrete floors are useful in corridors, auditoriums, and similar places; however, special consideration for their hardness is essential or the floors tend to become dusty. Terrazzo floors are attractive if properly sealed and serviced; however, they are expensive and may be slippery unless nonskid chips are used in the surfacing. Slate and marble are too soft for heavy use and tend to crack and chip. Quarry tile is useful in laboratories, kitchens, and similar places. Plastic tile, linoleum, and grease-resistant rubber tile have been found useful in kitchens and lunchrooms, where ease of cleaning is essential.

For interior walls the recent trend has been toward the use of exposed brick and cinder block. They are cheaper than plaster walls and present a pleasing appearance when painted. For partition walls, Sheetrock, plywood, and other light materials are popular, since they permit economical remodeling. Chalk boards are found in nearly all classrooms and usually become part of the wall surface. Slate boards are losing favor since their light absorption is very high. Glass, composition, and plastic boards, usually green in color and with a light reflectivity of 20 to 25 per cent, are now commonly used. With most composition boards, care must be taken not to allow moisture to be absorbed, or they will deteriorate rapidly.

In schools with a heavy dependence on natural light, the prismatic glass block has been used extensively with clear-glass vision strips below the glass-block area. The vision strip is usually placed in windows of the awning or pivot type to permit ventilation.

Wall surfaces in classrooms should usually have a light-colored smooth mat finish. For kitchens, dining rooms, and similar areas the finish should be smooth and washable.

Ceiling surfaces receive attention for acoustical treatment, and Fiberglas board and vegetable fiber board as well as Sheetrock are extensively used. A flat white finish is essential for good light reflectivity.

16-7. Light and Color. The importance of good lighting and some of the various factors which enter into providing an acceptable visual environment have been mentioned in Chaps. 14 and 15. Modern educational methods are dependent upon a well-lighted environment for much of their effectiveness, and more research and development have gone into this aspect of school plants than into any other one phase. It has been said that what is learned by the child is learned by the whole child, and what is seen by the child is seen by the whole child—not just the eye. The whole body is involved in seeing; nerves, muscles, and circulation all play a part.

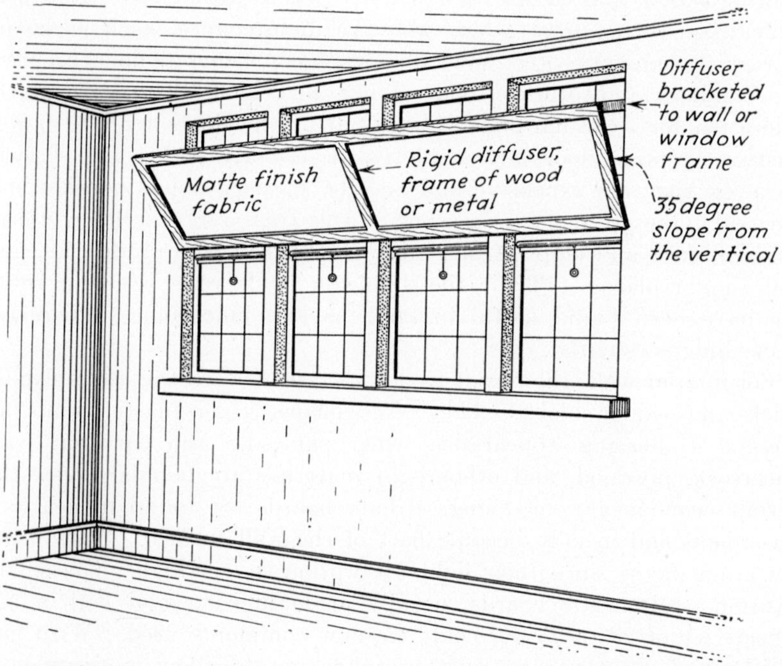

FIG. 16-2. Diffusers for schoolroom windows. The lower sashes are shaded if necessary; the upper sashes are not shaded. (*Courtesy of Texas State Department of Health.*)

To see with ease and comfort results in a minimum use of energy, and fatigue does not occur as readily. The handicaps to seeing, such as glare, dim lights, and poor balance of illumination, all tend to create muscular and nervous tension which prematurely brings on fatigue. The function of school lighting is to produce conditions which permit the performance of visual tasks efficiently with a minimum of strain and effort. Children's energies should be used for growth of sturdy bodies and the development of sound mental and emotional processes, not for combating the visual difficulties which result from poor lighting.

Until recent years, the intensity of light was considered the only criterion worthy of consideration, but now the quality of the light is also considered important for proper eye comfort and visual efficiency. Quality includes, in addition to quantity or intensity, such things as location of source, color, brightness, and the reflective characteristics of floor, ceiling, walls, and furnishings. All of these factors make up the brightness balance not only of the visual task but of the entire visual field. It is desirable to have no area in the entire visual field brighter than the task, nor should any area be less than one-third as bright as the task. These conditions, along with a general high level of illumination, are the goal which we should attempt to reach.

For classroom conditions, the reflective factor of the various surfaces must be considered. The ceiling must reflect 85 to 90 per cent of the light, walls 55 to 70 per cent, floors 20 to 30 per cent, furniture 25 to 35 per cent, and chalk boards 20 to 25 per cent. In addition, light sources which are in the visual field, such as windows and light bulbs, must be toned to diffuse and distribute the light over a wider area.

TABLE 16-1. RECOMMENDED MINIMUM ILLUMINATION LEVELS

Type of room	*Illumination level, foot-candles*
Classrooms	30
Libraries, laboratories, art rooms	30
Classrooms for partially seeing pupils	50
Drafting, typing, and sewing rooms	50
Reception rooms, gymnasiums	20
Auditoriums, lunchrooms, washrooms, corridors, and stairways	10
Storerooms	5

This is accomplished by using some type of shielding which diffuses and distributes the light. For windows, such equipment as translucent diffusers and deflectors are practical, as are blinds and light shades. Drapes and other dark or opaque materials reduce the available light without accomplishing the desired distribution. For light bulbs the indirect-light fixture directs the light rays to reflecting surfaces where further diffusion is accomplished. All these procedures tend to reduce the local or spot brightness; thus, a step toward smaller brightness ratios in the visual field is accomplished.

The Illuminating Engineering Society has suggested that school lighting for various types of visual tasks be sufficient to maintain levels on the task area corresponding to the values in Table 16-1.

The most common source of light used in schools until recent years has been natural light, and it is still used very extensively in most schools. The variables of natural light, such as orientation of light openings, sun rotation, cloud cover, and seasonal conditions, make the effective use of natural light a complex matter and can be coordinated for efficient use only part of the time. Formerly, it was considered advisable to have windows on one side of the room and to arrange the seating so that the light came to the child from the left side. Now the consideration of brightness, contrasts, limitations, glare control, shadow reduction, and other quality factors and the efforts being made to obtain a high over-all illumination level have opened the lighting design to the use of multilevel lighting. Bilateral window arrangements, entire upper wall areas of prismatic, light-directional glass blocks, improved elementary roof design, and skylights have been used effectively. The trend toward single-story construction and the use of open and single-loaded corridors have freed the designer of many of the handicaps to light utilization which previously existed. Multiple light sources make it mandatory that glare be eliminated and that light diffusion and direction be applied with a minimum of light loss.

In orienting the classrooms of the South and particularly the Southwest, direct sunrays should be kept out of the major light openings, and shielding, direction, and diffusing should be practiced if any direct sunlight is used. In the northern part of the country direct sunlight is considered psychologically desirable, and glare, as well as high brightness contrast results. To offset these handicaps more attention is given to seating arrangements, and for extremely difficult cases some internal shielding is applied.

Sky light represents sunrays that have been diffused and thus rendered more usable. Every effort should be made to utilize sky light and to inhibit the entrance of direct sunlight. Such external shields as canopies, overhanging roofs, louvered overhangs for windows, and external horizontal or vertical venetian blinds have been used successfully, so that in the warmer climates the heat control effected is of considerable value. Shielding and diffusing by interior equipment is accomplished by using venetian blinds, center-hung double shades, diffusers, and louvers.

In planning for a balance of brightness, it is necessary to consider artificial light either to supplement the natural light or to provide all light if the facilities are to be used in the evenings. Frequently the artificial lighting is placed in both roles. To utilize one set of lighting fixtures for all purposes, it is suggested that the various fixtures be placed on separate switch circuits which permit using only selected fixtures in the supplementing role and all fixtures when natural light is eliminated. Light fixtures may be divided into five classes: direct, semidirect, general-diffusing, semi-indirect, and indirect. As indicated by the names, the percentage of light directed downward and the percentage of light directed toward a reflecting surface are different in the five categories, varying from 90 per cent of the light directed down in the first class to 90 per cent directed to reflecting surfaces in the fifth class. The direct-type fixture is not considered satisfactory except for very limited use—for example, local lighting for tasks such as operating machines, reading dictionaries, etc. The semidirect fixture has limited school use in corridors, locker rooms, and storerooms. The general-diffusing fixture produces glare and shadow, which are undesirable features for classroom lighting. In spite of these defects, this type of equipment has been extensively used in the past. The semi-indirect fixture utilizes the ceiling as a primary reflecting source with a small percentage of light directed down and a limited amount of glare. This type of fixture can be successfully used in most classrooms. The indirect fixture usually is equipped with an opaque or only slightly translucent surface on the bottom and sides, with the light being reflected against the ceiling for further redirecting and diffusing. This type of fixture produces light with the most desirable qualities, but it does have a lower efficiency of light production per energy-unit input than do the other types.

Since the advent of fluorescent-light fixtures, there have been many discussions on the relative advantages of the two types of artificial lighting. In general, it is usually possible to provide satisfactory lighting utilizing either incandescent- or fluorescent-light fixtures if proper consideration is given to wattage, glare, location, and the reflective values of the various room surroundings. Local conditions usually control the relative advantages of one or the other, and thus some of the major points to be investigated are outlined below.

Incandescent fixtures and bulbs are cheaper in first cost than fluorescent fixtures; however, the incandescent light requires a higher wattage to produce a given brightness and, thus, is more expensive to operate. Incandescent lights produce large quantities of heat, whereas fluorescent lights are relatively cool. Fluorescent lights may be advantageous if the local building wiring is overloaded, since the current requirements are lower. Both types of light bulbs have been improved to give longer-lasting service, and, likewise, new light fixtures of both types are designed for easy maintenance, cleaning, and high efficiency. Formerly, the phosphorus used in fluorescent light bulbs was a toxic material and the danger from broken tubes was rather extensive; however, the present day material is relatively inert, and broken tubes are no more hazardous than any other cutting object.

The use of color in schools is of great significance since it plays a very important part in establishing the brightness ratios which are essential for visual ease and comfort. Another consideration in choice of color is the utilization of various light sources. Color may differ in its qualities under different light sources, depending on the components of the light. Color exerts an important influence on the alertness of the room occupants and may tend to soothe the user or, if clashing colors or sharp hues are used, to produce nervousness and fidgeting on the part of the teachers and children. From the standpoint of lighting, the reflective factors of the various colored surfaces are of such importance in imparting the proper light brightness for visual tasks that precedence should be given to these factors in selecting colors.

The reflective factor of ceilings and the upper wall above the picture molding in high-ceiling rooms should be 85 per cent or higher. This requires a white or nearly white finish and may be difficult to obtain and retain if acoustical finish ceiling materials are used. The side walls should have a reflective factor of 55 to 70 per cent and may be obtained by using pastel colors. Lower wall surfaces, trim, and baseboard should have a light reflectivity of about 30 per cent, and the finish should be one that permits frequent cleaning. Likewise, the chalk board should have a light reflectivity of 25 per cent or more, and the floors should have a similar reflectivity. These brightnesses preclude the use of slate boards, oiled floors, or dark finish tile.

A nongloss finish should be used on all surfaces to eliminate glare. Colors have usually been associated with warmth or coolness—blue and green indicating coolness and yellow, orange, and red suggesting warmth. Usually the cool colors are used in sunny rooms and warm colors in sunless rooms. Likewise, color plays a part in making rooms seem large or small. The light colors seem to enlarge the room, and dark colors make the room appear smaller.

Another use of color which should not be neglected is in safety work. The standardizing of colors for moving parts on machinery as well as fire-fighting equipment is a practical procedure that should be considered in school plants.

16-8. Heating and Ventilation. The atmosphere of the various parts of the school must be healthful and comfortable for the particular activities for which the room is used. It thus becomes necessary for the heating and ventilation systems to accomplish the following:

1. Supply clean air in sufficient quantities to dilute the room air below the threshold of body-odor detection and to remove dust, fumes, obnoxious gases, and humidity. (A system that accomplishes these goals also supplies sufficient oxygen for the occupants.)
2. Maintain a uniform room temperature without rapid fluctuations.
3. Supply heat for balancing losses from the human body.
4. Supply make-up heat for room and building losses.
5. Remove excess heat caused by body radiation, conduction, evaporation, or external conditions.
6. Diffuse the atmospheric temperature without pronounced drafts or stratification.

As may be noted, some problems require constant attention while others occur alternately, such as provision of make-up heat under certain conditions and the removal of excess heat under other conditions.

In some climates, the provision of proper heating of the schools takes precedence over ventilating, while in areas where a mild climate exists, the ventilating and cooling must receive major attention. There are numerous methods of heating; however, all depend on radiation, conduction, convection, or a combination of them to distribute the heat uniformly from the source to the room generally. It is usually better to have a central heating plant than room-fired heaters, which multiply the maintenance and operation duties of the custodial staff. Simple systems usually offer advantages in that the school staff is able to service and maintain the equipment, while the more complex types require skilled specialists. The fuel chosen depends on the locality; however, oil and gas fuels usually permit more nearly automatic operation and eliminate the problem of ash removal and disposal. Also, recent experiences in prolonged interruption of coal deliveries suggest the necessity of installing a large bunker space to store coal. Special consideration for student safety must be included in the planning, particularly if gaseous fuels are used. Explosions may result in mass injuries and death as well as a rapid spread of fire over a wide area.

For many years, the most common heating system used in schools consisted of a low-pressure steam boiler with steam radiators located in the various rooms. The systems have been modified to the extent that hot-water boilers have been added and the distribution of the heat may be accomplished by means of hot-water radiators, forced warm-air systems, or radiant-heating panels. The forced-air system offers certain advantages in that it may be designed for cooling as well as heating, and it permits control of fresh air, which may be filtered and tempered.

While central heating is usually more desirable than room-fired heaters, there are numerous installations which lend themselves to individual control for convenience and economy. Room heaters which are equipped with circulating fans permit good distribution of heat.

The effectiveness, safety, and economy of any heating system is dependent upon the controls. The fuel controls, pressure relief valves, and make-up water valves should be the best available, since the safety of the facility and of the occupants are dependent upon their prompt operation. Automatic controls produce more efficient operation, and the economies in fuel and man-hours more than offset the initial investment. Thermostats and humidostats, if humidity-control equipment is utilized, provide much more sensitive control of these atmospheric qualities than does manual adjustment using thermometers and psychrometers for indicating instruments. Locked controls which prevent tampering by unauthorized persons should be used in all public locations, such as classrooms, corridors, etc.

Ventilation standards are much more flexible than heating standards since the socioeconomic status of occupants, the activity for which the room is used, and general climatic conditions all have valid effects on the design criteria. Studies have been made to determine the minimum amount of fresh air per person needed to keep body odor below an objectionable level on the basis of cubic space per person, as affected by the age and socioeconomic status of the occupants. For example, a study by the Harvard School of Public Health, in which grade school children were used as subjects, shows that with 200 cubic feet of space per person of average economic background there is a need for 21 cubic feet of fresh air per person per minute but that occupants of a lower-than-average socioeconomic status require 38 cubic feet of fresh air per person per minute. Likewise, greater supplies of air are necessary if vigorous rather than sedentary activity is taking place.

Except in the case of exceedingly warm conditions, the ventilation requirements are based on body-odor control. For dissipating heat the quantity of air supplied, the temperature of the incoming air, the water-vapor content of the air, and the air movement are all factors which affect the comfort of the room occupants. Drafts may be uncomfortable if velocities of over 25 feet per minute are obtained when the air is appreciably cooler than the body; however, during warm weather, velocities of up to 100 feet per minute may be tolerated very well.

The dissipation of body heat is dependent upon the surrounding atmosphere's taking up the heat in one form or another. Most of the heat disposal in warm weather is accomplished by vaporization of perspiration from the body surfaces. The vapor content of the air thus materially influences the effectiveness of this process. Dehumidification of incoming air could effect a material benefit even if the air was not cooled in the process. It is obvious that the conductive effect of room air in cooling is dependent upon the temperature differential between the body to be cooled and the air. The heat-absorption capacity of dry air is very low, and thus the quantity of air which is needed to remove excess heat by the process of raising the air temperature is large.

The use of air conditioning in schools has not gained favor to any great extent, in that the cost of operation is rather high and the initial investment is likewise considerable. Another factor in the slow application of air conditioning is the relatively light use of school buildings during the warmest months of the year. Many of the newer schools have provided limited air conditioning for audio-visual rooms, auditoriums, cafeterias, and other similar special-service rooms. Most of these air conditioners provide dehumidification, cooling, and filtration of the air with a comparatively high percentage of air being recirculated.

In arid parts of the country, the conditioning is accomplished by air filtration and vaporization of water with little or no recirculation. This desert-type equipment is much more economical in initial cost, as well as in operation, than the mechanical refrigeration type, but it has a limited effectiveness in that it is useful only if the incoming air has a low vapor content. Central air-conditioning equipment can be used most economically with hot-air heating systems which permit the use of the air-filtration equipment and the distribution ducts and grilles for all-year heating and cooling.

In the southern part of the United States, various types of fans have been used to increase the air movement and circulation. The most satisfactory installations are of the exhaust type which permit gravity replacement of exhausted air. The primary advantages are that these systems permit lower fan speeds with less noise, fewer drafts, and a high rate of air change. Blower-type fans which are located to have an air intake from the outside permit an increased air change. With these, however, drafts are common, and high-speed operation, with its concomitant of increased noise, is frequently required. General circulating fans, such as ceiling fans, floor fans, and stand fans, are not recommended. One of the primary objections to their use is the increased opportunity for disease transmission as a result of the spread of droplet-borne infectious organisms as well as dust- and lint-carried organisms.

Natural ventilation, depending on windows, doors, transoms, and louvers, is widely used and can be rather effective if properly designed, installed, and utilized. One of the most serious deficiencies noted in natural ventilation systems is the lack of an adequate opening for the exit of stale air. In general, there is no static-pressure differential, and the velocity force is only sufficient to function effectively if the exit-air area is equal to the entrance area and is located to permit cross-ventilation movement without short-circuiting. Since used air which is to be exhausted is usually warmer than incoming air, the exhaust opening should be near the ceiling where the warm air accumulates. Fresh air that enters the room at a low height, at least 18 inches above the floor to avoid excess pickup of dust and lint, contacts the occupant's body and breathing zone. After this contact and use, the air is warmed and rises out of the occupied area of the room. If natural ventilation is used during the heating portion of the year, some tempering of the intake air should be accomplished by passage over heated surfaces before it contacts the occupants.

In this country, the comfort temperature is between 68 and 72°F for most people; however, older persons may find that temperatures nearer 75°F are desirable. Likewise, if vigorous activity is being performed by the occupants, lower temperatures may be desirable. If humidity control is being practiced, the range from 30 per cent to 50 per cent is most comfortable and healthful for normal individuals.

16-9. Furnishings. School furniture which is not designed for the particular use to which it is put can create hardships that interfere with the educational programs of the users and promote the development of physical deformities, even to the extent of permanently accentuating abnormalities. Properly designed desks, tables, and chairs are particularly important, since the students use this equipment for prolonged periods. Size and shape should be considered in the light of the age, stages of physical development, and functional requirements of the potential users. Adjustable furniture is available, and while the initial cost is higher than that of some other types, it may prove more economical in the long run if the cost of education and of treatment for physical deformities is considered.

The furnishings should also be selected to harmonize with the lighting, and to suit climatic conditions and educational uses. Furniture should be light and sturdy to permit movement as needed. In primary grades the extensive use of paints, clays, and other handiwork objects requires that the finish be durable and resistant to cleaning materials, as well as to the supplies provided students for school use. Special finishes may be required in certain educational rooms, involving such factors as heat resistance in rooms where cooking, pottery making, and certain physical sciences are taught. In warm or humid climates such furniture as desks and chairs should fit the users in a manner that permits them to wear loose clothing and allows intimate ventilation of the body surfaces. In all instances the coloring of the furnishings should blend with other interior finishes, particularly as to depth of color. This may be explained as a method of obtaining uniformity of brightness, regardless of the light intensity.

16-10. Plumbing. School plumbing fixtures include commodes, urinals, lavatories, and drinking fountains in all buildings. Under some conditions such special fixtures as sinks, showers, and hydrotherapeutic vessels may also be utilized. To avoid repetition, only the basic fixtures are discussed in this chapter; information on special fixtures is given in Chap. 6, which deals with their general uses.

Fundamentally, all plumbing fixtures used in schools should be smooth, attractive, and corrosion-resistant. They should be designed without sharp edges, corners, and crevices. White or bright finishes permit easy visibility of dirt, and this promotes better cleaning. Toilets and lavatories should be installed in well-lighted and well-ventilated rooms.

Dry, clean restrooms and plumbing fixtures can be maintained free from fecal and urine odors. School management which practices good restroom cleanliness, good ventilation, and normal maintenance finds that chemical deodorants are unnecessary.

The commodes used in the primary grades should be small in size, 11 or 12 inches high. Preschool age groups may find the 10-inch height useful. The regular sized commode, 14 inches high, should prove satisfactory for all older school groups. Some manufacturers build a 13-inch commode for intermediate grades, but the majority of administrators do not feel that this special size is needed. All commodes should be equipped with a U-shaped seat of impervious material that is not subject to checking or cracking.

If the water pressure is at least 18 pounds per square inch, the flushometer-valve type of flushing device is the most acceptable. The advantages of this type of valve are that a more vigorous flushing action is obtained, less water is used, and no delay between flushing cycles exists. The maintenance problems are reported as less frequent with the flushometer-valve unit than with the holding tank. Where low water pressure exists, the flush-tank commode is required. In both types a siphon breaker or anti-backflow device is required to prevent possible pollution. These devices should be inspected at least once a year to determine if they are still in good condition, since infrequent use permits corrosion and deterioration to occur without noticeable effect on the operation of the flushing device.

The same consideration regarding height of the fixture should apply to urinals. The urinal should be wall-hung rather than floor-mounted. The latter is difficult to clean, easily soiled, and frequently subject to clogging.

Lavatories should be mounted at various heights from 24 to 30 inches from the floor, depending on the age of the children to be served. The 24-inch, 26-inch, and 30-inch have been found most useful. To promote proper handwashing, all lavatories should be equipped with hot and cold water discharged through a mixing faucet. The discharge should be located above the overflow, and the valves should not be spring-loaded. Flush-valve types are very beneficial if the water is not of a scale-forming quality. They do serve to save water, avoid water-hammer problems, and avoid overflows, but for many waters the positive-action manually operated valves prove most sensible. Training in the school, as in the home, can effectively eliminate the objection commonly raised to the use of this type of valve. Schools are in existence to teach conservation of manpower and resources, and water is one of America's critical resources.

School lavatories should not be equipped with drain stoppers as all hand and face washing should be accomplished with running water that has not been contaminated from water in the lavatory bowl left by a previous user.

Drinking fountains should never be located in close proximity to other plumbing fixtures, particularly waste disposal fixtures. The drinking fountain should be mounted 30 to 40 inches above the floor with the 30-, 36-, and 40-inch fixtures being the most popular. Measurement of height on these units is the vertical distance from floor to fountain orifice, while on other fixtures the measurement is from floor to overflow rim. The fountainhead should be of the angle-jet mouth-guard type with an antisquirt device. The valve should be either manual or foot-operated, and a pressure-control regulator should be an integral part of the valve. The jet from the orifice should be regulated to rise not more than 4 inches vertically above the orifice and the arc should not extend more than 10 inches horizontally from the orifice. The discharge orifice should be not less than $\frac{3}{4}$ inch above the overflow rim of the waterbasin.

In warm climates, there is a trend toward installing refrigerated drinking fountains, and while this practice is common and readily accepted, special precautions should be taken to prevent school pupils from drinking cold water while they are overheated. This may be accomplished by providing two supplies of different temperature or by connecting only tap water to fountains in places where students congregate following strenuous exercise.

The number of plumbing fixtures needed per student is a widely debated subject, and there are many standards. Table 16-2 lists minimum facilities recommended by the Coordinating Committee for a National Plumbing Code[1]. Recommendations for institutions other than schools are included.

16-11. Water Supply and Sewage Disposal. The water supply should be obtained from a public supply, and sewage disposal should be conducted via a public sanitary sewer if practicable. In the absence of public service, the principles as set out in this book for individual water systems and private sewage systems should be used as a guide (see Chaps. 4 and 5).

Water use for domestic purposes at day schools is usually less than 20 gallons per person per day even in schools that have gymnasiums and cafeterias. Many elementary schools use 5 gallons per person per day or less for domestic purposes. In the more arid regions, extensive use of water for maintenance of lawns, athletic fields, and playgrounds greatly exceeds the domestic water use. The design of the school water-service lines should be made with this consideration.

Usually a design figure of 15 gallons of sewage per person per day is adequate. For individual-system design the sewage should be classed as weak with less than 0.07 pound of biochemical oxygen demand per capita per day with the suspended-solids content also low. Rarely does grease present a problem.

In choosing a type of sewage disposal system it should be remembered that the school is closed for a long period of each year and that it is advisable to avoid plant processes that require close supervision or highly technical operation since operation will be in the hands of school personnel who are not sanitation specialists.

16-12. Cleaning and Maintenance. The cleaning and maintenance program of a school plays an important part in the health and education of the building users. Of importance to the tax-paying public is the improved serviceability of a plant which is preserved through an effective maintenance program. A schedule which includes the various tasks—both daily and weekly duties and those that must be performed only at infrequent intervals—pays dividends through the avoidance of neglect of critical matters.

Cleaning is usually considered a separate function from maintenance; yet one of the primary records of a complete cleaning program is the reduction of deterioration due to excess wear, corrosion, and grit. Many large and well-organized school systems have training programs for their custodial staffs which are designed to stress proper cleaning procedures and maintenance practices. Many expensive repairs can be avoided if the custodial staff is alert to the care of the equipment it services.

The various surfaces to be cleaned require different kinds of cleaners and different types of brooms, brushes, or mops. Some surfaces may be cleaned with detergents in water, while other surfaces may be seriously damaged by the water or the ionization of the detergent. Some surfaces require vigorous buffing, while others are scratched and permanently damaged by stiff bristles. Most suppliers of cleaning supplies have developed charts which specify the type of agent and the applicator needed for various surfaces. Many of these charts refer to a specific kind of material which is handled by the cleaning-supply house but this is a handicap in preparing specifications for open bidding by the purchasing agent. Most manufacturers and trade associations have prepared instruction for the installation and care of their product. By the use of these informative guides, the school may develop its own charts based on ingredients and results without reference to brands.

The properly equipped, alert, and trained custodian can and will perform preventive maintenance in the course of his routine duties. Examples of such actions are replacing washers and gaskets in plumbing fixtures; adjusting pressure controls; replacing pull cords, tapes, or other frayed or broken items; tightening bolts or screws; oiling moving

Table 16-2. Minimum Facilities[a]

Type of building or occupancy	Water closets	Urinals	Lavatories	Bathtubs or showers	Drinking fountains[b]
Schools:[c]					
Elementary	1 per 100 males, 1 per 35 females	1 per 30 males	1 per 60 persons	......	1 per 75 persons
Secondary	1 per 100 males, 1 per 45 females	1 per 30 males	1 per 100 persons	......	1 per 75 persons
Office or public buildings	1 per 1–15 persons 2 per 16–35 persons 3 per 36–55 persons 4 per 56–80 persons 5 per 81–110 persons 6 per 111–150 persons 1 for each 40 additional persons	Wherever urinals are provided for men, 1 water closet less than the number specified may be provided for each urinal installed, except that the number of water closets in such cases shall not be reduced to less than two-thirds of the minimum specified	1 per 1–15 persons 2 per 16–35 persons 3 per 36–60 persons 4 per 61–90 persons 5 per 91–125 persons	......	1 per 75 persons
Manufacturing, warehouses, workshops, loft buildings, foundries, and similar establishments[d]	1 per 1–9 persons 2 per 10–24 persons 3 per 25–49 persons 4 per 50–74 persons 5 per 75–100 persons 1 for each additional 30 employees	Same substitution as above	1 fixture for each 45 additional persons 1–100 persons, 1 for each 10 persons; over 100, 1 for each additional 15 persons[e,f]	1 shower for each 15 persons exposed to excessive heat or to skin contamination with poisonous, infectious, or irritating material	1 per 75 persons
Dormitories[g]	1 for each 10 males 1 for each 8 females Over 10 persons, 1 for each 25 additional males and 1 for each 20 additional females	1 for each 25 men; over 150 persons, 1 for each additional 50 men	1 for each 12 persons (separate dental lavatories should be provided in community toilet rooms; ratio of 1 dental lavatory for each 50 persons is recommended); over 12, add 1 for each additional 20 males and 1 for each additional 15 females	1 for each 8 persons; in the case of women's dormitories, additional bathtubs should be installed at the ratio of 1 for each 30 females; over 150, 1 for each additional 20 persons	1 per 75 persons

TABLE 16-2. MINIMUM FACILITIES[a] (*Continued*)

Type of building or occupancy	Water closets	Urinals	Lavatories	Bathtubs or showers	Drinking fountains[b]
Theaters, auditoriums	1 per 1–100 persons 2 per 101–200 persons 3 per 201–400 persons Over 400, 1 for each additional 500 males and 1 for each 300 females	1 per 1–200 males 2 per 201–400 males 3 per 401–600 males Over 600, 1 for each additional 300 males	1 per 1–200 persons 2 per 201–400 persons 3 per 401–750 persons Over 750, 1 for each additional 500 persons	....	1 per 100 persons

[a] The figures shown are based upon 1 fixture as the minimum required for the number of persons indicated or any fraction thereof. Building category not shown on this table. Will be considered separately by the administrative authority.

In applying this schedule of facilities, consideration must be given to the accessibility of the fixtures. Conformity purely on a numerical basis may not result in an installation suited to the need of the individual establishment. For example, schools should be provided with toilet facilities on each floor having classrooms. Temporary workingmen facilities: 1 water closet and 1 urinal for each 30 workmen; 24-inch trough = 1 urinal; 36-inch trough = 2 urinals; 48-inch trough = 3 urinals; 60-inch trough = 4 urinals.

[b] Drinking fountains shall not be installed in toilet rooms.

[c] This schedule has been adopted (1945) by the National Council on Schoolhouse Construction.

[d] As required by the American Standard Safety Code for Industrial Sanitation in Manufacturing Establishments (ASA Z4.1–1935).

[e] Where there is exposure to skin contamination with poisonous, infectious, or irritating materials, provide 1 lavatory for each 5 persons.

[f] Twenty-four lineal inches of wash sink or 18 inches of a circular basin, when provided with water outlets for such space, shall be considered equivalent to 1 lavatory.

[g] Laundry trays, 1 for each 50 persons. Slop sinks, 1 for each 100 persons.

parts; and noting for early repair defects that require future attention. The tasks in this last category might include touching up disfiguring marks, filling cracks, removing small spots of corrosion, replacing cracked or broken window glass, etc. For the proper procedure for accomplishing this type of care, the manufacturer's instructions are the most reliable.

In addition to the routine preventive maintenance, some major and highly specialized jobs occur. Only in very large school systems is it practical to have specialized personnel on the staff. Other schools find it economical to hire the service required in the open market. Quite frequently, permitting the handy-man type of employee to do technical and delicate work results in permanent damage to expensive equipment.

The most effective cleaning and maintenance program is found where the admininstration not only furnishes good equipment and high-quality supplies but also hires alert and progressive personnel and provides them with basic training and frequent refresher courses.

HOSPITALS

16-13. The basic concepts of sanitation in a hospital are no different from those related to hotels, schools, and eating establishments since certain areas of the hospital render the same basic services. The major difference is in the greater degree to which cleanliness and sterilization are practiced; for the patient in the hospital, perhaps a simple medical, surgical, or obstetrical case, may develop some communicable disease after admission, or the patient may be admitted because of a communicable disease.

16-14. Physical Structure and Maintenance. The basic physical structure of a hospital is the same as that of any fireproof hotel. Special precautions are taken in the way of exits, fireproofing, wiring, etc., to reduce the possibility of fire and to make it easy to remove bedfast patients. Schools and hotels are designed to be cleaned regularly, but in a hospital the cleaning is much more frequent and important. Halls and other public areas should be mopped and washed every day. The patient rooms must be thoroughly scrubbed after each patient leaves. Because of the frequent washing and the strong disinfectants which are often used, the wall and floor surfaces must be designed to take this punishment as well as the abuse of being struck by carts and stretchers and being maltreated by the public. For this reason, some form of glazed tile or a vinyl plastic sheeting is frequently used. All paint is usually a high-quality enamel.

In general, the food-handling and dish-sterilization rules followed are the same as those observed in a good modern restaurant; however, extra care must be taken in dish and eating-utensil sterilization. The smallest of hospitals should have a dishwashing and a sanitizing machine.

16-15. Central Supply and Sterilizing Areas. The typical hospital has several features that are not found in any other type of building. The central supply and sterilizing area is responsible for the sterile and sanitary condition of nearly all items used by the patients that are not supplied by the kitchen. High-pressure steam autoclaves are used to sterilize surgical supplies and equipment, gloves, syringes, towels and sheets employed in surgery or deliveries, and any other article used for more than one patient. There are many special machines built to do the jobs of sterilization, the number and type depending upon the size of hospital. The most common is probably a bedpan sterilizer and washer, which washes bedpans by water under high pressure and sterilizes them with steam. There are special machines for washing and sterilizing surgical rubber gloves, surgical instruments, baby bottles and nipples, syringes, and other supplies.

16-16. Hospital Plumbing. The plumbing fixtures differ to some extent from normal units. All bedrooms and examining rooms should have hand-washing facilities, but the faucets should be of the gooseneck type and the handles should have wrist or elbow blades. Some units have foot- or knee-operated controls. Many toilets are equipped to wash bedpans and thus save the nurse time. Many sinks used in surgery and delivery areas are equipped with flushing rims or special traps to catch plaster and instruments overlooked in the linen.

No under-rim plumbing fixtures of any kind should be permitted (Art. 6-24). The danger of back siphonage from a bedpan washer, for example, is easily apparent.

16-17. Operating and Delivery Rooms and Nurseries. The operating rooms and delivery rooms present many sanitation problems. Safety from explosive mixtures of anesthetic gases and oxygen must be ensured by using conductive floors and explosion-proof electrical outlets. The areas must be particularly easy to clean and be scrubbed and disinfected after each patient, since one case may have an infection that could be transmitted to another patient. Year-round air conditioning with humidity control is almost a necessity in these sections of the hospital. The maintenance of a relative humidity of 50 to 60 per cent helps reduce the static electricity and the possibility of explosions, and the air-conditioning system filters out all dust and with it a large percentage of the air-borne bacteria which might cause infection of open wounds. Since the air is not recirculated in the room but is exhausted to the outside, the concentration of gases is kept low.

The nursery also requires a high degree of sanitation control. Here also, the washing of the room and bassinets is almost continuous. The air is usually conditioned the year around to control temperature and humidity, since it is known that a newborn infant is best taken care of in an environment of 80°F and 50 per cent relative humidity. The air-conditioning machine must supply the same type of air as provided for the operating and delivery room, but from an independent source.

16-18. Isolation Areas. The handling of contagious diseases in a hospital requires, in some cases, the reservation of special sections for diseased patients in which there is no recirculated air from or to other parts of the hospital (all air is supplied from the outside and is exhausted to the outside). No equipment leaves the area. Even the dishes are washed and sterilized in a special workroom set up for this purpose. If provision for complete segregation in this manner is not made, the isolation must be accomplished through the technique of the personnel.

16-19. Refuse Disposal. There is always a considerable amount of refuse from a hospital presenting unusual problems. The normal rubbish, such as paper, boxes, etc., may be handled in the conventional manner. The edible garbage must be stored in closed containers and in a screened area. It should not be fed to hogs, for the possibility of the garbage being contaminated by infectious agents is always present. Hot water or steam should be provided for cleaning the cans.

One form of rubbish that is always present is a wet, contaminated group of items that come from surgery and delivery rooms. The infective or bloody bandages and human wastes that cannot be permitted to enter a sanitary sewer require special consideration. Usually a gas-fired incinerator is supplied that can accommodate material containing 80 to 90 per cent moisture.

NURSING HOMES AND RELATED INSTITUTIONS

16-20. Nursing Homes. These are homes designed to care for the aged and infirm. They should be planned from the standpoint of the safety, health, and convenience of the patient or guest residing in the home. It is recommended that such homes be single-story buildings constructed of the most fire-resistive materials and that the building be located on adequate grounds with access to public transportation, churches, shopping centers, and hospitals.

Special features of the building and general equipment should include slip-resistant floors and corridors not less than 8 feet in width equipped with handrails on each side. All patient rooms should be outside rooms opening onto the corridor. It is recommended that ceilings in corridors, recreation rooms, detention rooms, nurses' stations, and utility rooms be acoustically treated. Wherever possible, ramps should be installed in lieu of steps; however, if steps are required they should be easy-tread and equipped with handrails. Handrails or safety grips are also needed in bathrooms, adjacent to the bathtub, shower, commode, and lavatory. Drinking fountains and lavatories should be projected from the wall in order that they may be easily approached at the front by wheel-chair patients.

Doors to bathrooms and toilets should be 3 feet wide with metal kick plates on both sides and should swing out. An inswinging door could be blocked if the patient should meet with some accident and fall against the door. Toilet stalls should be equipped with curtains instead of doors. Bathtubs should be set on the floor, and it is recommended that the tub be accessible from both sides and one end. It is important that hot water at all fixtures used by patients be thermostatically controlled to provide a temperature of not more than 110°F. Emergency call buttons should be installed in all toilets and bathrooms as well as in the individual patient quarters.

More liberal allowance should be made for storage space in nursing homes and other related facilities than in most public institutions. A room for medicine preparation and storage should be directly connected to the nurses' station. A utility room large enough to contain a small electric pressure sterilizer; nonpressure utensil sterilizer with booster; and a clinical sink with drainboards, counter, and storage cabinets is needed. Provision should also be made for the storage of stretchers and wheel chairs as well as for linen-supply and general-equipment storage. In addition to the closet space provided in bedrooms for the personal possessions of patients, a unit should be provided for the storage of such bulky items as trunks, luggage, and seasonal changes of clothing.

Special consideration should be given in designing a heating system that maintains constant uniform temperatures, avoids drafts, and controls odors.

JAILS

16-21. Physical Structure. Buildings which are used for jails should be structurally sound, secure, fire-resistive, properly heated, ventilated, and lighted. The plumbing should include a commode and a washbowl for each cell. The elimination of exposed wiring, wood partitions, and other combustible material is essential.

16-22. Cleanliness and Maintenance. Proper cleanliness and sanitation are absolute essentials in jail operation to maintain the health and morale of the inmates as well as to provide protection of the community against the spread of disease which might originate with the inmates. The jail authorities are obligated to maintain high standards of maintenance and repair practices through the allocation of funds in sufficient quantity to meet the needs. There is no excuse for lack of cleanliness, since a liberal supply of labor is readily available as long as the jail is occupied. This, along with soap, hot water, brushes, and mops, permits the administration to enforce the provision of a clean and sanitary building at all times. The official in charge should establish routine rules and regulations, as well as a policy, which ensure proper cleanliness, and then supervise the strict application of these instructions. A daily routine of work should be instituted with provision for incorporation of weekly and other periodic duties into various daily schedules. Allocation of specific tasks to prisoners, supervision of their progress, and inspection of the results should be the responsibility of paid employees rather than of trusties or other prisoners.

16-23. Examination of Inmates and Inspections. The local health officer or medical officer should examine all inmates upon admission or as soon thereafter as possible. He should also promulgate rules for care of sick prisoners and prescribe standards for isolation of all patients suspected or known to have communicable diseases. The health officer or his representative should make frequent inspections of the premises for unsanitary or unsafe conditions. Likewise, the fire marshal should be called upon to assist the jail administration in maintaining proper fire safety facilities and services.

16-24. Lighting and Ventilation. The building should be well lighted, ventilated, and heated to promote a healthful and clean environment. All cells should receive some natural light, and the artificial lighting should be sufficient throughout the building to permit easy visibility at all times. Cells, dormitories, dayrooms, and work areas should have sufficient artificial light to permit reading without eyestrain.

The interior of the jail should be of a durable finish which permits effective cleaning. The surfaces should be light in color to reflect light effectively. The pastel colors also tend to make the environment more pleasant and materially assist in promoting cleanliness.

Natural ventilation is not always sufficient to keep the air fresh and free from disagreeable odors, especially during periods of inclement weather. The use of a forced-air ventilation system has many advantages, since it can be designed to operate effectively in all types of weather. The heating system should be so installed that a uniform temperature can be maintained throughout the building. It is preferable to have a day temperature of 68 to 72°F and a night temperature of 60°F in the cells and dormitories, offices, guardrooms, and similar areas.

16-25. Water Supply and Sewerage. The water-supply and sewage disposal systems are usually a part of the community system, so that other local authorities are responsible for the provision of the necessary safeguards. The installation of sanitary drinking fountains throughout the jail is essential, and if the water is tepid to warm, it may be advisable to provide coolers. In those rare instances where the jail must maintain its own water-supply or sewage disposal systems, the standards for individual systems explained in Chaps. 5 and 4, respectively, should be applied. Under these circumstances it is also advisable to request the local health authorities to make inspections and tests at regular intervals.

16-26. Pest Control. Vermin, insect, and rodent control is an essential administrative responsibility. The building should be ratproof, and every effort to eliminate rat feeding or harborage in the immediate vicinity should be applied. Likewise, all exterior windows and doors should be effectively screened, and insect breeding on or near the jail premises should be eliminated. Head and body lice, bedbugs, and roaches can be effectively controlled by thorough inspection of the new prisoners and their garments; enforcement of high standards of personal hygiene, including frequent bathing and laundering of clothes, bed linen, bath towels, and other washable items; and the maintenance of clean premises, particularly the kitchen, dining room, and prisoners' living quarters. Personal cleanliness should include required bathing for all prisoners at least twice a week and daily bathing for food handlers, cleaning personnel, and prisoners who do heavy labor. If possible, any prisoner should be permitted to bathe daily if he so desires. In the event that an infestation of vermin, insects, or rodents should occur, the services of a competent exterminator should be engaged.

A well-secured enclosure which is clean, free from sharp or dangerous objects, and well drained should be provided for outdoor exercise of all prisoners. If an outdoor area is not available, a well-ventilated enclosure which admits sunlight should be provided.

16-27. Food Service. The food for prisoners should be procured, prepared, and served in accordance with the provisions cited in Chap. 12. Since prisoner labor is available, every effort should be made to operate a food service within the jail rather than to obtain food from an outside source, except in extremely small jails. Three meals should be served daily; however, if only two meals can be provided, the quantity of food supplied should be the same. The serving periods should be spaced to avoid any unduly long period without food, and the administration should take particular care to make sure that no prisoner is required to go to bed hungry. Prisoners are interested in the quantity, taste appeal, and variety of food rather than in its nutritional value. Good and attractive food proves valuable in maintaining discipline, high morale, and reasonable health, whereas monotonous or unpalatable food is a source of illness and resentment and may even provoke violence or an attempted jailbreak.

While the prisoner helpers in the food service should be inspected for communicable disease and closely supervised for cleanliness, it is essential that a well-qualified employee-cook, capable of planning menus and preparing and serving food in an appetizing manner, be in charge of the kitchen and dining room.

16-28. Cell Furnishings. Each cell or dormitory room should be equipped with a metal bed and a clean mattress, mattress cover, pillow, pillowcase, sheets, and blankets for each inmate. There should also be a cabinet or locker for each inmate's personal belongings, a stool or chair, and a table. Each room or cell should have a trash container and a unit for the disposition of cigarettes. The cells should have a washbowl and a commode, and community facilities may be used in dormitory rooms. There should be one shower for each fifteen inmates and one commode and one lavatory for each eight prisoners where community facilities are used. The cell should be designed to provide 50 square feet of floor space for each prisoner, and in the case of dormitory rooms additional space is highly desirable.

BIBLIOGRAPHY

1. "Report of the Coordinating Committee for a National Plumbing Code," U.S. Department of Commerce, Domestic Commerce Series, no. 28, 1952.
2. Good and Bad School Plants, *U.S. Dep. Health, Education, Welfare Special Pub.* 2.
3. "Responsibilities of State Departments of Education and Health for School Health Services," National Council of Chief State School Officers and the Association of State and Territorial Health Officers.
4. Improving School Custodial Service, *Federal Security Agency Bull.* 13, 1949.
5. School Lighting and Visual Environment, *Natl. Soc. Prevention Blindness Pub.* S-12.
6. "Manual of Jail Management," U.S. Bureau of Prisons, April, 1948.

CHAPTER 17

INDUSTRIAL HYGIENE

17-1. Industrial hygiene is concerned with conservation of the health of the worker. Insofar as it accomplishes this end it affects not only his well-being but also the prosperity of his family and the community. It also influences favorably his employer's production, labor turnover, and profits. The fact that science can eliminate work hazards and improve the worker's health has so proved itself to industrialists that the cost of industrial hygiene in many of the more progressive industries is now charged off to production. This cost averages about $15 per year per employee, although it varies considerably in the various industries, but it pays returns, not only in the ways already mentioned but also in reduced absenteeism and improved employee morale.

The newer concept of industrial hygiene embraces nonoccupational as well as occupational influences on the worker's health. It is also being extended to all the gainfully employed, not only to industrial workers; *i.e.*, the occupational hazards of the nonmanufacturing group are being studied and protection applied to workers in various services, such as transportation and the utilities. The more progressive states are also becoming concerned with the 8,600,000 agricultural workers who may be exposed to various insect poisons, herbicides, fungicides, and fertilizers under conditions approximating those of manufacture. The migratory farm workers present an additional and special problem. They are particularly exposed to nonoccupational diseases by reason of their poverty, nomadic life, and lack of sanitary facilities in their usual environment.

17-2. Industrial Hygiene Service in Industry. Authorities consider that an effective industrial hygiene program in an industrial plant should include four types of service: medical, engineering, safety, and welfare. These services will be discussed in detail.

1. *Medical Service.* This work is carried on by physicians, dentists, and nurses. It can be further subdivided as follows:

a. PHYSICAL EXAMINATIONS. These are given to new employees in order to eliminate those unfit for work, or those who have some latent condition which could be aggravated by a new exposure, and also to guide in assigning applicants to suitable work. Current practice tends to "preplacement" examinations since it is now recognized that certain operations can be satisfactorily performed by persons with limited disabilities. The examinations in many cases, and preferably so, are as searching as those given for life insurance. They also have a value for the workman in that they uncover both major and minor defects that he or the plant physician may take steps to remedy. Included under this activity may also be the instruction of new employees as to the occupational hazards they will encounter in the plant. Periodical physical examinations are important since they have the advantage of revealing previously unsuspected working hazards. The physician then is responsible not only for seeing that proper treatment is given but also for notifying the employer and the governmental authority having jurisdiction so that corrective measures can be taken to prevent injury to other workers. Workers known to be exposed to poisons or other hazards should be examined frequently. Periodical routine examinations are also useful in the discovery of nonoccupational defects which can be remedied before irreparable harm is done. In this phase of the examination the usual confidential relationship between doctor and patient should be preserved in order to overcome the employee's possible objections and to obtain his cooperation in the examination program.

b. SUPERVISION OVER WORKING CONDITIONS. The physician is the health officer of the plant. In this capacity he should acquaint himself with the toxic materials and harmful processes that exist there and their effects upon the workers. He should analyze sickness records as an aid to discovering hazards and be able to recommend or outline the necessary preventive measures. He should be able to interpret the engineers' reports on health hazards and apply them effectively.

c. HEALTH PRESERVATION IN THE PLANT. This includes dental and optical services and treatment of injuries and illnesses. Under this heading may also be placed provision for rest and recreation and supervision or inspection of food-handling establishments. Health education should be stressed in the industrial plant. This may be the function of the nurse who treats injuries. Furthermore, the prevention of health hazards requires not only the installation of preventive measures but also their intelligent use. Hence the employee should be fully informed as to what has been done and the reasons therefor. Through educational measures he can be given an accurate evaluation of the conditions under which he works so that he will be neither unnecessarily alarmed nor unduly careless at his work. These and other aspects of health education may be discussed by the same employee groups who meet periodically to discuss the safety problems of their plant. In other words, reduction or elimination of health hazards is a product of teamwork between management and the employee.

d. HOME AND COMMUNITY PROBLEMS. While too much work in this direction may result in the accusation of paternalism, which, by that name at least, is distasteful to many Americans, undoubtedly much good can be done by visiting nurses and by advice of the industrial physician as to bettering home conditions. At this point it may be well to point out that a few employers now realize, as in all likelihood many more will later, that the stimulation of municipalities to obtain good water and milk supplies and the application of health measures in general pay dividends to industry. Since the large industries are heavy taxpayers, their influence may do much in this respect.

2. *Engineering and Safety Services.* The application of engineering to industrial hygiene requires basic engineering training in addition to knowledge of ventilation; chemistry of dusts, fumes, gases, and vapors; physiology; toxicology; industrial sanitation; and the broad field of public health. Many industrial plants have no engineers on their staffs, and very few have their own industrial hygiene specialists. These plants may utilize the services of the governmental industrial hygiene bureaus, Federal, state, or local, to obtain impartial surveys and expert consultation. If this is done, the plant management should assign some responsible person, preferably an engineer, to work with the industrial hygiene consultant—this, of course, in addition to the necessary cooperation with the plant physician.

The safety engineering service is more likely to be organized by the plant. It may be headed by a safety engineer or by a man who is acquainted with the plant processes and who is required to familiarize himself with accident hazards and methods of prevention.

a. ENGINEERING IN INDUSTRIAL HYGIENE. After the physician has recognized the physical injury or disease caused by the hazardous process or environment, engineering methods leading to remedies should then be applied. These are (1) determination of the plant conditions that are causing the hazard; (2) the use of precise quantitative measurements or statistics to establish the exposure or other factors that result in injury or disease; (3) the devising of methods of controlling or minimizing the dangerous conditions and study of their effectiveness.

b. SAFETY. The safety engineer has the necessary training or knowledge to recognize conditions or practices that might result in accidental injuries to workers. His work might well be correlated with the physical examinations mentioned above. If a complete physical record is kept of each employee, including aptitude tests, individuals who are especially prone to accidents may be eliminated from certain occupations. All industrial operations must be designed so they can be done safely. Moving parts likely to injure workers must be guarded. In certain operations, workmen are required to wear safety shoes, goggles, hard hats, special gloves, and other protective clothing. Women workers should wear hair nets and practical work clothes, of designs made by the U.S. Women's Bureau. Stairways and pits must have adequate hand- and guardrails. Daily inspections of all operations should be made by the safety engineer. Safety committees, made up of workmen, one for each shop and operating under a central plant committee, have been found useful in investigating accidents, formulating safety rules, and making recommendations and seeing that rules are complied with. The plant physician and safety engineer should be members of the central safety committee. Each plant should have at least one first-aid or stretcher crew composed of interested employees who have had some special training.

17-3. Governmental Control. While some large industries are able to provide all the health services mentioned in the previous articles, the many workers in small industries must depend for health protection upon the state and local health departments, which, in turn, must be supported by adequate laws. The national laws affecting the health of workers are concerned mainly with hours of employment of Federal employees, safety devices for railroads, etc. The states have many and varied laws governing factories and mines, some of the earliest being concerned with inspection of steam boilers, dust removal, regulating working hours of minors and women, provision for fire exits, later followed by requirements for reporting occupational disease, the installation of safety devices, proper ventilation and lighting, and sanitation of workrooms and toilet rooms. To enforce these requirements most states have corps of factory inspectors. In addition, all states have workmen's compensation laws applying in most states to accidental injuries only, but in others covering occupational diseases also.

Laws that are more specific and comprehensive are required. Preferably such laws, or city ordinances, should be enabling in their nature. This would allow health officials to make and enforce regulations and would have the advantage of flexibility to meet changing conditions.

17-4. Organization for Industrial Hygiene. The real and potential progress in the field of industrial hygiene is indicated by the fact that each state and territory has industrial hygiene services in actual operation on the state level. In addition to this, many of the larger municipalities, such as Detroit, Houston, and Los Angeles, have full-time industrial hygiene programs, while over 254 other city health departments are prepared to offer some type of related service in this field. However, most of these cities provide more extensive services of a technical nature in cooperation with the state industrial hygiene organization. In most states, the work is in a separate division or bureau of the health department, where it is also identified occasionally as the occupational health division or the industrial health division. In three states, it is a function of the labor department. The Navy, Army, Air Forces, and Atomic Energy Commission have well-organized industrial hygiene units which conduct programs and surveys of their major installations. The Navy has an industrial hygienist at most of its shore stations. The Army and Air Forces have traveling teams to cover the United States and some overseas installations.

A separate unit has a director who may be a physician, an engineer, or a chemist. The work is divided between a medical section and an engineering section. The physician handles medical and clinical investigations of occupational disease and serves as a connecting link between industry and the various preventive medical services offered by the state health department. Such contact will also include consultation and cooperation with the health services provided by the larger industries of the state.

The engineer handles all problems dealing with environmental control of industrial hazards, makes investigations in industrial plants, and collects samples as needed. He is the connecting link between industry and the environmental control services offered by the state health department.

The laboratory is separate from other state laboratories and is available for such medical, chemical, and biological tests as may be required. Administratively it is responsible to the director, but the physician and engineer work directly with it, the former for medical laboratory work, the latter for engineering investigations.

Nursing consultation is carried on under the direction of the physician with as much coordination as may be necessary on the part of the engineer.

Many variations are noted from the above type of organization, whether in the state or municipal service. If the unit is in the bureau of sanitary engineering, the medical services are obtained as needed from some other bureau, probably that for control of communicable diseases, which may have a specialist in industrial medicine. Or all the technicians, physicians, engineers, and nurses may work together in the same office as a functional unit, but each type of personnel will be administratively responsible to some bureau, as the physicians to the bureau of communicable disease and the engineers to the bureau of sanitary engineering. The general health department laboratory may perform the laboratory services needed.

The U.S. Public Health Service has an Occupational Health Program, with the Occupational Health Field Headquarters located in Cincinnati, and a field station in Salt Lake City. This organization carries on extensive research work in the field of occupational health hazards, offers related laboratory services, and assists in organizing state work and training its personnel. Results of research and major field studies are published in bulletins and technical publications. It also provides a directory, which is revised periodically, of all local, state, and Federal government industrial hygiene personnel.

17-5. Occupational Hazards. Most processes and operations of industry involve one or more potential threats to the health and safety of the worker. These are called occupational hazards. Most of them may be eliminated, or much reduced, by the application of engineering methods. Lists of these hazards are available from various sources[1,2]. Here very broad classifications of the most important hazards are given:

1. Excessive heat, cold, or humidity
2. Compressed air
3. Dust, fumes, and gases
4. Poisons
5. Excessive noise
6. Poor illumination, glare, and extreme light
7. Repeated motion, pressure, or shock
8. Infections
9. Radiation hazards
10. Accidents
11. Poor plant sanitation

17-6. Industrial Poisons. In many industries, poisonous materials are produced, used, or appear as impurities in otherwise safe substances. Some occur as gases, fumes, mists, vapors, or dusts which are breathed with the air; others are liquids or solids which may be absorbed through the skin, while some which are solids or liquids may form fumes or gases and thus be absorbed in several ways. Note that the poisons mentioned are not ingested and, generally speaking, industrial poisons are not taken through the mouth, although it is possible for a workman to handle food while he has poison on his hands. Inspired poisons are far more important. As an example, a person can safely ingest twenty times the lead concentration which, if inhaled, would show systemic toxic effects.

Poisons absorbed through the skin may cause dermatitis or skin inflammation, which is a common industrial ailment. In some cases it may occur as an individual sensitivity to a substance, or allergy, when other workers have no difficulty. One of the most common of industrial poisonings is that due to lead, and it is encountered in lead smelting and refining, the manufacture and use of paints, the printing trades, and the glazing of china and earthenware. The preparation of arsenic and the making of commercial poisons have also been found to be dangerous. In the zinc, brass, and copper trades the fumes of the metals themselves and their impurities are deleterious. Carbon monoxide, being a product of incomplete combustion, has caused deaths through the agency of blast furnaces, mine explosions, and various exhausts. Mercury poisoning was formerly found among hatters and in trades where amalgams of mercury are used. Benzol and other coal-tar products, petroleum products, and many new organic solvents used as spray-paint thinners and degreasing agents represent other occupational hazards. A partial list of industrial poisons is given in Appendix B.

The prevention of sickness and death from these causes requires recognition of the hazard and the application of expert medical and engineering knowledge. These measures cannot be discussed in detail here, although some general rules for the protection of workers may be mentioned:

1. Construction of buildings so that the dangerous processes are isolated.

2. Use of apparatus that is adapted to its special purpose, kept in good order, and constructed, so far as possible, to prevent escape of dangerous materials.

3. Use of exhaust fans and ducts, placed as close to the source as possible, so that poisonous air-borne materials are removed quickly. These require careful design, with due consideration to the character of the dust, fumes, or gases and the allowable concentration of the deleterious material in the air[3].

4. Avoidance, so far as possible, of direct contact between the workmen and dangerous substances.

5. Replacement of particularly dangerous production methods with less dangerous methods and substitution of less dangerous chemicals or agents for the more dangerous ones, even though greater production expense results thereby. This is often not feasible.

6. Instruction of workmen as to the hazards of the process they are working in, with frequent repetition of such instructions. These instructions should include the signs of the poisoning or other injury that may be expected, consultation with the plant physician when suspicious signs appear, and precautions that should be taken by the worker to avoid poisoning or other injury. Warning placards should be used to supplement other instructions.

7. Supervision of dangerous operations by responsible and well-informed persons.

8. Employment of all personal means appropriate to the hazards encountered, as suitable clothing, gloves, goggles, and respirators. These devices should not, however, replace the better alternative of attacking the basic causes of the hazards. Furthermore, such safety devices are not always used and may get out of order or otherwise lose their efficiency without being suspected. The only respiratory equipment that should be used is that which has the approval of the U.S. Bureau of Mines.

9. Periodical medical examinations with provision for transferring workmen who show signs of poisoning to other occupations. In occupations that may give rise to chronic poisoning, periodic shifting of workers may be advisable.

10. Requiring of body cleanliness on the part of workers. This includes bathing and changing of clothing at the end of the working day. Work clothing must be frequently cleaned in nonhazardous ways. This requirement places upon the industry the responsibility of furnishing suitable clothing lockers, washrooms, and shower baths.

11. Lunches should not be eaten in the workrooms. This requires the industry to furnish lunchroom facilities.

12. Working hours in the hazardous operations should be as short as possible.

Many of the industrial poisons are air-borne, as fumes, gases, dusts, and vapors, and are difficult to collect and determine. The impinger or the electrostatic precipitator may be used if it is known that the poisonous material is a dust. Impingers are also useful for most toxic gases. Sampling methods have been developed for many atmospheric contaminants, and concentrations which may be tolerated by workmen have been established for some[4,5,6,7].

17-7. Maximum Allowable Concentrations. As a result of many observations and much experience a great deal has been learned of the effects of certain substances upon workers, and this knowledge has been translated into allowable concentrations. The knowledge is by no means complete and, especially where the experience is limited, there are differences of opinion as to allowable maximums. Each year the Threshold Limits Committee of the American Conference of Governmental Industrial Hygienists reviews the list of Threshold Limit Values published the preceding year. Revisions or additions are made as the result of toxicological research on specific substances or from actual industrial exposures encountered. The 1955 list appears in Appendix B. These values serve as a guide for Federal, state, and local agencies in determining compliance with codes or safe practices and are helpful to industry as bases for the design of protective measures.

The maximum concentration is defined as that amount of atmospheric contaminant which can be tolerated by man for continuous daily exposure with no impairment of health or well-being either immediately or after years of exposure. The specific figures listed in Appendix B refer to average concentrations of an eight-hour working shift rather than a maximum which is not to be exceeded momentarily. The amount which these figures may be exceeded for short periods depends upon a number of factors, such as the nature of the contaminant, whether short periods of high concentration produce acute poisoning, whether results are cumulative, and the frequency of occurrence of high values and for what periods of time. All these must be considered before deciding whether a hazard exists.

17-8. The Dust Hazard. The workers in many industries are exposed to a serious health hazard as a result of dust inhalation. The injurious effects of the inhalation of a harmful dust are proportional to the amount of dust breathed, which, in turn, is related to the amount of dust in the atmosphere and the length of time it is breathed.

Dusts may be classified as inert, irritating, and toxic. The inert ones do not poison the body, although they may cause undesirable effects. Irritating dusts have an immediate and local effect. They include lime and other caustics, picric acid, soap powder, and some cereal dusts. Toxic dusts are differentiated from irritating dusts in that they result in remote or systemic poisoning rather than immediate local effects.

The inert dusts include those of vegetable and animal origin, such as are encountered in woolen and carpet manufacturing, spinning and weaving, and jute and paper manufacturing, and are less harmful than other types, although a considerable amount of respiratory disease is attributed to them. Metallic and mineral dusts, to which grinders, polishers, printers, and file-and-tool workers are exposed, are considered more dangerous in predisposing persons to respiratory disease.

Dusts containing silica, which are incident to stonecutting, sandblasting, rock drilling, and certain processes in coal mining, are especially dangerous. Silica enters into a chemical reaction in the lungs to form fibrous tissue, the resulting injury being known as "silicosis," which in turn sets up conditions favorable for a fatal pulmonary tuberculosis. Asbestos dust has the same effect as silica, the resulting disease being known as "asbestosis," with pulmonary tuberculosis as the aftermath. Preventive measures include mechanical removal of the dusts by exhaust systems, which should be properly designed and then tested to make sure that they are reducing the atmospheric dust content below the danger point; enclosure of the work, such as the barrel method of sandblasting; the use of wet processes to diminish dust production; and the requirement that workmen wear respirators or helmets (either plain or, in especially dangerous processes, with special air supplies pumped under pressure to the helmets) over the nose and mouth.

Maximum allowable atmospheric dust contents, as given in Appendix B, are expressed in millions of particles per cubic foot as measured by various types of apparatus. The commonly used dust measurer is known as the "Greenburg-Smith impinger." It consists of a pump which draws the air to be sampled through a glass tube and impinges it at high velocity against a glass plate which is submerged in water, or other suitable liquid, in a flask. The dust is arrested, wetted by the liquid, and trapped.

After sufficient air has been sampled, a portion of the liquid is removed to a suitable counting chamber or cell for a microscopic count of the particles[9,10]. Another type is the electrostatic precipitator which can be used for the collection of dusts, fumes, and mists for chemical analyses. It has been discovered that silica dust particles in numbers over 10 million per cubic foot of air[11] will be injurious to workmen

FIG. 17-1. Collecting an air sample with a precipitator to determine the lead content near a soldering machine used in can making. (*Courtesy of Texas State Department of Health.*)

habitually breathing such air, although to improve the margin of safety most states recommend that not more than 5 million particles per cubic foot be allowed. The dust concentrations in stonecutting establishments where exhaust systems have not been installed sometimes exceed 80 million per cubic foot of air. Some investigations also indicate that in certain of the lead-using trades, such as storage-battery manufacturing, the limit of safety in the lead dust content of the air is 1.5 milligrams per 10 cubic meters of air (approximately the amount breathed per day),. except for prolonged exposure in excess of eight hours daily.

17-9. Radiation Hazards. The general subject of radiation hazards is discussed in Chap. 18. The industrial use of radioactive compounds, such as luminous paints, has long been recognized as a serious industrial health hazard. Other hazards noted in this field involve shoe-store clerks who operate or work near fluoroscopic shoe-fitting machines. In textile and paper mills radioactive static eliminators which are improperly shielded or stored have been reported. In the future, as nuclear energy is adapted for industrial purposes and betatrons, radioactive isotopes, and atomic power piles become commonplace, the accompanying hazards from both dangerous radiation and radioactive salts and gases will increase the demands for industrial hygiene services. Two of the most widespread uses of radioactivity in industry are in static-electricity eliminators and in gauging thickness or density.

A fund of knowledge is being developed by the United States government in its atomic energy researches which is applicable to this hazard. Physicists, engineers, and chemists have cooperated to develop protective measures which include proper construction of laboratories and buildings, disposal of radioactive wastes, a service that determines radiation present in the air, and personal protective measures. The last-named include protective clothing and various devices which indicate the amount of radiation to which the worker has been subjected. Among these devices are film badges, pocket ionization chambers, and dosimeters. These devices are usually attached to the worker's clothing, and the first two devices may be worn on the wrist or as a finger ring. These indicate the accumulated dose to which the wearer has been subjected. Standards have been set up for allowable exposures, but these are based upon knowledge gained from X-ray work and are subject to changes resulting from further research. These standards may be obtained from various handbooks on the subject issued by the National Bureau of Standards. Limiting exposures to radioisotopes are given in Appendix D.

A problem important to both the worker and the community is the disposal of wastes. Air and water are used in large amounts to cool the reactors or piles, and these become radioactive to a degree depending upon the nature of the impurities they contain. This activity is lost by decay in a period also depending upon the nature of the impurities. Water and liquid wastes in general are stored in ponds until they have lost radioactivity sufficiently to be discharged into streams. If the decay period is too long, they may be buried in lead and concrete containers. Air is filtered to remove most contaminants before use, but it is still radioactive, principally because of its argon content. Therefore air is discharged only through high stacks and at times when meteorologists say that atmospheric conditions are right for good dispersal to the upper atmosphere by winds. The half-life of most radioactive isotopes is known, and this provides a guide for the disposal of other waste, burial often being practiced to permit short-half-life contaminants to decay. Progress has been made in methods for the decontamination of material and equipment[11]. Detergents and decontaminants are also used.

17-10. Noise. Noise and its undesirable effects are discussed in Arts. 19-18 to 19-20. Noise levels at or near 100 decibels are harmful

FIG. 17-2. Noise-evaluation study being made with sound-level meter and frequency analyzer in an industrial shop. (*Photograph courtesy of General Radio Corporation, Cambridge, Mass.*)

to the human ear. Since many factories are noisy and workers are exposed continuously for long periods, noise prevention is even more important than for the nonindustrial worker. To safeguard the worker and also to eliminate production loss, noise should be reduced by use of the following expedients: (1) diminution of sound at its sources;

(2) isolation of noisy operations; (3) reduction by sound insulation; (4) use of personal protective devices.

Noise is becoming increasingly significant in industrial operations, for compensation awards have recently been made to employees who have sustained a partial hearing loss even though no lost time was involved. This court action has stimulated a review of the potential hazards throughout the United States; and in addition to noise control and evaluation studies, many progressive companies are now including audiometric examinations both on a preemployment basis and at periodic intervals. All this has contributed greatly to the improvement of various types of noise- and sound-analyzing equipment in recent years. Most state occupational health programs are now giving increased attention to the problem of industrial noise. The Public Health Service is engaged in a study of the acute and chronic effects of noise exposure on workers in the shops at some of the Federal penal institutions. *Noise Control,* a publication available from the Acoustical Society of America, contains much helpful information as to instrumentation, some of which is of special assistance to the nontechnical reader.

17-11. Light as a Hazard. Workers required to handle or view glowing materials, such as furnacemen, smelters, electro-welders, and glass-workers, show eye affections caused by the excessive exposures to radiant heat and ultraviolet rays. Glasses which are opaque to, or reduce the transmission of, these rays give protection. Excessive eyestrain may be caused in industrial processes by poor illumination as in mining, by glare, improper brightness contrasts, flicker, and by poor illumination combined with close use of the eyes for long periods (see Chap. 14).

17-12. Heat. Excessive heat is a hazard to stokers, smelters, blast-furnace men, glass blowers, kiln and pottery men, etc. The effects are heat exhaustion, colic, and cramps. If there are rapid variations in temperature, congestion of the internal organs may result with possibility of rheumatic and neuralgic affections, gastrointestinal catarrh, pneumonia, and other disorders. Radiant heat may cause dermatoses, eye inflammations, and perhaps cataract. Heat combined with high humidity affects workers in breweries, laundries, tanneries, textile mills, and canneries, causing disorders of the sweat glands. Exposure to a cold, humid atmosphere lowers the power of resistance and is conducive to rheumatic and pulmonary diseases. Preventive measures include air conditioning to obtain proper temperature and humidity with use of helmets and goggles to protect from radiant heat. Humidity and temperature relations should follow those indicated in Chap. 13.

17-13. Compressed Air. Divers and workmen in caissons who work in air at greater than atmospheric pressure are exposed to a disease known as the bends. The increased pressure causes air to be dissolved in the blood, a condition which is not dangerous unless the air pressure is suddenly greatly reduced. Bubbles of nitrogen then form in the veins and arteries and interfere with circulation, collapse and death being very likely to occur. The danger is overcome by reducing the air pressure gradually. Deep-sea divers are raised to the surface in successive stages. Caisson workers after leaving work are held in a special air lock or chamber for several hours while the pressure is slowly reduced. This permits the dissolved nitrogen to leave the blood without bubble formation. In addition to problems arising from compressed air, certain adverse exposures can occur where the environmental pressure is below that of the atmospheric level.

17-14. Repeated Motion, Vibration, Pressure, Shock. Using the same muscles in the same motion for many hours in the day may affect them so that the worker loses the ability to continue the operation, although the muscles respond to his will in all other respects. This condition is called an "occupational neurosis." The well-known writer's cramp is an example, but trap drummers, cigar rollers, milkers, engravers, dancers, letter sorters, and followers of many other occupations are sometimes affected. The use of vibratory tools in industry, especially in automobile and aircraft factories, is increasing. No one knows very much about the effects of vibration at the present; however, the Occupational Health Program of the Public Health Service is currently studying this particular type of exposure. Rest and medical attention are required by the victims of this condition.

17-15. Infections. Certain occupations present hazards from infections. Anthrax is not uncommon among tanners, hide handlers, and workers in leather and hair. So far as possible, hides and hair should be disinfected. Workers with open cuts should not handle unsterilized hides or hair; gloves should be worn; and washing facilities are necessary. Dust can be reduced by ventilation but should be removed by downward ventilation to carry the dangerous material away from the faces of the workers. Tetanus, ringworm, and septic infections are common among workers handling earth or earthy material. Dairymen, butchers, and slaughterhouse employees are exposed to brucellosis or undulant fever. Millers, dishwashers, and cigar makers are liable to fungus diseases.

Metalworkers use oily or soapy liquids to cool the metal while it is being cut. Such cutting compounds are used and returned many times. Frequently they become vehicles for large numbers of pus-forming bacteria and are responsible for spreading wound infections and furunculosis (boils). The remedy is sterilization of the compound by heat in a central reservoir before it is recirculated. Some of the newer disinfectants are now being investigated and may prove satisfactory to add to cutting compounds.

PLANT SANITATION

17-16. The sanitation of industrial plants is directed toward obtaining proper conditions for conserving health and improving the efficiency of the worker. This includes proper ventilation, heating, and lighting, the furnishing of pure drinking water; adequate toilet facilities; adequate and clean lunchrooms; and good housekeeping of the plant in general. A highly important provision is the delegation of responsibility for sanitary conditions to some qualified person. In factories having organized medical or health service the necessary inspections should be made by some member of the health organization. Leaving this important matter to the individual foremen of various departments is unsatisfactory. Even in the smaller plants where more dependence must be placed upon state or city factory inspectors, instructions, responsibility, and the necessary authority should be given to some permanent member of the working force. It has been suggested recently that the personnel manager be charged with this responsibility because of his advantageous relationship with labor and management.

17-17. Ventilation. The ventilation of industrial plants should be based upon the comfort standard discussed in Chap. 13, with the necessary attention paid to the activity required of the worker by his occupation. This may change the usual relationships of temperature, humidity, and air movement to bring the atmospheric conditions into the comfort zone. Natural or artificial means may be employed to get this result. An additional requirement is that at least 20 square feet of floor space and 200 cubic feet of air space be provided for each workman.

In addition to what may be called normal ventilation, the problem of removing injurious dusts, fumes, vapors, and gases must be solved. This requires exhaust systems that should be designed by experienced engineers to remove the undesirable substances at their source. Of equal importance is the fact that such systems should be operated at all times when protection is needed and that they should be properly maintained.

Ventilation systems, particularly in the Northern states, include recirculation of air in order to conserve heat. If the recirculated air contains dust or other contaminants, air-cleaning equipment should be installed. Air recirculation should not be practiced unless there is assurance that such equipment will operate efficiently at all times.

17-18. Illumination. Many states have adopted lighting codes to ensure sufficient lighting to reduce unnecessary eyestrain and to prevent accidents. Table 17-1 gives standards as recommended by authorities on the subject. The illumination should be measured by a foot-candle meter at the place of work with due attention to proper brightness ratios and prevention of glare (Table 17-1, footnote). Supplementary lighting is sometimes necessary to give proper illumination for special types of work. Here also care should be taken to avoid high brightness ratios in the field of vision. A ratio of 10:1 should not be exceeded, and 5:1 is a

TABLE 17-1. GENERAL RECOMMENDED VALUES OF ILLUMINATION

	Current recommended practice, foot-candles in service on task or 30 inches above floor
Most difficult seeing tasks	200–1000*
Finest precision work	
Involving finest detail, poor contrasts, long periods of time	
Such as extra-fine assembly, precision grading, extra-fine finishing	
Very difficult seeing tasks	100
Precision work	
Involving fine detail, fair contrasts, long periods of time	
Such as fine assembly, high-speed work, fine finishing	
Difficult and critical seeing tasks	50
Prolonged work	
Involving fine detail, moderate contrasts, long periods of time	
Such as ordinary bench work and assembly, machine-shop work, finishing of medium-to-fine parts, office work	
Ordinary seeing tasks	30
Involving moderately fine detail, normal contrasts, intermittent periods of time	
Such as automatic machine operation, rough grinding, garage work areas, switchboards, continuous processes, conference and file rooms, packing and shipping	
Casual seeing tasks	10+
Such as stairways; reception rooms, washrooms and other service areas; active storage	
Rough seeing tasks	5
Such as hallways, corridors, passageways, inactive storage	

* Obtained with a combination of general lighting plus specialized supplementary lighting. Care should be taken to keep within the general brightness ratios indicated below and to avoid glare conditions when light-colored materials are involved. Recommended brightness ratios: 5:1 between tasks and adjacent surroundings; 20:1 between tasks and more remote surfaces; 40:1 between luminaires (or sky) and surfaces adjacent to them; 50:1 anywhere within the environment of the worker. (These values are through courtesy of the Illuminating Engineering Society, as published in "American Standards Practice for Industrial Lighting," ASA A-11.1—1952.)

preferable limit. As many industrial plants are dusty, special attention should be paid to the cleaning of reflectors and bulbs and replacement of old or burned-out bulbs. Reflection factors of walls and ceilings must be maintained by repainting. Without such maintenance the illumination may be only 50 per cent of that to be expected from the design and electric current consumed.

For natural illumination of one-story industrial buildings the window area should be at least 30 per cent of the floor area. If only one wall has windows, the width of the room should not exceed twice the height from the floor to the top of the windows. If windows are in two parallel walls, the width between should not exceed six times this height. In some industrial plants which rely upon natural lighting, the illumination is kept at a desirable minimum level by means of photoelectric cells which turn on artificial illumination automatically. This makes it unnecessary to rely upon the human eye and ensures against forgetfulness.

17-19. Water Supply. The supply should, of course, be pure, satisfying the standards of the U.S. Public Health Service. If the water is derived from a private source, precautions outlined in Chap. 5 should be applied to prevent contamination, and tests should be made periodically. Not less than 20 gallons per capita per working day are required for drinking, washing, and other purposes. The consumption of drinking water alone varies from 2 quarts to 2 gallons, depending on the type of work and the temperature.

A possible danger is the use of unsafe supplies for fire protection or industrial purposes. Too often the auxiliary water is accessible for drinking by careless or uninformed workmen, or, if the two supplies are cross connected, the supposedly safe supply may become polluted. Cross connections are so dangerous that they should not be permitted. Exposed piping should be distinctively colored or lettered, and taps or faucets on unsafe supplies should be placarded or removed.

The common drinking cup should be prohibited in favor of drinking fountains, readily accessible and preferably furnishing water at not under 46°F. The number of fountains required varies from 1 for 50 men to 1 for 200 men depending upon the plant arrangement. If the workmen perspire a great deal, it is advisable to prevent excessive loss of salt from the body. The normal intake of sodium chloride is 10 to 20 grams daily mostly as seasoning in food. Manual work in a hot atmosphere may cause excessive perspiration with much loss of salts from the body. The occurrence of cramps and prostration has been attributed to this loss. In some industrial plants, workers are supplied with salt tablets and urged to take an amount equivalent to 15 grams of sodium chloride per day. Steel companies have found that a water containing 0.1 per cent of sodium chloride and cooled to 46°F is agreeable and beneficial. This would supply about 1 gram to 1 quart of water. In some cases the tablets furnished also supply potassium chloride in the proportion of 40 per cent potassium to 60 per cent sodium chloride.

17-20. Toilet Facilities. Observation of many plants indicates that the workmen may be protected against plant hazards but not against those of the toilet and washroom. In all toilet rooms the floor and side walls should be watertight and impervious to moisture to a height of 6 inches, including the angle formed by the floor and side walls. The floors, side walls, and ceilings should be of a finish that can be cleaned easily. All toilet and washrooms should have window openings to the outside air or be provided with ventilation systems which change the air at least six times per hour. Ventilation ducts serving toilet rooms should have no connection with other ventilating ducts. The proportion of glass window surface should be not less than 1 square foot to each 10 square feet of floor area. If insufficient natural illumination is available, artificial light should be provided sufficient in amount to encourage cleanliness and allow easy inspection.

Water closets, lavatories, and sinks should be of porcelain or vitreous china. The most sanitary closet seats are of impervious material, of the U-shaped or split-type open front and back. Water-closet bowls should be set free from all enclosing walls and should be so installed that space around them can be easily cleaned. If the washroom is not combined with the toilet room, one or more washing faucets should be placed in the toilet room.

The following numbers of toilets are recommended by the American Standards Association[14]:

No. of persons	*Minimum no. of facilities*
1–9	1
10–24	2
25–49	3
50–74	4
75–100	5
Over 100	1 for each additional 30 persons

For each urinal provided, one less than the above number of toilets may be provided, except that the number of toilets may not be reduced to less than two-thirds of the number specified. Two feet of acid-resistant porcelain enamel urinal is considered as equivalent to one urinal. The recommended type of urinal is the vitreous china individual stall with the waste pipe in the floor. Urinals may be located at convenient points in the plant, but there should always be urinals in the toilet room to prevent use of seat fixtures for this purpose.

One washing faucet should be provided for each 10 employees or one for 15 in large plants. The washing faucet is far more desirable than the individual washbasin or lavatory, as being less likely to spread infections among the users. Hot and cold water should run from the same faucet, and it is highly desirable that there should be automatic regulation of the hot water to not more than 125°F. Circular wash fountains with treadle-operated water valve and soap dispenser have been found satisfactory. Liquid soap, in dispensing containers, rather than cake soap, should be furnished, and no common towels should be used.

Shower baths, with an ample supply of hot and cold water from the same fixture, should be provided in the ratio of one for each 15 workers or fraction thereof in industries where there is exposure to excessive heat or skin contamination with infectious, poisonous, or irritating substances. The showers should discharge at an angle from the wall rather than from overhead. Hoods may be advisable to carry off vapors. As much privacy as possible should be provided in baths and dressing rooms, particularly where women are employed.

The floors and ceilings of locker rooms should conform to the requirements for toilet and washrooms. In fact, locker and washrooms are frequently combined. A well-ventilated locker should be furnished to every employee. The room itself also requires good ventilation, or the odors from used clothing will be noticeable. An alternative to lockers is the ceiling hook, an arrangement which allows complete drying and airing of clothing. Each workman is allotted a combination of two hooks and a wire basket for shoes, etc., all of which are attached to a chain which runs over a pulley suspended close to the ceiling. After the clothing is raised to the ceiling, the chain is locked to a device below. This system has been widely used at steel plants, mines, and chemical works.

Where 10 or more women are employed at any one time, at least one retiring room should be provided for their exclusive use. The space provided should be at least 60 square feet of floor area, with an increase of 2 square feet for each additional woman employee above 10. At least one couch or bed should be provided where 10 women are employed. The recommended minimum number of beds is one for 100 women or less; two beds for 100 to 250; and one additional for each additional 250 women employed.

It is of great importance that janitors be made reponsible for the condition of toilet, wash-, and locker rooms and for the placement of soap, towels, and paper. But this is not sufficient. There should be frequent inspections of the rooms by responsible executives of the plant staff.

Where employees are permitted to eat their lunches at their place of employment, a space should be provided for this purpose that will be adequate for as many workers as may wish to use it at one time. A covered receptacle is supplied for waste food, paper, etc., and employees should be required to use it for the disposal of all such wastes. No employee should be permitted to eat any food where there are poisonous materials or other substances injurious to health.

BIBLIOGRAPHY

1. Occupational Hazards and Diagnostic Signs, *U.S. Dep. Labor Bull.* 582.
2. "Useful Criteria for the Identification of Certain Occupational Health Hazards," Utah State Department of Health, 1942.
3. Brandt, A.: "Industrial Health Engineering," John Wiley & Sons, Inc., New York, 1947.
4. Jacobs, M. D.: "The Analytical Chemistry of Industrial Poisons, Hazards and Solvents," 2d ed., Interscience Publishers, Inc., New York, 1941.
5. Sampling for Control of Atmospheric Impurities, *Ind. Hyg. Foundation Amer. Preventive Eng. Ser. Bull.* 2, pt. 8, 1939.
6. Bailey, J. F., and B. H. Jennings: "Toxic Gases and Vapors in Industry," Northwestern University, The Technological Institute, Evanston, Ill., 1944.
7. *Am. Public Health Assoc. Year Books*, 1935–1936, 1937–1938, 1940–1941.
8. Silverman, Leslie: Sampling and Analyzing Air for Contaminants, *Air Conditioning, Heating and Ventilating*, vol. 52, pp. 88–100, August, 1955.
9. Bloomfield, J. J.: Dust Procedures in Air Analysis, *Am. Public Health Assoc. Year Book*, 1935–1936.
10. Comparative Tests of Instruments for Determining Atmospheric Dusts, *U.S. Public Health Bull.* 144.
11. Health of Workers in Dusty Trades, *U.S. Public Health Bull.* 187.
12. "Radiological Decontamination in Civil Defense," Federal Civil Defense Administration, TM-11-6.
13. Yaffe, C. D.: A Study of Industrial Noise and Hearing Loss in a Controlled Population, *Public Health Repts.*, vol. 69, no. 9, 1954.
14. "American Standards Minimum Requirements for Sanitation in Places of Employment," American Standards Association, Inc., Z4.1-1955.
15. Drinker, P., and T. Hatch: "Industrial Dust: Hygienic Significance, Measurement, and Control," 2d ed., McGraw-Hill Book Company, Inc., New York, 1954.
16. Patty, Frank A. (ed.): "Industrial Hygiene and Toxicology," vols. I and II, Interscience Publishers, Inc., New York.
17. Elkins, Harvey B.: "The Chemistry of Industrial Toxicology," John Wiley & Sons, Inc., New York.
18. "Industrial Ventilation: A Manual of Recommended Practice," American Conference of Industrial Hygienists, Committee on Industrial Ventilation.
19. "Encyclopedia of Instrumentation for Industrial Hygiene," University of Michigan Press, Ann Arbor, Mich.

CHAPTER 18

RADIOLOGICAL SANITATION

18-1. Radiological health, which is the public health aspect of the use of ionizing radiation, is becoming increasingly important as nuclear energy is used to an ever-increasing extent in medicine and industry.

18-2. Atomic Structure. All matter is made up of "atoms."[1] Physicists have succeeded in establishing that the atom consists of a "nucleus" surrounded by a group of "electrons" moving about the nucleus. The nucleus is a combination of particles called "protons" and "neutrons." The former have positive electrical charges, the latter are neutral, and the electrons have negative charges. The single positive charge on each proton is balanced by the negative charge on each electron. The number of protons, or of electrons, is called the "atomic number," and each chemical element has an atomic number according to the number of its protons or electrons. For example, hydrogen, the simplest element, has only one proton and one electron, and thus its atomic number is 1. Lithium has three protons and three electrons, and its number is 3. The atomic number for chlorine is 17; for iron, 26; and for lead, 82. The atomic number of an element should be distinguished from its "mass number," which is based upon the mass or quantity of matter in its nucleus. It is the mass number which is used in making chemical calculations in which mass is involved.

An atom of the same element may have differing numbers of neutrons in its nucleus. Chemically it remains the same, but its mass is slightly different. These slightly varying atoms are known as "isotopes." Every element has three or more known isotopes. For example, hydrogen, as mentioned above, has one proton and one electron in its atom, with an atomic number 1 and mass number 1. But there are other isotopes of hydrogen. One has a single neutron in its nucleus, in addition to its single proton. The atomic number remains the same, but the mass number is 2. Another hydrogen isotope has two neutrons in the nucleus, and its mass number is 3. These three isotopes are known as H^1, H^2, and H^3 and are also called "protium," "deuterium," and "tritium," respectively. Carbon has at least five isotopes, carbon 10, 11, 12, 13, and

[1] A glossary of the terms used in this chapter is provided in Appendix C.

14, the figures indicating the mass numbers, but the atomic number remaining the same.

What are called "nuclear forces" keep the nuclear particles together, while others tend to thrust them apart. In the nuclei of most atoms the forces are balanced, and the balance is hard to upset. Nuclei of this sort are called "stable." In other nuclei there is spontaneous rearrangement with ejection of charged particles and final attainment of more stable combinations of protons and neutrons. These unstable isotopes are called "radioactive isotopes," or "radioisotopes."

Each element has at least one radioisotope. Some occur in nature, as those of radium, thorium, and uranium, while others can be made artificially by means of the nuclear reactor or other means. In both types, radioactive decay takes place, and simpler nuclei result with other combinations of protons and neutrons and differing chemical characteristics.

18-3. Radioactivity. "Radioactivity" is the process whereby unstable nuclei undergo spontaneous atomic disintegration with liberation of energy. The process, also known as decay, is characterized by the emission of one or more types of radiation, as alpha particles, beta particles, and gamma radiation.

The alpha radiations are high-energy particles consisting of two protons and two neutrons and thus have two positive electric charges. A stream of them is called an alpha ray. Alpha particles quickly dissipate their energy and can penetrate matter for only short distances. They are usually a health hazard only when the radioisotope has been ingested or otherwise absorbed into the body and they radiate internally.

Beta rays are streams of charged beta particles, which have a mass and electric charge equal in magnitude to those of an electron. The charge may be positive or negative; if the former, they are called "positrons." Beta particles are moderately penetrative and dissipate their energies relatively quickly, but they can be a health hazard either as internal or external radiation.

Gamma rays are high-energy "photons," rays similar to light and radio waves but much shorter in wavelength and of much higher frequency. They have no electric charge. They resemble X rays and actually the longer gamma rays are identical with the shorter X rays so that the radiations are indistinguishable. The term "gamma ray," however, is applied to radiations of short wavelength having their origin in atomic nuclei. The emission of gamma rays is an important way in which a nucleus in a high state of internal energy can rid itself of the excess energy.

X rays are produced by subjecting a metal or other dense target to bombardment with a stream of high-speed electrons. The electrons are formed by passing a high-voltage current through a vacuum from a cathode to an anode. The atoms of the target anode are surrounded by intense electric fields; when the electrons strike these fields, a part of their energy is converted into X rays, which emerge in all directions from the target. The vacuum tube is enclosed by a shield of lead or other dense material to leave a small opening through which the useful beam can pass. The higher the voltage used to form the electron stream, the more penetrating the resulting X rays. The voltage used may be from 50,000 to more than 10 million. X-ray machines and fluoroscopes are, of course, in common use in hospitals and the offices of physicians and dentists. They are also used in industry to determine the internal structure of materials. A common use is in fitting shoes. Other man-made radioactivity is caused by some radio transmitters, high-voltage, projection-type television receivers,[1] and high-voltage rectifiers for changing alternating current to direct current. Cyclotrons, betatrons, and similar machines are used to accelerate protons, electrons, or other charged particles and so produce ionizing radiations, usually for experimental purposes.

Background radioactivity is the radiation produced by cosmic rays, the trace amounts of radioactive isotopes that are naturally present in the environment, and those that have been disseminated as a result of man's use of nuclear energy.

The amount of energy released in nuclear reactions is of importance in the effects it may have upon persons or matter exposed to the various rays. One method of calculating energy is of interest. It utilizes the fact that the forces in atomic nuclei manifest themselves in their respective nuclear masses. According to Einstein's theory of relativity, the relationship can be expressed as

$$E = mc^2$$

in which E is the energy equivalent of the mass m, and c is the velocity of light. If m is expressed in grams and c is taken as 3×10^{10} centimeters per second, then E will be in ergs; that is,

$$E \text{ (ergs)} = 3^2 \times 10^{20}\, m \text{ (grams)}$$

In order to change this to calories, it would be divided by 4.2×10^7. The energy change in any nuclear reaction can be obtained by inserting for m in the equation the difference in mass resulting from the nuclear reaction.

Measurement of the energy actually generated, however, is made by

[1] This does not apply to the ordinary, direct-view television receivers now in general use. They present no hazard, as the soft radiations produced within the picture tubes are absorbed by the thick glass of the tubes.

other means, and the energy is expressed in units related to the means of measurement. A special unit, the electron volt, is used in relation to the energies of radiations of atoms and of molecules. One electron volt is the energy given to a single electron as it moves across an electrical potential difference of one volt. The volt is the same unit used to measure electrical potential in its ordinary use. One electron volt is 1.6×10^{-12} erg. One million electron volts (Mev) is enough energy to lift a milligram one-millionth of a centimeter. The energy of the bonds holding molecules of chemical compounds range from fractions of electron volts to 10 or 12 electron volts. The nuclear binding energy holding protons and neutrons together in the nuclei of atoms is of the order of millions of electron volts.

18-4. Half-life of Radioisotopes. Decay of a radioactive isotope is caused by the disintegration of the individual atoms of which it is composed, with the release of energy in the forms of alpha, beta, and gamma rays. Scientists have no means of speeding or slowing the rate of decay. Among the identical radioactive atoms, disintegrations occur at random, and no prediction can be made as to when a particular nucleus will decay. It is possible, however, to estimate with accuracy the number that will disintegrate in any given length of time. Since very large numbers disintegrate, the number doing so in any one time interval follows the laws of probability, and the number decaying in any given interval of time is proportional to the number originally present and can be estimated with sufficient accuracy. If the interval chosen is that in which 50 per cent of the atoms disintegrate, then in each successive interval of the same length 50 per cent of the remaining radioactive atoms will decay. Such a time interval is known as the radioactive half-life. After seven half-lives the radioactivity of a radioisotope will have been reduced to about 1 per cent.

The half-lives of the known radioisotopes range from fractions of seconds to billions of years. Nitrogen 12† has a half-life of 13/1,000 of a second; iodine 131 has a half-life of 8.14 days; carbon 14 has 5,580 years; radium 226 has 1,622 years. Very long half-lives are more conveniently expressed exponentially. For example, uranium 238 has a half-life of 4.49×10^9 years, or 4,490 million years.

18-5. Ionization. Ionizing radiations—whether they are the alpha, beta, gamma, or other rays produced by radioactive decay, from radiation-producing machines, or from cosmic sources—all react upon any matter which absorbs them by splitting molecules into pairs of electrically charged fragments called "ions." This ionization can occur in any kind of matter, and when it takes place in living tissue, animal

† Nitrogen 12 means that the mass number of this particular isotope is 12, whereas the commonly stated mass number for nitrogen is 14.

or plant, changes occur that may affect health. The extent of the ionization and damage depends upon the length of exposure and the energy level of the radiation received.

The fact that charged particles or photons ionize gases is made use of to measure radioactivity. If an electrical potential is maintained across a gas, a small charge flows through the gas chamber each time a charged particle traverses it, as the result of positive ions and electrons collecting on the cathode and anode respectively. The Geiger-Mueller counter makes use of this method and is used principally for the measurement of beta and gamma rays. The scintillation counter shows visible scintillations when alpha particles impinge upon zinc sulfide crystals. This method now employs a multiplier tube which is highly sensitive and is also used to measure gamma radiation.

Background radioactivity is first obtained before a counter is used to determine the radioactivity of some radioactive material.

18-6. Units of Radiation and Radioactivity. Radiological health workers commonly make use of several units of radiation and radioactivity. The "curie" is the unit of radioactive disintegration. It is the quantity of any radioactive material in which the number of disintegrations per second is 3.700×10^{10}. This is a large amount of radioactivity. Practically speaking, a gram of pure radium is one curie of radium. Two smaller units, the millicurie, or 1/1,000 curie, and the microcurie, or 1/1,000,000 curie, are frequently used. Some types of counters can be calibrated to give results in curies. Others merely give the number of disintegrations per unit of time, and these are known as counters. How these are used is shown by the following example:

Example. A counter, after the calibration and other corrections have been applied, indicates a disintegration rate of 3,000 per minute or 50 per second. This expressed in curies would be $50/(3.7 \times 10^{10})$ or 1.4×10^{-9}. This would also be expressed as 1.4×10^{-6} millicurie or 1.4×10^{-3} microcurie. This may seem a very small amount of radioactivity, but the permissible amount (see Art. 18-10) of phosphorus 32 in water gives off 2×10^{-4} microcurie per milliliter.

If the number of disintegrations from a known radioisotope have been counted, it is possible to determine the weight of the isotope producing them. Of course the curies per gram of the isotope must be known. The calculations can be shown by an example:

Example. It is desired to know the number of curies that will be given off by 1 gram of the radioisotope phosphorus 32 and also the number of grams that will give off 1 curie. The curies per gram can be calculated by the following equation:

$$\text{Curies per gram} = \frac{1.308 \times 10^{8}}{(T_{\frac{1}{2}})(\text{atomic weight})}$$

in which $T_{\frac{1}{2}}$ is the half-life of the radioisotope in days. Phosphorus 32 has a half-life of 14.3 days. The atomic weight is taken as the mass number or 32 in this case. Substituting in the formula we obtain curies per gram as 2.85×10^5. Grams per curie will be the reciprocal of this or 3.5×10^{-6}. The amount of phosphorus 32 that would have the disintegrations in the previous example would be $1.4 \times 10^{-9}/2.85 \times 10^5$, or 4.9×10^{-15} gram. This demonstrates the very small amounts of radioisotopes that produce considerable radioactivity. The allowable amount of phosphorus 32 in water is even less per milliliter.

The "roentgen" is a measure of the absorption of gamma and X rays only, primarily in the ionization of air. It is also used as a measure of radiation dosage to human beings. In practical work, mixed radiation (*e.g.* beta-gamma) and particulate (*e.g.*, beta) radiation fields are sometimes measured with gamma-standardized measuring instruments, and the readings may be recorded as roentgens. These are only approximations, however, and the need for proper evaluation must be kept in mind. In the application of the roentgen to dosages, the milliroentgen, or 1/1,000 roentgen is often used.

Two other units are used. The "roentgen equivalent physical" is applied to dosages of particulate ionizing radiations. It may be defined as the amount of alpha, beta, or other particulate ionizing radiation whose absorption exposes tissue to the same amount of energy as does the absorption of a roentgen of gamma or X radiation. The "roentgen equivalent man" is the quantity of radiation of any type which, when absorbed by man, produces a biologic effect equivalent to that produced by the absorption of 1 roentgen of gamma or X radiation. These equivalents are computed and not measured.

18-7. Harmful Effects of Radiation. Massive doses of radiation produce such conspicuous conditions in man as nausea, vomiting, bleeding, anemia, and leukemia. Public health workers should be more concerned with the less evident results of repeated small exposures. These include shorter life span, debility, loss of vigor, increased susceptibility to illness, retardation of recovery from illness, and other health impairments which affect earning capacity or increase the possibility of an individual's requiring community care. While the adverse health effects are important, they should not obscure the fact that radioactive materials are important in medicine and industry and will become more so.

The above effects are the results of injury or destruction to body cells caused by ionization. Cells may be affected in such a way that cancers may result; mutations in future generations and decreased fertility are injuries that are likely to occur after heavy exposures accompanying atomic bomb explosions or repeated exposures to which workers around X-ray machines or other radiation producers are subject. Such repeated exposures can be prevented by appropriate safeguards.

The effects of acute or large single doses of ionizing radiation vary from possible blood changes at 25 to 50 roentgens and obvious injury, but not disability, at 100 roentgens to possible death at 400 roentgens. A dose of 400 roentgens, which is likely to kill 50 per cent of the persons exposed, is sometimes called the "mean lethal dose." At doses above this, the proportion of deaths increases. At 600 the chance of survival is very small. It should be emphasized that these dosages must be applied to the entire body. Application of 400 roentgens to a cancerous area of the body may result in injury to the cancer but in no other damage.

Chronic or continuous doses also have bad effects. The allowable exposures, however, are not as well established. It has been said that a dose of 0.3 roentgen per week can be delivered continuously to the whole body without danger. Many radiologists now believe that this amount does not provide a sufficient factor of safety. It is of interest to note that the Atomic Energy Commission[1] has set up a standard of 0.03 roentgen per forty-eight-hour work week in connection with licenses issued by the Commission for certain activities.

Typical exposures of patients or others exposed to X-ray radiations are as follows:

Routine chest X ray	0.05–0.3 roentgen
Routine gastrointestinal X ray	1.0 roentgen per exposure
X ray of extremities	0.25–1.0 roentgen
Fluoroscopic examination	10–20 roentgens per minute

These exposures are only to the parts of the body concerned, and danger is reduced as the percentage of the body exposed is decreased.

18-8. Safety Measures. Protection against injury by radioactivity is attained by (1) checking to determine the amount of exposure of an individual, (2) by shielding the worker against radiation, and (3) by safeguarding the public against radioactive waste products.

Various types of device are used to check the exposure of individuals to radiation. Use of such devices is known as monitoring. Some types are worn in or on the clothing of the person.

One type is the film badge, which contains photographic film enclosed in a container that is readily penetrated by beta, gamma, and X rays. The film is developed after exposure, and the density of the film, which is measured by an instrument called a densitometer, indicates the total exposure in roentgens.

Another type is shaped like a fountain pen and has an ionizing chamber. The outer wall is an electrode, and another electrode is located within the chamber. To it is attached a quartz fiber, which shows by its curvature the amount of charge. As ionization caused by gamma or other rays decreases the charge, the curve of the quartz fiber decreases, and this, as shown by a scale which can be seen through an eyepiece, indicates the roentgens of exposure.

Area-survey types of instruments, also depending upon ionization of air, can be used to detect beta, gamma, and X radiation in terms of roentgens at various points in a laboratory or plant.

Shielding of personnel is the placing of barriers between the emitter of radiation and the exposed persons. The thickness of the shield required depends inversely upon its distance from the source and directly upon the energy level of the radiation. If the shield does not absorb all the energy, the exposure of the worker is reduced by increased distance from the shield. Alpha rays can be stopped by almost any material. Beta rays are absorbed by 1 inch of wood or ½ inch of dense metal. Gamma and X rays require more protective material. The denser the material, the more efficient it is. Accordingly, lead is much used for this purpose, and concrete is useful in walls. Protective barriers do not absorb all the radiation. Scattered and secondary radiation result from the impact of the rays upon the atoms of the shielding substance. Some of the rays are deviated in direction, and some, by their impact upon the atoms of the barrier, cause changes which release energy, and this leaves the barrier material. Arrival at necessary thickness of the shield for protection against X rays depends upon the voltage and current used and the absorbent characteristics of the material[2].

Shielding included in doors, partition walls, or ceilings of X-ray rooms should be carefully done, or there may be considerable leakage to unsuspecting persons. Shielding, in general, should be checked by the use of an area-survey apparatus. If the work week is forty-eight hours, the roentgens per minute should not exceed 10^{-4} per minute at the working point if the standard of 0.3 roentgen per week is not to be exceeded.

18-9. Radioactive Wastes. Low-level radioactive wastes, since they are usually diluted by water or air, are far larger in volume than the high-level wastes, which are higher in radioactivity and toxicity. The low-level wastes include drainage from research laboratories where radioactive materials are used; drainage from laundries which launder clothing, etc., used by laboratory workers and from hospitals where radioisotopes are used; wash water which is used to decontaminate surfaces which have become coated with radioactive substances; and water used in basins to shield workers from radioactive materials that are being stored or worked on.

High-level wastes are relatively low in quantity but very high in radioactivity. They are derived from the chemical processing of spent fuels from nuclear reactors and from research laboratories dealing with "hot" radioactive materials.

High-level wastes with long half-lives have been stored in underground tanks. Evaporation has also been used to concentrate such wastes prior to storage. Ion exchange and precipitation with coagulants have been used, followed by filtration. Sludges obtained are partially dewatered and stored. Ultimate disposal includes land burial and disposal at sea. Burial grounds should not be located in or near creviced limestone or gravel beds. The soil should preferably be of such type that it will absorb radioactivity. Dense clays are favorable in this respect. There has been some disposal of radioactive wastes at sea into deep water beyond the continental shelves on the Atlantic and Pacific Coasts. The wastes are placed in steel drums, and these are encased in concrete. It is believed that this method requires further investigation before it is used to a great extent.

Solid radioactive wastes, which include laboratory table covers, wiping papers, etc., have been burned. This method concentrates about 85 per cent of the activity, at least for certain isotopes, in the ash, which must then be disposed of. The gases of combustion need decontamination by costly air-cleaning facilities.

From air-cooled reactors large volumes of irradiated air may be discharged to the atmosphere, and the air may require removal of particulate matter. The disposal of radioactive gaseous wastes poses problems of cleaning the gases of smoke and dust, stack heights, and the meteorology of the area. Stack heights are important, since the radioactive gases should be released at a high level into the atmosphere. The permissible level of radioactive contaminants in air is 10^{-9} microcurie per milliliter for beta and gamma emitters and 5×10^{-12} microcurie per milliliter for alpha emitters. These values are considered safe for exposures of several months[3].

18-10. Radioactive Isotopes in Water. Radioactive isotopes gain entrance to water by being discharged along with other wastes into the sewers or by direct dilution into streams from industrial or other users or producers of radioactive isotopes. Another method of water contamination is by fallout of radioactive dusts resulting from the explosion of atomic bombs. In the last case dust particles become contaminated with radioactive products of fission, and some radioisotopes are formed by neutrons bombarding certain elements. The amount of radioactive dust depends upon the location of the explosion with regard to the ground surface.

Radioactive wastes can be diluted in water to below the allowable limit. This is taken as 10^{-7} microcurie per milliliter when the activity is caused by an unknown mixture of beta- and gamma-emitting isotopes[3]. For certain known radioisotopes the limits may be higher. As examples, for strontium 89 the limit is 7×10^{-5} microcurie per milliliter, for phosphorus 32 it is 2×10^{-4} microcurie per milliliter, and for iodine 131 it is 3×10^{-5} microcurie per milliliter. Dilution, however, does not give complete protection, for radioactivity may be concentrated to dangerous limits in water life which may be consumed in some form by humans.

Dilution is made less hazardous by procedures that prevent excessive concentrations of radioactivity. For example, recommendations of the Subcommittee on Waste Disposal and Decontamination of the National Committee on Radiation Protection have pointed out that the maximum permissible levels of phosphorus 32 and iodine 131 that may be discharged into a sewer should not exceed the following:

1. Short-period concentration of 100 microcuries of either isotope per liter of sewage.
2. A single-batch discharge of 10 millicuries.
3. When a uniform discharge device is used, 100 millicuries of these isotopes may be discharged in any six-hour daylight period into a sewer system having an average dry-weather flow of 1 million gallons per day.

Reduction of radioactivity in sewage is reduced in unknown amounts by sewage treatment processes through concentration in biological films and sludges. There natural decay takes place, but the problem of safe disposal of these materials remains. The radioactivity remaining in the treated sewage is, of course, present in the body of water receiving it, where it may be taken up, in part, by algae. These may be consumed by higher forms of life which, in turn, may be eaten by fish, which may present a hazard to human consumption.

Fallout of radioactive dusts from atomic bomb explosions into reservoirs[4] or upon watersheds has not, so far, constituted a hazard to public water supplies where investigations have been made[5].

The water treatment processes, including coagulation and filtration, remove some of the radioisotopes from water, but the removal is only in the neighborhood of 30 per cent of mixed isotopes[5]. Water treatment in itself, therefore, cannot be considered as a safeguard for heavy contamination, particularly since the removal rate varies with the radioisotope. Investigations are in process leading toward the discovery of better methods of treating low-level wastes.

BIBLIOGRAPHY

1. "Standards for Protection against Radiation," U.S. Atomic Energy Commission, F.R. Document 55-5625, July, 1955.
2. "X-ray Protection Design," National Bureau of Standards, Handbook 50, May, 1952.
3. "Maximum Permissible Amounts of Radioisotopes in the Human Body and Maximum Permissible Concentrations in Air and Water," National Bureau of Standards, Handbook 52, 1953.

4. Eliassen, Rolf, and R. A. Lauderdale: Radioactive Fallout in Water Supply of Portland, Me., *J. Am. Water Works Assoc.*, vol. 48, p. 665, June, 1956.
5. Morton, R. J., and C. P. Straub: Removal of Radionuclides from Water by Water Treatment Processes, *J. Am. Water Works Assoc.*, vol. 48, p. 545, May, 1956.
6. "Assuring Public Safety in Continental Weapons Test," U.S. Atomic Energy Commission, 1953.
7. "Effects of Atomic Weapons," U.S. Atomic Energy Commission, 1950.

CHAPTER 19

MISCELLANEOUS

HOOKWORM CONTROL

19-1. This plague of mankind is now widely spread throughout the tropics and also in many subtropical regions. There is a belt encircling the earth extending from 38° North to 34° South in which hookworm is likely to be prevalent. In other areas with favorable temperatures it is also likely to be encountered, and in the mines of cooler countries it is frequently found. In this country it is present more or less in all the Southern states and as far west as and including Texas, also in some mines of California and the East. The rate of infestation is sometimes found to be very high. In certain areas of the Southern states, 50 per cent or more of the rural school children may show infestation. In some tropical regions including the West Indies, northern South America, and the Orient even higher rates of infestation have been found. Rates of infestation do not necessarily indicate the magnitude of hookworm as a public health problem, as it is only the severe cases which have appreciable effects upon the individual.

The life history of the hookworm and the means by which infestation is transmitted from person to person and the factors affecting such transmittal are known in detail. The universal wearing of stout boots and shoes, for instance, would effectually bar the usual entrance point of hookworms into the human body. Specific treatments are also available for curing the persons infected. The methods of control and the cure are comparatively simple, and therefore hookworm elimination should be easily attained. The most important obstacles, however, are the ignorance, poverty, and apathetic attitude too often encountered among that portion of the population which is exposed to the disease.

19-2. Hookworm Disease. All persons harboring hookworms do not have hookworm disease. The worms must be present in sufficient numbers in the intestines to cause the weakness, dullness, loss of energy, and anemia characteristic of the disease. The number required to cause the symptoms varies with the age of the infected person, but in adults probably 100 or more worms show some evil effects. When complicated by malaria or other debilitating influences, however, this number may cause real suffering, while greater numbers are responsible for more severe disturbances. It must be recognized that all infected persons are carriers and may spread the infection.

19-3. Life History of the Hookworm. There are several species of hookworm which infect man. The two most important are *Ancylostoma duodenale* and *Necator americanus*. The latter is the most prevalent in the United States. It appears to be somewhat less virulent than the other. There are several other hookworms occasionally found in the intestines of man but never in sufficient numbers to cause hookworm disease. Still other types confine their activities to dogs, cats, and other animals. The adult hookworm is about the thickness of hairpin wire and is 3/8 to 1/2 inch long. The adults live in the intestines, fastening themselves to the walls by means of their strong mouth parts. The biting injures the walls and causes loss of blood. In addition, there are toxins liberated which are responsible for anemia. The adult worm is supposed to live for six to eight years, spending all its adult life in the intestines. The female worms are constantly producing large numbers of eggs, which leave the host in the feces. Examination of feces under the microscope for the presence of eggs is the regular method of establishing infection. Within twenty-four hours the eggs hatch if temperature and moisture conditions are favorable. The larva is able to move about to a limited extent and feeds on the excrement. It molts once and in four to five days after hatching molts for the second time but remains within the loose skin from which it has detached itself. At this period the larva becomes infective and is able to enter a victim at the first opportunity. It may exist in this stage for as long as six weeks, although in general its life is not so long. Should a barefooted person step on soil in which the larva is present, the larva clings to the skin and starts to bore its way in. A favorite point of attack is the tender skin between the toes. Its passage through the skin sets up an irritation which has been given the popular name of "ground itch." The larval worm makes its way into the lymph vessels and veins and is carried with the blood to the heart and finally to the lungs. It leaves the blood vessels of the lungs and penetrates the air passages, thus obtaining a clear route up the bronchial tubes and windpipe to the throat. From the throat it is swallowed, going to the stomach and intestines. This journey requires about ten days, and during the process the worm becomes sexually mature.

While the great majority of infestations are obtained through the bare feet, the worms may also enter through other parts of the body. In the mines infestation is frequently obtained through the hands' coming in contact with infected soil or in the climbing of ladders which have received infective material from shoes. It is also possible to become infected through the mouth by means of vegetables which have been grown in fields fertilized by human excreta and possibly through drinking of infected water.

19-4. Characteristics of Eggs and Larvae. Hookworm eggs may survive for long periods in the soil. Stiles, of the U.S. Public Health Service, found infected soil under privies which had been abandoned five months previously. The infection does not usually last that long however. Eggs in fecal matter which is decomposing under water are killed after three months. Apparently they hatch only in the presence of oxygen. This suggests the possible danger in the use of sludge from septic and Imhoff tanks for fertilizer. It is known that the eggs may come unharmed through septic tanks with the effluent. Disinfectants appear to have no effect upon them.

The larvae, while capable of movement, apparently do not travel horizontally. Payne found them capable of traveling vertically 36 inches in loose sandy soil which was frequently wet by tropical showers. Cort found them able to travel vertically 8 inches in moist soil but less than 4 inches in dry soil. This information is significant in connection with the burial of infective materials. There appears also to be a possibility of larvae reaching the surface from the disposal fields used in subsurface irrigation, particularly in sandy soil which is fairly moist. They do not climb up grass blades, as was formerly believed. Larvae are quickly killed by drying and by frost.

In addition to favorable temperature, favorable soil and favorable rainfall characteristics are necessary to maintain a high rate of infestation in a population. A heavy clay soil is unfavorable because it quickly dries and becomes hard. A sandy soil that is continually dry is also unfavorable. A sandy soil or a sandy loam combined with a well-distributed rainfall is most favorable. This permits the larval worms to retreat downward when the soil surface becomes too dry and to return to the surface when a rain wets the topsoil. Larvae caught in pools of water soon drown. For the same reason they are not likely to be washed very far. There appears to be no danger that they can make their way out of the pit of a pit privy, even though there may be no curb or cover to prevent them. Apparently, in their upward travel, they remain on the first horizontal or approximately horizontal surface they may reach, even though it is only a small roughness of the side of the pit.

The inability of the worm to travel horizontally indicates that, unless it is transported by animals or insects, the danger occurs where fecal matter is indiscriminately scattered on the ground where the bare feet of children or adults may come in contact with the polluted soil. This is likely to occur where no privies are in use and especially where certain areas are used for defecating purposes, with no privies of any type. This custom is not uncommon in India and elsewhere.

19-5. Medical Control Methods. Medical treatment of hookworm disease is simple. The worms are killed or numbed by various medicines, following the taking of which a purgative is given to expel the worms. Generally three doses of the vermicide are given at weekly intervals, and the cure is checked by means of feces examinations for the presence of eggs. In the work of the International Health Board the giving of medicines in the United States is usually left to the families of the persons affected. In the West Indies and elsewhere, in treating a population of lower intelligence, medicines are administered by nurses. The nurses are usually men of the country, capable of receiving a small amount of special training for the work. This was considered necessary to ensure the proper taking of the medicine and also to avoid the possibility of damage by the vermicides, these being somewhat injurious to the health if taken improperly.

Routine treatment of infested persons has been demonstrated as being insufficient alone to control hookworm disease, since the treated population is likely to be reinfested to the pretreatment level within a year after treatment stops. Sanitation must be improved through the construction of sanitary toilets.

While many mines at present have toilets for the use of the workmen underground, it is almost impossible to prevent pollution of the ground in the various passageways. The safest means of hookworm control in mines is to exclude infested workmen by giving them medical treatment and keeping them at work above ground until a feces examination demonstrates freedom from the worms.

19-6. Sanitary Control. In those areas where hookworm is prevalent, toilet facilities are of the most primitive kind. At many schools and rural homes either there are no toilets whatever or the existing ones are in such filthy condition that they are avoided. The open-back surface toilet is also a contributor to the spread of hookworm as chickens, pigs, and surface water may spread the infection out upon the near-by ground. Sanitary control of hookworm must, therefore, be directed against soil pollution. This requires direction and inspection through some governmental agency. Of the toilets which may be constructed with this purpose in view, the improved pit toilet is the most applicable. Its low first cost and operation and its underground disposal of excreta render it valuable for rural homes and schools. If the water table is high so that the working of the pit toilet is interfered with, probably the septic privy is next in value. This type of privy, however, should have a retention period of at least three months. The chemical toilet can also be used, but its somewhat high cost probably confines its use to schools. For schools and homes with running water the septic tank with subsurface irrigation is the best means available.

Control of hookworm by sanitary measures in primitive communities where sanitary or unsanitary habits have been the custom for centuries may present special difficulties. The sanitarian may introduce elaborate privies that combine all the safeguards possible and find that they are not used or are abused in such a manner that their usefulness is lost. This difficulty has been noted in the Orient. The bored-hole latrine with squat-type cover may be applicable here. In any case the habits, beliefs, and customs of the people should be carefully studied, and the improvements installed should conform as far as possible to them.

RABIES CONTROL

19-7. Rabies is an acute fatal encephalitis caused by a specific virus. Reservoirs of this virus include any of a large group of wild and domestic mammals. Vampire and fruit-eating bats are infected in South and Central America and Mexico. Recently insectivorous bats have been found infected in the United States. The disease is transmitted by the bite of a rabid animal or, rarely, by the contact of infectious saliva from such animals on abraded areas of the skin. The incubation period of rabies in man varies from two to six weeks or longer, and this variation depends on the severity of the laceration, relationship of the bite wound to richly supplied nerve areas, and the length of the nerve path from the bite wound to the brain. Bites on the head and face are particularly dangerous because of the richness of the nerve supply to these areas and the short distance to the brain.

19-8. Treatment of Suspected Human Cases. When there is ample evidence to suspect that a person has been bitten by a rabid animal, the Pasteur treatment is indicated. This consists of a regimen of 14 consecutive daily doses of the rabies vaccine. The vaccine is generally prepared from rabbit spinal cord tissue in which the rabies virus has been cultivated and attenuated. Postvaccinal paralysis may occur when using this nerve tissue vaccine. Consequently, the need for vaccination must be critically evaluated.

Maximum protection is probably not imparted with this vaccine until three to four weeks after treatment is begun. For this reason, in the case of short-incubation face and head bites, it is imperative that the treatment be started as soon as possible after exposure. Hyperimmune antirabies serum has recently come into usage. Immediate protection is provided by serum; however, it is of short duration. Antirabies serum in conjunction with vaccination is of particular value in severe exposures such as occur in head and face bites.

19-9. Treatment of Suspected Animals. An animal that has bitten a person should be caught, if possible, and confined under observation by a veterinarian for a period of fourteen days. If at the end of this interval the animal has shown no signs and symptoms of rabies and is still alive, there is no reason to suspect that the bitten individual has been exposed to rabies virus. Should the animal show signs and symptoms of rabies or die during this interval, the Pasteur treatment for the bitten person should be initiated and laboratory confirmation of rabies in the animal should be sought. Other animals known to be exposed to rabies should be either treated, and held in quarantine for not less than sixty days, and preferably longer, or destroyed. When laboratory confirmation is desired, the head should be removed, packed in a watertight container, iced, and expressed to the laboratory. Pertinent information relative to the reason for shipping the specimen should accompany the specimen to the laboratory:

19-10. Rabies Prevention. The successful control of rabies is based upon the application of three essential principles:

1. Impoundage and disposal of all stray and ownerless dogs.
2. Annual antirabies vaccination of all claimed dogs; however, if phenoliozer vaccine (an attenuated live rabies as grown in chick embryos) is used, an immunity for three years is secured.
3. The reduction of wildlife populations, *i.e.*, foxes, skunks, etc., when that population is serving as a reservoir of rabies.

Rabies is best controlled at the local health levels, for it is here that the enforcement of a program is carried out. The adoption of local ordinances, which in some way encompass the three broad principles stated above, is the key to effective rabies control. It must be remembered that no matter how well a program of control is drafted, it does not have its desired effect unless a well-planned educational program goes along with it.

INSECTS

19-11. Roaches. These pests are frequently found in homes, bakeries, restaurants, and other warm places where food is prepared. They feed upon any kind of animal matter and cereal products and also gnaw woolens and leather. They frequently do damage to books, the glue or sizing used in bookbinding being particularly attractive.

Bacteriological examinations made of their intestinal contents indicate that their feces contain at times bacteria which are associated with gastrointestinal disorders or so-called food poisoning. They may also carry infectious material on their bodies and feet from the sewers which they frequently inhabit to kitchens and other food-handling establishments. Their presence, therefore, can be considered as a sanitary defect.

There are four common species[1] of roaches which inhabit houses. They are all somewhat alike in appearance and differ not at all in habits, except that the smallest, the German cockroach, also known as Croton bug or water bug, prefers the dampness around water pipes and sinks and is more wary than its cousins. They are all nocturnal in their habits, so that many more may be present than might be suspected from a daylight inspection. They pass through successive stages from egg to adult, the period of development being rather long, possibly a year.

The roach population may be kept down by cleanliness and by protection of all foods in jars or other containers. Cracks and other hiding places should be eliminated. Powdered borax mixed with meal or flour and scattered on floor, shelves, or runways is an effective poison. Sodium fluoride prepared in the same way is probably still better. Sodium fluoride used alone is very good if it is blown by means of a dust gun into cracks of walls, floors, and furniture and into other dark corners where the roaches hide. It must be used with caution, however, as it is very poisonous to humans. Pyrethrum powders are also useful, particularly if rotenone is also a constituent of the powder and if it is dusted into cracks.

Chlordane has been found to be very effective against roaches and is the preferred insecticide for their control. It is not as dangerous as sodium fluoride and has a more lasting effect. For best results, all cracks formed by floors, baseboards, cabinets, shelves, the undersides of tables and chairs, and other hiding places are sprayed with a 2.5 per cent oil solution or a 2.5 per cent emulsion. Many of the roaches then emerge and thus disclose their hiding places. These are then dusted with a 10 per cent DDT dust or a 5 per cent chlordane dust, using a hand dust gun. It may be three days to a week before a great reduction in the roaches is noted, but thereafter they should be rare or completely absent for a period of months. In some locations where there is a nightly influx of roaches from outdoors, it may be advisable to apply chlordane to garages, outside lavatories, garbage cans, and disposal points, incinerators, etc. Of course, precautions must be taken to protect food, dishes, and utensils from the chlordane. In recent years some species of roaches, particularly the German roach, have become resistant to chlordane treatments in certain localities. Other insecticides have to be substituted in these areas (see Arts. 10-29 and 10-33).

19-12. Bedbugs. There is no convincing evidence that the bedbug is ordinarily a carrier of disease[2]. It is possible, however, that it may be involved in the transmission of plague, leprosy, and other diseases. It is usually nocturnal in its habits and spends the daylight hours in cracks of wooden beds, under wallpaper, or behind wainscoting—retreats for which, by reason of its flat body, it is well fitted. The young are hatched from eggs in a week or ten days after laying, although cold may lengthen the incubation period. The young at first are yellowish-white, but during successive molts they gradually assume the dark-red or brown color of the adult. About seven weeks is required from egg to adult. The most remarkable characteristic of the bedbug is its ability to live for a year or more without food. Its normal food is man, but in the absence of human blood it preys upon rats and mice. It usually feeds every three or four days.

Bedbugs are easily controlled by DDT. A 5 per cent solution of DDT applied to mattresses, bedsteads, and other furniture where they occur eliminates them. About half a cup (¼ pint) of the solution is sufficient for a double bed. Three or four days may elapse before the bugs are noticeably reduced, but they must come from their hiding places to feed and the DDT then destroys them. The residue of DDT kills the bugs for many months, and new bugs brought into the house are killed before they can multiply. In those few localities where resistance to DDT has developed, lindane may be substituted (see Art. 10-32).

Bedbugs are not very sensitive to cold, a month or more of exposure to weather well below freezing being required to destroy them. They are much more easily killed by high temperatures. At 96 to 100°F, particularly if the humidity is high, newly hatched bugs are killed in a few days. At 113°F, regardless of humidity, they, together with their eggs, are killed in a few minutes. This method has been used by contractors to free bunkhouses of bedbugs[3]. Steam pipes are run into the house, live steam forced in, and the temperature held at 160°F for several hours.

19-13. Control of Lice. Epidemics of typhus fever can be controlled by use of DDT for the eradication of lice. Since body lice are usually found in the clothing, the underwear is dusted with a 10 per cent DDT powder. Special care should be taken to rub the powder into the seams. The insides of shirts, trousers, hats, and other articles of clothing should be treated at the same time. About 30 grams is required to treat the clothing of one person. Underwear so treated retains killing power after one washing with warm soapy water. DDT does not destroy the eggs of lice, but the young lice are killed by it as they hatch. As an emergency measure during the war, threatened typhus epidemics were prevented by dusting clothing while it was being worn. This was done by using hand dust guns to blow the dust up sleeves and into neck and trouser openings.

Crab lice are killed by lightly dusting the hairy portions of the body with 10 per cent DDT powder. A second application should be made after eight to ten days to kill young lice which have hatched from eggs. Head lice are killed by rubbing a teaspoonful of the powder thoroughly into the hair. The head should not be washed within twenty-four hours. A second application should be made in eight to ten days. The hat also should be dusted. In some areas of the world, lice have developed a pronounced resistance to DDT. In these localities, allethrin or lindane may be substituted (see Arts. 10-23 and 10-32).

SANITATION OF PUBLIC CONVEYANCES

19-14. Railways. The Sanitary Engineering Division of the U.S. Public Health Service has jurisdiction over the sanitation of interstate carriers, and details as to sanitary requirements and procedures are obtainable from that agency. The term "interstate carrier" as applied to railways is very broad and includes, by court decision, railways which are entirely within a state but which connect with a line that crosses the state boundary. Hence practically all railways are under Federal supervision, in regard to sanitation as well as other matters. The sanitary problems of railways are concerned with dining cars, water supply, and excreta disposal. The first-named presents the usual problems of food handling and is not discussed here. Only an outline of the requirements for the latter two can be given; for more details the reader is referred to the "Handbook of Sanitation" of the U.S. Public Health Service[4,5,6].

Water Supply. The water supplies of the railways are carefully supervised. The standards of quality mentioned in Art. 5-9 were formulated by the Public Health Service to apply to interstate carriers, but they have been widely adopted by the states and cities. Actual inspections of the sources of supply, usually municipal systems, are made by sanitary engineers of the state health departments, who also take samples for testing in the state laboratory. The results of the survey and tests are sent to the Public Health Service, together with a recommendation by the inspecting engineer. If findings are favorable, a certificate of approval is issued. If minor deficiencies are found, a provisional certificate is issued pending the making of improvements. If they are not made or if major deficiencies are found at the first inspection, the supply is disapproved and it connot be used.

The water-supply problem, therefore, is largely a matter of safety in production, treatment, and distribution of municipal supplies. However, safety must also be attained at the points where the water tanks of the cars are filled, which frequently are the railway yards. The filling is done by hose from faucets which must not be flush with the ground surface, lest contaminated water accumulate around them; they must be placed or guarded in such fashion that they are not exposed to spattering from car toilets. Guards are placed over the ends of hoses so that they cannot come into contact with the ground. If buckets are used, they must have covers and be used for this purpose only. Water tanks must be kept clean, and since ice may be contaminated by handling, it is placed in a separate compartment from the water. The ice must, however, be handled in a sanitary manner.

Excreta Disposal. In yards and terminals toilets are kept closed, and tanks are attached during cleaning and flushing. These tanks are emptied and cleaned in such fashion that the water supply is not endangered. Railway car toilets discharge wastes and flushing water directly to the tracks, and the only sanitary restriction has been the locking of toilets while cars are in stations or the placing of signs in the toilets requesting that no flushing be done while the train is in or passing through a station. Sanitary authorities have been concerned with possible danger to water supplies near railways and to track workmen by discharge to the tracks, but an inquiry by Maxcy[7] indicated no definite proof that the practice had caused water-borne epidemics or had any effect upon the death rate for typhoid fever among track and yard employees of railroads.

The practice of scattering fecal matter along tracks is disagreeable to contemplate. Studies have been made[8] to determine the amount and character of the discharges, and further investigations are in progress to develop some device to reduce the wastes to a finely divided condition so that they will not be conspicuous and then to disinfect them by means of heat before they are scattered to the track.

19-15. Vessels. The sanitary problems of passenger and other vessels include food handling, water supply, and rat control. The water-supply problem for interstate vessels is handled in the same manner as for railways, with the same precautions as to quality and distribution at the docks. Careful attention must be given to the ship's plumbing to prevent cross connections of the drinking-water system to polluted supplies. This is particularly necessary on vessels plying the Great Lakes. Rats must be controlled by fumigation or otherwise. Vessels which make international voyages and come from known plague-infested ports are fumigated to kill rats under the supervision of the Sanitary Engineering Division of the U.S. Public Health Service. Other vessels may also make use of the same service from time to time. The Division also gives consultation service to ship designers and builders to the end that rat harborages may be reduced.

19-16. Airplanes. Planes engaged in interstate service present the same problems as to food and water as do railways. Excreta are caught in tanks and cared for at the airport. The principal sanitary problem concerns planes on international flights which may convey infected mosquitoes for long distances in a few hours. Jungle yellow fever is endemic in large areas of Africa and South and Central America; occasional epidemics of urban yellow fever arise in the cities. Obviously, unless precautions are taken, an infected mosquito may enter a plane and be carried to another country and an epidemic may result. Obviously too, precautions should be taken whether there is a known epidemic in an airport city or not. Another danger is the introduction of a new vector of mosquito-borne disease to an area. An instance of this was the appearance in eastern Brazil of *Anopheles gambiae*, apparently introduced by a fast boat from Africa. This mosquito is a very efficient malaria vector and, as it found conditions in that portion of Brazil very favorable, it caused a severe epidemic of malaria. The Rockefeller Foundation in cooperation with the Brazilian government was able to exterminate the species in Brazil by careful work adapted to the breeding habits of the species.

Mosquitoes in airplanes are killed by aerosols containing pyrethrins and DDT. The aerosol should be released before passengers enter the plane at the beginning of a trip. Since mosquitoes may enter with passengers, another release should be made just before the next stop. This is not always done, but certainly there should be a final release just before landing at the last airport of the trip.

19-17. Buses. The principal sanitary problem which may arise in connection with buses or motor coaches is the motor exhaust. The exhaust gases include dangerous carbon monoxide (Art. 13-24) and should not be allowed to enter the conveyance. Some cities, therefore, have ordinances requiring that exhaust pipes be free from leaks and that the discharge point be located so that there is a minimum of danger of exhaust gases entering the coach.

NOISE ABATEMENT

19-18. Effects of Noise. Noise has increased to such an extent in cities that there is much popular demand for remedial measures. Health departments and other agencies have studied the matter, notably in New York City[9], and methods of prevention have been formulated. The bad effects of noise are given as follows:

1. Hearing is likely to be permanently impaired among those constantly exposed to loud noises. Not only those exposed to city noise at its worst, such as traffic policemen and taxicab and truck drivers, are affected, but also boilermakers, structural steel riveters, and factory workers.

2. Noise decreases efficiency of workers. Reduction of noise by 90 per cent in an office was found to increase output by 12 per cent.

3. Great strain is put on the nervous system in the attempt to over-

come the effects of noise. This leads to abnormal states necessitating frequent recuperation to maintain mental efficiency.

4. Noise interferes with sleep, even though actual wakefulness may not occur.

5. Normal development of infants is interfered with by constant loud noises. Experiments made at Colgate University, showed that young animals kept under quiet conditions consumed more food and grew faster than others in noisy compartments.

19-19. Measurement of Noise. Noise is measured by decibels. Strictly speaking the decibel rating is a ratio, and as used in measuring city noise it expresses the ratio of the sound in question to the smallest distinguishable noise. For example, if two sounds are in the ratio of 10:1, the sounds are said to differ by 10 decibels; if they are as 100:1 (or 10^2:1), the sounds differ by 20 decibels; if they are as 1,000:1 (or 10^3:1), they differ by 30 decibels. Stated mathematically, the common logarithm of the intensity ratio multiplied by 10 expresses the ratio in decibels. As an example: One sound is 1,000,000 times as intense as another. The common logarithm of this number is 6. Accordingly the two sounds differ by 60 decibels.

Noise-measuring instruments show the sound intensities in decibels as compared with the smallest noise distinguishable to the human ear. The New York noise survey indicated that the regular din of street traffic ranged from 60 to 80 decibels. The noise of a subway train reached 94 decibels and a steamship whistle 93 decibels. In residences the average noise was 31 decibels, with variations from 22 to 45. In offices the noise varied from 72 to 32 decibels with an average of 51.

The sources of noise are many and various. Some are unavoidable, but many can be eliminated. Among the latter are automobile horns, use of cutouts, rattling trucks, noisy brakes, unnecessarily loud radios, newsboys, and peddlers. Most annoying are the sharp dissonances which rise above the steady roar of sound.

19-20. Noise Prevention. Overcoming the noise nuisance requires (1) education of the public; (2) cooperation of industrial firms, utility companies, truck owners, businessmen, and city authorities; (3) a reasonable and enforceable antinoise ordinance; and (4) a coordinating agency or commission.

The public must be informed as to the desirability of reducing unnecessary noise, particularly with regard to blowing of automobile horns, loud radios, etc.

Utility companies may cooperate by reducing noises of streetcars, elevated railways, and subways. With streetcars improvement is possible by keeping equipment in good repair and eliminating loose joints in rails and wide gaps at crossings. Subways and elevated railways can be so constructed in the future that noise is much decreased, although remedying existing conditions is impracticable. Trucks and taxis can be kept in repair and drivers instructed to avoid unnecessary noise. Steel buildings may be constructed by welding rather than riveting. Automobile horns can be used that are free from shrill and inharmonic overtones.

Soundproofing of homes and office buildings should not be overlooked. Materials are available that reduce transmission of sound through walls and damp it after it has entered. In offices noisy processes, such as typewriting, can be segregated in small rooms rather than placed all in one large room, where the resultant noise is the sum of all. Such precautions make it possible to keep the noise of homes and offices below 30 and 35 decibels, respectively, and in any case the noise level in homes should not exceed 50 decibels.

An ordinance[1] is necessary to define unnecessary noises and provide for punishment of infractions. Heavy penalties defeat the purpose of the ordinance. Small fines, up to $5, should be levied for violations, and enforcement is easier and more efficient if violators who admit their guilt can pay their fines to the tax receiver without having to appear in court. Of course, provision must also be made for trial of the accused who claims that he is not guilty. Policemen should have the responsibility of enforcing the ordinance.

Some agency should be established to coordinate antinoise activities and keep the matter before the public. If this is not done, enforcement soon becomes perfunctory and then ceases altogether. The commission should be made up of interested persons and city officials, with a sanitary engineer from the health department as technical consultant.

TOURIST COURTS, TRAILER PARKS, AND SUMMER CAMPS

19-21. With the increased dependence of the public on the automobile as a means of long-distance transportation, the need for roadside lodging places became evident. Tourist rooms in residences provided one means of meeting this need and probably offered few problems for the sanitarian. "Roadside cabins" and the earlier "tourist camps," on the other hand, became items of concern because of the haphazard construction of facilities and maintenance. The first attempts to provide private cabins for the tourist resulted in erecting anything that would pass for sleeping quarters and a community toilet and shower. These presented problems of sanitation. As increased use of the tourist

[1] A model noise ordinance is obtainable from Public Administration Service, Chicago.

camp was made by the motorist, capital investments in this type of facility made feasible the construction of accommodations of a more appealing character. Efforts of state health departments, automotive associations, and the motorists themselves brought about significant changes in the "camps" to convert them to "courts" and finally to the present "motel" status. In the modern motel, one may now expect every attempt at providing comfort and convenience. Sanitation standards have, of course, been greatly improved in the process.

FIG. 19-1. A modern tourist court. (*Courtesy of Tourist Court Journal, Temple, Tex.*)

Improved and more widespread public health education and immunization have also served to minimize what was popularly known as "vacation typhoid"—a sharp rise in the incidence of typhoid fever during the summer and early fall. The disappearance of the privy and greater well-water protection at summer camps and resorts are, in part, responsible. Resorts can present sanitation problems, however, especially where individual private cottages are maintained. Facilities are used only seasonally and are allowed to fall into a state of poor maintenance and repair. Supervision by public health workers of summer camp sites should serve to inform owners of sanitation hazards when they appear.

The house trailer or "mobile home" has presented sanitation problems of somewhat different nature—how to provide a water supply, toilet and bathing facilities, and garbage disposal for an individual who carries his own living quarters with him. Improperly supervised trailer parks can become eyesores to a community as well as present it with a means of disease harborage and conveyance. The problem is one of requiring the parking of trailers only at recognized and well-maintained parking places and exercising supervision of the latter to see that rules of sanitation are continually observed.

19-22. Sewage Disposal. Water carriage as a means of sewage disposal is a must at tourist courts, motels, and trailer parks. Privies, especially those provided for community use, cannot be kept flytight and seldom are clean. If city sewerage is available, connection to the sewer system should, of course, be enforced. Otherwise, septic tanks must be constructed in accordance with the principles outlined in Chap. 4. Cesspools are not to be condoned. Chemical toilets have limited application, particularly where water under pressure cannot be obtained. This is discussed in Chap. 3.

Where community toilets are provided, the toilet house should be well constructed, with impervious floors and walls, and carefully maintained. They require cleaning at least once a day, sometimes oftener, depending on use. At least one commode should be provided for each 15 potential users. The place should be well-ventilated, well-lighted, and screened—not only against flies but mosquitoes as well.

19-23. Water Supply. Municipal water supplies are usually of better quality than small private supplies and should be piped to courts and motels where practicable. Dug wells are shallow, collect water of questionable quality, and should always be suspected of being hazardous; if they are necessary, protection should be provided as discussed in Chap. 5.

Springs may also be dangerous, and in no case should they be used without protection against the entrance of surface water, by methods described in Chap. 5. Driven wells are more satisfactory than springs or dug wells, and deep drilled wells are usually the safest of all. Surface water, unless boiled or otherwise sterilized or given complete coagulation, filtration, and disinfection treatment, should never be used for drinking purposes.

Motor tourists should provide themselves with emergency disinfectants that can be depended upon to make suspicious water safe for drinking purposes. Such disinfectants are discussed in Arts. 5-18, 5-20, and 5-40.

19-24. Refuse Disposal. In the modern motel, cooking is seldom permitted unless kitchenettes are provided. Consequently, a wastebasket usually suffices for refuse. Otherwise, covered garbage cans are necessary, an individual receptacle for each dwelling unit. This, however, necessitates the provision of some central collection and disposal agency. At trailer parks, readily available incinerators provide a convenient solution to the problem, with the use of outside garbage cans discouraged. Tenants can then carry their refuse, as it accumulates, to the incinerators, avoiding the problem of the overloaded and unsightly garbage cans. The incinerators must be kept constantly burning and be well supervised. Otherwise, they may not answer the problem. Incompletely burned garbage can easily become a source of fly breeding. Mixed refuse should be discharged to incinerators. Garbage alone presents a problem in operation.

The most convenient method of disposal at roadside camps, summer camps, and parks is by sanitary fill (Art. 8-30), which can be easily done on a small scale by opening a trench, placing the day's collection in it, and immediately covering with earth. Compaction of the fill before covering is desirable.

19-25. Sanitary Inspection. Sanitary inspections of tourist courts, motels, and camp grounds should also cover other items: adequate bathing facilities, with provision for keeping them clean; proper lighting of the dwelling units and grounds; sufficient ventilation of dwelling units and common washrooms, bathrooms, laundries, and kitchens; the screening of dwelling units and kitchens; control of rats, mice, roaches, and other vermin; cleanliness of the dwelling units, including floors and rugs, mattresses, and linens, and whether linens are changed after each use. If gas is available for heating or cooking, heaters and ranges should be carefully checked (see Arts. 13-17 and 13-23). If a restaurant or lunchroom is operated, the matters discussed in Chap. 12 should be inspected insofar as they apply.

19-26. Trailer Parks and Courts. The trailer as a means of housing travelers and migratory workers has received considerable attention from sanitarians. Trailers are of three types. Some have no toilets, some have a chemical toilet, and others have a water flush toilet discharging into a tank. They may or may not have a sink or lavatory. It is recognized that the use of trailers results in the dumping of tanks of fecal matter along roadsides, but there appears to be no practical method of preventing this. A greater danger results, however, when trailers are parked, either singly or in numbers, on the same site for considerable periods. A good rule to apply to trailers is that no stopover of more than twenty-four hours should be permitted in populous areas, except in properly equipped and approved trailer camps.

A trailer park or camp should satisfy the following requirements. The space for each trailer coach should be well defined and provide not less than 1,000 square feet. Parking should be so arranged that there is at least 15 feet of clearance between coaches. Walkways not less than 2 feet wide leading to the service buildings should be provided and should be lighted at night. The park must provide service buildings to house toilet, bathing, and laundry facilities. Toilet facilities for women should be not less than one flush toilet and tub or shower for each 10 coach spaces and one lavatory for each 20 spaces. For men there should be one flush toilet and urinal for each 15 spaces and one tub or shower and lavatory for each 10 spaces. For each sex, toilets and bathing facilities should be in private compartments. A slop-water closet should be available in a separate room in the service building. Service buildings housing toilet facilities should be not more than 200 feet or less than

FIG. 19-2. A modern trailer court.

10 feet from any trailer space. Laundry facilities should be in the ratio of one double tub and ironing board with electrical outlet for each 20 spaces. An area for drying clothes should also be provided. Safe drinking water must be supplied from faucets located on each trailer space. Garbage requirements are as in Art. 19-24.

At most modern trailer parks, each trailer space is provided with a water connection and a separate sewer connection, with terminal points embedded in concrete to minimize damage and to promote cleanliness. The water connection should terminate well above ground and be protected against freezing. The sewer connection should be of the type that permits a tight coupling of a flexible hose.

Trailers parked on vacant city lots have sometimes proved to be difficult to control under existing laws and city ordinances. At least one court case in Michigan was decided by the court ruling that a trailer parked a considerable time on vacant property became a house and was thereupon subject to local ordinances controlling houses. This, of course, would require a water supply and sewer connection. Adoption of this viewpoint would tend to concentrate trailers into trailer camps, where they can be controlled.

19-27. Camps for Migratory Workers. In some parts of the country, workers move about for the picking of fruits and vegetables and for periods of work at canneries. The problem of housing them has been made more acute by the housing shortage. Wherever possible, such workers should camp in designated areas where safe water and sanitary facilities can be furnished and where supervision can be exercised over sanitation. If barracks are provided for the workers and their families, the minimum requirements for satisfactory housing should be satisfied, including 50 square feet of floor space per person, window space equal to 15 per cent of the floor area, windows that can be opened completely, and tight screening of doors and windows. The application of insecticides for the control of mosquitoes, flies, bedbugs, etc. is important. Flush-type toilet facilities should be available if at all possible.

19-28. Caretaker. If not supervised by a competent and conscientious caretaker, camps, even with the best of equipment, are invariably in an insanitary condition. No one factor is more important. It is important also that caretakers have some knowledge of sanitation, and they should therefore be taught sanitation principles. In some areas, schools have been held for this purpose. Associations and organizations of tourist-court owners have served to acquaint members of this business with acceptable practices through publications and meetings. Sanitarians can expect and receive cooperation from such agencies.

19-29. State Supervision of Tourist Courts, Trailer Parks, and Summer Camps. The problem of camp sanitation and roadside water supplies has assumed such importance, because of the numbers of the camps and the multitudes of people who patronize them, that health authorities have been much concerned as to the best methods of protecting the public. Where located within the limits of cities having active health departments, good sanitation may be assured through the city authorities. The majority of camps and resorts, however, are located in rural sections where control measures are possible only through the state health department.

District sanitary engineers of the state health department are usually responsible for the sanitation of tourist courts and roadside water supplies in their districts, although an attempt is usually made to have the local health officers, *i.e.*, of the county or city in which they are located, or their sanitary inspectors assume the duty of regular inspections. If an inspection indicates that the court is sanitary and tests indicate that the water is safe, an approval certificate is given by the state health department, and this is posted in a conspicuous spot in the court. If the approval is based upon a report made to the state health officer by the local health officer, the latter also signs the approval certificate and thereby also assumes responsibility. Some state health departments publish lists of tourist courts that have been inspected and approved.

In some states, roadside water supplies found to be unsafe had warning signs posted near them. This was found to be unsatisfactory, as the owners removed the signs. The practice now is to warn the owners against allowing the public to use the water. Water supplies found to be safe were distinguished by having small metal tags or seals fastened to pipes, faucets, or pumps. This was also found to be unsatisfactory, as the metal tags were frequently removed. A better method is to use a decalcomania transfer on the pump barrel and to renew it every two years.

RAGWEED CONTROL

19-30. It has been estimated that over 3 million persons in the United States suffer from hay fever caused by ragweed pollen. The U.S. Public Health Service states that 2 to 3 per cent of the population east of the Rocky Mountains have symptoms of ragweed hay fever. Ragweed in its two forms, the common and giant varieties, is frequently present in vacant city lots, roadsides, ditches, and wherever the original topsoil has been removed or disturbed. Ragweed is classed as pioneer vegetation since it is among the first plants to establish itself in such unfavorable surroundings. Later it will probably give way to grasses and similar plants classed as intermediate vegetation. It is not competitive, however, and cannot establish itself in areas of intermediate vegetation. In the normal course of events the intermediate stage is followed by climax vegetation, which is typified by forests and the lush grass of the prairies. According to one authority the Indians had no hay fever because they lived in a land of climax vegetation.

The fact that ragweed tends to concentrate in highly populous areas and that highly effective weed killers are now available indicates that ragweed control may become a part of the sanitary work of the large city. New York, after determining by experience that attempting to clear vacant lots of ragweed by formal notices to owners was unsuccessful, embarked upon a campaign using the weed killer 2,4-D[10]. This chemical kills broad-leaved plants but does not harm grasses and other resistant vegetation, and it is noninflammable, noncorrosive, and not poisonous to human beings. It was applied as a 0.1 per cent solution, wetting about 90 per cent of the plant foliage. About 200 gallons was required for

1 acre of ragweed, and a crew consisting of a spraying unit and three men could spray 2½ acres in a day.

The ragweed is an annual plant and produces one crop of seeds per year. If all plants are killed before the seed crop is produced, it would appear that ragweed would be eradicated, but for various reasons some seeds remain viable for two years or more before coming up. Therefore

FIG. 19-3. *A*, giant ragweed; *B*, common ragweed. (*Courtesy of U.S. Department of Agriculture.*)

some follow-up work may be necessary. In general, however, killing of ragweeds encourages a better growth of grasses, and this is unfavorable to their reappearance.

Campaigns against ragweed should be preceded by studies of the pollen content of air in the city. Particular attention should also be given to the presence and effect of ragweed in the metropolitan or suburban area of the city, since it may be necessary to extend control beyond the city limits in order to give relief to residents of the city proper. The Public

Health Section of the Weed Society of America, at their 1956 meeting, reported some progress in the control of plants detrimental to health.

DISASTER SANITATION

19-31. Public health is often endangered when disasters occur and should be considered in preparedness measures. Congress created the Federal Civil Defense Administration to cushion the impact and to function in the relief of natural disasters as well as those which are due to bombing or other military action. A system of radar stations has been established and warning procedures developed. To cope with an enemy attack, F.C.D.A. provides training in rescue work, evacuation, gas and radiation defense, decontamination, and construction of bomb shelters. Its disaster activities are closely coordinated with those of the Department of Defense, the Department of Health, Education, and Welfare, the American Red Cross, and the state and local civil defense organizations. The Federal Civil Defense Administration publishes bulletins on various phases of defense. The discussion here, however, is confined to relief matters, particularly sanitation, relating to nonwar disasters, with the work carried out by representatives of the state health department, local authorities, the Red Cross, and volunteer workers. Frequently the sanitary engineer, particularly if he has a thorough knowledge of needs and procedures, may find himself in complete charge of all work until higher state officials and local authorities have mobilized their resources. He should in any case encourage local officials and other county and municipal residents to take over all the responsibilities of which they are capable.

Types of Disasters. The emergencies to be expected and the damages they may cause are as follows. *Floods* in rural areas may drown persons and stock and destroy homes or make them temporarily uninhabitable; in urban areas they may also flood the water pumping and treatment plants and perhaps contaminate the whole water distribution system. If motors have been covered with water, the pumps will be unable to operate until time-consuming repairs have been made. The sewage treatment plant may also be damaged and some sewers choked with mud or sand. *Hurricanes* may destroy buildings and also put water pumping and treatment plants out of operation. Collapse of buildings means extensive plumbing damages and heavy leakage of water. All city services, including light, power, and telephone, may be disrupted. *Fires and explosions*, if extensive, may have all the effects of hurricanes. *Earthquakes*, which are sometimes accompanied by fires, may result in much breakage of water mains and sewers, in addition to causing the other damages cited.

Preparation. The state health department which has prepared itself has designated a sanitary engineer in each district to function in case of disasters. He should have available for instant use a mobile water filter and chlorinator with a stock of chlorine or hypochlorite, depending upon the type of apparatus. The representatives of chlorinator manufacturers sometimes have portable units which they are willing to place at the disposal of an engineer in emergencies, and he should be ready to call for this assistance when needed. He should also know where gasoline- or motor-driven pumps can be obtained for emergency water service. Fire department pumpers have sometimes been used for this purpose. For information as to such emergency shelter as tents, he should make contact with Army, including National Guard, and Navy authorities in his district. If there are local committees for relief work, the engineer should confer with them, explain his plans, and learn theirs. The same applies to the representatives of the Red Cross. If there are regional waterworks associations, he should encourage them to form emergency sanitation committees that will obtain the following lists: names of trained waterworks and sewage works operators in the area; equipment that can be obtained for use during an emergency, such as tank trucks, repair equipment, insect sprayers, refuse collection equipment; the major plumbing concerns; and local utility concerns. If waterworks associations are not available, he must use other methods to obtain such information. He should also have on hand a list of equipment and supplies that can be obtained from the state and local health departments.

Relief Work. The primary human needs in an area which has been struck by disaster are medical services, safe water, food, and shelter. If the weather is severe, fuel and warm clothing are also essential.

Medical services, which may include immunization against typhoid fever, are furnished by state, local, or Red Cross authorities, which also furnish the supplies.

If a refugee camp is set up, an emergency water supply may be established by means of a mobile water treatment plant and chlorinator; if tank trucks are available, they may be used to convey water from some safe supply. The food, including milk, should come from safe sources and be properly handled in the camp. If warehouses or similar buildings are not available for emergency housing, it may be necessary to obtain tents which must be properly placed on a suitable, well-drained site. Refuse must be collected and removed. If no city service is available, it may be possible to obtain trucks and drivers from the state highway department. If sewerage is not available, some type of emergency latrines may have to be established to be replaced with pit privies as quickly as possible. Tools and materials should be available, and able-bodied male refugees should be put to work under skilled supervision at digging pits for privies and refuse disposal, construction of privy buildings, tent floors, rough tables, benches, and other necessities. If the camp is located in an undamaged urban area, it may be possible to have electric lines and gas pipes run for lighting and cooking at a central kitchen.

Dead bodies must be collected and placed in temporary morgues for identification and later burial. Carcasses of animals may be removed by meat-packing plants, which usually have trucks and hoists. Insecticides should be used freely around garbage storage and disposal areas, toilets, barracks, and food-handling points. Airplane application of DDT may be advisable to control flies and to prevent malaria in areas which have been flooded. Observations should be made as to the need for rodent control.

In cities it may be necessary to chlorinate the water distribution system throughout if it has been contaminated by unsafe water. Emergency pumps may have to be set up. If important damage has been done to the waterworks, pipe, fittings, and other equipment may be needed. Reference to the lists mentioned above will enable the engineer or local waterworks man to obtain them quickly. If he needs skilled assistance, he can call upon men listed as available. If many plumbing systems have been damaged, it may be necessary to plug broken lines so that adequate water pressure can be built up. Thereafter permanent repairs may be made. If sewers are clogged, rods and other cleaning apparatus will be needed for rapid cleaning.

SMOKE ABATEMENT

19-32. Smoke Abatement. In many cities smoke is a major problem. Aside from aesthetic grounds for smoke elimination there are economic and humanitarian reasons. Smoke and soot are unburned fuel which is being lost. Another result is the spoiling of clothing, rugs, curtains, and the exterior finish of buildings. Smoke also affects health by shutting out the life-giving rays of the sun. It also contains substances that are irritating to the nose and throat.

In some large industrial cities, such as Los Angeles, Cincinnati, and Pittsburgh, the problem of "smog" has attracted public and official attention. Smog, a combination of fog, smoke, and chemical fumes from various industries, has caused illness in extreme conditions. The remedy is to reduce smoke and atmospheric pollution from industrial chemical fumes by measures applied at the factories. Automobile, truck, and bus exhaust is considered a contributing factor in atmospheric pollution in urban areas.

The main sources of smoke are the incomplete combustion of coal in industrial plants, which furnish about 45 per cent of smoke; locomotives, which furnish 15 to 20 per cent; and domestic furnaces and heaters. Another source is dust or vapor from manufacturing processes which mingle with the true smoke. Ordinances are in force in many cities which prohibit excessive smoke production by industrial plants and locomotives. The validity of such ordinances has been upheld by the U.S. Supreme Court. The regulation of smoke production in homes is, however, largely a matter of education, to be handled through publicity and through the schools.

Smoke standards have been formulated to aid in the enforcement of ordinances. These are based upon the density of the smoke, which has been classified into five grades[11]. No. 1 smoke is 20 per cent dense, or shuts out 20 per cent of the light; No. 2 smoke is 40 per cent dense; No. 3 is 60 per cent dense; No. 4 is 80 per cent dense; and No. 5 is 100

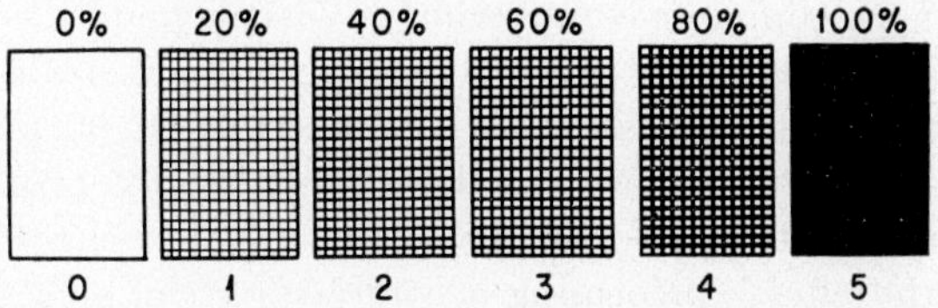

Fig. 19-4. The Ringelmann smoke-inspection chart. Observe from distance of 10 feet for smoke density.

per cent dense or completely opaque. Smoke inspectors make observations of the smoke as it issues from chimneys. The observations are taken at fifteen-second intervals over a period of one hour and the smoke densities are recorded. The smoke ordinances usually provide that dense smoke shall be emitted no more than six minutes in any one hour for industrial plants and that there shall be no more than one minute of continuous dense smoke from locomotives. Dense smoke is No. 3 or worse, or smoke which cannot be seen through directly over the stack top. The enforcement of smoke prevention is sometimes placed among the functions of city health departments and sometimes elsewhere, such as in the department of public safety. In Massachusetts it is a state activity. Figure 19-4 shows the Ringelmann chart, which is used to indicate the density of smoke.

Smoke prevention can be accomplished to a large extent in domestic ranges and heaters by alternate firing, *i.e.*, by piling coal on one side of the fire only. This allows the heat from the strongly burning coal on the other side to consume the volatile matter as it distills off. In the coking methods the grate is first shaken and the live coals pushed back, clearing the fire pot to the grate. Coal is then placed on the bare grate, piling it up to the fire door. The draft should be regulated according to the weather, and the slide in the furnace door should be left open. Ignition takes place from the side and top without soot formation and with minimum smoke. Firing furnaces from below, or the underfeed method, also reduces smoke production. The starting of fires may also be accomplished with a minimum of smoke by placing a layer of coarse coal on the grate, laying a small amount of paper over the coal, and placing the wood over the paper. As the paper and wood burn, the coal is heated, and the volatile matter comes off and is ignited as it passes through the burning wood. A high heat is quickly obtained without the smoke caused by the usual method of covering burning wood with coal. The size of the chimney is also involved in smoke production. A chimney 8 by 8 inches is necessary for a grate surface of 1.5 to 3 square feet, 10 by 12 inches for 3 to 5 square feet, 12 by 12 inches for 5 to 9 square feet.

Prevention of smoke in industrial plants is accomplished by using alternate firing or, better still, installing automatic stokers. Space should be allowed for the complete combustion of volatile matter before it strikes and is chilled by the boiler tubes. Proper chimney size and height are also important. The Bureau of Mines asserts that 90 per cent of the smoke from industrial plants can be eliminated by proper firing and design of equipment. In locomotives the installation of brick arches, which have the effect of forming a combustion chamber, has produced good results. Special draft equipment also helps. Careful firing is necessary at all times. The expense of installing smoke-prevention equipment is usually offset by the increased economy in fuel.

BARBERSHOP SANITATION

19-33. Regulations governing barbershops and beauty parlors are a part of the sanitary laws of many states and cities. Connecticut, which has a state board of examiners for barbers, has adopted a comprehensive set of regulations for barbers and barbershops of which the following are the most important provisions[13]:

Barbers must keep themselves and their wearing apparel clean, thoroughly cleanse their hands immediately before serving each customer, and must be free from communicable disease. No persons suffering from communicable disease or eruption of the face, scalp, or neck shall be served in a barber shop.

The same piece of solid soap must not be used for more than one customer. Shaving mugs and lather brushes must be thoroughly cleansed with hot water before being used. All razors, scissors, needles, pincers, and other instruments shall be cleansed and sterilized after each separate use either by boiling in water for 5 minutes or by some other method approved by the State Department of Health. Combs and brushes must be kept thoroughly cleansed with soap and hot water. The use of styptic sticks or pencils is prohibited. Materials used for this purpose must be in powdered or liquid form. The use of powder puffs and sponges is prohibited. Towels must be laundered and sterilized outside of the shop. A separate towel must be used for each patron.

NUISANCES

19-34. A comprehensive definition of a nuisance is anything which is injurious to the health, offensive to the senses, indecent, or detrimental to the free use of property, so as to cause inconvenience or discomfort to the community, neighborhood, or any considerable number of persons. To the health worker, however, the term "nuisance" has a somewhat restricted meaning and is applied to conditions offensive to the senses or interfering with property but having no effect upon health, or at most only an indirect effect. The most common nuisance complaints encountered in cities are against the odors of poultry yards, pig pens, or other animals and the means of keeping them. The odors in themselves are harmless, and the only effect upon health is the possibility of breeding and attracting flies and rats. Noise, smoke, fumes, and dust are nuisances which, unless present over prolonged periods or in high intensities, may have no effect upon health whatever. Nuisance inspection, however, is usually one of the duties of sanitary inspectors. Cities have ordinances prohibiting the maintenance by any person or corporation of anything which is a hazard or danger to public health, and some also say that no nuisance may be maintained, yet in many cases there are no definitions given, particularly of nuisances, a defect which greatly hampers enforcement. The following discussion attempts to set out the usual procedure in connection with nuisances and their abatement.

19-35. Responsibility for Nuisances. Whether or not a nuisance exists is a matter of fact. The declaration of an administrative officer that a condition is a nuisance must be proved, and whoever abates it, except under court authority, does so on his own responsibility. The responsibility for the nuisance itself, however, rests upon the person who causes it. In general, the occupant of land is responsible for nuisances originating thereon. Following the usual doctrine in connection with municipalities, a municipal corporation is not responsible for a nuisance arising by reason of its performance of governmental or political duties, but may be responsible if the nuisance results from its exercise of private powers. The distinction can be well brought out by the following. Fire protection is a governmental function; therefore the city could not be held responsible for nuisances arising from a stable for horses used with the fire-fighting equipment. In furnishing water the city is acting in a private capacity; therefore it would be responsible for nuisances arising from a stable used by water department horses.

19-36. Remedies for Nuisances. Three methods of abating nuisances are in use. (1) Damage suits may be brought, and if actual injury can be proved the injured party may be awarded damages. If the nuisance is not abated new suits may be brought. (2) An injunction may be obtained which orders immediate abatement, and if it is not obeyed, fine or imprisonment may be imposed for contempt of court. (3) Or a health official may remedy the nuisance without the formality of court action. Notice should be given before this is done, but if an emergency exists notice may be dispensed with. In this method the person who maintained the nuisance may sue the health officer for damages. If the official acts in a reasonable and prudent manner, however, he is not liable for injury.

The real remedy for nuisances, however, is the passage of laws or ordinances preventing them. The prohibition of manure storage in stables, the restriction against raising pigs within the city, the insistence on covered garbage pails—all tend to prevent nuisances. If legally prohibited nuisances are complained of, it is only necessary to proceed against the offender for a violation of the ordinance, with no vexing question as to the actual nature of the nuisance entering into the matter. In this connection and also with regard to larger questions, such as stream pollution, Tobey[14] says:

> It may be more efficient, for instance, for the state by means of adequate legislation, to prohibit the pollution of streams than to pass legislation penalizing those who do pollute them or stating that such pollution constitutes a nuisance. The latter provisions may be necessary corollaries of the former, but the forbidding of the pollution in the first instance is the important element. This holds good for any and all kinds of public health nuisances, and is a proposition which has been upheld by the U.S. Supreme Court.

COMFORT STATIONS

19-37. American visitors to European cities, particularly Paris, are struck by the numerous and conveniently located public comfort stations. Public toilets for both sexes are, of course, necessities and should receive far more attention from municipalities in the United States than is given at present. Large cities should place them near important street-car intersections; in parks, squares, and plazas; in the business sections; and in such public buildings as city halls, courthouses, and libraries. The small city also needs at least one toilet in its business section, particularly if it is the center of a farming district and has a heavy influx of rural visitors for trading purposes. In some cases, however, public toilets in small towns are poorly designed and uncared for, with resulting nuisances. Responsible caretakers are absolutely necessary. It is possible to combine revenue-producing projects with comfort stations. One or two pay toilets, a bootblack stand, and possibly a cigar or newsstand might pay the cost of attendance.

In congested districts with space restricted, comfort stations must frequently be placed underground. This arrangement complicates the problems of ventilation and lighting, especially important in a structure of this kind. An above-ground location is far better. Windows, if used, should be of frosted glass. Skylights may also be necessary. Fan ventilation may be required in large installations.

A convenient and economical arrangement of comfort station is a rectangular space divided into two compartments by a narrow passage about 30 inches wide. This affords separate toilet rooms for women and men with entrances on opposite sides of the building. The toilets and urinals are so placed that the flush tanks and most of the piping are in the passage, which is accessible to the caretaker only. Toilets should be the wall-hung type, but they should also be the elongated type with an open-front seat. The plumbing fixtures should be of porcelain with valves and faucets of very rugged and simple character. Lavatories should, of course, be installed. Partitions between booths should extend only to within 8 inches of the floor to allow easy cleaning and flushing. All corners, including that between the floor and side walls, should be rounded or "covered" for the same purpose. Concrete, asphalt, tile, or terrazzo floors with drains are most satisfactory. Walls, partitions, and floors should preferably be white in order that the toilet room may be as well lighted as possible. Illumination at the floor level should be at least 5 foot-candles.

BIBLIOGRAPHY

1. Marlatt, C. L.: Cockroaches, *U.S. Dept. Agr. Farmers' Bull.* 658.
2. The Bedbug, *Public Health Repts.*, reprint 626.
3. *Public Health Repts.*, vol. 34, no. 48, Nov. 28, 1919.
4. Handbook on Sanitation of Railroad Passenger Car Construction, *U.S. Public Health Service Pub.* 95.
5. Handbook on Sanitation of Railroad Servicing Areas, *U.S. Public Health Service Pub.* 66.
6. Handbook on Sanitation of Dining Cars in Operation, *U.S. Public Health Service Pub.* 83.
7. Maxcy, Kenneth F.: "An Inquiry into the Public Health Hazard of Sewage Disposal from Railway Conveyances," Association of American Railroads, 1946.
8. Wolman, A., and L. K. Clark, Human Waste Disposal from Railroad Passenger Cars, *Am. J. Public Health,* vol. 38, no. 5, May, 1948.
9. "City Noise," New York City Department of Health, Noise Abatement Commission, 1930.
10. Weinstein, I., and A. H. Fletcher: Essentials for Ragweed Control, *Am. J. Public Health,* vol. 38, no. 5, May, 1948.

11. Monnett, Osborne: Smoke Abatement, *U.S. Bur. Mines Tech. Paper* 273.
12. "Trailer Court Sanitation," U.S. Public Health Service, reprinted by the Trailer Coach Manufacturers Association, 1953.
13. *State Dept. Health Bull.*, vol. 40, no. 7, *Hartford, Conn.*, July, 1926.
14. Tobey, J. A.: "Public Health Law," The Williams & Wilkins Company, Baltimore.
15. Handbook on Sanitation of Airlines, *U.S. Public Health Service Pub.* 308.
16. Handbook on Sanitation of Vessel Construction, *U.S. Public Health Service Pub.* 393.
17. Handbook on Sanitation of Vessels in Operation, *U.S. Public Health Service Pub.* 68.
18. Rosenau, M. J.: "Preventive Medicine and Hygiene," 7th ed., by Kenneth F. Maxcy, Appleton-Century-Crofts, Inc., New York, 1951.
19. Chandler, A. C.: "Introduction to Human Parasitology," John Wiley & Sons, Inc., New York.
20. Chandler, A. C.: "Hookworm Disease," The Macmillan Company, New York.
21. Bartlett, F. C., and C. S. Myers: "The Problem of Noise," The Macmillan Company, New York.

CHAPTER 20

VITAL STATISTICS

20-1. While the sanitarian cannot ordinarily be a statistician, he should be sufficiently acquainted with vital statistics and their uses to be able to apply them to his work. Morbidity statistics, which are the statistics of disease, and mortality statistics, which are concerned with death and the causes of death, indicate more or less clearly the healthfulness of a community and the success or failure of health work. What is even more important, they may give valuable clues as to the character of work that is required. Birth rates are of somewhat less importance to the sanitarian but are useful in other lines of health activities. The prediction of future population is essential in connection with the planning of such sanitary improvements as water treatment plants, sewage disposal works, and sewer extensions. Complete studies of vital statistics include many other items, such as marriage and divorce rates, and characteristics of the population of the country as to age, race, etc.

20-2. Sources of Vital Statistics. Vital statistics are obtained from several different agencies. Population and its characteristics are obtained from the official enumerations made by the Bureau of the Census. Birth, death, and morbidity statistics are obtained from certificates and reports required of physicians and undertakers. Life insurance reports give information as to causes of death, and hospital records are of value. Information of a more general nature, particularly in regard to morbidity, can sometimes be obtained through questioning school teachers, druggists, and citizens in general. Information of this sort should be considered as only supplementary to other data, such as physicians' reports. The important sources of vital statistics are discussed in detail below.

20-3. Census. The United States census is taken every ten years by the Bureau of the Census, which is a part of the Department of Commerce. A staff of enumerators works simultaneously in all parts of the country and of the outlying possessions, completing the collection of data in about thirty days. The information is obtained through questions which may be classified under the following headings: place of abode, tenure of home, personal description, citizenship, nativity, and occupa-

TEXAS DEPARTMENT OF HEALTH
BUREAU OF VITAL STATISTICS

STATE OF TEXAS — CERTIFICATE OF DEATH — STATE FILE NO.

NOTE, THE INFORMATION CALLED FOR ON THE REVERSE SIDE

1. PLACE OF DEATH
a. COUNTY
b. CITY OR TOWN (If outside corporate limits, write RURAL and give precinct no.)
c. LENGTH OF STAY (in this place)
d. FULL NAME OF HOSPITAL OR INSTITUTION (If not in hospital or institution, give street address or location)

2. USUAL RESIDENCE (Where deceased lived. If institution: residence before admission).
a. STATE
b. COUNTY
c. CITY OR TOWN (If outside corporate limits, write RURAL and give precinct no.)
d. STREET ADDRESS (If rural, give location)

3. NAME OF DECEASED (Type or Print) a. (First) b. (Middle) c. (Last)
4. DATE OF DEATH

5. SEX
6. COLOR OR RACE
7. MARRIED, NEVER MARRIED, WIDOWED, DIVORCED (Specify)
8. DATE OF BIRTH
9. AGE YEARS | MONTHS | DAYS | IF UNDER 24 HRS. Hours | Min.

10a. USUAL OCCUPATION (Give kind of work done during most of working life, even if retired)
10b. KIND OF BUSINESS OR INDUSTRY
11. BIRTHPLACE (State or foreign country)

12. FATHER'S NAME — BIRTHPLACE
13. MOTHER'S MAIDEN NAME — BIRTHPLACE

14. WAS DECEASED EVER IN U.S. ARMED FORCES? (Yes, no, or unknown) | (If yes, give war or dates of service)
15. SOCIAL SECURITY NO.
16. INFORMANT'S SIGNATURE

MEDICAL CERTIFICATION

17. CAUSE OF DEATH
Enter only one cause per line for (a), (b), and (c)

*This does not mean the mode of dying, such as heart failure, asthenia, etc. It means the disease, injury, or complication which caused death

I. DISEASE OR CONDITION DIRECTLY LEADING TO DEATH* (a) ____________

ANTECEDENT CAUSES
Morbid conditions, if any, giving rise to the above cause (a) stating the underlying cause last.
DUE TO (b) ____________
DUE TO (c) ____________

II. OTHER SIGNIFICANT CONDITIONS
Conditions contributing to the death but not related to the disease or condition causing death.

INTERVAL BETWEEN ONSET AND DEATH

18a. DATE OF OPERATION
18b. MAJOR FINDINGS OF OPERATION
19. AUTOPSY? YES ☐ NO ☐

20a. ACCIDENT SUICIDE HOMICIDE (Specify)
20b. PLACE OF INJURY (e.g., in or about home, farm, factory, street, office bldg., etc.)
20c. (CITY, TOWN, OR PRECINCT NO.) (COUNTY) (STATE)

20d. TIME OF INJURY (Month) (Day) (Year) (Hour) m.
20e. INJURY OCCURRED WHILE AT WORK ☐ NOT WHILE AT WORK ☐
20f. HOW DID INJURY OCCUR?

21. *I hereby certify that I attended the deceased from ________, 19___, to ________, 19___, that I last saw the deceased alive on ________, 19___, and that death occurred at ______ m., from the causes and on the date stated above.*

22a. SIGNATURE (Degree or title)
22b. ADDRESS
22c. DATE SIGNED

23a. BURIAL, CREMATION, REMOVAL (Specify)
23b. DATE
23c. NAME OF CEMETERY OR CREMATORY

23d. LOCATION (City, town, or county) (State)
24. FUNERAL DIRECTOR'S SIGNATURE

25a. REGISTRAR'S FILE NO.
25b. DATE REC'D BY LOCAL REGISTRAR
25c. REGISTRAR'S SIGNATURE

IF DECEASED HAS RENDERED MILITARY SERVICE, FILL OUT THE FOLLOWING:

(a) Is the deceased reported to have been in such service?
(b) Name of organization in which service was rendered?
(c) Serial number of discharge papers or adjusted service certificate?
(d) Name of next of kin or of next friend?
(e) Post Office Address?

PLEASE FILL OUT FOR ALL DEATHS

(f) Deceased was citizen of what country? | (g) Name of husband or wife | (h) Age in years

IF DECEASED IS UNIDENTIFIED, FILL OUT THE FOLLOWING:

(i) Color of Hair? | (j) Color of Eyes? | (k) Height? Ft. In. | (l) Weight?
(m) Deformities? | (n) Tattoo Marks?
(o) Other marks of identification?

FIG. 20-1. The standard death certificate.

tion. The census reports give the population by various civil divisions. The continental population is divided into states; the states into counties; the counties into cities, boroughs, and towns; the cities into wards. The population of the rural regions and villages is also indicated. The study of the vital statistics of any section of the country must be based upon its total population and the characteristics, age grouping, sex distribution, etc., of that population. The importance of the census reports which give this fundamental information, therefore, cannot be overestimated.

20-4. Death Certificates. Death certificates are required by the laws of the various states. They include information as to name, age, race, nativity, conjugal condition, occupation, and date of death of the deceased. These questions may be filled in by any competent person. The cause or causes of death and circumstances surrounding it must be given by the physician in attendance. Place and date of burial or removal must be given by the undertaker. If no physician has been in attendance, the required burial-transit permit is not issued until the case has been referred to the local health officer. In suspicious cases an investigation must be made by the coroner, justice of the peace, or other proper official, before burial is permitted. The death certificate, after being made out and signed by the physician and the undertaker, must be filed by the latter with the local registrar, and a burial-transit permit is issued. Copies of death certificates and burial permits are kept by the local registrar, who transmits the original death records to the state registrar for permanent filing in the state bureau of vital statistics. Copies of vital records are filed locally by the county or city clerks and/or by the county or city health departments.

Death registration assists in the prevention and detection of crime. It is valuable in the settlement of property, inheritance, and life insurance cases. The fact that causes of death are recorded has resulted in statistics which have played a large part in the control of disease. The records have a local value in the detection and suppression of epidemics of communicable disease.

20-5. Birth Certificates. Birth registration is invariably required by the states. Registration is carried out by means of birth certificates, which are made out by the physician or midwife who attended the birth or, if the birth was nonattended, by the parents. The certificate contains the date and place of birth; the name and sex of the child; and the name, age, race, birthplace, residence, and occupation of the parents. As in the case of death certificates, birth certificates are filed with the local registrar, who should keep a permanent record of them and transmit them to the state registrar, in whose department they are permanently filed.

As registration of birth is of great importance not only to the com-

TEXAS DEPARTMENT OF HEALTH
BUREAU OF VITAL STATISTICS
CERTIFICATE OF BIRTH

STATE OF TEXAS

BIRTH NO.

NOTE THE INFORMATION CALLED FOR ON THE REVERSE SIDE

1. PLACE OF BIRTH a. COUNTY	2. USUAL RESIDENCE OF MOTHER (Where does mother live?) a. STATE b. COUNTY
b. CITY OR TOWN (If outside corporate limits, write RURAL and give precinct no.)	c. CITY OR TOWN (If outside corporate limits, write RURAL and give precinct no.)
c. FULL NAME OF HOSPITAL OR INSTITUTION (If NOT in hospital or institution, give street address or location).	d. STREET ADDRESS (If rural, give location)

3. CHILD'S NAME (Type or print) a. (First) b. (Middle) c. (Last)

4. SEX | 5a. THIS BIRTH SINGLE ☐ TWIN ☐ TRIPLET ☐ | 5b. IF TWIN OR TRIPLET (This child born) 1ST ☐ 2ND ☐ 3RD ☐ | 6. LEGITIMATE? | 7. DATE OF BIRTH

FATHER OF CHILD

8. FULL NAME a. (First) b. (Middle) c. (Last)			9. COLOR OR RACE
10. AGE (At time of this birth) YEARS	11. BIRTHPLACE (State or foreign country)	12a. USUAL OCCUPATION	12b. KIND OF BUSINESS OR INDUSTRY

MOTHER OF CHILD

13. FULL MAIDEN NAME a. (First) b. (Middle) c. (Last)			14. COLOR OR RACE
15. AGE (At time of this birth) YEARS	16. BIRTHPLACE (State or foreign country)	17a. USUAL OCCUPATION	17b. KIND OF BUSINESS OR INDUSTRY

18. CHILDREN PREVIOUSLY BORN TO THIS MOTHER (Do NOT include this child)
a. How many OTHER children are now living? | b. How many OTHER children were born alive but are now dead? | c. How many OTHER children were stillborn (born dead after 20 weeks pregnancy)?

19a. INFORMANT

19b. ADDRESS

20. *I hereby certify that I attended the birth of this child who was* ***born alive / born dead*** *on the date stated above at ________ M.*

21a. ATTENDANT'S SIGNATURE

21b. ATTENDANT AT BIRTH M.D. ☐ D.O. ☐ MIDWIFE ☐ OTHER (Specify)

21c. ATTENDANT'S ADDRESS

21d. DATE SIGNED

22a. REGISTRAR'S FILE NO.	22b. DATE REC'D BY LOCAL REGISTRAR	22c. REGISTRAR'S SIGNATURE

FOR MEDICAL AND HEALTH USE ONLY (*This section MUST be filled out*)

23. LENGTH OF PREGNANCY	24. WEIGHT AT BIRTH	25. WAS EYE PROPHYLAXIS USED?	26. WAS STANDARD SEROLOGIC TEST MADE? (H.B. 597, 51st. Leg., 1949)
WEEKS	LBS. OZS.	YES ☐ NO ☐	YES ☐ NO ☐

FIG. 20-2. The standard birth certificate.

munity but to the individual, parents should insist that the physician file a birth certificate without delay. The local health officer should know how many infants there are in his community and what proportion of the total have died. From birth certificates, he can plan his infant and child hygiene work to safeguard the health of the newborn child and the mother. In cities where health work is well organized, public health nurses visit every home in which a birth has been registered. Some of the more frequent uses of birth records are for obtaining passports, marriage licenses, drivers' licenses, and pension benefits. They are also used for entering military service, obtaining employment, and receiving retirement benefits. To summarize, a birth certificate is important to the individual as the best means of proving age, parentage, and citizenship.

20-6. Physicians' Reports. These apply to morbidity and in general cover communicable diseases and the more important industrial diseases. The lists of notifiable diseases are not uniform in all parts of the country.

PLEASE ANSWER THESE QUESTIONS AS TO ALL BIRTHS

MILITARY SERVICE RECORD OF FATHER 21

(a) Is the father reported to have been in such service?	
(b) Name of organization in which service was rendered	
(c) Serial Number of Discharge Papers or Adjusted Service Certificate	

THIS INFORMATION FOR STATISTICAL PURPOSES ONLY

(d) Describe congenital malformation or defects	
(e) Describe any birth injury	
(f) Was prenatal care given?	Approximate date when first seen?
(g) What anesthetic was used?	How administered?
(h) What analgesic was used?	How administered?
(i) Was forceps used?	Pituitrin during labor?
(j) Complications of pregnancy	
(k) Complications of labor	
(l) Did a Midwife precede you in this case?	Name Address
(m) Was there an operation for delivery?	
(n) Describe fully all operations	

IF STILLBIRTH FILL OUT THE FOLLOWING:

(o) Did child die before labor?	After labor?	(p) Did child die before operation?	During operation?

FIG. 20-2. *Continued.*

Some states may require that a certain disease be reported while in others it is ignored. A partial list of the diseases that some or all of the states have made notifiable is given below:

INFECTIOUS DISEASES

Anthrax
Chicken pox
Cholera, Asiatic
Dengue
Diphtheria
Dysentery:
  1. Amoebic
  2. Bacillary
Glanders
Hookworm disease
Influenza
Leprosy

Malaria
Measles
Meningitis:
  1. Epidemic cerebrospinal
  2. Tuberculous
Mumps
Paratyphoid fever
Plague
Pneumonia (lobar)
Poliomyelitis (acute infectious)
Rabies
Scarlet fever

Smallpox
Tetanus
Trachoma
Trichinosis
Tuberculosis (all forms)
Typhoid fever
Typhus fever
Whooping cough
Yellow fever

Occupational Diseases and Injuries

Arsenic poisoning
Brass poisoning
Carbon monoxide poisoning
Lead poisoning
Mercury poisoning
Natural gas poisoning
Phosphorus poisoning
Wood alcohol poisoning
Naphtha poisoning
Carbon bisulphide poisoning
Dinitrobenzene poisoning
Caisson disease
Any other disability or illness resulting from the nature of a person's employment

Venereal Diseases

Syphilis
Gonococcus infection

Other Diseases

Pellagra
Cancer

State laws usually specify that such diseases must be reported to the local health officer immediately after the diagnosis has been made. The local health officer keeps a record of the diseases reported and usually makes a monthly report covering these particular diseases to the state board of health. The importance to the local health officer of the prompt reporting of diseases by the attending physician cannot be overestimated. It enables him promptly to apply quarantine, isolation, and other measures and thereby prevent an epidemic. His knowledge of the occurrence of a few cases of such a disease as typhoid fever may allow him to apply measures which will stop an incipient typhoid outbreak. In tuberculosis control prompt registration of the cases ensures the valuable preventive and educational work of the nursing service. A comparison of current morbidity reports with those of former years gives some indication of the value and efficiency of public health work. Morbidity reports are, of course, dependent upon the cooperation of the physician and his compliance with the law. The health officer is frequently called upon to take a firm stand in the enforcement of the state laws requiring such reports. Enforcement of such requirements is as much a part of the public health work as the study of epidemics or milk sanitation.

20-7. Registration Area. The states were not equally progressive in passing adequate laws requiring the registration of births and deaths, and in some cases enforcement of law was neglected. The result of this condition was that the statistics of some states were not complete and were far from reliable. The Bureau of the Census recognized the birth and death records of a state or any subdivision if, after a careful check, it became convinced that at least 90 per cent of births and deaths were registered, and such recognition placed the state, city, or county in the registration area. A relaxation of diligence in collection and registration might cause it to be dropped from the area. At present all the states are included in the birth- and death-registration areas.

20-8. Population. The vital statistics of any particular subdivision are based upon its population, and this information may be obtained from the census reports. However the census gives the population only at ten-year intervals. The calculation of a death rate based upon the population given in the census report of five or six years previous may be far from accurate. It becomes necessary, therefore, to make some approximation of the population for the year in question. This may be done in several ways. The simplest method is by arithmetical progression. The increase per year during the preceding census period is found by dividing the total increase for that period by 10. It is then assumed that the yearly increase for the following census period will be the same. For example: A city of 100,000 population in 1950 gained 20,000 from 1940 to 1950, or an average annual increase of 2,000. The arithmetical method assumes that the annual gain will continue to be 2,000 and will have reached 6,000 by 1953, therefore the population of the city will be 106,000 in 1953. This method has the merit of simplicity and is widely used. It cannot be extended too far into the future, but this is not a particularly serious limitation, since there is a new census every ten years. Local conditions which tend to modify population growth and local information such as number of voters, number of names in the directory, and the school attendance should also be considered in population estimates.

Populations tend somewhat to increase by geometrical progression, *i.e.*, in the same manner as money increases by compound interest. Therefore, applying this method to population increase is sometimes more correct than the arithmetical method. It can be applied easily by means of a formula identical with that used in compound interest computations. It is

$$P_n = P_c(1 + r)^n$$

in which P_c is the population at the last census, r is the annual rate of increase expressed as a decimal, n is the number of years after the census, and P_n is the population at n years after the census. To use this formula the average rate of increase for the preceding ten years must be obtained by substituting 100,000 and 80,000 for P_n and P_c, respectively, and 10 for n, and solving for r. In the case given above r, on this basis, is found to be 0.0226. To find the population in 1953: 100,000 is substituted for P_c, 0.0226 for r, 3 for n, and P_n (the answer) is found to be 106,993.

The prediction of population of cities over long periods, fifteen years or more, is somewhat more complicated. The possibility of annexations is a larger factor. It should also be recognized that there is a tendency for decreased rates of growth as cities become larger and that the annual rate of population increase in general tends to approach 1 per cent. The method of making forecasts, briefly outlined, is as follows:

1. Plot a curve over the past census reports.
2. Extend this curve, following the general direction of the known points.
3. Plot the curves of older and larger cities.
4. Other curves showing the arithmetical, geometrical, and 1 per cent rates of growth may also be plotted as guidelines.

After carefully considering the possible decreased rate of growth, possible annexations, the industrial and commercial situation, etc., as well as the previously plotted curves, draw a curve to show the expected increase.

20-9. Death Rates. These are expressed as so many per year per 1,000 of the population. The crude death rate is expressed as the number of deaths in one year occurring per 1,000 of the whole population and may be found from the following formula:

$$\text{Death rate per 1,000} = \frac{\text{number of deaths}}{\text{total population}} \times 1{,}000$$

The crude death rates of various localities are sometimes compared for the purpose of arriving at their relative healthfulness. A little consideration demonstrates that crude death rates are not always indicative of the health of the community. Death rates are high among very young children and among the aged. Therefore the locality containing a large percentage of either of these two classes will have a higher crude death rate than another community having a high percentage of young adults, irrespective of sanitary conditions. Comparisons can be made by means of specific death rates, *i.e.*, finding the death rate among the population of a certain class. For instance, the specific death rate for children from five to ten years of age is as follows:

$$\text{Specific death rate} = \frac{\begin{array}{c}\text{number of deaths of children}\\ \text{5 to 10 years of age}\end{array}}{\begin{array}{c}\text{total number of children 5 to}\\ \text{10 years of age}\end{array}} \times 1{,}000$$

The specific death rate may be similarly found for other ages, for the sexes, and for locality of dwelling, *i.e.*, urban or rural. The specific death rates which may be computed are, of course, dependent upon the tabulations given by the census reports for various localities. Dr. Raymond Pearl[3] points out the value of specific death rates covering such other factors as race, including color and country of birth of person and parents, and occupation. All these factors combined allow specific death rates covering, for example, the probability that a male person, age twenty, native-born of native white parents, living in the country and working as a farmer, will die within one year.

Since the death rates vary for different ages it is apparent that the variation in age distribution of populations makes it impossible to compare death rates unless they are standardized or corrected. The standardized death rate, also known as the adjusted death rate, is obtained by applying the specific death rates for the various age and sex groups of some standard population, say that of the registration area, to the corresponding age and sex groups of the living population of the particular locality. This gives the number of deaths that would have occurred in the particular locality if the specific death rate of the standard population had prevailed there, and dividing the number of deaths so obtained by the actual total living population of the locality gives the standardized death rate. The ratio

$$\frac{\text{Death rate in the standard population}}{\text{Standard death rate of the living population}}$$

gives the corrective factor which measures the amount that the crude death rate of the local population is altered from the death rate of the standard population as a result of the difference between the two populations in respect of the age distribution of the living.

A corrected death rate is the reverse of the standardized death rate. It is obtained by applying the specific death rate observed in a local population to the age and sex distribution of the chosen standard population. This allows comparison of the death rate of a city with that of the standard population.

20-10. Causes of Death. Since the causes of death as reported on the death certificates are of great value in studies of vital statistics, it is important that there be uniformity in the medical terms used to describe them. To bring about such uniformity international commissions have met from time to time to adopt standard classifications of causes of death. The latest, or sixth, classification was made in Paris in 1948, by the International Conference for the Decennial Revision of the International Lists of Diseases and Causes of Death. This list is used by the states in compiling vital statistics. The International List is divided into 17 groups as follows:

Section	*Numbers*
1. Infective and parasitic diseases	001–138
2. Neoplasms	140–239
3. Allergic, endocrine system, metabolic, and nutritional diseases	240–289
4. Diseases of the blood and blood-forming organs	290–299
5. Mental, psychoneurotic, and personality disorders	300–326
6. Diseases of the nervous system and sense organs	330–398
7. Diseases of the circulatory system	400–468
8. Diseases of the respiratory system	470–527
9. Diseases of the digestive system	530–587
10. Diseases of the genitourinary system	590–637
11. Deliveries and complications of pregnancy, childbirth, and the puerperium	640–689
12. Diseases of the skin and cellular tissue	690–716
13. Diseases of the bones and organs of movement	720–749
14. Congenital malformations	750–759
15. Certain diseases of early infancy	760–776
16. Symptoms, senility, and ill-defined conditions	780–795
17. Accidents, poisonings, and violence	800–999

20-11. Some Factors Affecting Death Rates. In addition to the age groupings which have already been mentioned as affecting death rates there are other factors concerned. There may be a large number of nonresident deaths in an area because of the presence of hospitals which attract patients from other communities, thereby unfavorably affecting the local death rate.

Also, since immigration is likely to be very largely of young adults, a locality with a large balance of immigrants over emigrants may have large groups with low specific death rates that tend to lower the crude death rate. A large and continuous excess of births over deaths has the same effect.

20-12. Birth Rates. These are usually expressed as so many per year per 1,000 population. The birth rate based on the whole population is termed the crude birth rate, which can be found by using the following formula:

$$\text{Birth rate per 1,000} = \frac{\text{number of births in 1 year}}{\text{total population}} \times 1{,}000$$

While the crude birth rate is the one most generally used, it is apparent that the birth rates for various localities cannot be properly compared in many cases. Obviously, the number of births depends to a considerable extent upon the age distribution of the population, to a greater degree upon the sex distribution, and still more so upon the number of the female population of the child-bearing ages (ordinarily considered as being from fifteen to forty-five years). The birth rate based upon the number of females of child-bearing age may be three times as great as the crude birth rate.

In some 2 to 3 per cent of all deliveries, the child is born dead. This is termed a fetal death and is not considered as either a birth or death in the computation of birth, death, and infant-mortality rates. The standard certificate of fetal death (stillbirth) is used in registering these events.

If birth rates for local areas are to be compared, it is necessary that such rates be computed on the number of births for the area by place of residence of the mother rather than by place of occurrence.

20-13. Infant Mortality. One of the most important divisions of vital statistics is the study of infant mortality. The infant-mortality rate is suggestive of several things. It reflects very closely the social welfare of a community and also serves as one of the most sensitive indexes of its sanitary condition. This is due to the close connection between the health of infants and the quality of the milk supply, the presence of flies, the condition of housing, and, to some extent, the purity of the water. Therefore the alert health officer scrutinizes very closely the infant-mortality figures. These figures are expressed as the number of deaths of infants under one year of age to every 1,000 births occurring in the same year and expressed as the following formula:

$$\text{Infant mortality} = \frac{\text{infant deaths in 1 year}}{\text{births in same year}} \times 1{,}000$$

It is almost impossible to determine in midyear the total number of infants under one year of age, but with good registration of births and with a fairly stable population the number of births registered for any one year is practically equal to the number of infants under one year of age. The infant mortality varies greatly in different cities and even in the different sections of a city. In general, there has been a decline in infant-mortality rates during the last quarter century. For instance, in the registration area of the United States, the infant mortality was 161 in 1900, 100 in 1915, 76 in 1921, 32.2 in 1948, and 28.4 in 1952. It must be remembered that the infant-mortality rate for a local area may be adversely affected if the percentage completeness of birth registration is considerably below that for death registration.

20-14. Morbidity Rates. These are expressed as the number of cases of a specific disease occurring in one year, to the midyear population expressed in thousands, or more frequently in hundred thousands. It is usually based upon the entire population but may be computed for certain age groups or classes. Incompleteness due to poor reporting of diseases is the weak point of morbidity rates. To a great extent morbidity rates depend upon the environmental conditions which directly and indirectly cause disease or lowering of resistance. The study of the morbidity rates of diseases which are specifically connected with some particular condition, such as industrial diseases, typhoid fever, and malaria, is of great value to the health officer and sanitarian.

The fatality of a disease is the ratio between the number of deaths and the number of cases and is usually expressed as a percentage. The determination of the fatality rate of a disease is complicated by incompleteness of morbidity reports. For instance, typhoid fever was for many years considered as having a fatality rate of 10 per cent. On the basis of case and death reports it may appear even higher. Careful investigations in connection with typhoid epidemics have established the fact that the fatality rate is considerably less than 10 per cent under usual conditions.

BIBLIOGRAPHY

1. Whipple, G. C.: "Vital Statistics," John Wiley & Sons, Inc., New York.
2. Falk, I. S.: "Principles of Vital Statistics," W. B. Saunders Company, Philadelphia.
3. Pearl, Raymond: "Introduction to Medical Biometry and Statistics," W. B. Saunders Company, Philadelphia.
4. Davenport, C. B., and M. P. Ekas: "Statistical Methods in Biology, Medicine and Psychology," John Wiley & Sons, Inc., New York.
5. Arkin, H., and R. R. Colton: "Graphs: How to Make and Use Them," Harper & Brothers, New York.

CHAPTER 21

PUBLIC HEALTH ORGANIZATIONS

21-1. The protection of the health of the citizen is a function of government. The needs, however, vary according to the governmental agency involved. The principal health agency of the national government, the U.S. Public Health Service, is organized to meet specific emergencies and to carry out particular routine duties. The health departments of the various states, in general, resemble each other in organization and functions. There is resemblance also between the organizations of the state departments and the local agencies, those of the cities and counties. But the detailed functions of the various departmental divisions of the local departments are necessarily different from those of the states. For instance, the bureau of communicable disease control in a state department, though having the same object as a similarly named division or bureau of a city health department, has a different field to cover and directs its activities accordingly.

In addition to governmental health organizations there are a number of private health agencies, supported by endowments, contributions, or public subscription, which cover certain fields of health work either independently or in cooperation with the governmental agencies.

21-2. Health Activities. The activities of health departments vary somewhat not only according to the governmental agency involved but also according to the size of the community served and, to some degree, the local conditions. In some cities, by custom, health departments have retained certain functions which, it is felt, should be undertaken by other agencies—for instance, street cleaning and garbage collection and disposal. However, health authorities are agreed that certain activities should be duties of public health services, and these are listed below. Of course, many of them are not included by certain departments, possibly because funds or interest is lacking or perhaps because the particular problem is absent.

A. Vital statistics
  1. Registration
  2. Classification

3. Verification
4. Interpretation

B. Communicable disease control
1. Reporting
2. Record keeping
3. Verification of diagnoses
4. Laboratory control
5. Control practices
6. Investigation of sources of infection
7. Isolation, quarantine, release, disinfection

C. Child hygiene
1. Prenatal service
2. Infant hygiene
3. Care of the preschool child
4. Health of the school child
   a. Physical examinations
   b. Correction of defects
   c. Sanitation of school buildings
   d. Health education
   e. Recreation

D. Chronic diseases
1. Reporting on registration
2. Screening and detection
3. Statistical studies
4. Follow-up

E. Sanitation
1. Water supply
2. Sewerage
3. Food sanitation
   a. Milk sanitation
   b. Meat inspection
   c. Sanitation of food-handling establishments
4. Housing
5. Insect control
6. Rodent control
7. Industrial hygiene
8. Swimming-pool sanitation
7. Nuisances

F. Laboratory
1. Bacteriological examinations
2. Chemical examinations
3. Research

G. Public health education
1. Bulletins, circulars, and periodicals

2. Newspaper articles, radio, and telecasts
3. Exhibits
4. Lectures, motion pictures

In addition to the above activities a few cities also conduct clinics for mental hygiene, drug addiction, and various other special purposes. Clinics for infants and children, for tuberculosis, and venereal diseases are usual. A newcomer in the public health field is geriatrics, which is concerned with diseases and health conditions of old age. The greater proportion of persons in the older age groups is focusing attention on the need for planning an acceptable and realistic program and guide for the older age group.

21-3. Vital Statistics. This work, as discussed in Chap. 20, is the registration of births, marriages, and deaths. It should also include the tabulation and analysis at monthly intervals of the data obtained, including also the reports of the reportable diseases sent in to the division or bureau of communicable diseases. Such information is of special value to the local health departments.

Although a register is kept by active city and county health departments, the state organization is the final repository for the death and birth certificates. The National Office of Vital Statistics in the U.S. Public Health Service at Washington collects tabulated reports of births, deaths, and causes of death from the states and some municipalities. It publishes annual reports and occasional bulletins in addition to the regular decennial report.

The Metropolitan Life Insurance Company of New York also keeps vital statistics of a group of 17 million insured persons. Various bulletins and studies based upon its records are issued by the company from time to time and are of great value.

21-4. Communicable Disease Control. As this has been discussed to some extent elsewhere, it is touched upon but briefly here. The epidemiological work of this division includes a system of reporting of all the ordinary communicable diseases with systematic investigation of each reported case. In the more serious diseases, such as diphtheria, smallpox, bubonic plague, and poliomyelitis, verification should be made by a medical officer. Specimens are taken for laboratory diagnosis or release, or both, in diphtheria, typhoid fever, syphilis, and epidemic cerebrospinal meningitis. All cases are hospitalized if proper precautions cannot be taken at home. Many health departments furnish biologics for prevention of infectious diseases. Public health education pays dividends in stimulating and securing adequate community immunization levels of such diseases as smallpox, diphtheria, whooping cough, tetanus, typhoid fever, poliomyelitis, bubonic plague, and cholera. From the public health standpoint, health departments are primarily interested in securing immunization levels of a community to prevent a major outbreak of the disease. Should an epidemic of a communicable disease occur, this division institutes measures to determine the natural history of the disease and, utilizing this knowledge, plans a strategy of control at strategic points where control measures may be applied.[1]

Tuberculosis control, through the use of mass case-finding techniques, antimicrobial drugs, and major chest surgery, has brought about a marked decline in the mortality rate. However, in certain states and larger cities where tuberculosis is still a major problem, separate divisions are maintained. In some areas, however, certain parts of this work, such as that of outpatient clinics and visiting nurses, are supported or furnished by voluntary health agencies. The control methods used include effective reporting of cases; consultation service; screening techniques, such as mass chest X-ray surveys and tuberculin testing; ascertaining that each case receives proper nursing and medical care in adequately staffed hospitals or at home; and provision for adequate follow-up and vocational rehabilitation for arrested cases.

Much progress has also been made in venereal disease control. With the advancement of modern therapy, the treatment of gonorrhea is as trifling as that of the common cold, and more certain. Today complications of the disease are rarely encountered; but because of its reinfectious nature, the morbidity of gonorrhea, despite modern treatment, remains high, and control is therefore very difficult. Modern therapy, however, has brought about a remarkable decline in the morbidity of syphilis, bringing us close to the reservoirs of infection, and it is now timely to consider eradication rather than mere control. If syphilis is to be numbered, as it should be, with smallpox, yellow fever, typhoid fever, and diphtheria among the extinct or nearly extinct diseases, we shall need to revise our epidemiologic approach to it. In the control program of today, emphasis must be placed upon reporting of all cases to the local health authorities, contact investigation, and prophylactic use of penicillin. There should be precise legislation providing for the examination of the presumably infected and their compulsory treatment when indicated.

21-5. Maternal and Child Health. This very important branch of health work may be divided into two major classifications: complete maternity care and a program for child health.

Maternity care includes premarital education and counseling, preconceptive advice and instruction, prenatal care, delivery care, and postnatal care. In planning these services, consideration is given not

[1] See "Control of Communicable Diseases in Man," an official report of the American Public Health Association.

only to the physical factors involved but also to the mental, emotional, social, and economic situations.

A health program for children must take into consideration the physical factors in the child's life situation and, here again, also the emotional, social, mental, and economic aspects. This program can be subdivided impartially into the care of the newborn, or neonatal care; infant care; care of the preschool child; and a health program for the school-age child. A comprehensive program varies according to the age levels and includes health appraisal; counseling; mental health; communicable disease control; nutrition instructions; dental health; health education, including special activities for the handicapped child; and the control of environmental conditions which affect the child's growth and development.

21-6. Chronic Diseases. The treatment of chronic diseases is strictly a function of the private physician; however, health authorities have recognized that through community effort, early detection of the disease can be stimulated, early treatment started, the disease arrested, and the burden of aftercare of the the indigent patients reduced.

Heart disease and cancer are leading causes of death. Diabetes is a major chronic degenerative disease affecting over 2 per cent of our population. Tuberculosis is communicable but chronic in character. Arthritis is the chief cause of morbidity and disability. These diseases are often silent in their early stages.

The activities of the local health authorities in regard to chronic diseases include:

1. Detection or case finding from the reports of physicians, hospitals, and clinics and through mass screening. This procedure permits early treatment.
2. Programming measures to arrest the disease.
3. Advising on nursing homes and aftercare for indigent patients.

21-7. Sanitation. That control of environment which makes up the practice of sanitation has been discussed in detail elsewhere and needs no further elaboration here. All sanitary work, however, is not included in the work of the health department, although practice varies in this regard. In general only those activities which are directly concerned with health are placed in the city health department, the idea being that funds appropriated for health purposes should give maximum returns in health. Refuse collection and disposal, for instance, are often excluded and handled by some other department. Research along such lines has, however, been carried on by the state health agencies and by the U.S. Public Health Service. In cities the care of small water supplies, from the standpoint of safety, is invariably entrusted to the health department, but purification of the public supply is supervised by the water department. Excreta disposal in unsewered areas is a recognized activity of health departments, but maintenance and operation of city sewers and sewage treatment plants are likely to be functions of some other city agency. Plumbing inspection may or may not be included in the health department, but in most cases the city sanitary engineer or some other health official is placed on the examination board which licenses plumbers. Nuisance inspection is invariably conducted by the health department inspectors of cities and counties, but of late its removal elsewhere has been strongly urged. Other instances might be given.

The theory of such elimination of activities is good, particularly so in the case of refuse collection and disposal. There are other practical considerations, however, which, for some time to come at least, may necessitate a departure from theory. To the average person many of these functions, particularly nuisance inspection, belong in the health department, and it will be blamed for poor performance even though not responsible. On the other hand, such work is conspicuous and if well done may gain financial support for the less spectacular though more important activities.

In all sanitary activities, however, the health department may be called upon to give advice; hence it is important for health officials to have a thorough understanding of all branches of sanitation. Also, since all the allied sanitary matters are strictly of an engineering nature, it is of value for the health department to have a sanitary engineer who can represent the health department and at the same time meet the engineers of other city departments on common ground.

Good administration indicates that safety and sanitation features be incorporated in the design, construction, and maintenance of streets, utilities, public buildings, industrial plants, recreational areas, and housing projects. Good communication with most governmental and some private agencies is highly desirable.

21-8. Laboratory. The laboratory of a health department makes chemical and bacteriological examinations of milk, water from public and private supplies, bottled waters, and possibly sewage or sewage-polluted waters; chemical, bacteriological, and microscopical examinations of foods and drugs; and bacteriological and microscopical examinations for diagnosis and release in diphtheria, tuberculosis, typhoid fever, malaria, syphilis, gonorrhea, pneumonia, and, in the South, hookworm and other intestinal parasitic diseases. Research should also be carried on along the lines of bacteriology and chemistry as they pertain to public health.

21-9. Public Health Education. Health education not only teaches healthful living to children and adults but also instructs in the principles of community hygiene. It therefore is doubly valuable in that it helps the individual directly and also brings about recognition of the value of public health work, resulting in better cooperation between the citizen and the health department. The recognized methods of health education as accomplished by health departments are as follows: the preparation of an annual report showing clearly the work done, results accomplished, costs, and future needs; publishing and distribution of weekly or monthly bulletins to physicians, nurses, teachers, social workers, and prominent persons, so that they may be informed about current health problems; preparation of radio script, television recordings, and newspaper stories and articles on timely subjects; exhibits illustrating and demonstrating health work; lecture service for various organizations; and stimulation of health instruction in the schools by arousing the interest of the school authorities and teachers and cooperating in instruction. Departments of education of many of the larger cities have health education specialists on their staffs.

HEALTH ORGANIZATIONS

21-10. The World Health Organization. The World Health Organization came into existence Apr. 7, 1948, when the necessary 26 nations had notified the Secretary General of the United Nations that the constitution of the proposed organization had been ratified. Its organization includes a Health Assembly made up of delegates representing the member countries. Countries that are not members of the United Nations may join the Organization. The Health Assembly appoints an Executive Board and a Director General, who is the chief technical and administrative officer of the Organization. The functions of the Organization as given in its constitution are:

(*a*) to act as the directing and co-ordinating authority on international health work;

(*b*) to establish and maintain effective collaboration with the United Nations, specialized agencies, governmental health administrations, professional groups and such other organizations as may be deemed appropriate;

(*c*) to assist governments, upon request, in strengthening health services;

(*d*) to furnish appropriate technical assistance and, in emergencies, necessary aid upon the request or acceptance of governments;

(*e*) to provide or assist in providing, upon the request of the United Nations, health services and facilities to special groups, such as the peoples of trust territories;

(*f*) to establish and maintain such administrative and technical services as may be required, including epidemiological and statistical services;

(*g*) to stimulate and advance work to eradicate epidemic, endemic and other diseases;

(*h*) to promote, in co-operation with other specialized agencies where necessary, the prevention of accidental injuries;

(*i*) to promote, in co-operation with other specialized agencies where necessary, the improvement of nutrition, housing, sanitation, recreation, economic or working conditions and other aspects of environmental hygiene;

(*j*) to promote co-operation among scientific and professional groups which contribute to the advancement of health;

(*k*) to propose conventions, agreements and regulations, and make recommendations with respect to international health matters and to perform such duties as may be assigned thereby to the Organization and are consistent with its objective;

(*l*) to promote maternal and child health and welfare and to foster the ability to live harmoniously in a changing total environment;

(*m*) to foster activities in the field of mental health, especially those affecting the harmony of human relations;

(*n*) to promote and conduct research in the field of health;

(*o*) to promote improved standards of teaching and training in the health, medical and related professions;

(*p*) to study and report on, in co-operation with other specialized agencies where necessary, administrative and social techniques affecting public health and medical care from preventive and curative points of view, including hospital services and social security;

(*q*) to provide information, counsel and assistance in the field of health;

(*r*) to assist in developing an informed public opinion among all peoples on matters of health;

(*s*) to establish and revise as necessary international nomenclatures of diseases, of causes of death and of public health practices;

(*t*) to standardize diagnostic procedures as necessary;

(*u*) to develop, establish and promote international standards with respect to food, biological, pharmaceutical and similar products;

(*v*) generally to take all necessary action to attain the objective of the Organization.

At the 1948 meeting of the Organization permanent headquarters were set up in Geneva, the Director General and Executive Board were appointed, and a program was adopted. Top priority was given to six major problems: malaria, maternal and child health, tuberculosis, venereal diseases, environmental sanitation, and nutrition. For these, funds were set up for staffs and travel costs in order to give expert advice and to provide demonstration teams and training programs. Second priority was given to four problems: public health nursing, parasitic diseases, virus diseases, and mental health. To each of these were assigned a staff member and a small committee of experts.

Funds for the World Health Organization are derived from the member countries. An annual budget is prepared by the Director General and presented to the Executive Board, which submits it to the Health Assembly with any recommendations it cares to make. The Assembly after reviewing and approving the budget apportions the expenses according to some plan adopted by the Assembly. Six geographic divisions were set up to be served by regional offices.

21-11. The United States Public Health Service. This is a part of the U.S. Department of Health, Education, and Welfare and is directed by a Surgeon General. It has a corps of commissioned officers, including physicians, sanitary engineers, and other technicians, who hold corresponding rank to officers in the Army, Navy, and Coast Guard. It is by far the most important health agency in the Federal government, and in the space available here it is difficult to do justice to its contributions to public health in the United States. Its major functions include the following:

1. Provision of medical and hospital care for merchant seamen, officers, and enlisted men of the Coast Guard and others as authorized by Congress
2. Administration of quarantine service to prevent the introduction of certain epidemic diseases into the United States
3. Medical inspection of aliens arriving in the United States
4. Prevention of the spread of communicable diseases from state to state
5. Licensing of biologic products (vaccines, serums, etc.) applicable to the treatment of man which are sold in interstate traffic
6. Conduct of scientific research, investigations, and demonstrations related to the cause, prevention, and cure of diseases of man, including provision for engaging in various cooperative public health studies and demonstrations with state and local health agencies, other Federal agencies, and voluntary or nonofficial organizations
7. Administration of grants-in-aid of funds to states for various public health services
8. Administration of grants-in-aid to qualified institutions or individual scientists for research in the physical and mental diseases
9. Provision of technical assistance and consultant services to the states and other Federal agencies
10. Collection and dissemination of statistical and other information on health problems
11. Training of professional personnel in the public health and medical sciences through (*a*) fellowships for research scientists; (*b*) payments of tuition and stipends for individuals employed by state and local health departments and for physicians intending to become specialists in the diagnosis and treatment of cancer; (*c*) grants to approved institutions for

training of psychiatrists and other personnel concerned with care of mental patients

12. Collaboration with the governments of other countries and with international organizations in activities for the improvement of world health, as well as with private national organizations and institutions concerned with health

In order to carry on its functions the Public Health Service has many divisions, bureaus, offices, hospitals, and laboratories. Those which are of special interest to the sanitary engineer are described briefly below.

The Division of Sanitary Engineering Services has general supervision over all sanitation activities of the Service. Its activities include:

1. Inspection and certification of sanitary facilities, food and drink used on interstate carriers (railroads, vessels, and airplanes), including the certification of water supplies
2. Cooperation with state agencies in certification of shellfish shippers
3. Certification of shippers of shaving brushes sold in interstate commerce, as a means of preventing anthrax
4. Review of vessel plans and coordination of the inspection and certification of water systems, plumbing, food storage, and ratproofing of vessels
5. Administration of the Federal Water Pollution Control Act
6. Providing technical services and equipment in emergencies through the states
7. Furnishing consulting service to other agencies of the Federal government and the states
8. Initiating and conducting studies on many phases in the field of environmental sanitation
9. Preparation of suggestive ordinances or regulations on housing, air, milk, frozen desserts, and restaurant sanitation

The Milk Ordinance and Code developed by the U.S. Public Health Service Engineering Services has been adopted by many cities and has greatly contributed to the decline in milk-borne epidemics.

The Robert A. Taft Sanitary Engineering Center, Cincinnati, Ohio, is engaged in research in the fields of water and sewage treatment and is developing data upon which to base standards in air, milk, and food sanitation.

The Bureau of State Services includes a number of important divisions which give technical and consultative aid to the state health departments. These divisions also grant funds to the states to carry on projects in the fields of venereal disease, tuberculosis, and the planning and construction of hospital facilities.

The National Institutes of Health, an agency of the U.S. Public Health Service, located at Bethesda, Md., do research on cancer, heart, mental, dental, and many other diseases. They also make grants to support research projects in educational institutes and award fellowships to develop research talent in certain medical areas.

The Communicable Disease Center, a section of the U.S. Public Health Service located in Atlanta, Ga., provides consulting services and general assistance to states in matters pertaining to the control of communicable diseases. It is composed of epidemiology, laboratory, technology, and training branches. The Technology Branch has subsections concerned with insect vector control, emergency disaster aid, and research in the development and safe use of pesticides and of efficient equipment for dispensing this material.

21-12. Other Health Agencies of the National Government. There are numerous other agencies of the national government which are concerned to a greater or less degree with health matters. Of these, only the more important can be mentioned here.

The Food and Drug Administration has the responsibility for developing, directing, and supervising the nation-wide food and drug and cosmetic regulatory program in order to prohibit the manufacture and sale of adulterated, misbranded, or dangerous foods, drugs, and cosmetics.

In the Department of Agriculture the Bureau of Animal Industry inspects meat and meat products and deals with dairying, dairy sanitation, and animal diseases. The Bureau of Entomology studies insects which affect the health of man, and the Biological Survey cooperates in the eradication of rodents.

In the Department of the Interior the Bureau of Mines cooperates with the Public Health Service in the investigation of health hazards in mining and industry, smoke prevention, and methods of ventilation.

The Labor Department maintains a Children's Bureau, which investigates infant mortality, diseases of children, and administers maternity and infancy laws; a Women's Bureau, which is concerned with the health of women in industry; and a Bureau of Labor Statistics, which studies problems of industrial hygiene.

The Civil Defense Administration is charged with the development of a nation-wide plan for the defense of the civilians in the event of an emergency. It has issued many informative bulletins on preparedness.

The Labor Department and many other Federal agencies are interested in certain phases of health and sanitation. The Labor Department carries on certain studies in the field of health in industry.

Since all the above bureaus or divisions publish pamphlets and bulletins giving the results of their investigations, anyone interested in these fields has valuable mines of information available on request from the agency concerned.

21-13. State Health Departments. The health departments of the various states vary considerably in their organizations and powers. In general they are given control over the health work of the states and enforce the health laws enacted by the state legislatures. The laws generally cover such matters as the control of communicable disease, reporting of diseases, registration of births and deaths, control of the quality and sanitation of foods, child and maternal hygiene, and prevention and investigation of stream pollution. They usually require the submission and approval of plans for sewerage and waterworks before construction by a municipality or private agency.

In some cases, a somewhat centralized control of health matters, with decentralization of the state organization, has been obtained through the division of the state into districts and the placing of a state official or district health officer in each. In general, however, the formation of local health departments in the individual cities and counties and their assumption of responsibility are encouraged, and the state cooperates with these local departments, advises them, and gives aid in emergencies. Where no local department is functioning, the state renders the only health service which such an unfortunate community receives.

The organization of a state health department is prescribed by the state law. Invariably the chief officer, generally known as the state health officer or the commissioner of public health, is required to be a physician; preferably he should be trained and experienced in public health work, although this requirement is not the rule as yet. Generally also there is a state board of health which acts in an advisory capacity to the state health officer but exercises no executive functions. In most cases the health officer and the state board of health are appointed by the governor, although the practice of having the state board choose the health officer is currently followed in some states and advocated in others. In this case the board is rotating, two of six members, for instance, being replaced every two years. This arrangement makes for continuity of policy and tends to take the health department out of politics.

As mentioned before, the state health activities are very largely advisory and cooperative although they follow closely the lines described in the first section of this chapter. The communicable disease division keeps records of communicable diseases so that it may recognize emergencies. It aids local health departments and communities without health departments to overcome epidemics and keeps on hand supplies of vaccine, antitoxin, and other immunizing agents for use and distribution where needed.

The division of vital statistics is the final repository of birth and death

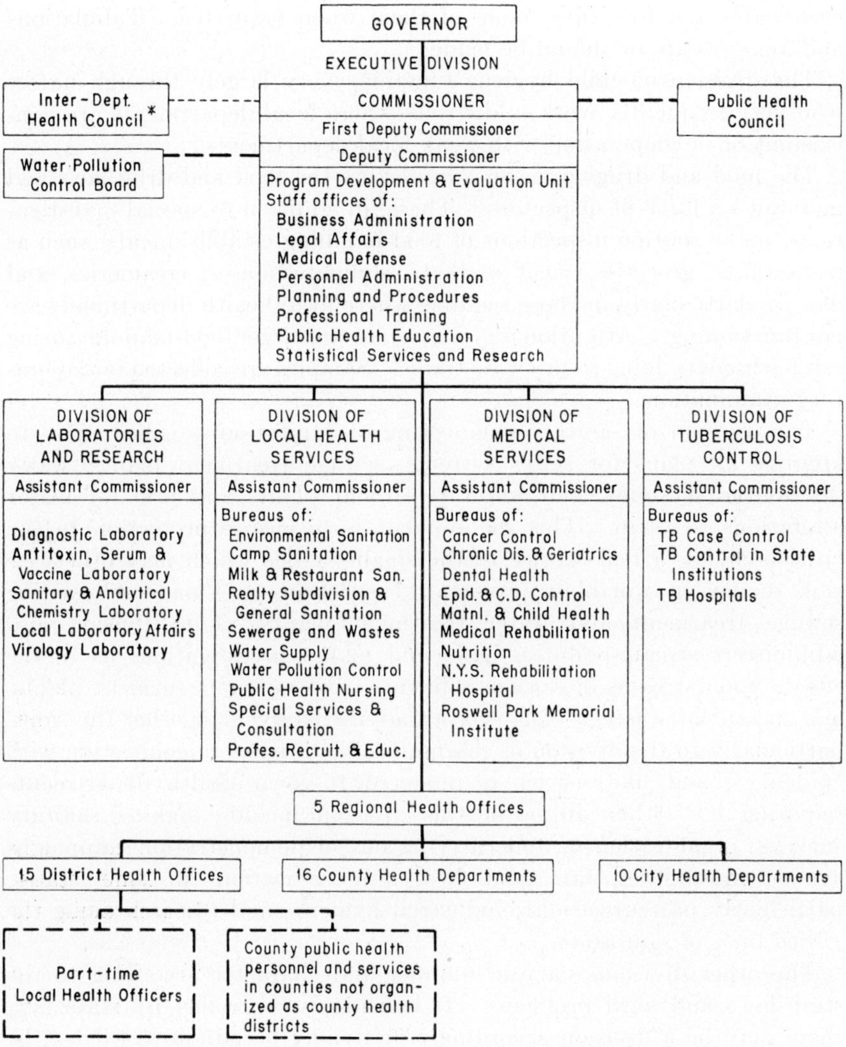

*Coordinates health activities of all state agencies. It is comprised of the Commissioners of Health (Chairman), Social Welfare, Education, Mental Hygiene, Labor, Correction, the Chairman of the Parole Board, and the Chairman of the Workmen's Compensation Board.

--------- Advisory relationship ——— Functional relationship

FIG. 21-1. Organization chart of the New York State Health Department.

certificates and furnishes copies of them when requested. Tabulations and analyses are or should be made.

The division of child hygiene functions very largely through nurses who very frequently work in districts where local departments are non-existent or in cooperation with weak local departments.

The food and drugs division administers the food and drug laws and maintains a force of inspectors. These, in addition to special investigations, make routine inspections of food-handling establishments, such as restaurants, groceries, meat markets, slaughterhouses, creameries, and dairies, particularly in those sections where local health departments are not functioning. Attention is also given to the larger food-manufacturing establishments doing a statewide trade. Samples are collected for laboratory examination.

The division of sanitary engineering or sanitation is called upon to approve all plans for sewer systems, sewage treatment plants, water distribution systems, and water treatment plants and also for major alterations to them. This requirement is to ensure protection to the citizens and is a real service to the smaller cities which may otherwise sink money in worthless projects. Inspections are made of existing sewage treatment and water treatment plants. This division also administers stream-pollution laws and makes investigations as to the effects upon streams of sewage, effluents from sewage treatment plants, and industrial wastes. Engineering advice is given to other divisions, particularly to the division of communicable diseases in connection with epidemics, and like service is rendered to local health departments requiring it. Other duties of this division include making sanitary surveys; organization of and carrying out of demonstration campaigns against mosquitoes, rats, and flies; milk sanitation (in some states, particularly pasteurization); industrial hygiene; and research along the varied lines of sanitation.

The other divisions vary in number and character according to the state laws and local problems. If housing is controlled by state law, there may be a division accordingly or it may be administered by the sanitary engineering division. The division of local health services is mainly concerned with the stimulation of local health work and the formation of local health departments. A division of public health nursing furnishes to the other divisions the required number of nurses, thus allowing great flexibility.

As mentioned before, the state health officer is invariably a physician. The chiefs of bureaus or divisions are also physicians, with some exceptions. The division of foods and drugs is sometimes headed by a chemist. The chief of the division of sanitary engineering is in all cases a sanitary engineer and is sometimes called the state sanitary engineer. His assistants are, in general, engineers also, with sanitarians and inspectors sometimes used for special purposes. Milk sanitation is frequently carried on by veterinarians and sometimes by sanitarians.

21-14. City Health Departments. While the state health department performs important duties in supervising, standardizing, and cooperating in state health work as a whole, it is the local health department which must serve the average citizen in the matters which touch him closely. In a city it is the municipal health department or the city health officer who must solve the local problems and do the detail work. This need, in the large cities, calls for an organization differing but little in form from that of the state but showing differences in duties and personnel.

In the smaller cities the problem of obtaining effective local health work is still far from solution. Most states require health officers (usually they must be licensed physicians) for each county and incorporated city. But the compensation of such officers is left to the city or county and is frequently so small that the incumbent can afford to take little or no time from his regular practice to attend to public duties. Theoretically he is required by the state to enforce the control, isolation, placarding, etc., of communicable diseases and register vital statistics. The authority of city health officers is also enlarged by city ordinances to include sanitary inspection and abatement of nuisances. But the part-time official is at a disadvantage here since enforcement of such ordinances makes enemies and the practice by which he makes his living may suffer. The possibilities of accomplishing effective health work under such conditions is discussed later.

21-15. The Health Department of a Large City. Figure 21-2 is an organization chart based upon recommendations by Winslow and Harris[1] for a city of 100,000 population. It would also serve for a city of considerably greater size with the possible addition of such divisions as mental hygiene and industrial hygiene. It will be noted that there is provision for a board of health. This is advisory and deliberative only, without executive duties, though possibly with the power to formulate a sanitary code. The health officer or director of public health is head of the department and should be full-time and specially trained and experienced in public health work. The duties and personnel of the various bureaus and divisions are briefly given below, the discussions being based upon the recommendations of Winslow and Harris in the report previously referred to.

The bureau of administration is directly under the supervision of the health officer and includes the two divisions of administration and education. The former handles the routine office business of the department, and the latter, which also receives much of the attention of the health officer, performs the work described in Art. 21-9. The educational division should include a man or woman experienced in writing who can obtain and put into popular form the technical matter furnished by the other bureaus.

The bureau of sanitation for a city of 100,000 should be in the charge of a sanitary engineer whose technical advice is available for the other

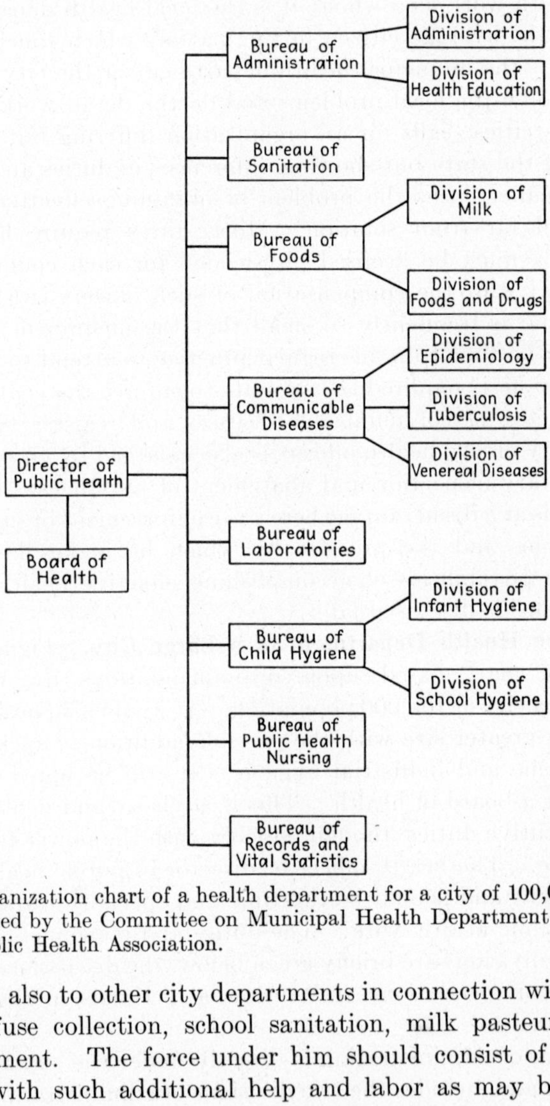

FIG. 21-2. Organization chart of a health department for a city of 100,000 population, as recommended by the Committee on Municipal Health Department Practice of the American Public Health Association.

bureaus and also to other city departments in connection with plumbing, housing, refuse collection, school sanitation, milk pasteurization, and water treatment. The force under him should consist of four district inspectors with such additional help and labor as may be needed for mosquito control or other special measures. The routine work would include inspection of privies and of fly breeding conditions, particularly manure, possibly also ratproofing and rat extermination, the investigation of complaints, and the remedying of nuisances. The supervision of housing conditions should also be placed in the jurisdiction of this bureau. To further its acitvities there should be comprehensive ordinances furnishing a housing code, defining nuisances, and regulating offensive trades.

The bureau of foods should have as its head a technically trained man, perhaps a veterinarian, whose time is divided between the two divisions—milk, and foods and drugs. In some instances this work, and especially milk sanitation, is placed under the sanitary engineer. Each division requires two inspectors. The milk division should carry out the work as outlined in Chap. 11 and modified to some extent by the particular milk ordinance of the city in question. The food and drugs division inspects, and preferably grades, all food-handling establishments and enforces state laws and ordinances regulating the quality and handling of foods, including the regular examination of food handlers. Both divisions of this bureau are greatly strengthened by ordinances requiring the licensing or holding of permits by all food establishments, including dairies, hotels, restaurants, bakeries, candy stores, groceries, markets, slaughterhouses (including poultry), soda fountains, ice-cream stands, and fruit stands. No provision is made for meat inspection in this organization. A practical and desirable arrangement is the establishment of a municipal abattoir upon a fee system that makes it completely self-supporting, including the salary of the meat inspector, who should be a veterinarian.

The bureau of communicable diseases is divided into the three divisions of epidemiology, tuberculosis, and venereal diseases. The work of this bureau is outlined in Art. 21-4. Each division is in the charge of a full-time physician who should be an expert in his line. The division of epidemiology also requires the services of a nurse and an inspector. The inspector's duties include placarding of houses, supervision of terminal cleansing, disinfection, and fumigation in the case of insect-borne disease. The tuberculosis division, in addition to the director, requires a part-time physician to assist in the work at the clinic or dispensary. Half of the time of a social worker could profitably be used to visit the homes of patients, and the services of four nurses are essential. The venereal diseases need a part-time physician to assist at the clinic and could also make use of the other half of the time of the social worker. For assistance at the clinic and home visiting, two nurses are needed.

The bureau of child hygiene is composed of two divisions: infant hygiene, which is concerned with the health of mothers and young children; and school hygiene, which deals with the health of children of school age. The activities of these divisions are briefly given in Art. 21-5. A clinic is required for infant hygiene and necessitates the use of part-time physicians who are specialists in infant and maternal care. The advisability of placing school health work under the health department has been mentioned elsewhere. The chief of the bureau divides his time between the two divisions, being assisted in the inspection of school children by five part-time medical inspectors, two dentists, and five dental hygienists. The nursing service would be required to furnish 15 nurses for infant hygiene and 8 for school hygiene.

The bureau of public health nursing should furnish the nurses for the various activities previously mentioned. A force of 30 nurses is needed under such an arrangement. If provision for care of the sick in their homes is also to be made, 10 to 20 more nurses are required, making a total of 50 with 6 supervisors, the latter to be specialists in the various branches of the work. The head of this bureau should be a nurse with special qualifications for the position. Winslow suggests that the home-nursing work might be defrayed in part on an hourly basis by persons who are able to pay. Under such an arrangement the city would probably be divided into districts with a nurse in each. While the nursing force may seem large, it should be considered that this arrangement presupposes that all work is done by the city. In most municipalities much of the nursing work is done by agencies other than the city health department, such as the schools and various private charitable organizations. When these are all summarized, the force as recommended may not appear so large.

The work of the laboratory has been described elsewhere. Its director should be a bacteriologist with a trained assistant, preferably a chemist who is able to assist in bacteriological work. A helper with no special training may also be required.

The activities of the bureau of records and vital statistics have already been described. The chief should be a person having training in health work with special study in statistics. A combination clerk and draftman would also be useful.

The budget to care for the salaries, including the clerical assistance which most of the divisions need, and the supplies for such a complete city health department requires an expenditure of $2.30 per capita per year, which is about two to four times the average expenditure of cities for municipal health departments at present. In cities having adequate facilities, however, if all the expenditures of other agencies for health work were totaled and added to the city appropriation, there would probably be no great difference in cost.

It should be mentioned that in some cities welfare work is placed under the director of public health, the combined department being called "public health and welfare." The welfare work includes free care of the diseased, dependent, and defective. Welfare work includes treatment of indigent persons in hospitals. By some authorities this has been considered as charitable work and not as a part of health work, which is preventive medicine and not curative medicine. There are advantages, however, in having hospitals closely related to the health department, and accordingly there is some disposition on the part of health officers to encourage placing of publicly supported hospitals in the county or city health departments.

21-16. Health Department of a Medium-sized City. The health department of a city of 50,000 population is, of course, considerably modified over that of the large city, although the activities are along the same lines. Figure 21-3 is a chart of the health department organization recommended to a city of this size by the American Public

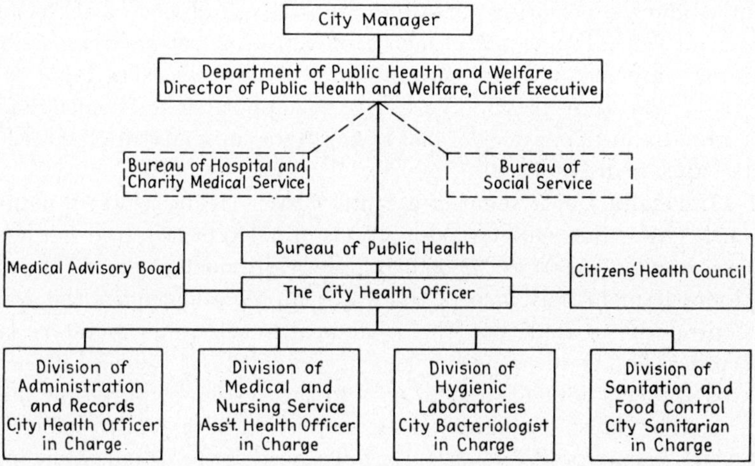

FIG. 21-3. Proposed organization of a health department for a city with a population of 50,000, as recommended by the American Public Health Association.

Health Association. It illustrates very well the combination of functions and duties necessitated by the smaller personnel. In the proposed organization the director of public health and welfare is also the city health officer and in addition is in direct charge of the division of administration and records. This division also includes educational work. The division of medical and nursing service, with an assistant health officer in charge, combines communicable disease control, child hygiene, and nursing. All the work of sanitation, including milk and food sanitation, is concentrated in one division, with a sanitarian, or sanitary engineer, in charge.

The medical advisory board and citizens' health council replace the old-fashioned board of health. As usually constituted, the medical advisory board consists of four or five physicians and a dentist, the members to be as agreed upon or appointed jointly by the local medical and dental societies and by the city council, mayor, or city manager. The citizens' health council consists of representatives of the chamber of commerce and other civic organizations, the members to be appointed by agreement. Since the health department must cooperate with physicians, dentists, and the public, the value of advisory boards of this sort, with the possibility of getting various viewpoints on health problems or emergencies, is very apparent. Such boards serve without pay.

The personnel aside from the chiefs required to carry on the necessary activities of a department of this size are somewhat as follows: division of administration and records, one clerical assistant or secretary; division of medical and nursing service, a dentist for the schools, 10 nurses and a supervising nurse, a quarantine officer, a clerical assistant; division of sanitation, a meat inspector who is a veterinarian, a dairy inspector, three or at least two sanitary inspectors, extra labor when required. The appropriation necessary to support such a health department would approximate $125,000 annually or, in a city of 50,000, a per capita expenditure of $2.50.

21-17. Health Department of a Small City. Health work in many of the small cities, those having populations of 5,000 or less, and frequently in those having 15,000 to 20,000, is practically nonexistent. The state health department may inspect the water supply and require the sewage to be properly treated, but the local health work in general is sadly neglected. This is due in part to lack of recognition of the need for health work by the city councils and in part to the system of part-time health officers. The laws of many states require that a health officer be appointed, usually a physician. He must necessarily be part-time in the small cities, and generally, since at best he can do but little, his salary is nominal and the work that he does is commensurate.

In a city of 5,000, it may be taken for granted that with school examinations and other work a public health nurse would find herself a busy woman. There is also sufficient sanitary work to take the full time of a sanitary inspector. It is better still to obtain a sanitarian with sufficient knowledge to do routine bacteriological testing of water and milk. It is also necessary in most cases to satisfy the state requirement of a medical health officer, and in any event the services of a physician are necessary in connection with the isolation of communicable diseases. He may, therefore, be retained on part time. This arrangement, aside from the salary paid to the part-time health officer, would cost the city about $10,000.

This organization may easily be expanded for larger cities and the costs varied to meet the local conditions, but to meet the needs of smaller communities is more difficult. It may be possible in very small towns to cooperate with the county in obtaining the services of a nurse and sanitary inspector on a part-time basis. A small city may also cut down expenses by contenting itself with a cheaper inspector or requiring the city marshal or policeman to give to sanitation the attention it deserves. Little will be gained, however, unless the inspector or policeman has been given some instruction or training. Such training, in some states, may be obtained through the state health department. A better solution is the combined city-county health department, which is discussed in the following article.

21-18. County Health Department. Less than one-half of the counties in 1953 had full-time health service; 2,229 were served by local district or state health districts, while 839 did not even receive this service.

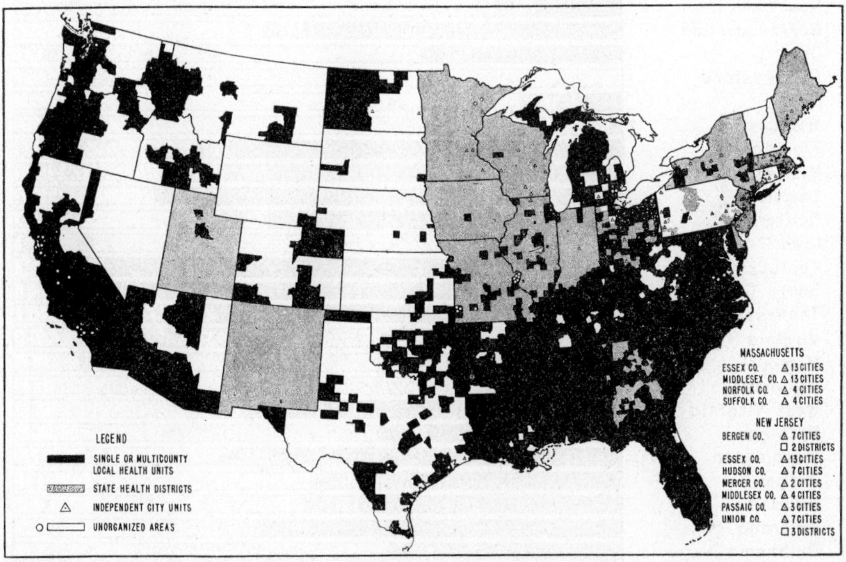

FIG. 21-4. Areas reporting full-time local health service. (*From "Organization and Staffing for Full-time Local Health Service," U.S. Public Health Service, December,* 1953.)

The services rendered by state districts are inadequate in most instances. Yet rural communities are in need of health service to a degree as great as, if not greater than, municipalities. The county health department is a local health agency, and in addition to providing basic services, frequently carries on activities to control special local health problems not common in other areas.

The work of a county health department follows very closely that of the city. A rural program may be summarized as including the following activities: records and vital statistics; isolation, quarantine, immunization, and bedside instruction to prevent the spread of communicable disease; discovery and instruction as to treatment and care of tuberculosis cases and incipient cases; child hygiene, including prenatal care,

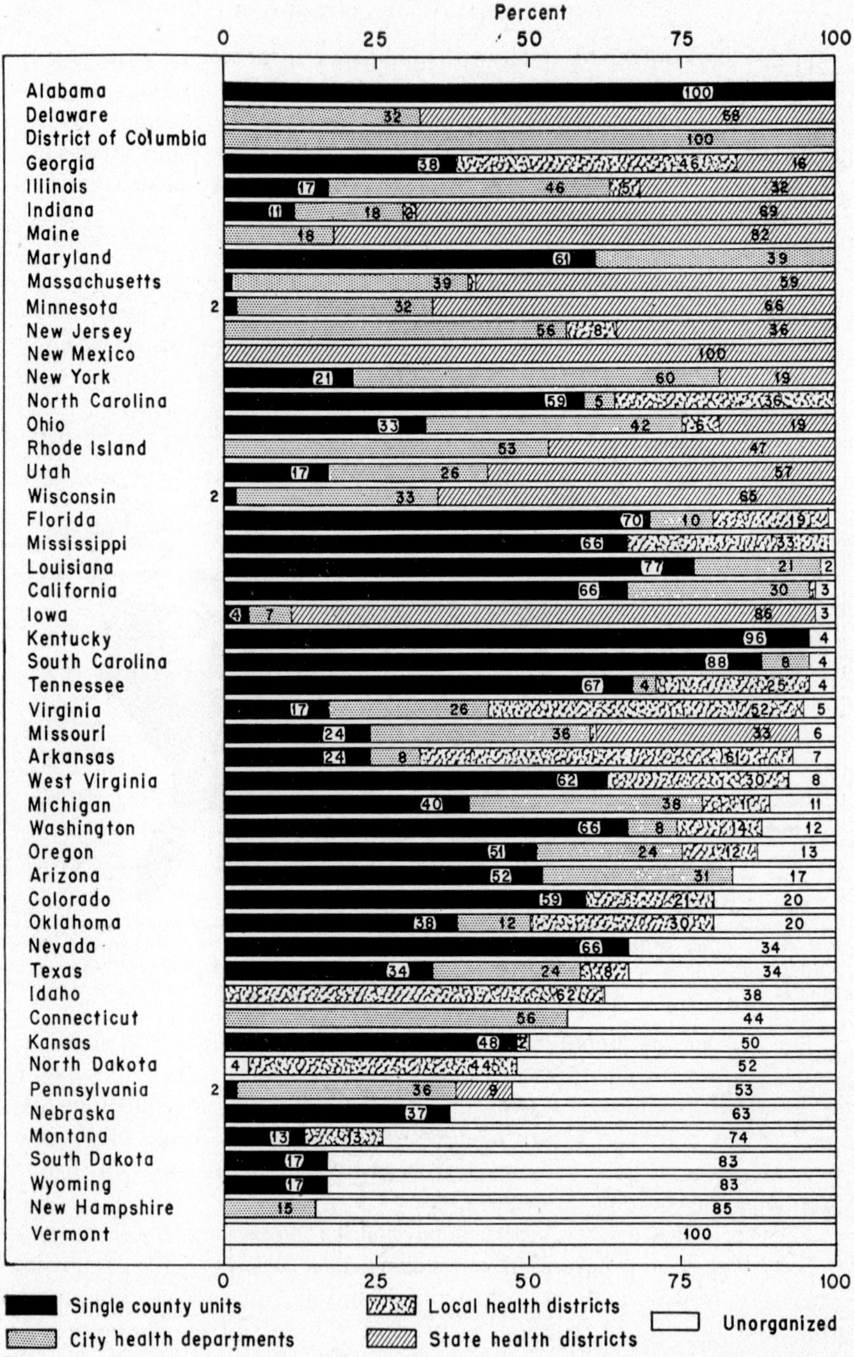

FIG. 21-5. Per cent of each state's total population served by various types of local organization. (*From "Organization and Staffing for Full-time Local Health Service," U.S. Public Health Service, December, 1953.*)

infant hygiene, care of the preschool child, examination of school children, and sanitation of schools; instruction of midwives; safeguarding of the water supplies of the villages and farms; provision for proper excreta disposal to prevent soil and water pollution and fly carriage of disease; food sanitation by inspection of food-handling establishments, dairies, and slaughterhouses and examination of food handlers; control of insects and rodents, if necessary; educational measures by means of lectures, motion pictures, demonstrations, printed matter, formation of clubs for instruction in hygiene, and physical training.

In most cases rural health work on a county basis has resulted through the cooperation of state and county governments, with financial assistance from the Federal government allotted by the U.S. Public Health Service. The last-named agency may start work in a county with the understanding that it will be continued with funds contributed jointly by the state and county. Following several demonstration years it is expected that the county will assume a greater share of the budget.

An economical arrangement, which also encourages greater efficiency in health work, is the formation of city-county health departments. Obviously epidemics and health problems in general are not limited by political boundaries, and the health department which can operate without regard to city limits is in a stronger position than if it cannot do so. Pooling of financial resources also allows an organization that is more complete and staffed by better qualified personnel. The city-county department is, in fact, the answer to the problem of furnishing a well-rounded health program, not only, to the rural inhabitants of a county, but also to the small towns. Unfortunately this logical arrangement is frequently opposed by county politicians and farmers. The former, of course, are opposed to changes of any kind because of fear that they will be disadvantageous to them politically, while the farmers tend to distrust the municipalities. Legal obstacles to the formation of such departments are met with in some states, but these can be eliminated by legislative action or amendment to the state constitution. Progress has been slow in the formation of combination health departments, but it is probably safe to predict that they will become more numerous as time goes on. Counties have also combined to form multicounty or local district health units. This is especially valuable for sparsely populated counties.

21-19. District Organization. In some states, state health work has been decentralized to a very considerable extent. The state is subdivided into districts, and a district health officer, with assisting personnel, is placed in each area. This arrangement is defended by some as permitting closer state supervision over sections which may otherwise be neglected and also for its usefulness in giving health service to those areas where economic conditions or lack of interest has operated to prevent establishment of city and county health organizations. The following considerations enter into any discussion of this subject.

The solution of local health problems is primarily a responsibility of local authorities. Only where emergencies exist and other communities are endangered or the lives of people are threatened through gross local neglect should the state assume responsibility and control. This conforms to the American idea that local self-government is desirable and even necessary. In populous areas, when public sentiment for adequate health work arises, it is provided, and the state should contribute to the crystallization of that sentiment.

Recognition should also be given to the fact that there are many areas in some states, such as the sparsely settled sections of the poorer agricultural districts, where it is a practical certainty that sufficient local funds will never be available for health protection. Here the district organization, created by the state, can mobilize and employ all available financial resources, Federal, state, and local, for the required protection. It should be recognized, however, that where the district plan is widely adopted a closely integrated system results which, at a whim of the state legislature, may be swept away entirely. On the other hand, county health units, while tending to be unstable individually, permit gains to be made slowly without danger of complete disappearance.

21-20. Private Health Organizations. The work of the public health agencies is supplemented by many private organizations. In fact, many of the most important of the present-day functions of public health departments were first developed by private agencies and later taken over by governmental departments. A few of the more important organizations are mentioned below.

The International Health Board of the Rockefeller Foundation has done work both in the United States and abroad in the control of hookworm, malaria, and yellow fever. It has also aided in the organization of rural health work and conducted studies leading to the bettering of public health organizations. The policy of the board in general is to work in cooperation with governmental agencies, and its assistance has been welcomed by the U.S. Public Health Service, states, counties, municipalities, and foreign countries whose funds for adequate health work have been limited.

The American Public Health Association has a membership of over 13,000 persons who are engaged or interested in health work. It publishes the *American Journal of Public Health* and conducts meetings and section meetings at which there are valuable interchanges of ideas. The association is divided into sections corresponding to the various lines of health work. These are health officers, public health engineering, epidemiology, laboratory, vital statistics, industrial hygiene, health education, food and nutrition, public health nursing, and child hygiene. In cooperation with the U.S. Public Health Service it conducted an investigation of municipal health department practice. It has also made surveys and evaluations of the health work of individual cities. The committee reports and other publications of the association have been very influential and useful in advancing and standardizing practice in all public health fields.

The American National Red Cross, in addition to its military and emergency work, also performs community service. This consists of the formation and instruction of classes in nursing hygiene and nutrition.

In addition to the above there are the National Tuberculosis Association, the American Social Hygiene Association, the Council on Health and Public Instruction of the American Medical Association, the Russell Sage Foundation, the National Physical Education Service, the Milbank Foundation, the Commonwealth Foundation, the Kellogg, Hogg, and Cullen Foundations, and others. Much work is also done by state public health associations, state tuberculosis associations, and similar bodies which are organized on a city or county basis.

21-21. Appraisal of Public Health Work. Any local department of health, whether city, county, or combined, should be aware of its shortcomings and anxious to improve its facilities. One method of attaining knowledge of weak spots is a comparison with other departments or, in other words, with commonly accepted practice. An excellent means of doing this is to use the "Health Practice Indices," published by the American Public Health Association. These indices are based upon schedules submitted by the local health officers of 276 communities with a total population of 26 million, or about 30 per cent of the total of 87.6 million people served by full-time organized health departments. They represent, therefore, a good picture of health practice. Charts have been prepared covering the significant phases of health work. For example, in the field of sanitation, a chart showing percentage of rural school population served with approved water supplies indicated that in the median county the percentage was 80. Therefore a county having a smaller percentage of rural children served with safe water supplies is lagging in its efforts. In the field of communicable disease there is a chart for cases of tuberculosis reported per tuberculosis death. The median for this relationship is 2.6. Therefore a city or county reporting a smaller number is lagging in this important activity and is not finding cases which might be saved by proper measures.

BIBLIOGRAPHY

1. Report of the Committee on Municipal Health Department Practice, *U.S. Public Health Bull.* 136.

2. "Organization and Staffing for Full-time Local Health Service," U.S. Public Health Service, December, 1953.
3. Smillie, W. G.: "Public Health Administration in the United States," 2d ed., The Macmillan Company, New York.
4. McCombs, C. E.: "City Health Administration," The Macmillan Company, New York.
5. Mustard, H. S.: "Rural Health Practice," The Commonwealth Fund, New York.
6. Hiscock, I. V. (ed.): "Community Health Organization," The Commonwealth Fund, New York.
7. Horwood, M. P.: "Public Health Surveys," John Wiley & Sons, Inc., New York.
8. "Health Practice Indices, 1943–46," American Public Health Association, New York.
9. Emerson, H.: "Local Health Units for the Nation," The Commonwealth Fund, New York.

APPENDIX A

INSTRUCTIONS FOR THE CONSTRUCTION OF A PIT PRIVY, CONCRETE-SLAB TYPE

Figure A-1 illustrates a single-seat privy of this kind. The steps in construction are as follows:

Dig a hole 4 feet 10 inches deep and 3 feet 6 inches square. Construct a box, open at top and bottom, of 1-inch rough lumber with 2- by 4-inch verticals at the corners, and 5 feet deep. Place the box in the hole.

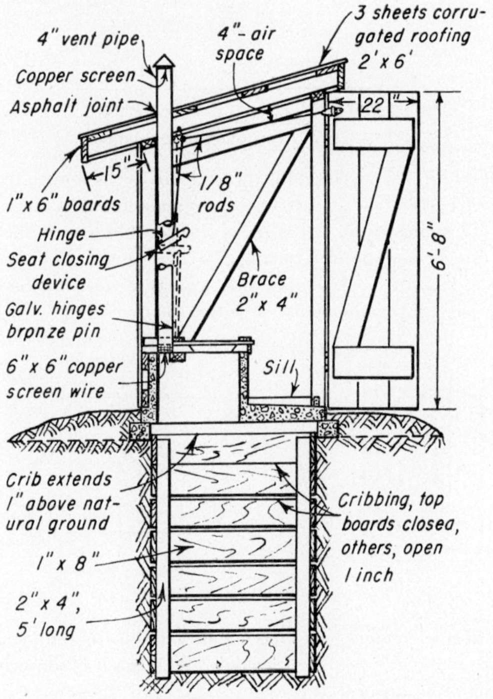

FIG. A-1. Pit privy, concrete-slab type.

The concrete slab and riser are then constructed. On a clean level surface four pieces of 2- by 4-inch lumber are nailed together as forms and pegged down so that a slab 4 feet square and 3 to 3½ inches thick can be poured. It is advisable to cover the surface with paper before pouring the concrete. The slab may be poured in place over the pit if labor is not available to move it, but this requires using forms for the underside of the slab. In either case the reinforcing is next placed so that it is 1 inch above the undersurface of the finished slab. Heavy hog-wire fencing with one 3/8-inch round steel rod placed parallel to and 6 inches from each side is used for this purpose. Before the hog wire is placed, a hole is cut in it large enough to admit the riser form with the wire turned up 4 inches or more into the riser so that a good tie results. The riser form is then set in the hole cut for it. This form should be made of 12-gauge or heavier galvanized iron, the outside in two pieces and the inside in three pieces with pin hinges so that it can be easily assembled and taken down and yet make tight forms.

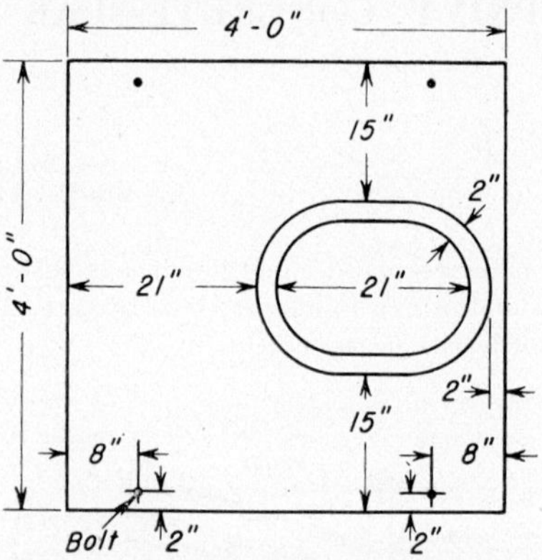

FIG. A-2. Plan of concrete slab.

The riser is 13 inches high above the slab top, and this is the length of the form. Figure A-2 shows a plan of the slab with the inside dimensions of the riser and its location. The riser walls are 2 inches thick. Figure A-3 shows details of the riser forms. The concrete is then mixed and poured, using a 1:2:3 mix. If only sand and cement are available, use a 1:2 mix. The concrete is poured and finished to a thickness of 3½ inches at the riser and 3 inches at the edges of the slab.

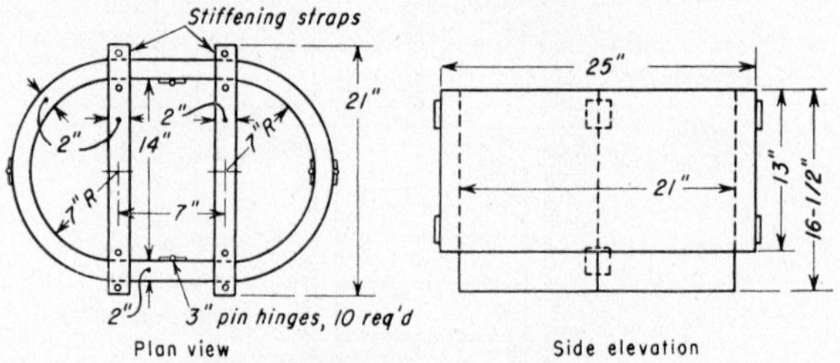

FIG. A-3. Details of riser form.

The curbing is also of concrete. It is usually made in four sections, each 4 feet 1 inch long, 5 inches wide, and 3¾ inches thick, although it is sometimes poured monolithically. Put together around the edge of the pit, these sections make a square curb 4 feet 6 inches (outside dimensions). Before the slab is set, several thicknesses of newspaper and a little cement grout are placed on the curb.

A bolt ½ by 5 inches is set at each corner of the slab to extend high enough to go through the house sill. In the top of the riser three bolts ¼ by 6 inches are set to hold the seat and cover.

The seat and cover are arranged as shown in Fig. A-4. Both are hinged to prevent soiling of the seat when the privy is used as a urinal. Strips of old inner tube can be tacked to the undersides of the seat and cover as gaskets to make tight joints. A ventilator pipe of 4-inch 24-gauge galvanized iron rises from the fixed portion of the seat to extend through the roof. It should be screened with 16-mesh copper wire to prevent entrance of flies and mosquitoes.

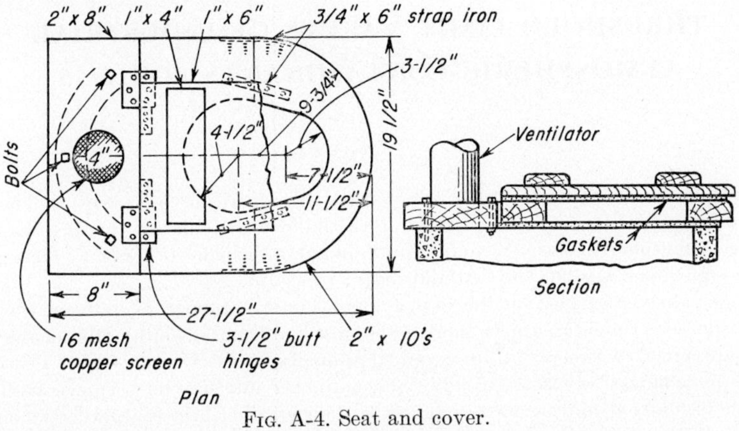

FIG. A-4. Seat and cover.

The house should be substantially constructed. A corrugated iron roof may be used with an opening between the roof sheathing and end rafters for ventilating purposes, as shown in Fig. A-1. The sills are framed as shown in Fig. A-5 and are bolted to the slab. Finally earth is banked up to and around the curbing to keep surface water and roof drippings from entering the pit.

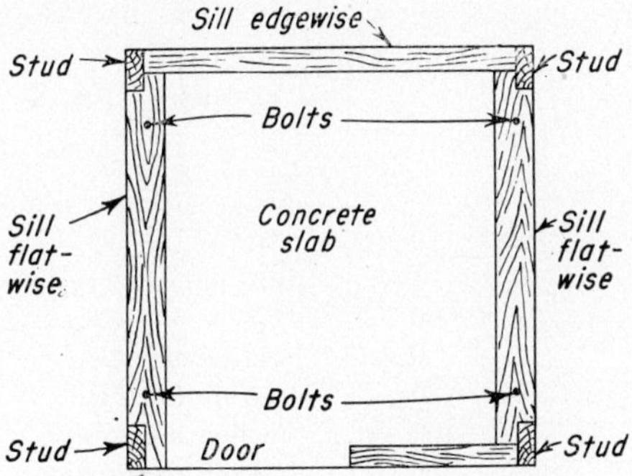

FIG. A-5. Plan of building sills.

The seat cover should be kept closed at all times when the privy is not in use to keep flies from the pit. A self-closing device is shown in Fig. A-1. It does not permit raising of the whole seat, however, and has the further disadvantage of easily getting out of order.

Metal slabs with metal risers welded to them are made commercially.

APPENDIX B

THRESHOLD LIMIT VALUES OF INDUSTRIAL ATMOSPHERIC CONTAMINANTS FOR 1955

Threshold limit values for 1955, adopted by the American Conference of Governmental Industrial Hygienists, are given in the following tabulation for the maximum average atmospheric concentration of contaminants to which workers may be exposed for an eight-hour working day without injury to health.

These values are based on the best available information from industrial experience, from experimental studies, and, when possible, from a combination of the two. They are not fixed values but are reviewed annually by the Committee on Threshold Limits for changes, revisions, or additions as further information becomes available. Threshold limits should be used as guides in the control of health hazards and should not be regarded as fine lines between safe and dangerous concentrations. They represent conditions only within which it is felt that workers may be repeatedly exposed, day after day, without their health being adversely affected. It is felt, at the present time, that workers should not be exposed to a working environment containing any of these substances in excess of the value indicated.

These values are not intended for use, or for modification for use, in the evaluation or control of community air pollution or air pollution nuisances.

Gases and Vapors

Substance	*Ppm**
Acetaldehyde	200
Acetic acid	10
Acetic anhydride	5
Acetone	1,000
Acrolein	0.5
Acrylonitrile	20
Ammonia	100
Amyl acetate	200
Amyl alcohol (isoamyl alcohol)	100
Aniline	5
Arsine	0.05
Benzene (benzol)	35
Bromine	1
Butadiene (1,3-butadiene)	1,000
Butanone (methyl ethyl ketone)	250
Butyl acetate (*n*-butyl acetate)	200
Butyl alcohol (*n*-butanol)	100
Butyl cellosolve (2-butoxyethanol)	200
Carbon dioxide	5,000
Carbon disulfide	20
Carbon monoxide	100
Carbon tetrachloride	25
Cellosolve (2-ethoxyethanol)	200
Cellosolve acetate (hydroxyethyl acetate)	100
Chlorine	1
Chlorobenzene (monochlorobenzene)	75
Chloroform (trichloromethane)	100

* Parts of vapor or gas per million parts of air, by volume.

Substance	*Ppm**
1-Chloro-1-nitropropane	20
Chloroprene (2-chlorobutadiene)	25
Cresol (all isomers)	5
Cyclohexane	400
Cyclohexanol	100
Cyclohexanone	100
Cyclohexene	400
Cyclopropane	400
o-Dichlorobenzene	50
Dichlorodifluoromethane	1,000
1,1-Dichloroethane	100
1,2-Dichloroethylene	200
Dichloroethyl ether	15
Dichloromonofluoromethane	1,000
1,1-Dichloro-1-nitroethane	10
Dichlorotetrafluoroethane	1,000
Diethylamine	25
Dimethylaniline (*N*-dimethylaniline)	5
Dimethylsulfate	1
Dioxan (diethylene dioxide)	100
Ethyl acetate	400
Ethyl alcohol (ethanol)	1,000
Ethylamine	25
Ethyl benzene	200
Ethyl bromide	200
Ethyl chloride	1,000
Ethyl ether	400
Ethyl formate	100
Ethyl silicate	100
Ethylene chlorohydrin	5
Ethylene dibromide (1,2-dibromoethane)	25
Ethylene dichloride (1,2-chloroethane)	100
Ethylene oxide	100
Fluorine	0.1
Fluorotrichloromethane	1,000
Formaldehyde	5
Gasoline	500
Heptane (*n*-heptane)	500
Hexane (*n*-hexane)	500
Hexanone (methyl butyl ketone)	100
Hexone (methyl isobutyl ketone)	100
Hydrogen chloride	5
Hydrogen cyanide	10
Hydrogen fluoride	3
Hydrogen selenide	0.05
Hydrogen sulfide	20
Iodine	1
Isophorone	25
Mesityl oxide	50
Methyl acetate	200
Methyl alcohol (methanol)	200
Methyl bromide	20
Methyl cellosolve (methoxyethanol)	25
Methyl cellosolve acetate (ethylene glycol monoethyl ether acetate)	25
Methyl chloride	100
Methylal (dimethoxymethane)	1,000
Methyl chloroform (1,1,1-trichloroethane)	500
Methylcyclohexane	500
Methylcyclohexanol	100
Methylcyclohexanone	100
Methyl formate	100
Methylene chloride (dichloromethane)	500
Naphtha (coal tar)	200
Naphtha (petroleum)	500
Nickel carbonyl	0.001
Nitrobenzene	1
Nitroethane	100
Nitrogen dioxide	5
Nitroglycerin	0.5
Nitromethane	100
2-Nitropropane	50
Nitrotoluene	5
Octane	500
Ozone	0.1
Pentane	1,000
Pentanone (methyl propyl ketone)	200
Perchlorethylene (tetrachloroethylene)	200
Phenol	5
Phosgene (carbonyl chloride)	1
Phosphine	0.05
Phosphorus trichloride	0.5
Propyl acetate	200

* Parts of vapor or gas per million parts of air, by volume.

Substance	*Ppm**	*Substance*	*Ppm**
Propyl alcohol (isopropyl alcohol)	400	Sulfur monochloride	1
Propyl ether (isopropyl ether)	500	Sulfur dioxide	10
Propylene dichloride (1,2-dichloropropane)	75	1,1,2,2-Tetrachloroethane	5
Stibine	0.1	Toluene	200
Stoddard solvent	500	*o*-Toluidine	5
Styrene monomer (phenyl ethylene)	200	Trichloroethylene	200
		Turpentine	100
		Vinyl chloride (chloroethene)	500
		Xylene	200

* Parts of vapor or gas per million parts of air, by volume.

Toxic Dusts, Fumes, and Mists

Substance	*Mg/m^3**	*Substance*	*Mg/m^3**
Antimony	0.5	Pentachloronaphthalene	0.5
Arsenic	0.5	Pentachlorophenol	0.5
Barium (soluble compounds)	0.5	Phosphorus (yellow)	0.1
Cadmium	0.1	Phosphorus pentachloride	1
Chlorodiphenyl	1	Phosphorus pentasulfide	1
Chromic acid and chromates as CrO_3	0.1	Selenium compounds (as Se)	0.1
Cyanide as CN	5	Sulfuric acid	1
Dinitrotoluene	1.5	Tellurium	0.1
Dinitro-*o*-cresol	0.2	Tetryl (2,4,6-trinitrophenylmethylnitramine)	1.5
Fluoride	2.5	Trichloronaphthalene	5
Iron oxide fume	15	Trinitrotoluene	1.5
Lead	0.15	Uranium (soluble compounds)	0.05
Magnesium oxide fume	15	Uranium (insoluble compounds)	0.25
Manganese	6	Zinc oxide fumes (as Zn)	15
Mercury	0.1		
Parathion (O,O-diethyl-O-*p*-nitrophenyl thiophosphate)	0.1		

* Milligrams of dust, fume, or mist per cubic meter of air.

Radioactivity

For permissible concentrations of radioisotopes in air, see Appendix D.

Mineral Dusts

Substance	*MPPCF**	*Substance*	*MPPCF**
Alundum (aluminum oxide)	50	Silica	
Asbestos	5	High (above 50% free SiO_2)	5
Carborundum (silicon carbide)	50	Medium (5 to 50% free SiO_2)	20
Dust (nuisance, no free silica)	50	Low (below 5% free SiO_2)	50
Mica (below 5% free silica)	20	Slate (below 5% free SiO_2)	50
Portland cement	50	Soapstone (below 5% free SiO_2)	20
Talc	20	Total dust (below 5% free SiO_2)	50

* Millions of particles per cubic foot of air.

The following threshold limit values (unclassified) were adopted at the meeting of the American Conference of Governmental Industrial Hygienists in 1956:

Aldrin (1,2,3,4,10,10-hexachloro-1,4,4a,5,8,8a-hexahydro-1,4,5,8-dimethanonaphthalene)	0.25	mg/m^3
Allyl alcohol	5	ppm
Allyl propyl disulfide	2	ppm
Ammate (ammonium amidosulfate)	15	mg/m^3
Benzyl chloride	1	ppm
Butyl amine	5	ppm
Butyl mercaptan	10	ppm
Calcium arsenate	0.3	mg/m^3
Chlordane (1,2,4,5,6,7,8,8-octachloro-3a,4,7,7a-tetrahydro-4,7-methanoindane)	2.0	mg/m^3
Chlorine trifluoride	0.1	ppm
Chlorinated diphenyl oxide	0.5	mg/m^3
Crag herbicide (sodium-2,4-dichlorophenoxy ethyl sulfate)	13	mg/m^3
2,4-D (2,4-dichlorophenoxy acetic acid)	10	mg/m^3
DDT (2,2-bis-(*p*-chlorophenyl)-1,1,1-trichlorethane)	2.0	mg/m^3
Diacetone alcohol (4-hydroxy-4-methyl pentanone-2)	50	ppm
Diborane	0.1	ppm
Dieldrin (1,2,3,4,10,10-hexachloro-6,7-epoxy-1,4,4a,5,6,7,8,8a-octahydro-1,4,5,8-dimethanonaphthalene)	0.25	mg/m^3
Difluorodibromomethane	100	ppm
Diisobutyl ketone	50	ppm
EPN (ethyl-*p*-nitrophenyl thionobenzene phosphonate)	0.5	mg/m^3
Ethyl mercaptan	250	ppm
Ethylene diamine	10	ppm
Ethylene imine	5	ppm
Ferro vanadium dust	1	mg/m^3
Furfural	5	ppm
Furfuryl alcohol	200	ppm
Hydrazine	1	ppm
Hydrogen bromide	5	ppm
Hydrogen peroxide	1	ppm
Hydroquinone	2	mg/m^3
Isopropylamine	5	ppm
Lead arsenate	0.2	mg/m^3
Lindane (hexachlorocyclohexane)	0.5	mg/m^3
Malathion (O,O-dimethyl dithiophosphate of diethyl mercapto-succinate)	15	mg/m^3
Methoxychlor (2,2-diparamethoxyphenyl-1,1,1-trichloroethane)	15	mg/m^3
Methyl acetylene	1,000	ppm
Methyl isobutyl carbinol (methyl amyl alcohol)	25	ppm
Methyl mercaptan	50	ppm
Molybdenum:		
Soluble compounds	5	mg/m^3
Insoluble compounds	15	mg/m^3
p-Nitroaniline	1	ppm
Organo mercurials (as mercury)	0.01	mg/m^3
Perchlormethyl mercaptan	0.1	ppm
Phenylhydrazine	5	ppm

Picric acid	0.1	mg/m^3
Propylene imine	25	ppm
Pyridine	10	ppm
Quinone	0.1	ppm
Sodium hydroxide	2	mg/m^3
Sulfur hexafluoride	1,000	ppm
Sulfur pentafluoride	0.025	ppm
TEDP (tetraethyl dithionopyrophosphate)	0.2	mg/m^3
TEPP (tetraethyl pyrophosphate)	0.05	mg/m^3
p-Tertiary butyl toluene	10	ppm
Tetrahydrofuran	75	ppm
Tetranitromethane	1	ppm
Titanium dioxide	15	mg/m^3
Trifluoromonobromomethane	1,000	ppm
Vanadium:		
V_2O_5 dust	0.5	mg/m^3
V_2O_5 fume	0.1	mg/m^3
Zirconium	5	mg/m^3

APPENDIX C

GLOSSARY OF RADIOLOGICAL HEALTH TERMS

The following are terms commonly used in radiological health as given in Concepts of Radiological Health, *U S. Public Health Service Pub.* 336:

absorption Transformation of radiant energy into other forms of energy when passing through a material substance.

alpha particles Charged particles emitted from the nuclei of some atoms, having a mass of four units and two-unit positive electrical charges. They are composed of two neutrons and two protons.

alpha ray Stream of fast-moving alpha particles; a strongly ionizing and weakly penetrating radiation.

atoms The chemical units of which all matter is made. The atom may be defined as the smallest particle of an element which is capable of entering into a chemical reaction.

atomic mass The mass of an atom of an element compared with one-sixteenth the mass of an oxygen 16 atom.

atomic number Number of protons in the nucleus, hence the number of positive charges on the nucleus. Also the number of electrons outside the nucleus of a neutral atom. Symbol: Z.

atomic radiation Radiation produced by energy changes in atomic nuclei or atomic electron clouds: ionizing radiation.

background The counting rate or the ionizing radiation produced by cosmic radiation and naturally occurring trace amounts of radioactive elements.

beta particle Charged particle emitted from the nucleus and having a mass and charge equal in magnitude to those of the electron.

beta ray A stream of beta particles, more penetrating but less ionizing than alpha rays; a stream of high-speed electrons.

betatron A machine used to accelerate electrons.

binding energy The energy that holds the nucleus together; it is quantitatively related to the difference in mass of the separate component parts and the actual mass of the nucleus.

chain reaction Any chemical or nuclear process in which some of the products of the process are instrumental in the continuation or magnification of the process.

curie Standard measure of rate of radioactive decay; the quantity of any radioactive nuclide in which the number of disintegrations per second is 3.700×10^{10}.

cyclotron A machine which accelerates charged particles by electric and magnetic forces.

decay Disintegration of the nucleus of an unstable element by the spontaneous emission of charged particles and/or photons.

decay time See *half-life.*

dosimeter Instrument used to detect and measure an accumulated dosage of radiation; usually a pocket electroscope.

electron Negatively charged particle which is a constituent of every atom. Unit of negative electricity equal to 4.80×10^{-10} electrostatic unit (esu). Its mass is about 1/2,000 of that of a proton.

electron cloud The group of electrons surrounding an atomic nucleus and, with it, forming the neutral atom.

electron volt Amount of energy gained by an electron in passing across a potential difference of one volt. Abbreviated ev; a million electron volts is abbreviated Mev.

electroscope An instrument used to measure cumulative exposure to ionizing radiation.

element A substance consisting of atoms of the same atomic (Z) number.

equivalent roentgen (er) That amount of radiation other than X or gamma which produces in air an amount of ionization equal to that produced by one roentgen of X or gamma radiation.

erg Unit of work done by a force of one dyne acting through a distance of one centimeter. Unit of energy which can exert a force of one dyne through a distance of one centimeter.

external radiation Radiation entering the body from without.

film badge Small piece of X ray or similar photographic film enclosed in a lightproof paper usually crossed by lead or cadmium strips, carried in a small metal or plastic frame. The badge is used to estimate the amount of radiation to which an individual has been exposed.

gamma ray Electromagnetic radiation emitted from the nucleus of a radioactive atom.

Geiger-Mueller (G-M) counter Highly sensitive instrument for detecting radiation.

half-life Time required for a radioactive substance to lose by decay 50 per cent of its activity.

half-thickness Thickness of absorbing material necessary to reduce the intensity of radiation by one-half.

internal radiation Radiation arising from inside the body; as from radioisotopes assimilated and contained within the tissues.

ion Atomic particle, atom, or chemical radical (group of chemically combined atoms) bearing an electrical charge, either positive or negative, caused by an excess or deficiency of electrons.

ionization Act or result of any process by which a neutral atom or molecule acquires either a positive or a negative charge.

ionizing radiation Radiation possessing sufficient energy to ionize the atoms or molecules absorbing it.

isotope One or two or more forms of an element having the same atomic number (nuclear charge) and hence occupying the same position in the periodic table. All isotopes are identical in chemical behavior, but are distinguishable by small differences in atomic weight. The nuclei of all isotopes of a given element have the same number of protons but differ in the number of neutrons.

mass Quantity of matter, popularly thought of as identical to "weight."

mass number The number of nucleons in the nucleus of an atom. Symbol: A.

mass unit (mu) Unit of mass, one-sixteenth of the mass of an oxygen atom (O^{16}) taken as 16.00000.

maximum permissible dose The amount of radiation which a normal human being may receive day in and day out without any harmful effects to himself becoming evident during his lifetime.

Mev Abbreviation for million electron volts. See *electron volt.*

microcurie A millionth of a curie (37,000 disintegrations per second).

millicurie A thousandth of a curie.

molecule Orderly group of atoms joined together by chemical bonds. Some molecules are small and simple, such as water (H_2O): others are large and complex such as chlorophyll *a* ($C_{55}H_{72}O_5N_4Mg$).

neutron A nuclear particle with a mass approximately the same as that of a proton and electrically neutral; a constituent of the atomic nucleus. Its mass is 1.00893 *mu.*

nuclear energy The energy released by fission or fusion of atomic nuclei.

nuclear fission A special type of nuclear transformation characterized by the splitting of a nucleus into at least two other nuclei and the release of a relatively large amount of energy.

nuclear fusion Act of coalescing two or more nuclei.

nuclear reactor A device or machine for producing energy by fission or fusion of atomic nuclei.

nucleon Generic name for the constituent parts of the nucleus. At present applied to protons and neutrons, but will include any other particle found to exist in the nucleus.

nucleus Heavy central part of an atom in which most of the mass and the total positive electrical charge are concentrated.

nuclide A general term referring to any nuclear species of the chemical elements capable of existing for a measurable time.

photon A quantity of energy emitted in the form of electromagnetic radiation, such as radio waves, light, X rays and gamma rays.

positron Nuclear particle equal in mass to the electron and having an equal but opposite charge. Its mass is 0.000548 mu.

potential difference Difference in potential between any two points in a circuit; work required to carry a unit positive charge from one point to another.

proportional counter Gas-filled radiation detection tube in which the pulse produced is proportional to the number of ions formed in the gas by the primary ionizing particle.

proton Nuclear particle with a positive electric charge equal numerically to the charge of the electron and having a mass of 1.007575 mu.

radiation Propagation of energy through space; an electromagnetic wave or rapidly moving atomic or subatomic particle.

radiation sickness The group of symptoms developed consequent to an overexposure to ionizing radiation; symptoms include weakness, nausea, vomiting, diarrhea, leukocytopenia, anemia, and spontaneous bleeding.

radioactivity Process whereby unstable nuclei undergo spontaneous atomic disintegration with liberation of energy, generally resulting in the formation of new elements. The process is accompanied by the emission of one or more types of radiation, such as alpha particles, beta particles, and gamma radiation.

radioisotope A radioactive isotope.

radiological health The public health aspects of the use of ionizing radiation.

roentgen Standard unit of absorption of X and gamma radiation; quantity of X or gamma radiation such that the associated corpuscular emission per 0.0012938 gram of air (dry and at standard temperatures and pressure) produces, in air, ions carrying one electrostatic unit of quantity of electricity of either sign.

roentgen equivalent man (rem) That quantity of radiation of any type which when absorbed by man produces a biologic effect equivalent to that produced by the absorption of one roentgen of X or gamma radiation.

roentgen equivalent physical (rep) That amount of ionizing radiation which in tissue produces the same amount of ionization as that produced by one roentgen in air; the dose of radiation (other than that covered by definition of the roentgen) which produces energy absorption of 93 ergs per gram of tissue.

Van de Graaff accelerator A machine using static electricity to accelerate charged particles.

X ray A penetrating electromagnetic radiation similar to gamma radiation. This radiation is produced as a result of sudden decrease in electron energy.

APPENDIX D

MAXIMUM PERMISSIBLE AMOUNT OF RADIOISOTOPE IN TOTAL BODY AND MAXIMUM PERMISSIBLE CONCENTRATION IN AIR AND WATER FOR CONTINUOUS EXPOSURE (OCTOBER, 1951)

The following tabulation gives the maximum permissible amount of radioisotope in total body and maximum permissible concentration in air and water for continuous exposure (October, 1951), as given in "Maximum Permissible Amounts of Radioisotopes in Human Body and Maximum Permissible Concentrations in Air and Water," National Bureau of Standards, Handbook 52, March, 1953. This table is subject to revision. The latest table may be secured from the National Bureau of Standards.

Element and percentage in body[a]	Organ, grams	Microcuries in total body[b]	Microcuries per milliliter of water[b]	Microcuries per milliliter of air[b]
A. Common Radioisotopes That Are Alpha Emitters				
Po^{210} (soluble)	Spleen, 150	0.02	3×10^{-5}	2×10^{-10}
Po^{210} (insoluble)	Lungs, 10^3	7×10^{-3}	...	7×10^{-11}
Rn^{222} + daughter[c]	Body, 7×10^4	...	2×10^{-6} [d]	
	Lungs, 10^3	...	...	10^{-8}
Ra^{226} + ½ daughter[c]	Bone, 7×10^3	0.1	4×10^{-8}	8×10^{-12}
U, natural (soluble)	Kidneys, 300	0.2[e]	7×10^{-5} [e]	1.7×10^{-11} [e]
U, natural (insoluble)	Lungs, 10^3	0.009	...	1.7×10^{-11} [e]
U^{233} (soluble)	Bone, 7×10^3	0.04	1.5×10^{-4}	1×10^{-10}
U^{233} (insoluble)	Lungs, 10^3	0.008	...	1.6×10^{-11}
Pu^{239} (soluble)	Bone, 7×10^3	0.04	1.5×10^{6}	2×10^{-12}
Pu^{239} (insoluble)	Lungs, 10^3	0.008	...	2×10^{-12}
B. Beta- and Gamma-emitting Radioisotopes That Are of Interest because They Are Common Body Elements				
H^3 (HTO) or $H^3{}_2O$), 10%	Total body, 7×10^4	10^4	0.2	2×10^{-5}
C^{14} (CO_2), 18%	Fat, 10^4	250	3×10^{-3}	10^{-6}
	Bone, 7×10^3	1,500	4×10^{-3}	5×10^{-7}
Na^{24}, 0.15%	Total body, 7×10^4	15	8×10^{-3}	2×10^{-6}
P^{32}, 1.0%	Bone, 7×10^3	10	2×10^{-4}	1×10^{-7}
S^{35}, 0.25%	Skin, 2×10^3	100	5×10^{-3}	10^{-6}
Cl^{36}, 0.15%	Total body, 7×10^4	200	2×10^{-3}	4×10^{-7}
K^{42}, 0.35%	Muscle, 3×10^4	20	1×10^{-2}	2×10^{-6}
Ca^{45}, 1.5%	Bone, 7×10^3	65	5×10^{-4}	3×10^{-8}

Element and percentage in body[a]	Organ, grams	Microcuries in total body[b]	Microcuries per milliliter of water[b]	Microcuries per milliliter of air[b]
B. Beta- and Gamma-emitting Radioisotopes That Are of Interest because They Are Common Body Elements (*Continued*)				
Mn^{56}, 3×10^{-4}%	Kidneys, 300	....	0.15	3×10^{-6}
	Liver, 1.7×10^3	7.5	0.3	4×10^{-6}
Fe^{55} } 0.004%	Blood, 5×10^3	1×10^3	4×10^{-3}	6×10^{-7}
Fe^{59} } 0.004%	Blood, 5×10^3	11	1×10^{-4}	1.5×10^{-8}
Cu^{64}, 2×10^{-4}%	Liver, 1.7×10^3	1.5×10^2	8×10^{-2}	6×10^{-6}
Zn^{65}, 0.003%	Bone, 7×10^3	430	6×10^{-2}	2×10^{-6}
I^{131}, 4×10^{-5}%	Thyroid, 20	0.3	3×10^{-5}	3×10^{-9}
C. Other Radioisotopes of Current Interest				
Be^7	Bone, 7×10^3	670	1	4×10^{-6}
F^{18}	Bone, 7×10^3	24	0.9	10^{-4}
A^{41}	Total body, 7×10^4	30	5×10^{-4}	5×10^{-7}
Sc^{46}	Spleen, 150	6	0.4	7×10^{-8}
V^{48}	Bone, 7×10^3	20	0.5	10^{-6}
Cr^{51}	Kidneys, 300	390	0.5	8×10^{-6}
Co^{60}	Liver, 1.7×10^3	3	2×10^{-2}	10^{-6}
Ni^{59}	Liver, 1.7×10^3	39	0.25	2×10^{-5}
Ga^{72}	Bone, 7×10^3	8	9	3×10^{-6}
Ge^{71}	Kidneys, 300	67	9	4×10^{-5}
As^{76}	Kidneys, 300	10	0.2	2×10^{-6}
Rb^{86}	Muscle, 3×10^4	60	3×10^{-3}	4×10^{-7}
Sr^{89}	Bone, 7×10^3	2	7×10^{-5}[f]	2×10^{-8}[f]
Sr^{90} + Y^{90}[c]	Bone, 7×10^3	1	8×10^{-7}	2×10^{-10}
Y^{91}	Bone, 7×10^3	15	0.2	4×10^{-8}
Nb^{95}	Bone, 7×10^3	90	4×10^{-3}	4×10^{-7}
Mo^{99}	Bone, 7×10^3	50	14	2×10^{-3}
Tc^{96}	Kidneys, 300	5	3×10^{-2}	3×10^{-6}
Ru^{106} + Rh^{106}[c]	Kidneys, 300	4	0.1	3×10^{-8}
Rh^{105}	Kidneys, 300	9	1.5×10^{-2}	10^{-6}
Pd^{103} + Rh^{103}[c]	Kidneys, 300	6	1×10^{-2}	7×10^{-7}
Ag^{105}	Liver, 1.7×10^3	18	2	10^{-5}
Ag^{111}	Liver, 1.7×10^3	36	4	3×10^{-5}
Cd^{109} + Ag^{109m}[c]	Liver, 1.7×10^3	40	7×10^{-2}	7×10^{-8}
Sn^{113}	Bone, 7×10^3	80	0.2	6×10^{-7}
Te^{127}	Kidneys, 300	4	3×10^{-2}	10^{-7}
Te^{129}	Kidneys, 300	1.3	10^{-2}	4×10^{-8}
Xe^{133}	Total body, 7×10^4	300	4×10^{-3}	4×10^{-6}
Xe^{135}	Total body, 7×10^4	100	1×10^{-3}	2×10^{-6}
Cs^{137} + Ba^{137m}[c]	Muscle, 3×10^4	90	1.5×10^{-3}	2×10^{-7}
Ba^{140} + La^{140}[c]	Bone, 7×10^3	5	2×10^{-3}	6×10^{-8}
La^{140}	Bone, 7×10^3	24	1	10^{-6}
Ce^{144} + Pr^{144}[c]	Bone, 7×10^3	5	4×10^{-2}	7×10^{-9}

Element and percentage in body[a]	Organ, grams	Microcuries in total body[b]	Microcuries per milliliter of water[b]	Microcuries per milliliter of air[b]
C. Other Radioisotopes of Current Interest (*Continued*)				
Pr^{143}	Bone, 7×10^3	29	0.4	7.5×10^{-7}
Pm^{147}	Bone, 7×10^3	120	1	2×10^{-7}
Sm^{151}	Bone, 7×10^3	420	0.2	10^{-8}
Eu^{154}	Bone, 7×10^3	22	3×10^{-2}	6×10^{-9}
Ho^{166}	Bone, 7×10^3	17	23	3×10^{-6}
Tm^{170}	Bone, 7×10^3	19	0.25×10^{-1}	5×10^{-8}
Lu^{177}	Bone, 7×10^3	78	24	5×10^{-6}
Re^{183}	Thyroid, 20	35	8×10^{-2}	8×10^{-6}
	Skin, 2×10^3	600	0.2	2×10^{-5}
Ir^{190}	Kidneys, 300	21	10^{-2}	7×10^{-7}
Ir^{192}	Kidneys, 300	3.4	9×10^{-4}	5×10^{-8}
Au^{198}	Kidneys, 300	10	3×10^{-3}	1×10^{-7}
Au^{199}	Kidneys, 300	28	7×10^{-3}	2.5×10^{-7}
Pb^{203}	Bone, 7×10^3	57	0.1	6.5×10^{-6}
At^{211}	Thyroid, 20	6×10^{-4}	2×10^{-6}	3×10^{-10}
Th^{234}	Bone, 7×10^3	120	3	6×10^{-7}
Am^{241}	Bone, 7×10^3	0.056	10^{-4}	3×10^{-11}
Cm^{242}	Bone, 7×10^3	0.05	9×10^{-4}	2×10^{-10}

[a] Percentages of stable element by weight comprising total body. The other principal body elements, oxygen (65 per cent), nitrogen (3 per cent), and magnesium (4×10^{-3} per cent), are omitted because all their radioactive isotopes have very short half-lives.

[b] Calculated values were rounded off to one significant figure.

[c] Values of microcuries and of microcuries per milliliter are given for the parent element in equilibrium with its daughter element(s).

[d] This value actually applies to ingestion, although the submersion equation was used for the calculation, since it is considered that tissue in the gastrointestinal tract is submerged in a fluid. The equation for submersion was applied specifically to an element of tissue in the gastrointestinal tract that was surrounded by water contaminated with radon and its products and by other layers of tissue contaminated with such products.

In this case the total energy leaving the unit volume is approximately equal to the total energy absorbed in a unit volume, and one is justified in using this method of calculation, which gives 2×10^{-6} microcuries per milliliter of water. Approximately the same answer is obtained using the ingestion equation and the entire gastrointestinal tract as the critical organ.

If one is concerned with the case of submersion exposure due to a person's or animal's swimming continuously in the contaminated water, the value would be increased to about 2×10^{-4} microcuries per milliliter because in such a case the alpha radiation would not be effective and the value given here could be increased by a relative biological effectiveness of 20 and an energy ratio of 5.5.

[e] Based on chemical toxicity. The microcurie and microcurie-per-milliliter values are given for the natural mixture of U^{238}, U^{235}, and U^{234} with all the other radioisotopes removed.

[f] Obtained by a comparison of recommended values for Sr^{90} with the calculated values in the two cases.

INDEX